MACHINE TOOL
Technology

McKnight & McKnight
Publishing Company
Bloomington, Illinois

MACHINE TOOL
Technology

WILLARD J. McCARTHY
College of Applied Science and Technology
Illinois State University
Normal, Illinois

ROBERT E. SMITH

Preface to the Third Edition

This book includes information and procedures for a first course in machine shop theory and practice, regardless of the age level of the student. It also includes many operational units and technical units which sometimes are taught in machine shop classes of a more advanced or intermediate level. Prepared for text use, it may also be used for independent study and is also valuable as a general reference. The content is presented with abundant illustrations. The language and vocabulary used are simple, direct, and should be easily understood by machine shop students.

This third edition is completely revised and expanded to include many new technical units which are either directly or indirectly related to the machining of metal. The ninety units of the previous edition have been revised and many of them expanded considerably. In addition, fifty-five completely new units are included, fifty of which are technical theory or *knowing* units.

This new edition reflects many of the technical changes which have evolved in machine tools, cutting tools, and precision measurement. The new technical units emphasize precision measurement, screw threads, cutting tool materials, cutting fluids, machinability of metals, the production and selection of metals, basic metallurgical theory, and heat-treatment processes. A new unit concerning employment opportunities in metal machining occupations also is included.

The content in machine shop courses should emphasize the "technical theory" as well as the "doing" or skill aspects. In this book, the content is organized in a logical order for teaching purposes. The book is divided into major sections which are based on basic machines, basic machining arts, or basic areas of technical theory.

Most of the introductory units in each section are normally included in beginning machine shop courses. Some of the units in certain sections are more appropriate for students in classes studying machining technology at an intermediate level. The units may be studied in the order in which they are presented, or they may be studied in an order appropriate to fit any desired course of study.

The first section of the book includes a preview of the meaning and significance of the machining of metal in our present-day technical world. It presents an overview of the five basic machining techniques or arts. New machine tools of improved design are continually being developed for applying these basic techniques more efficiently. A fundamental understanding of the basic machining arts and the basic machine tools which perform operations based on these techniques is important for machinists, machine operators, manufacturing engineers, and those workers engaged in occupations related to machine design.

General safety practices for the machine shop are emphasized in Section II. Additional safety practices and precautions concerning each basic machine tool are included in succeeding sections.

The content in each section is centered around a basic type of machine tool or around a basic area of study related to the machining of metals. In each section concerned with a basic machine tool and its operation, the related technical theory is presented first, followed by step-by-step procedures used for performing operations on the machine.

The introductory units concerned with each basic machine explain and illustrate the machine, the operations which it is capable of performing, the principal parts of the machine, accessories used with the machine, cutting tools used on the machines, cutting speeds and feeds employed, and any special safety precautions.

This book is not intended to be comprehensive in all phases of machining operations and technical theory. Theory which is most important and most significant is presented. The student is referred to standard handbooks for machinists in securing further information related to many of the units. Handbooks such as *The New American Machinist's Handbook* and *Machinery's Handbook* are valuable references for this purpose and should be readily available.

A majority of the illustrations show equipment which is typically used in school machine shops. However, also shown are pictures of larger equipment typically used for similar purposes in industrial establishments. Hence, the relationship of operations performed on smaller basic machine tools and those performed on larger production machine tools is more readily understood.

A list of pertinent questions is included for each theoretical or *knowing* unit. These questions may be used as a guide in studying or reviewing a unit. The units which are largely theoretical are readily identified by their titles, when they are compared with the units which are largely operational or *doing* units. The operational units have titles which start with the words, *How To* such as *How to Drill A Hole*.

The use of automatically controlled machine tools has expanded rapidly during recent years, and this trend is expected to continue in future years. The type of automatic control generally employed is called Numerical Control (N/C).

The use of N/C machine tools involves transferring coded information from a drawing or blueprint to a program, and then punching cards or a tape. The tape is inserted in the machine tool, and the machine produces parts, with little physical effort on the part of the operator. However, the programer, the machine tool operator, and the machinist generally must possess a thorough understanding of pertinent machining operations and the directly related technical units in this book in order to satisfactorily utilize or operate modern, expensive N/C machine tools.

The cost of N/C machine tools at the present time prohibits their availability for use in many school machine shops. However, a basic understanding of machine shop theory and practice generally is considered a prerequisite for programing, operating, and maintaining N/C machine tools. The machine shop student with this knowledge and experience is considered as a more worthy applicant for apprenticeship or on-the-job training on N/C machine tools.

The authors wish to thank all of the individuals, companies and organizations who contributed illustrations, data, and suggestions used in the preparation of this book.

Considerable credit is due to Mrs. McCarthy for her work in typing the manuscript and various other materials.

The authors and the publishers welcome suggestions for improvement of the book for future printings and future revisions.

Acknowledgments

Acknowledgment for illustrative material is appreciatively extended to the following:

Airborn Instruments Laboratory, Division of
  Cutler Hammer,
  Long Island, New York
Allegheny Ludlum Steel Corporation,
  Pittsburgh, Pennsylvania
American Gas Furnace Company,
  Elizabeth, New Jersey
American Society of Mechanical Engineers,
  New York, New York
American Society for Metals,
  Metals Park, Ohio
American Society for Testing and Materials,
  Philadelphia, Pennsylvania
Ames Precision Machine Works,
  Needham Heights, Massachusetts
Armstrong Brothers Tool Company,
  Chicago, Illinois
Atlas Press Company,
  Kalamazoo, Michigan
Bausch and Lomb Incorporated,
  Rochester, New York
Boyar-Schultz Corporation,
  Broadview, Illinois
Brown and Sharpe Manufacturing Company,
  North Kingstown, Rhode Island
Adolph I. Buehler, Incorporated,
  Evanston, Illinois
Burgmaster Corporation,
  Gardena, California
The Carlton Machine Tool Company,
  Cincinnati, Ohio
Caterpillar Tractor Company,
  Peoria, Illinois
Cincinnati Lathe and Tool Company,
  Cincinnati, Ohio
The Cincinnati Milling Machine Company,
  Cincinnati, Ohio
The Cincinnati Shaper Company,
  Cincinnati, Ohio
The Cleveland Twist Drill Company,
  Cleveland, Ohio

The Desmond-Stephan Manufacturing Company,
  Urbana, Ohio
The Do All Company,
  DesPlains, Illinois
Federal Products Corporation,
  Providence, Rhode Island
The du Mont Corporation,
  Greenfield, Massachusetts
Metallurgical Products Department, General
  Electric Company,
  Detroit, Michigan
General Motors Corporation, Pontiac
  Motor Division,
  Pontiac, Michigan
The G. A. Gray Company,
  Cincinnati, Ohio
Greenfield Tap and Die, Division of United
  Greenfield Corporation,
  Greenfield, Massachusetts
Gulf Oil Corporation, Domestic Marketing
  Department,
  Houston, Texas
H and G Sales Corporation, A Subsidiary of
  The Eastern Machine Screw Corporation,
  New Haven, Connecticut
The Hanson-Whitney Company,
  Hartford, Connecticut
Heli-Coil Corporation,
  Danbury, Connecticut
Hughes Industrial Systems Division,
  Hughes Aircraft Company,
  Los Angeles, California
Illinois Gear and Machine Co.,
  Chicago, Illinois
The I. O. Johansson Company,
  Skokie, Illinois
Johnson Gas Appliance Company,
  Cedar Rapids, Iowa
E. Leitz Incorporated,
  New York, New York
The Lufkin Rule Company,
  Saginaw, Michigan
National Twist Drill and Tool Company,
  Rochester, Michigan

ACKNOWLEDGMENTS:

Norton Company,
  Worcester, Massachusetts
Pittsburgh Instrument and Machine Company,
  Pittsburgh, Pennsylvania
Precision Scientific Company,
  Chicago, Illinois
Precision Twist Drill and Machine Company,
  Crystal Lake, Illinois
Racine Hydraulics and Machinery, Incorporated,
  Machinery Division,
  Racine, Wisconsin
The Rigid Tool Company,
  Elyria, Ohio
Rockwell Manufacturing Company,
  Power Tool Division,
  Pittsburgh, Pennsylvania
Sheldon Machine Company, Incorporated,
  Chicago, Illinois
The Shore Instrument and Manufacturing
  Company, Incorporated,
  Jamaica, New York
South Bend Lathe, Incorporated,
  South Bend, Indiana

The L. S. Starrett Company,
  Athol, Massachusetts
Tempil° Corporation,
  New York, New York
Texaco Incorporated,
  New York, New York
Thermolyne Corporation,
  Dubuque, Iowa
Union Carbide Corporation, Linde Division,
  New York, New York
Union Carbide Corporation, Stellite Division,
  New York, New York
VanKeuren Company
  Watertown, Massachusetts
The Walton Company,
  Hartford, Connecticut
J. H. Williams and Company,
  Buffalo, New York
Wilson Mechanical Instrument Division,
  American Chain and Cable Company,
  Incorporated,
  New York, New York
Zagar, Incorporated,
  Cleveland, Ohio

8

Table of Contents

CONTENTS:

CONTENTS:

Useful Tables for Reference

References for Further Study

Handbooks

ASME Handbook, Metals Properties. Edited by Samuel L. Hoyt, Sponsored by the Metals Engineering Handbook Board of the American Society of Mechanical Engineers. New York: McGraw-Hill Book Co., Inc., 1954.

ASTME Die Design Handbook. Prepared by the American Society of Tool and Manufacturing Engineers, Frank W. Wilson, Editor-in-Chief. New York: McGraw-Hill Book Co., Inc., 1955.

ASTME Handbook of Fixture Design. Prepared by the American Society of Tool and Manufacturing Engineers, Frank W. Wilson, Editor-in-Chief. New York: McGraw-Hill Book Co., Inc., 1962.

Machinists Ready Reference. Compiled by C. Weingartner. Ann Arbor, Mich.: Praken Publications.

Metals Handbook, Vol. I: Properties and Selection, 8th Edition. Prepared under the direction of the Handbook Committee. Metals Park, Ohio: American Society for Metals, 1961.

Metals Handbook, Vol. II: Heat Treating, Cleaning and Finishing, 8th Edition. Prepared under the direction of the Handbook Committee. Metals Park, Ohio: American Society for Metals, 1964.

The New American Machinists' Handbook. Edited by Rupert Le Grand. Based upon earlier editions of *American Machinists' Handbook* edited by Fred H. Colvin and Frank A. Stanley. New York: McGraw-Hill Book Co., Inc., 1955.

Oberg, Erik, and Jones, F. D. *Machinery's Handbook*, 17th Edition. 93 Worth Street, New York 13, N.Y.: The Industrial Press, 1964.

Books

Anderson, James and Tatro, Earl. *Shop Theory*. Fifth Edition. New York: McGraw-Hill Book Co., Inc., 1968.

Ansley, Arthur C. *Manufacturing Methods and Processes*. Philadelphia: Chilton Co., 1957.

ASTME. *Numerical Control in Manufacturing*. Prepared by the American Society of Tool and Manufacturing Engineers; Frank W. Wilson, Editor-in-Chief. New York: McGraw-Hill Book Co., Inc., 1963.

Begman, Myron L., and Amstead, B. H. *Manufacturing Processes*. 5th Edition. New York: John Wiley and Sons, 1963.

Burghardt, Henry D., Axelrod, A., and Anderson, J. *Machine Tool Operation, Part I*. 5th Edition. New York: McGraw-Hill Book Co., Inc., 1959.

Burghardt, Henry D., Axelrod, A., and Anderson, J. *Machine Tool Operation, Part II*. 4th Edition. New York: McGraw-Hill Book Co., Inc., 1960.

Cincinnati Milling Machine Co. *A Treatise on Milling and Milling Machines*. 1951.

Clark, Donald, S. *Engineering Materials and Processes*. 3rd Edition. Scranton, Pa.: International Textbook Co., 1959.

Datsko, Joseph. *Material Properties and Manufacturing Processes*. New York: John Wiley and Sons, Inc., 1966.

DeGarmo, E. P. *Materials and Processes in Manufacturing*. New York: The Macmillan Co., 1962.

Doyle, Lawrence E. *Metal Machining*. New York: Prentice-Hall, Inc., 1953.

Edgar, Carroll. *Fundamentals of Manufacturing Processes and Materials*. Reading, Mass.: Addison-Wesley, Inc., 1965.

Henry Ford Trade School. *Shop Theory*. Revised by Fred Nicholson, 4th Edition. New York: McGraw-Hill Book Co., Inc., 1955.

Frier, W. T. *Elementary Metallurgy*. New York: McGraw-Hill Book Co., Inc., 1952.

Habicht, Frank. *Modern Machine Tools*. Princeton, N.J.: D. Van Nostrand Co., Inc., 1963.

Hine, Frank. *Machine Tools for Engineers*. New York: McGraw-Hill Book Co., Inc., 1959.

Johnson, Carl G., and Weeks, W. R. *Metallurgy*. 4th Edition. Chicago: American Technical Society, 1956.

Kauffman, H. J. *Machine Shop and Foundry Projects*. Bloomington, Ill.: McKnight and McKnight Publishing Co., 1959.

REFERENCES:

Knight, Roy E. *Machine Shop Projects*. Bloomington, Ill.: McKnight and McKnight Publishing Co., 1943.

Ostergaard, Eugene. *Basic Die Making*. Sponsored by National, Tool, Die and Precision Machining Association. New York: McGraw-Hill Book Co., Inc., 1963.

Palmer, Frank R., and Leurson, G. *Tool Steel Simplified*. Carpenter Steel Co., 1961.

Paquin, J. R. *Die Design Fundamentals, Book One*. Totowa, N. J.: The Industrial Press, 1962.

Porter, H. W., Lasco, O. D. and Nelson, C. A. *Machine Shop Operations and Setups*. 3rd Edition. Chicago: American Technical Society, 1967.

Rusinoff, S. E. *Manufacturing Processes*. Chicago: American Technical Society, 1962.

South Bend Lathe, Inc. *How to Run a Lathe*. South Bend, 22, Indiana: 1958.

Strasser, F. *Practical Design of Metal Stampings*. Philadelphia: Chilton Co., Book Division, 1959.

Umowski, Joseph S. *Ferrous Metallurgy: Laboratory Manual*. Chicago: American Technical Society, 1960.

American Standards

The American Standards Association works continually on the development of various standards. Of its many publications, the following relate to subjects in this book. A list of American Standards may be obtained upon application to the publisher, The American Society of Mechanical Engineers. 345 East 47th Street, New York, N. Y. 10017.

(ASA B1.1 — 1960) Unified Screw Threads
(ASA B1.5 — 1952) Acme Screw Threads
(ASA B1.12 — 1963) Class 5 Interference-Fit Thread
(ASA B4.1 — 1955) Preferred Limits and Fits for Cylindrical Parts
(ASA B5.3 — 1960) Milling Cutters
(ASA B5.4 — 1955) Taps — Cut and Ground Threads
(ASA B5.10 — 1963) Machine Tapers
(ASA B5.14 — 1959) Reamers
(ASA B5.17 — 1958) Markings for Identifying Grinding Wheels and Other Bonded Abrasives
(ASA B5.22 — 1950) Single-Point Tools and Tool Posts
(ASA B6.1 — 1932) Spur Gear Tooth Form
(ASA B6.5 — 1954) Letter Symbols for Gear Engineering
(ASA B6.7 — 1956) 20-Degree Involute Fine Pitch System for Spur and Helical Gears
(ASA B6.8 — 1950) Fine Pitch Straight Bevel Gears
(ASA B6.10 — 1954) Gear Nomenclature
(ASA B6.13 — 1955) System of Straight Bevel Gears
(ASA B46.1 — 1962) Surface Texture

Power with Precision — Essence of Machining Metal
(Cincinnati Milling Machine)

Introduction To The Machining of Metals

Fig. 1-1. Heavy-Duty Special Radial Drilling Machine (Caterpillar)

Machine Tools and Machining

Importance of Machine Tools

Every product known to man requires the use of machine tools for its manufacture or for its delivery to the consumer. Without these tools, our modern civilization would not be possible. Machine tools are used to cut metals and to produce metal parts of all sizes and shapes to very close limits of accuracy (Fig. 1-1).

Machine tools make the working parts for all machines and equipment used in the production of goods and in the service industries, Fig. 1-2. They are used to make parts for household appliances such as radios, televisions, refrigerators, washing machines, sewing machines, and vacuum cleaners. Machine tools make the working parts for all transportation equipment including automobiles, railroad equipment, ships, airplanes, and space vehicles. They also make the working parts for manufacturing machinery, mining machinery, agricultural machinery, and construction machinery.

Modern machine tools have made mass production methods possible. By reducing costs, these methods enable more people to afford products and services. Increased buying stimulates further production which, in turn, creates more jobs. This sequence applied to American production methods has made possible the high standard of living in America.

Machining of Metals Defined

The machining of metals generally involves cutting, shaping, or forming of metal parts with power-driven tools called *machine tools*. Machine tools cut, shape, or form metal parts—

(1) through the cutting and removal of metal chips by the use of edge tools, as in Figs. 1-6 and 1-8; (2) through shearing, in much the same manner as paper is sheared with a scissors; and (3) through the controlled corrosive action of either chemicals, electricity, or sound. In the third, more recently developed method, a combination of electrical and chemical action is used in several modern machining processes for ultra-hard materials. The use of sound with an ultrasonic process is employed in machining otherwise unmachinable materials.

Fig. 1-2. Machine Tools Produce Machines and Equipment for All Major Divisions of Industry

Of the three general ways in which machine tools produce metal parts, the first method is basic and most important for the machine shop student. Operations which involve the cutting and removal of metal chips are performed on all basic machine tools. They may also be performed on specialized production machine tools.

Before machine tools were developed, metals were shaped with hand tools such as the hammer, chisel, file, and abrasive stone. The chisel when struck with a hammer removed chips from the base metal. The abrasive stone removed fine grains or chips of material from the workpiece on which it was rubbed. Machine tools used in machining metals cut in a manner similar to hand tools, except that the cutting tools are power driven, thus cutting many times faster, and the workpiece is held rigidly in the machine. Some examples of machine tools are the drill press, metal lathe, grinder, milling machine, and metal shaper.

Machine Tools Contribute to Growth of Civilization

Have you ever wondered why there has been more progress in civilization during the past two-hundred years than during the previous period of all recorded history? This progress was due to the development and use of power-driven machine tools which produce metal parts by machining. Prior to this development, all material goods were shaped, formed, or made with hand tools, manipulated by human or animal muscle power. The rate of progress of civilization is traceable to the rate of man's development of tools — first, hand tools, and more recently, machine tools. Through the direction of human energy and tools, together with material resources, man has promoted his material welfare and the present status of civilization.

The earliest-known hand tools were made of wood, stone, animal bones, and animal teeth, and were manipulated entirely by human muscle power. Then, about 2400 B.C., the beginning of the bronze age, hand tools were made of copper and bronze, and energy was supplied by both human and animal muscle power. Since copper and bronze were very scarce, the supply of tools was limited. Hence, man's material wealth and the growth of civilization progressed slowly.

During the iron age, which started about 1000 B.C., hand tools were made of iron derived from iron ore. These tools were less expensive, more durable, and of better quality than those of wood, stone, or bronze. More people were able to acquire the iron tools and more products could be produced. In addition, animals became domesticated and were more widely used to replace human power.

Prior to the Industrial Revolution, hand tools were used to shape and form materials for construction of utensils, furniture, shelter, wagons, ships, and the many implements necessary for everyday life. Craftsmen attained great skills in producing material goods, though luxury items were available only for the wealthy.

The invention of the steam engine by James Watt in England in 1776 marks the beginning of the Industrial Revolution. With the use of mechanical power provided by the steam engine, man's energy was multiplied many times. Material goods could be produced more rapidly than ever because machines could be power driven. The key which unlocked the door to increased production of material goods was *power-driven machine tools* which were used to machine metals. With these tools, steam engines and many other machines and tools were developed, and their uses spread rapidly. Power-driven machine tools were used to build the first reapers, electrical generators, steam boats, railroad locomotives, diesel engines, gasoline engines, and the many machines which continued to be developed.

This brief historical review of the development and use of hand tools and machine tools provides a background of information which will enable you to study about the machining of metals with greater understanding. A further brief historical review of the development of several basic machine tools is presented in succeeding chapters concerned with particular machines such as the lathe and the milling machine.

Machine Tools and Mass Production

Mass production is a method of rapidly producing objects in standard sizes and in large numbers, by the use of mechanically powered machines or machine tools. Mass production involves the following basic factors: interchangeability of parts, specialization of work performed by each worker, the mechanical conveyance of parts to each worker, and the elimination of waste motion by each worker.

Almost every industrial product in America today, from light bulbs to automobiles, is mass-produced. Mass production techniques provide for rapid production of material goods by unskilled or semi-skilled workers. This further reduces the cost of industrial products and makes them readily available to more people.

Historical Background

During the American Colonial period, and during earlier periods of Medieval history, a skilled artisan or craftsman using hand tools produced all of the necessary parts for a carriage, a piece of furniture, or a musket. This method required highly skilled workers, it limited production, and the products were expensive. Since each part of an item, such as a musket, was made and fitted by one particular craftsman, the parts were not interchangeable with those of other muskets.

Eli Whitney, whom we have all heard of as the inventor of the cotton gin, is considered the father of mass production methods. In 1798 he agreed to produce 10,000 muskets for the United States Government during a two-year period. Toward the end of the two years, Whitney had produced only 500 muskets. The government called him to Washington to give an account of his agreement to fulfill the contract. Whitney placed a box before a group of arms experts representing the gov-

ernment. From the box he took ten stocks, ten triggers, ten barrels, and so on, and placed them in separate piles. He asked a member of the group to select one part from each pile. He then assembled the parts into a musket. He repeated this procedure until the ten muskets were assembled. Anyone could assemble a musket once the parts were properly made.

Whitney had used most of the two-year period *tooling up* for mass production. He constructed *jigs* for guiding cutting tools and *fixtures* for holding parts in position while they were being machined or formed. He designed and constructed special power-driven machines for performing specific *repetitive* operations or for making duplicate parts. He trained many of the workers to do specific jobs, so that much of the work involved in producing the muskets could be performed by unskilled or semi-skilled workers. Whitney could then produce the remaining order in a relatively short period of time. He received approval to complete his contract.

By today's production standards, much of Whitney's work was very crude. His products had a very rough finish and had to be filed, polished, and finally fitted together by hand. Part of this difficulty was due to the lack of precision measuring devices, systems of measurement, and standards of accuracy. However, Whitney's work established the concepts for the mass production methods which followed and became the basis for modern industrial production.

The American Engineering Standards Committee was created in 1918 for the purpose of establishing standards of quality and methods of mass production in most industries in the country. Today this organization is called the American Standards Association. The study and work of this group have contributed much toward improved mass production standards and techniques used in modern industry.

The Assembly Line

The *assembly line* method is another technique used in mass production. This method was pioneered by the American automobile industry during the early 1900's. After the parts of the automobile had been made, the frame was placed on a conveyor belt, and various workers were stationed along its length. As the frame was carried along the line, each worker performed a specialized task involving the assembly of a particular part or series of parts. Each worker had to perform his task accurately during a specified time, or the whole line was stopped. When the end of the line was reached, the automobile was completely assembled, painted, and ready for inspection and operation. Since its creation, the assembly line has been used as a method of rapidly assembling not only automobiles but many other machines and appliances throughout industry. This method has also reduced the cost of production.

Machine Tools Necessary for Mass Production

Mass production methods would not be possible today without the use of the basic machine tools which are necessary for construction of specialized machine tools, automated production machines, or other specialized production machines.

Machine tools often have been referred to as the "machines which make machines." They are used both directly and indirectly in the production of all manufactured industrial products, consumer goods, and consumer services. Machine tools are used *directly* when used to produce other machine tools or specialized production types of machine tools. They also are used directly when used to make machines for use in the mass production of parts for automobiles, television sets, home appliances, and other types of hard consumer goods. Machine tools are used *indirectly* when used to manufacture food-making machinery, packaging machinery, electric motors, agricultural machinery, dry cleaning machinery, textile machinery, and similar items necessary for production of modern goods and services.

Machine tools made possible the interchangeability of parts required in mass production. Several methods are used: The parts may be accurately machined on specialized production machine tools, as shown in Fig. 1-3. They may be stamped or formed by accurately machined dies or punches in punch presses. The parts also may be produced through the use of other specialized production machines or processes. Machine tools are required for the construction of machines and equipment necessary for all common mass production processes.

Machine tools are also important because metal parts very frequently can be produced at lower cost by machining than through the use of other processes such as casting, welding, forging, or forming. Machining is frequently the only method which can be utilized in modern manufacturing for producing parts requiring dimensions with very close tolerances.

Since the *gross national product* of a nation includes the total production of all goods and services, both it and the standard of living usually rise when production is increased. Thus, machine tools have contributed not only to increased production, but to rising standards of living and to our nation's wealth. They have made possible the production of more goods for more people at lower cost.

Fig. 1-3. Engine Blocks for Large Tractors Being Bored on Specialized Production Machine Tools (Caterpillar)

The Five Basic Machining Arts

There are many different machining operations which can be performed on many different specialized machine tools, but most of the common machining operations can be classified under the heading of *five basic machining techniques or arts — drilling, turning and boring, milling, shaping or planing*, and *grinding*. Machining operations such as reaming, tapping, facing, threading, broaching, sawing, or honing can be classified under one of the basic techniques based upon the principles involved in the operation.*

Although it is possible to demonstrate any one of the five basic machining techniques on several different types of specialized machine tools, they are most commonly performed on *five basic machine tools* — the drill press, the metalworking lathe, the milling machine, the shaper or planer, and the grinder. These tools commonly are included in school machine shops for teaching the basic arts of machining metals. The principles learned may be readily applied to setting up and operating many of the large specialized production machine tools and multipurpose machine tools used in modern industry.

The variety and number of combinations of machine tools in use today are almost unlimited. Some are so small they are mounted on a work bench, while others are as large as a three-story house. They range in cost from a few hundred dollars to hundreds of thousands of dollars. Some machine tools weigh several hundred tons and require a fairly large area for their operation. Large or small, however, most of the common machine tools can be considered as falling into major groups which are identified according to *five basic techniques of machining metal*.

Drilling

Drilling is a machining operation which involves making holes in metal workpieces. It is done with a rotating cutting tool called a twist drill, Fig. 1-4. The basic machine used for drilling is called a drilling machine or drill press, Fig. 1-5. Operations such as reaming and tapping usually are classified under the art of drilling. *Reaming* consists of finishing a hole already drilled, usually to very close tolerances. *Tapping* is the process of cutting a thread inside the hole so that a cap screw or machine screw may be used in it. Drilling operations also can be performed on lathes, jig boring machines, vertical milling machines, and on certain other special types of machines.

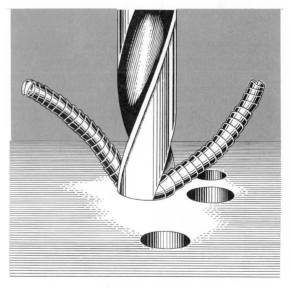

Fig. 1-4. Twist Drill Machining a Hole

*Numerous authorities concerned with metals manufacturing processes classify an additional group of *metal forming* processes as a *sixth basic technique*. Those processes most often included are shearing, stamping, pressing, and forging. These operations do not involve metal removal in the form of chips. Hence the principles involved are somewhat different than those of the first five basic techniques listed above. Although the metal forming operations classified as the sixth basic technique are very important in metals manufacturing industries, details concerning these operations are not within the scope of this book.

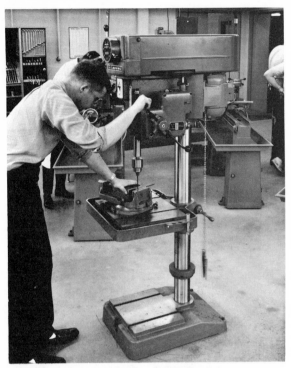

Fig. 1-5. Drilling with a Floor-Model Drill Press
(Clausing Div., Atlas Press)

**Fig. 1-6. Operator Turning Work Mounted in Chuck
on Metalworking Lathe** (South Bend Lathe)

Turning and Boring

The basic machine used for *turning* is the metalworking lathe, also called an engine lathe, Fig. 1-6. The lathe commonly is called the "father of the entire machine tool family." For turning operations, the lathe utilizes a single-point tool which removes metal as it travels longitudinally along work which is revolving, Figs. 1-7 and 1-8. Turning operations apply to machining many different cylindrical shapes, such as axles, gear blanks, pulleys, or threaded shafts. Turning may involve machining straight or tapered cylindrical objects or machining faces or shoulders on cylindrical objects. Turning operations also are performed on other specialized machines such as turret lathes or screw machines.

Boring involves enlarging and finishing a hole which has been drilled or cored. A hole is bored by means of a single-point tool which travels along the inside of the work, Fig. 1-9.

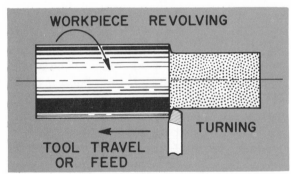

Fig. 1-7. Turning on a Lathe

**Fig. 1-8. Turning a Steel Shaft Mounted between
Centers** (South Bend Lathe)

26

Boring operations are performed to enlarge and accurately locate holes. Holes may be bored straight, tapered, or with a shoulder as in Fig. 1-9. When boring is performed on a lathe, the tool travels along the work longitudinally as the work revolves, Fig. 1-10. When boring is performed on a drill press, the work remains stationary while the boring tool revolves as it enters and bores the hole to the desired depth. Boring operations also are performed on milling machines, turret lathes, jig boring machines, and on many specialized production machine tools.

Although many authorities in the area of metal machining classify boring under turning, others classify this operation under drilling because it is a hole-forming operation. In this unit, boring is classified under turning because of the similarity between both turning and boring tools.

Milling

Milling is an operation which removes metal with a multiple-tip, rotating, cutting tool called

a milling cutter, Fig. 1-11. A milling cutter has two or more teeth. A narrow milling cutter resembles a circular saw which is familiar to most people. The basic machine used for milling operations is called a milling machine, Fig. 1-12. There are several different types of milling machines, such as the plain, universal, and vertical milling machines. Many different styles of milling cutters also are designed for various types of milling operations, e.g., ma-

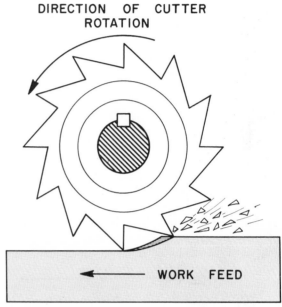

Fig. 1-11. Milling with a Plain Milling Cutter

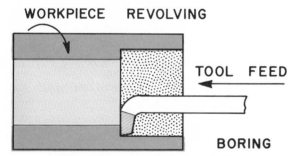

Fig. 1-9. Boring a Hole on a Lathe

Fig. 1-10. Boring Work Mounted in a Lathe Chuck
(South Bend Lathe)

Fig. 1-12. Milling Grooves in a Shaft with a Plain Horizontal Milling Machine
(Cincinnati Milling Machine)

chining flat surfaces, curved surfaces, grooves, shoulders, and many special shapes. Milling cutters also may be used on jig boring machines and on specialized production machine tools.

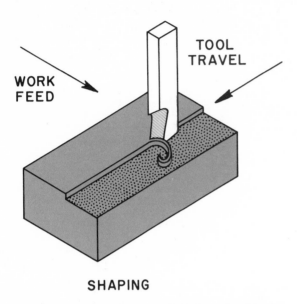

SHAPING

Fig. 1-13. Tool in Relation to Workpiece when Shaping

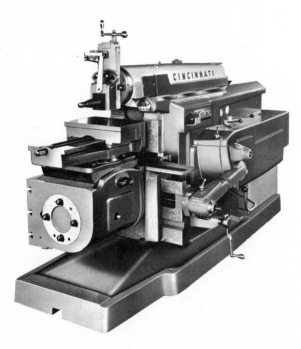

Fig. 1-14. Heavy-Duty Shaper (Cincinnati Shaper)

Shaping and Planing

Shaping and planing are operations which involve the machining of flat surfaces with a single-point edge tool, Fig. 1-13. The basic machine used for shaping is a shaper, Fig. 1-14. The basic machine used for planing is a planer, Fig. 1-15. You should understand the difference between these two machines.

The cutting tool on a *shaper* reciprocates back and forth along the work, while the work automatically feeds toward the tool a small amount for each new stroke, Fig. 1-13. The shaper commonly is used for machining short, flat surfaces or grooves. The surfaces may be horizontal, vertical, angular, or sometimes irregular.

Fig. 1-15. Large Industrial Planer with Two Tool Heads
(G. A. Gray)

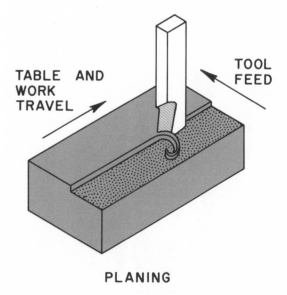

PLANING

Fig. 1-16. Tool in Relation to Workpiece when Planing

The work on a *planer* moves back and forth on a reciprocating table underneath the cutting tool. The cutting tool feeds automatically across the work a small amount for each cutting stroke as the table reciprocates, Fig. 1-16. The planer is commonly used for machining long, flat surfaces or grooves. The surfaces may be horizontal, vertical, or angular.

The shaper and planer are similar in several respects. A single-point cutting tool is used on both, except that the tool on the planer usually is heavier for heavier cuts. They both perform similar operations; however, the shaper is used for shorter cutting strokes on shorter workpieces. The planer is used for long cutting strokes which cannot be performed on a shaper. The principles involved in performing operations on both the shaper and planer are quite similar. Since planers are relatively expensive and occupy much floor space, they are not included in many school shops.

Broaching   Broaching is generally classified under the art of shaping and planing. Broaching is somewhat similar to shaping, except that a broaching tool is a multiple-tooth tool which completes a broaching operation in a single stroke. Many operations which can be performed on a shaper may be performed more economically by broaching.

Broaching operations involve both internal and external machining applications. Examples of internal broaching include making square holes, hexagonal holes, octagonal holes, irregularly shaped holes, serrations in holes, and keyways in gears or similar objects. Examples of external broaching include making grooves or splines on shafts. Although broaching may be done in special broaching machines, in the school shop it is most frequently performed with a hand-operated press.

The teeth of the broaching tool are equally spaced, and each tooth is so designed that it feeds further into the work, as in Fig. 1-17. The broaching operation is completed in a single stroke, as the broaching tool is pressed or drawn through (or over) the work. The action of a broaching tool used to cut a keyway in a gear can be observed in Fig. 1-18. The method used in cutting a keyway with a broaching tool in an arbor press is shown in Figs. 1-18 and 1-19. Broaching tools for use in cutting keyways with an arbor press are available in sets, as in Fig. 1-20. A square hole is made by drilling a round hole first and then pressing or drawing a square broaching tool through the hole.

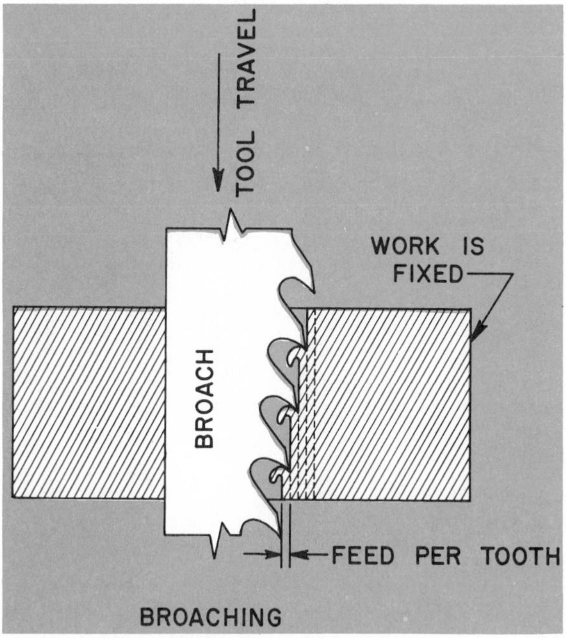

Fig. 1-17. Action of Broaching Tool

Fig. 1-18. Broaching Tool Used to Cut Keyway in Gear Blank (du Mont)

Grinding

Grinding is a machining operation which involves removal of very fine metallic chips from a workpiece which is rubbed by a grinding wheel, as in Figs. 1-21 and 1-22. Grinding is one of the most accurate of all the basic machining methods. Very close tolerances and very smooth surfaces can be produced. Parts may be ground to tolerances of plus or minus .0001" (one ten-thousandth of an inch) with a precision grinding machine.

The basic machine used for grinding is called a grinder. Grinding operations may be classified as either precision grinding or nonprecision grinding, depending on the purpose. *Precision grinding* is concerned with grinding to close tolerances with smooth surfaces. *Non-*

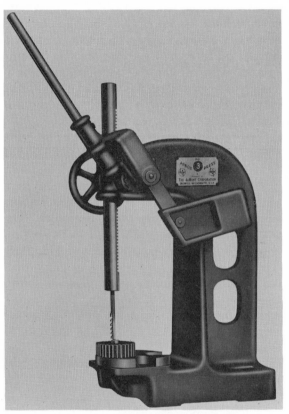

Fig. 1-19. Arbor Press Broaching Keyway in Gear Blank (du Mont)

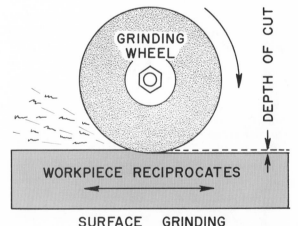

Fig. 1-21. Magnified View of Metal Chips Produced by Grinding Wheel (Norton)

Fig. 1-20. Keyway Broach Set (du Mont)

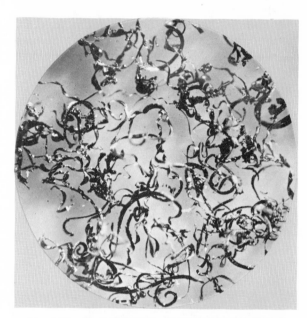

Fig. 1-22. Action of Grinding Wheel in Surface Grinding

precision grinding involves the removal of metal which cannot be removed any other way, or where accuracy is not a factor. Grinders are designed for use for one purpose or the other. Precision grinders are available for many types of grinding, including surface grinding, external cylindrical grinding, internal cylindrical grinding, thread grinding, and grinding of objects of many different shapes and sizes.

Flat surfaces are ground on a precision surface grinder, Fig. 1-23. The relationship of the grinding wheel and the work is shown in Fig. 1-22. The workpiece, mounted on the grinding machine table, reciprocates back and forth under the grinding wheel; when each stroke is completed, the work is cross-fed further under the wheel until the entire surface is ground. Surface grinders are available with either manual or power-operated feeding mechanisms.

Workpieces with a cylindrical shape are ground on cylindrical-type grinding machines, such as the plain cylindrical grinding machine shown in Fig. 1-24. The relationship of the grinding wheel and the work in cylindrical grinding is illustrated in Fig. 1-25. This and other types of grinding may be studied at greater depth in the sections of the book concerned with grinding.

Lapping generally is classified under the art of grinding. Lapping involves the use of abrasive pastes or compounds and, therefore, its use is limited to the removal of very small amounts of stock. It is used in instances where a high degree of surface finish and precision are required.

Honing is widely accepted as a process apart from lapping. It is used for extremely accurate finishing of holes. A common type of honing machine has a rotating head which carries abrasive inserts for producing accurately finished holes.

Specialized Production Machine Tools

Many specialized machine tools utilize one or more of the five basic machining arts listed above. The specialized machines are usually designed as a modification or as an adaptation of one or more of the five basic machine tools. For example, several specialized machine tools are adaptations of the metalwork-

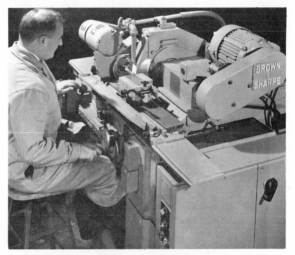

Fig. 1-24. Grinding a Part in a Plain Cylindrical Grinding Machine (Safety goggles are recommended.) (Brown & Sharpe)

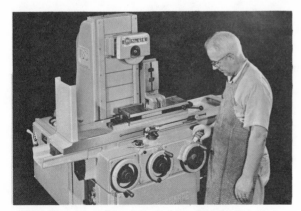

Fig. 1-23. Grinding a Part with a Surface Grinding Machine (Brown & Sharpe)

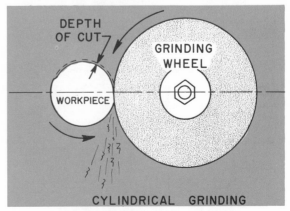

Fig. 1-25. Relationship of Grinding Wheel and Workpiece in Cylindrical Grinding

31

ing lathe and the drill press; these include the *hand screw machine*, the *turret lathe* (Fig. 1-26), and the *automatic screw machine*. These specialized machines are designed to perform turning, drilling, and many other operations rapidly and in sequence on one particular workpiece. They may be tooled to increase production through rapid repetition of the machining operations necessary for producing duplicate parts quickly. The specialized production machine tools make mass production methods possible.

Multipurpose Machine Tools

In recent years, numerous multipurpose machine tools have been developed. For example, the *machining center* shown in Fig. 1-27 performs many different operations commonly performed on several basic machine tools. These operations include milling, drilling, boring, tapping and reaming. In addition, this machine is *numerically controlled*. With this system, a sequence of operations to be performed is punched in the form of coded infor-

mation on a tape which is fed into the machine. Each operation is coded according to letters and numbers. With the use of an electronic control system, the machine automatically performs the sequence of operations indicated on the tape. The machine center automatically can change and replace up to thirty different tools from its universal tool head. This type of machine eliminates the need for constructing many expensive jigs and fixtures which frequently are necessary in modern production machining applications.

It should be noted that the use of numerically controlled machine tools is rapidly increasing throughout American industry. Numerical control systems are used on many kinds of machine tools, including drilling machines, lathes, milling machines, punching machines, and multipurpose machine tools.

Variations in Machining Applications

The purpose in machining metal is to produce workpieces or parts which have the desired shape, size, and surface finish. The size may vary from the small parts in a watch or mechanical pencil to the engine block of a

Fig. 1-26. A Turret Lathe (Sheldon)

large, earth-moving tractor. Some machined parts require great accuracy and very smooth surfaces, while other parts require less accuracy and may have rougher surfaces. Machinability of the metals used may vary from easy to difficult. The number of particular machined parts needed may vary considerably, as well as the amount of metal which needs to be removed from a workpiece.

The accuracy and finish required on a machined workpiece must be considered in selecting the type of machine tool on which the piece is to be machined, the type of cutting tool to be used, and the type of work-holding accessories and fixtures needed on the machine. For example, a hole one-half inch in diameter may be drilled with a drill press, a lathe, certain milling machines, or a jig boring machine. Several of these machine tools are simple in design, less costly, and require less skill to operate than others. Therefore, many factors must be understood and considered in selecting the method and tools required to machine certain workpieces in modern machine shop practice. The basic machine tools, their characteristics, and the operations which they will perform are described in greater detail in succeeding sections of this book.

Test Your Knowledge of Section 1

Unit I: Machine Tools and Machining

1. Explain what is meant by the phrase, *machining of metals*.
2. List three general ways in which machine tools cut or form metals.
3. How were metals cut to shape before the invention of machine tools?
4. Explain several basic differences between machine tools and hand tools used to cut metals.
5. List five examples of machine tools.
6. Why was progress in civilization greater during the past 200 years than during the previous period of all recorded history?
7. What factor largely determined the rate of man's progress?
8. From what materials were the earliest known hand tools made?
9. When were the first metal hand tools developed?
10. When were hand tools first made of iron?
11. What were the principal advantages of iron tools over previous tools.

Fig. 1-27. A Numerically Controlled Machining Center (Cincinnati Milling Machine)

12. How were material goods manufactured before the onset of the Industrial Revolution?
13. When did the Industrial Revolution occur?
14. What were the principal sources of power used to manipulate tools and to perform services before the Industrial Revolution?
15. What was the basic source of power used to drive machine tools at the onset of the Industrial Revolution?
16. List five early machines or inventions which were produced by power-driven machine tools.
17. Of what value is a knowledge of the history of hand and machine tools?

Unit 2: Machine Tools and Mass Production
1. Define *mass production*.
2. What basic factors are involved in mass production?
3. Why are products which are mass-produced less expensive than custom or individually made products?
4. Who is considered the father of mass production methods?
5. Why was Eli Whitney so slow in producing the first 500 muskets required in his contract for 10,000? Why do you think the Government did not cancel his contract?
6. Why was Whitney's work on his muskets considered crude by today's standards?
7. What group was established to develop standards of quality and methods which result in improved mass production?
8. Explain the assembly line method used in mass production of consumer goods.
9. What are the principal advantages in having an automobile assembled by the assembly line method, as compared with two men working in pairs to assemble the whole automobile?
10. What is meant by using machine tools "directly" to produce goods?
11. List several items which are made "directly" by machine tools.

12. What is meant by using tools "indirectly" to produce goods or services?
13. List several types of goods or services which have been produced or made possible "indirectly" by machine tools.
14. List several mass production methods which are used to make parts identical and interchangeable.
15. Are some metal parts or products mass-produced by machining? Explain.
16. Explain how machine tools affect the wealth of a nation and its people.

Unit 3: The Five Basic Machining Arts
1. List the five basic machining techniques.
2. Why can such operations as reaming, facing, and broaching be classified under the heading of one of the five basic machining techniques?
3. Name the five basic machine tools.
4. Why are the five basic machine tools frequently included in school machine shops?
5. Explain what drilling is, and list several machines on which drilling operations may be performed.
6. Explain what turning is, and indicate which basic machine is used for turning.
7. List several typical objects which are machined by turning on a lathe.
8. Explain what is meant by boring, and indicate a basic machine which frequently is used for boring.
9. List several machines which may be used for boring.
10. Explain what milling means, and indicate which basic machine is commonly used for milling.
11. Explain the principal difference between a milling cutter and a turning or boring tool.
12. Explain what shaping is, and indicate what basic machine tool is used for shaping.
13. Explain what planing is, and indicate what machine is used for planing.
14. Explain the principal difference between shaping and planing.
15. In what ways are the shaper and planer similar?

16. What similarities can you observe between cutting tools used for shaping, planing, turning, and boring operations?
17. Explain what broaching is and how it is performed.
18. What similarity exists between broaching and shaping?
19. List several types of operations which can be performed by broaching.
20. Explain what grinding means.
21. Explain the difference between precision grinding and nonprecision grinding.
22. List several types of precision grinding operations.
23. Explain the difference between a basic machine tool and a specialized machine tool.
24. Define a multipurpose machine tool.
25. Describe the system of numerical control.
26. Explain how knowledge and experience in operating the five basic machine tools can be of value in setting up and operating a modern multipurpose machine tool.

Remote Controls — Another Benefit is Safety
(Caterpillar Tractor Co.)

SECTION 2

Safety

Safety in the Machine Shop

Safety applied to procedures in a school or industrial shop resolves into using common sense and good judgment. Modern machinery is equipped with guards and devices designed to protect the operator and make operation of equipment as safe as possible. However, statistics show that guards and other safety devices afford only 15 percent protection. Thus, 85 percent of all accidents in school and industrial plants are due to a factor (or factors) that cannot be guarded against by mechanical devices. Strange as it may seem, the same percentage of accidents attributable to the human element in industrial plants applies to farming, homemaking, the operation of automobiles, and all other activities. Most accidents are a result of someone's thoughtlessness, carelessness, lack of knowledge, or lack of consideration for the rights of others and may be avoided by acquiring the habit of *thinking before doing*.

If persons who experience repeated accidents can be said to be habitually careless, thoughtless and reckless, the opposite usually may be said of persons whose records are reasonably clear; they may be classed as habitually careful, thoughtful, considerate, and informed of safe practices and procedures.

Safety is principally a matter of striving earnestly to learn and follow safe practices and procedures at all times. It is much more a matter of do's than don'ts. Specific practices and precautions concerned with the efficient operation and use of each of the basic machine tools are included in the sections of this book concerned with each machine.

Safe practices concerned with first aid, clothing worn in the machine shop, orderliness in the shop, general safe practices in the shop, and safety in the use of hand tools are included in this unit.

First Aid

1. Always notify the instructor immediately when injured in the school shop, regardless of how slight the injury may be.
2. Always apply *first aid treatment* to cuts or bruises, regardless of how slight. It is good practice to allow slight and moderate cuts to bleed for a minute or two before attempting to stop the flow of blood. Free bleeding will carry infectious particles out of the wound. Severe cuts or bruises should receive the immediate attention of a physician.
3. Always treat burns promptly, according to their degree of severity. A first-degree burn is one in which the skin is merely reddened; a second-degree burn is one in which the skin is blistered; and a third-degree, one in which the flesh is seared or charred. Treat first-degree burns with applications of cold water; then apply a sterile, dry bandage. Second- and third-degree burns should receive the *immediate attention of a physician*.

Clothing in the Machine Shop

1. Always wear appropriate clothing when working near machinery. Keep your necktie tucked into your shirt and the sleeves

rolled up. It is best to wear short-sleeved shirts, Fig. 2-1.

2. Avoid wearing watches, rings, bracelets or other loose jewelry which can catch in a machine.

3. It is dangerous to have long loose hair when working with machine tools, as it may become caught in a machine. Persons with long hair should wear a snug-fitting cap in the machine shop.

4. While operating machines, avoid wearing gloves. They may easily become caught in the machine. While sharp-edged tools or materials are being handled, gloves may be worn; however, the machine should be stopped during this time.

5. Wear safety goggles or a face shield of an approved type at all times in the machine or metalworking shop. See Fig. 2-1. They are more comfortable than a glass eye.

Orderly Procedures

1. Clean up all oil, grease, or other liquids spilled on the floor. They are slipping hazards.

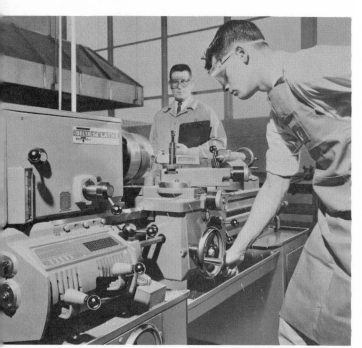

Fig. 2-1. Machine Tool Worker Dressed Appropriately for Safe Operation of Metal Lathe or Other Machine Tools (Rockwell)

2. Keep the aisles free of metal chips, shavings, and coils. One can be seriously injured by any of these.

3. Keep aisles free of stock, small metal remnants, or waste.

4. Return long metal bars to the proper storage place after cutting off the necessary stock.

5. Return all tools and machine accessories from work stations or machines after completing a job. Falling tools can cause injuries.

6. Place wiping cloths or waste materials in the proper container after use.

General Safety Procedures

1. Observe all rules of conduct, regardless of whether they were made by your classmates or by school authorities. Generally, rules are for the effective, wholesome, and safe operation of the institution in the best interest of all concerned.

2. Operate machines only after being authorized to do so, or under the supervision of the instructor.

3. Always follow the instructions of your teacher. By doing a job *differently*, you may remain *different* through the loss of a finger or through other injury.

4. The school shops and laboratories are places for purposeful activities, where the worker must direct his undivided attention to what he is doing. Do not divert his attention by play, needless conversation, shouting, whistling, or boisterousness of any form.

5. Avoid grasping metal you suspect of being hot. If doubtful, test by touching the piece very lightly with the moistened tips of the fingers.

6. When it is *necessary* to approach someone operating a machine, do so in a manner which will not annoy or alarm him.

7. Keep your fingers away from moving machinery or moving parts.

8. Avoid leaning on or touching a machine which someone else is operating.

9. Before starting a machine, be sure that all its safety devices are in place and operating effectively.

10. Always be sure that the work and the cutting tool are mounted securely before starting the machine.

11. Where two or more persons are working with a machine, only one person should operate the controls or switches.

12. Avoid *feeling* the machined surface of stock while the machine is running. Fingers can be lost easily this way.

13. Avoid leaving a machine while it is running or in motion, even if it is coasting with the power off. Someone else may not notice that it is still in motion and may be injured.

14. Make it a practice always to stop the machine when performing an operation where there is danger of the tool catching (for example, when using an inside caliper).

15. Make it a practice to stop machines when oiling, cleaning, adjusting, or repairing them. Be sure the power switch is off.

16. Avoid using your hands to stop a machine or a moving part such as a lathe spindle or a drill press spindle.

17. Use a brush or a thin piece of wood to remove metal chips. *Do not use your bare hands.*

18. Keep machines free of oil cans, wrenches, and measuring tools while in operation.

19. Whenever you have occasion to remove guards, or change the normal position of the machine, or remove parts to perform a specific operation, be sure that all are replaced properly before leaving the machine.

20. When closing electric switches, always grasp the switch by the insulated handle and keep your hands away from the metal parts of the switch or the switch box itself.

21. Avoid touching a moving belt or pulley.

22. When necessary to change V-belts, *stop the machine;* then change the belt.

23. Practice lending a cheerful helping hand when requested or when you observe someone in need.

24. When you desire the assistance of a fellow student, ask for it in a gentlemanly manner. Be sure to explain the nature of the assistance wanted and any risks that may be involved (for example, handling hot metal).

25. Ask for help in lifting or handling heavy stock or machine accessories. Also ask for assistance in handling long pieces of stock, in order to avoid injuring other persons or equipment.

26. Practice being courteous, considerate, and obliging at all times and under all circumstances.

27. Avoid standing in your own light. One needs the best light possible to do accurate work and avoid injury.

28. Avoid working in restricted areas which may be designated by floor markings.

29. When in the vicinity of a machine from which stock or parts are thrown occasionally, make it a practice to stand where you will be out of danger.

30. Be very cautious in using equipment with projecting setscrews. Where possible, they should be replaced with flush setscrews.

31. Avoid blowing metal chips from a machine or other work station with compressed air; be sure that you and all others in the area are wearing approved safety goggles when using compressed air for any purpose.

32. Carefully observe cautions as to safe practices when using specific machinery; safety precautions are given by your instructor and at appropriate places in the instruction units which follow.

33. Under all conditions — stop, look, and *think* — before you proceed in a dangerous or definitely unknown and unfamiliar situation.

Fire Precautions

1. Learn the location of the nearest fire alarm in the shop or in the building, in case of fire.

2. Learn the location and proper use of fire protection equipment in the building, in case of fire. Fire extinguishers which use a dry chemical or carbon dioxide should be readily accessible at all times.

3. Place oily rags or waste in the proper container provided.

4. Always store inflammable materials (such as cleaning solutions, paint thinners, and

lacquers) in a metal cabinet away from open flames. Keep a limited supply of these materials on hand — only enough for use over a short period of time.

Safety with Hand Tools

1. Use the right tool for the right job, and be sure that it is the right size for the job, Fig. 2-2.
2. Be sure the tool is wiped clean — free of grease, oil, and dirt.
3. Wipe your hands clean and free of grease before using tools.
4. Be sure tools are sharp and in good condition. Dull tools must be forced and cause accidents easily.
5. Carry only the number of tools needed to a work station. A shop tool falling on someone can be dangerous.
6. Carry sharp-edged tools with edges or points down. Avoid carrying them in your pockets.
7. When handing tools to fellow workers, give them handle first.
8. Check that the heads of cold chisels and punches are properly dressed; when they start to *mushroom* or *check*, small pieces may break off and cause serious injury.
9. When chiseling, be careful that small flying chips do not hit others in the shop.

Fig. 2-2. Many Accidents Happen in Using Hand Tools
(J. H. Williams)

10. Always use the right wrench for the right job. Your knuckles or hands can easily be injured when a wrench slips. See Fig. 2-3.
11. Check that file handles fit snugly to the tang of the file.
12. Always clean tools properly when you are through with them. Then store them in the proper place.
13. Always report tool damage to the instructor. Damaged tools are dangerous.

The person who has achieved recognition as a careful, considerate, thoughtful, far-seeing workman has daily practiced these virtues.

Test Your Knowledge of Section 2

Unit 4: Safety in the Machine Shop

1. What factors cause most accidents?
2. How can most accidents be prevented?
3. Where in this book can you find information on specific safe practices for each of the basic machine tools?
4. Who should be notified immediately in case of injury, even if the injury seems very slight?
5. What types of injuries should receive first aid treatments?
6. When should burns receive first aid treatment?
7. What type of burn injuries should always receive the attention of a physician?
8. What types of clothing are considered safe in the school shop?
9. What kinds of jewelry should be removed when working in the shop?
10. What dangers are involved in having long, loose hair when working with machines?
11. When should safety goggles or a face shield be worn in the machine shop?
12. Why is it dangerous to leave oil or grease on the floor?
13. What injuries can be caused by coiled metal chips on the floor?
14. Why should you make it a practice to see that work and cutting tools are mounted securely before starting a machine?

15. Explain several general safety procedures which should be practiced in the machine shop.
16. What procedure should be used in changing V-belts to change speeds on a machine?
17. What dangers are involved in blowing metal chips off a machine with compressed air?
18. What should you usually do before proceeding with a definitely unknown and unfamiliar situation?
19. What precautions should be taken to prevent fires in the shop?
20. List several safety precautions which should be taken when working with hand tools in the machine shop.
21. What safety precautions should be taken when chiseling a piece of metal?
22. What possible dangers are involved if you operate a machine before you are given instruction on how to use it?

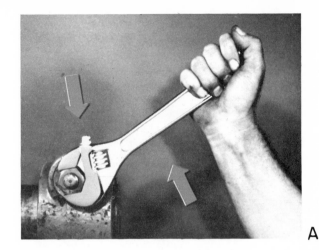

A

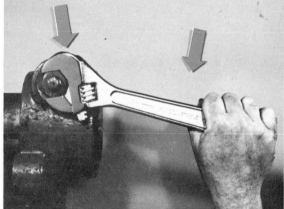

B

C

Fig. 2-3. Use a Wrench Properly (J. H. Williams)
(A) Wrong: Do not push on the handle; (B) Right: Pull
on the handle; (C) Use offset box wrench on bolts
and nuts in locations like this.

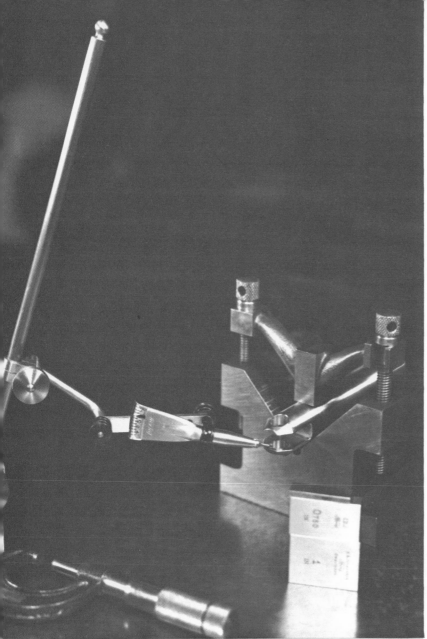

Measurement — An Art of the Precision Workman

Measurement, Measuring Tools, and Gages

Principles of Measurement

Accurate measurement is the basis for machine shop work and modern manufacturing. Every part produced in the machine shop must be accurate to size, within specified limits. Parts which are not accurately made will not assemble and fit properly with mating parts. Hence, the finished machine or mechanism will not operate properly.

Each worker in the machine shop is responsible for the accuracy of his work. Accurate workmanship depends primarily on accurate measurement and layout work. To insure accuracy in workmanship, the machinist must know the principles of measurement. He also must be familiar with and must know how to use the common hand tools, measuring tools, measuring instruments, and gages used in his trade.

The machinist uses many tools, instruments, and gages for making the measurements necessary in the course of his work. Some of these measurements need not be made with greater accuracy than one sixty-fourth of an inch. At other times, measurements must be made within one-thousandth or within one ten-thousandth of an inch. In the manufacture of special precision gage blocks and special measuring instruments, measurement sometimes must be within tolerances of two-millionths of an inch. In order to make accurate measurements, the machinist uses tools such as rules, micrometer calipers, gages, gage blocks, and special optical measuring instruments. These tools are presented in the next unit, after a review of some of the principles of measurement.

Linear Measurement

In the United States, Canada, and Great Britain, the *English* system of linear (straight line) measurement is used. Most other major countries use the *metric* system of linear measurement. The standard unit of measurement for the English system is the *inch*, while that for the metric system is the *meter*. One meter is equal to 39.37 inches.

English System: In the English system, the inch is divided into smaller parts for finer measurements. It may be divided into common fractions such as $\frac{1}{2}''$, $\frac{1}{4}''$, $\frac{1}{8}''$, $\frac{1}{16}''$, $\frac{1}{32}''$ and $\frac{1}{64}''$. It also may be divided into decimal fractions such as $\frac{1}{10}''$, $\frac{1}{100}''$, and $\frac{1}{1000}''$. These fractions may be expressed with a numerator and a denominator as shown; however, in the machine shop and on drawings and blueprints, they frequently are expressed in decimal form such as 0.1″, 0.01″, and 0.001″. Decimal fractions are expressed in the following manner:

$$\text{One-tenth inch} = \frac{1}{10}'' = 0.1''$$

$$\text{One-hundredth inch} = \frac{1}{100}'' = 0.01''$$

$$\text{One-thousandth inch} = \frac{1}{1,000}'' = 0.001''$$

$$\text{One ten-thousandth inch} = \frac{1}{10,000}'' = 0.000\,1''$$

$$\text{One hundred-thousandth inch} = \frac{1}{100,000}'' = 0.000\,01''$$

One-millionth inch =

$$\frac{1}{1,000,000}'' = 0.000\,001''$$

One-millionth inch = 1 microinch

Common fractions, such as the following, also are expressed in decimal form:

$\frac{1}{2}'' = 0.500''$	$\frac{1}{16}'' = 0.062\,5''$
$\frac{1}{4}'' = 0.250''$	$\frac{1}{32}'' = 0.031\,25''$
$\frac{1}{8}'' = 0.125''$	$\frac{1}{64}'' = 0.015\,625''$

Metric System: In the metric system, the meter is subdivided into the following parts:

1 meter = 10 decimeters (dm)
1 decimeter = 10 centimeters (cm)
1 centimeter = 10 millimeters (mm)

Hence, one *decimeter* is one-tenth meter, one *centimeter* is one-hundredth meter, and one *millimeter* is one-thousandth meter. Other subdivisions of the meter are also included in the metric system. One meter is equal to 39.37 inches. One inch is equal to 2.54 centimeters. Both dimensions are exact and are not rounded. (Further decimal positions would be zeros.)

Occasionally the machinist finds it necessary to convert measurements from the English system to the metric system or vice versa. The metric units of linear measure and equivalent English units are included in Table 42, appendix.

Standards for Measurement

Standards for linear measurement were established by the International Bureau of Weights and Measures. This bureau was created in 1875 and is located near Paris, France. It has representatives from most nations of the world. It keeps models or standards for units of metric measurement, including a standard for the meter.

The international standard for the meter is the length between two finely scribed lines on a platinum-iridium-alloy metal bar at a temperature of 32°F. (0°C.). This metal meter-bar was declared the International Prototype Meter, and all member nations received exact duplicate copies of it. The United States received its copy in 1889. It is kept at the Bureau of Standards at Washington, D. C.

The U.S. Bureau of Standards adopted the metric system in 1893 as a *standard* for legally defining the pound and the yard. The length of the U.S. yard was defined as $\frac{3600}{3937}$ meter. One inch was defined as 2.54 centimeters, exactly. Thus the units of linear measurement in the English system are defined in terms of equivalent metric units.

In 1959 the English-speaking countries, including the United States, Great Britain, and Canada, accepted the *International Inch* by general agreement, without specific legislation. The International Inch is equal to 2.54 centimeters, exactly. Prior to this date, the inch in Great Britain was defined in terms of the British Imperial Standard Yard which was a few millionths of a millimeter shorter than the U.S. yard.

The International Bureau of Weights and Measures also defined the length of the meter in terms of a specific number and kind of light-wave lengths. One meter equals 1,650,763.73 wave lengths of orange light emitted by Krypton-86 atoms in an electrical discharge; this is now the accepted standard. Since no standard of length is maintained for the English system, the International Inch, as defined in terms of metric units (2.54 centimeters), can be stated in terms of wave lengths of krypton light as follows:

1 inch = 0.0254 meters x 1,650,763.73 wave lengths per meter
1 inch = 41,929.3987 wave lengths
1 wave length = 0.000 023 8 inch

Measuring instruments for light-wave measurement also may utilize light emitted from sources such as helium or mercury.

Since light waves do not vary significantly with temperature and atmospheric conditions, this method of precise measurement may be duplicated in all parts of the world.

Without a standard for units of linear measurement, precision measurement, mass production methods, and interchangeability of parts would not be possible. Precision *gage blocks*, as shown in Fig. 3-131, are the practical standard of measurement used in machine shops the world over. Gage blocks are used for checking the accuracy of various measuring tools and instruments. They are also used for making extremely accurate measurements, as required for special work. Precision gage blocks are available with tolerances of plus or minus 2-millionths (0.000 002) inch. In their manufacture, size is measured to light-wave accuracy with optical instruments. Gage blocks and their use are explained in detail in Unit 13.

Limits and Tolerances for Interchangeability

Generally it is considered impossible to produce parts to absolute size, since some error or inaccuracy would always exist, even if a part were made to within one-millionth of an inch. Therefore, in most cases, it is impractical, costly, and wasteful to machine parts to a greater degree of accuracy than that which is required and specified on the drawing.

Interchangeability: Modern mass production methods require that parts be machined to size limitations which provide for interchangeability in use. The size limitations are indicated in notes or dimensions on working drawings.

The automobile is an example of the significance of interchangeability of parts. The parts are manufactured in different sections of the country and are shipped to an assembly plant where they are assembled. Other parts are sent to parts distributors where they are used later as replacements for worn-out parts. All of the parts, therefore, must be made within specific size limitations. The size limitations provide for interchangeability of parts on all automobiles of the make and model for which they were designed.

Terms Used: The terms used in dimensioning limits of size are so interrelated that they should be understood clearly

*American Standards Association, *Preferred Limits and Fits for Cylindrical Parts* (B4.1-1955), The American Society of Mechanical Engineers, 29 West 39th St., New York, New York. (Permission Granted).

for correct interpretation of dimensions. The following definitions are adapted from those by ASA:*

Actual size is a measured size.

Basic size is the size from which limits of size are derived by the application of allowances and tolerances. The basic size for the dimensions in Fig. 3-1 is 1.750".

Limits of size are the maximum and minimum permissible sizes which apply. Several methods are used in dimensioning to indicate limits of size, as shown in Fig. 3-1.

Tolerance is the total permissible variation of a size. It is the difference between the maximum and minimum limits of size. The tolerance for each of the examples in Fig. 3-1 is 0.002".

Fit is a general term which is used to signify the range of tightness which exists between two mating parts as a result of a specific combination of tolerances and allowances.

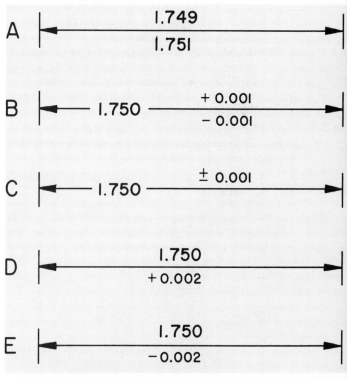

Fig. 3-1. Dimension Limits
In each case, the tolerance is 0.002".

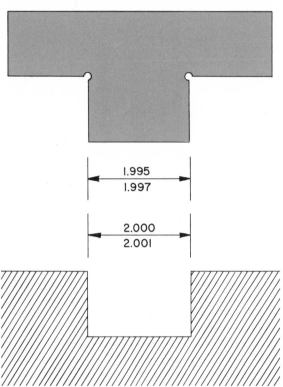

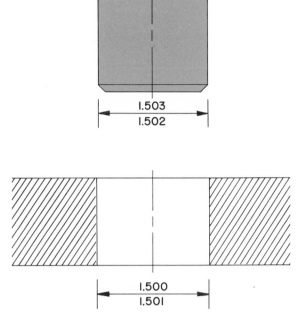

Fig. 3-3. Shaft and Hole Designed with Allowance (Negative) for Interference Fit
Loosest figure is 0.001″ interference; tightest figure is 0.003″ interference.

Fig. 3-2. An Example of Limit Dimensioning
Tolerance on tongue, 0.002″; tolerance on groove, 0.001″; allowance is 0.003″ (positive) for clearance fit.

Clearance fit is a fit which has limits of size which always provide a clearance between mating parts when assembled.

Interference fit is a fit which has limits of size which always provide for an interference between mating parts when assembled.

Allowance is an intentional difference between the maximum material size limits of mating parts. It is the minimum *clearance* (positive allowance) or maximum *interference* (negative allowance) between mating parts. Fig. 3-2 shows two parts which are designed to mate together with a clearance for a free-sliding fit. In this example, the tongue at a maximum material size (1.997″) and the groove at maximum material size (2.000″) provide for a 0.003″ *positive* allowance. The positive allowance provides for a free fit which is called a *clearance fit*.

The shaft and hole in Fig. 3-3 are designed with a *negative* allowance for a tight fit, which is called an *interference fit*. The loosest permissible fit has a 0.001″ interference. The tightest permissible fit has 0.003″ interference.

Reading Tolerances: Tolerances on a drawing may be *general*, *i.e.*, specified with a note; or they may be *specific*, *i.e.*, specified with a dimension. Whenever specific tolerances are not indicated on the drawing, general tolerances apply. When no tolerance is specified, the tolerance generally is assumed to be $\pm\frac{1}{64}$″ for fractional dimensions and $\pm\frac{1}{2}$° for angular dimensions. When no tolerance is specified for decimal dimensions, the tolerance generally is assumed to be $\pm$ one figure, to the nearest significant figure. For example, with a two-place decimal, the tolerance is ±0.01″; with a three-place decimal, the tolerance is ±0.001″.

Specific limits and tolerances may be indicated in several ways with a dimension value as shown in Fig. 3-1. The tolerance at *A* is indicated by writing the two limit sizes above and below the lines. The tolerance at *B* and *C* is shown by indicating the basic size, followed by the tolerance plus and minus. When only one tolerance is indicated, as at *D* and *E*, the other is assumed to be zero.

Measuring and Layout Tools

In machine shop work, the term *laying out* means the marking of lines, centers, or circles on metal workpieces. Layout work is necessary for showing the size, shape, holes, or areas which must be machined.

The machinist uses many common tools for measuring and laying out parts to be machined, as shown in Figs. 3-23 and 3-25. This unit is concerned with the study of measurement and layout tools such as rules, squares, calipers, and several other common measuring tools. Some of these tools also are used for inspection work.

Rules

The *steel rule* is the measuring tool used by the machinist for making rough measurements. See Fig. 3-4. Steel rules are available in lengths from 1″ to 72″; commonly used lengths are 3″, 6″, 9″, and 12″. The better ones are made of spring steel, hardened and tempered, and may be graduated on one or both sides.

The graduations on one side may be 8ths and 16ths and the other 32nds and 64ths. Some rules also have graduations in 10ths, 50ths, and 100ths. Most mechanics can measure accurately to $\frac{1}{64}$″ with a steel rule. When greater accuracy is required, the dimensions generally are specified in decimal fractions to three or four decimal places, such as 1.250″ or 1.2495″.

Some manufacturers specify all dimensions in decimals, including rough dimensions. A steel rule may be used to measure accurately within 0.020″ for this purpose. Hence, steel rules are available with graduations in tenths (0.100) and fiftieths (0.020) of an inch.

Caliper Rule: The steel slide caliper rule, Fig. 3-5, is used for accurately measuring the diameter of rods and tubing and the thicknesses of sheet metal and bars. The

outside measurements of various thicknesses are read at the *out* graduation line; the inside measurements, at the *in* graduation line.

The caliper rule has two knurled thumb pieces on the slide which make it easy to open and close the jaws. The clamping screw is used to lock the slide at any desired setting.

Rule Depth Gage: The rule depth gage, Fig. 3-6, is used to measure the depth of recesses accurately and quickly. The rule is adjusted to the depth of the recess being measured and is locked with a knurled nut and friction spring. Graduations are in 64ths.

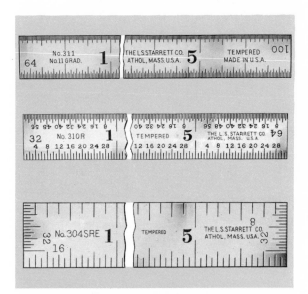

Fig. 3-4. Machinists' Steel Rules (L. S. Starrett)

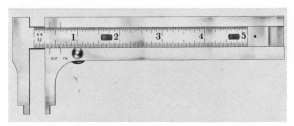

Fig. 3-5. Caliper Rule (L. S. Starrett)

A *combination depth and angle gage* is shown in Fig. 3-7. In addition to measuring the depth of recesses, this tool may be used to measure or lay out angles of 30°, 45°, and 60°. The tool may be set at any of these angles by swinging the rule so that the line on the center turret is aligned with the desired angle. The rule graduations are in 64ths.

Squares

Squares are used for several purposes, including laying out lines on parts and checking two surfaces for right-angle squareness. Several types of squares commonly are used.

Combination Set: A combination set consists of the steel rule or blade, a square head, a center head, and a protractor head, Fig. 3-8. The square head and the protractor head are furnished with a spirit level. Although the level is not a precision level, it may be used as an aid in measuring angles in relation to the vertical or horizontal plane.

Any one of the three parts may be used individually when inserted in the blade. The blade and the square head together make up a *combination square*, which may be used to lay out or test 90° or 45° angles and to lay out lines parallel to an edge. It also may be used to measure the height of parts (as in Fig. 3-9) or the depth of slots or grooves.

The *protractor head* is used to test, measure, or lay out angles to within 1° accuracy, Fig. 3-10. The head may be graduated from 0° to 90° or from 0° to 180° in either direction. Some protractor heads, called the *nonreversible type*, have a shoulder extending from one side of the blade only. A second type, the *reversible type*, has a shoulder on both sides for measuring from either side.

The *center head* is used in locating and laying out the center of round bars or other round objects, Fig. 3-11. It also is used to locate the center of square bars or square objects.

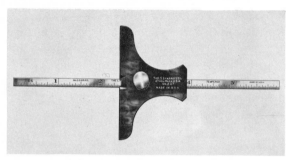

Fig. 3-6. Rule Depth Gage (L. S. Starrett)

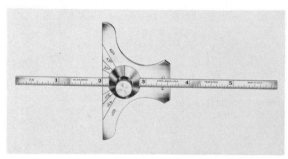

Fig. 3-7. Combination Depth and Angle Gage
(L. S. Starrett)

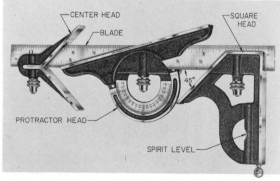

Fig. 3-8. Combination Set (L. S. Starrett)

Fig. 3-9. Measuring Height with a Combination Square
(Brown & Sharpe)

The combination set may be used to take the place of a number of common tools. It may serve as a steel rule, height gage, bevel protractor, level, depth gage, marking gage, or plumb. The combination set may be used for work which generally does not require extreme accuracy.

Precision Steel Square: The steel square, Fig. 3-12, is an L-shaped precision tool which is used when extreme accuracy is required. It is used for laying out lines, as in Fig. 3-23, or for testing the squareness of two surfaces with each other. Since it has no movable parts, it is extremely accurate. In comparison with other types of squares, it is relatively expensive. It is available in several sizes. The steel square is widely used by toolmakers and machinists for checking work on both surface plates and machine tools. Although it is hardened and tempered, the steel square should be handled carefully. Dropping or severe abuse may affect its accuracy.

Die Maker's Square: A die maker's square, Fig. 3-13, is used for measuring clearance on dies. It also is used for checking drafts and angles on patterns. The blade is graduated in 64ths and may be set at any angle up to 10°. The angle is indicated on the beam of the square by the line on the pointer. The offset blade may be used for measuring angles in places where the straight blade cannot be used.

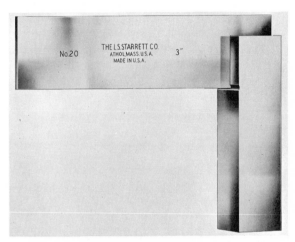

Fig. 3-12. Precision Steel Square (L. S. Starrett)

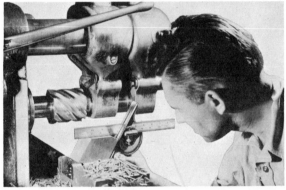

Fig. 3-10. Measuring an Angle with a Protractor Head (Brown & Sharpe)

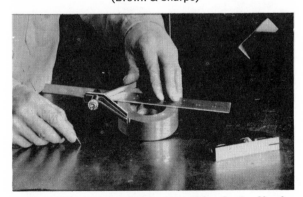

Fig. 3-11. Locating Center Line with a Center Head (Brown & Sharpe)

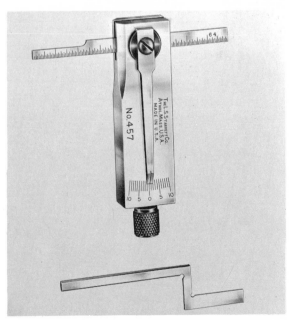

Fig. 3-13. Die Maker's Square (Top), with Offset Blade (Bottom) (L. S. Starrett)

Cylindrical Square: The cylindrical square is used to tell the *out-of-squareness* of work in units of 0.0002" without the use of transfer tools. See Fig. 3-14. It is a true cylinder, with one end lapped perfectly square and the other end lapped at a fixed angle in relation to the sides.

In checking for squareness, the square is placed on a surface plate with the angular end down. The base of the square is placed against the work and rotated until light is shut out. The topmost dotted curve in contact with the part is read, and the number at the top of the square indicates the out-of-squareness of the part in 2, 4, 6, 8, 10, or 12 ten-thousandths of an inch. The workpiece in Fig. 3-14 is out-of-squareness by 0.0010". The same reading may be obtained at two places on the circumference of the square. Thus the tool is self-checking.

Calipers

Calipers are used chiefly for determining diameters. *A*, *B*, and *C* in Fig. 3-15 are outside calipers used for measuring outside diameters. *D*, *E*, and *F* are inside calipers for measuring inside diameters. *C* and *F* are called firm joint calipers, while *A*, *B*, *D*, and *E* are spring type, commonly called spring calipers. Calipers are available in sizes from 3" to 10" or more. The procedures for setting and using calipers are outlined later in this section.

Hermaphrodite Calipers

The hermaphrodite caliper, Fig. 3-16, is used by machinists for scribing lines at a desired distance, parallel to a flat or curved sur-

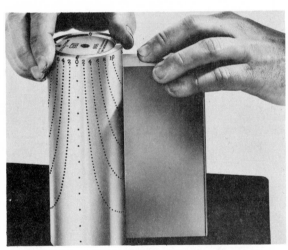

Fig. 3-14. Cylindrical Square (Brown & Sharpe)

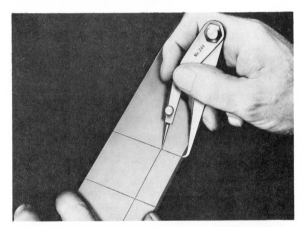

Fig. 3-16. Scribing Lines Parallel to a Surface with Hermaphrodite Caliper (L. S. Starrett)

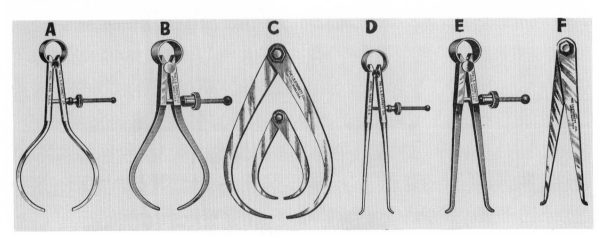

Fig. 3-15. Calipers (L. S. Starrett)

face. It also is used for locating the center of circular objects, as described later in this section.

Center Gage

The center gage, Fig. 3-17, is used principally for grinding and setting thread-cutting tools.

Screw Pitch Gage

The screw pitch gage, Fig. 3-18, is used to determine the pitch of a thread or to compare the threads of different objects, as, for example, the thread on a bolt with that on a nut. The gage has a number of notched blades. The notches on each blade are cut to match the pitch of a standard thread. Each blade is stamped with the pitch or number of threads per inch it represents.

Radius Gage

The radius gage, Fig. 3-19, is used for determining the radius of fillets and rounds on machine parts. It also may be used for laying out fillets and rounds. Each blade is marked with its radius. Other styles of radius gages also are available in larger sizes.

Layout Tools

The machinist, toolmaker, and mechanic in other occupations frequently must do layout work. In laying out work, the machinist accurately scribes lines, locates centers for holes and circles, and scribes lines which define the outline of parts. See Figs. 3-23 and 3-25. Layout work is similar to drafting. However, it generally is performed to greater accuracy, usually to $\frac{1}{64}''$ or closer tolerances. Also, layout work usually must be performed with less convenient tools than those used for drafting.

In laying out work, the machinist must know how to read prints, how to select and use layout tools, and how to transfer measurements accurately. The following tools are important in performing various kinds of layout work in the machine shop:

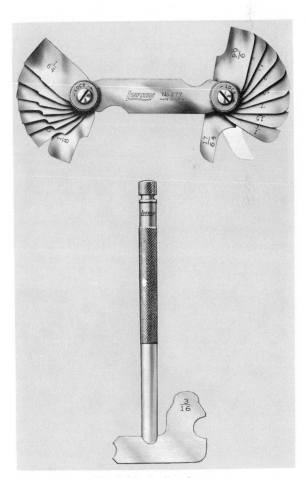

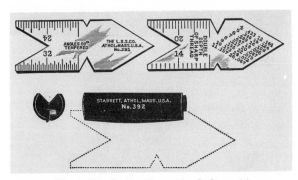

Fig. 3-17. Center Gages (L. S. Starrett)

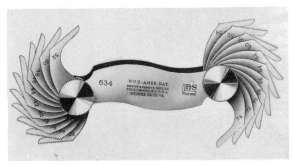

Fig. 3-18. Screw Pitch Gage (Brown & Sharpe)

Fig. 3-19. Radius Gages

Machinist's Vise: The machinist's vise, Fig. 3-20, is an essential piece of equipment for the machine shop, toolroom, and maintenance shop. It is mounted on a work bench and is used to hold work for various operations performed there.

Ball-Peen Hammer: The hammer most widely used by the machinist is the ball-peen hammer, Fig. 3-21. It is available in sizes which vary in weight from 2 ounces to 48 ounces.

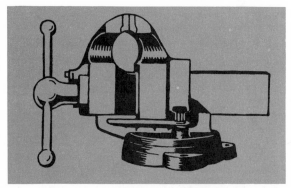

Fig. 3-20. Machinist's Vise (Smith Bros.)

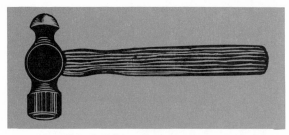

Fig. 3-21. Ball-Peen Hammer (Smith Bros.)

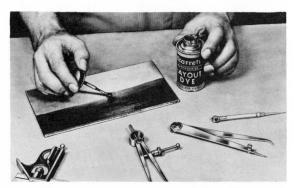

Fig. 3-22. Applying Layout Dye before Laying Out Work (L. S. Starrett)

Layout Dye: Several kinds of layout dye are available commercially for use in coloring metal workpieces before laying out the work, Fig. 3-22. The workpiece is first wiped clean; then the dye is brushed or sprayed on and is allowed to dry. The dye is available in various colors. With the use of layout dye, the lines may be seen more easily.

Scriber: The scriber, Fig. 3-23, is used for marking layout lines on workpieces. Several types of scribers are available. They usually are designed so that the hardened point may be replaced when it becomes badly worn. When the point becomes dull, it may be resharpened on an abrasive stone. The point of some scribers is bent at a 90° angle for use in scribing the inside of cylindrical objects.

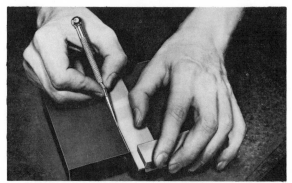

Fig. 3-23. Scribing Lines on Dyed Surface with Scriber and Precision Steel Square (L. S. Starrett)

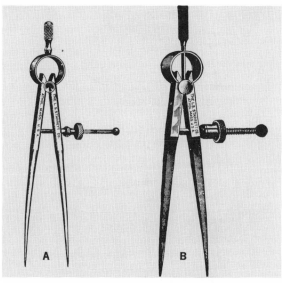

Fig. 3-24. Dividers (L. S. Starrett)

Dividers: Dividers, Fig. 3-24, are used chiefly for spacing, scribing circles (Fig. 3-25), and laying out work. Distances may be transferred directly from a rule to the work. *A*, Fig. 3-24, has a solid nut, while *B* has a quick-adjusting, automatic-closing nut. Dividers are available in sizes from 2″ to 12″.

Prick Punch: Fig. 3-26 shows a prick punch at the top. This tool is used in layout work for marking sharp, small points along layout lines, or preparatory to center punching before drilling. The prick punch is similar to a center punch, except that it has a sharper point. The included angle of the point on a prick punch usually is about 30° or less.

Center Punch: A center punch is shown below in Fig. 3-26. It is a hardened tool whose point usually is ground to an included angle of about 60° to 90°. This tool is used for *center punching* preparatory to drilling. The center punch mark aids in guiding the drill so that it will drill in the desired location without drifting to the side.

Surface Plate: A surface plate, Fig. 3-27, is a heavy plate of steel, cast iron, or granite, with a precision flat surface. The surface is machined, ground, and scraped for extreme flatness. It provides the necessary flat surface for making the accurate measurements required in precision layout and inspection work, as shown in Fig. 3-28.

Surface plates are available in sizes ranging from 12″ square to 4′ x 10′, or larger. They are expensive and should be used carefully. A surface plate never should be hammered or struck,

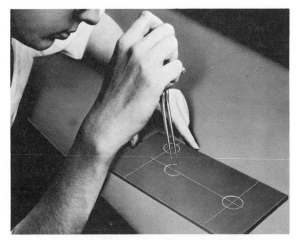
Fig. 3-25. Laying Out Circles with Dividers
(L. S. Starrett)

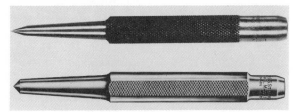
Fig. 3-26. Prick Punch (Upper) and Center Punch (Lower) (L. S. Starrett)

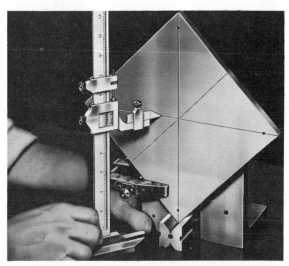
Fig. 3-28. Precision Layout Work on a Surface Plate
(L. S. Starrett)

Fig. 3-27. Surface Plate (Brown & Sharpe)

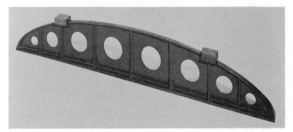
Fig. 3-29. Cast-Iron Straightedge (Brown & Sharpe)

since the smallest nick or dent will affect its accuracy. A thin film of oil should be applied to the surface of iron or steel plates, to prevent rust when not used regularly.

Straightedge: The straightedge in Fig. 3-29 is made of cast iron. This tool is portable and is placed on machined surfaces to check them for flatness or straightness. The straightedge is a scraped surface which should be protected with a wooden cover when not in use. Straightedges are available in various lengths ranging from 18″ to 180″.

V-Blocks: Several types of V-blocks commonly are used in doing layout work and for making machining setups. V-blocks may be used singly or in pairs. A pair of V-blocks with clamps is used for a drilling set-up in Fig. 3-30. A single V-block is used in a setup for layout work in Fig. 3-28.

A second type of V-block, Fig. 3-31, is used in holding work for machining operations. This V-block is held to the worktable of the machine with clamps. The work is held in the V-block with adjustable screws.

A third type of V-block is shown in Fig. 3-32. In this setup, the V-block is placed against an *angle plate* where it is held magnetically when the control knob is turned to the *on* position.

Toolmaker's Clamps: The toolmaker's clamps, Fig. 3-33, are used for clamping workpieces and accessories together for machining setups, inspection setups, and layout setups (as in Fig. 3-28).

Surface Gage: The surface gage, Fig. 3-34, may be used for a variety of purposes, but it is used chiefly for locating distances from a base and for locating points at a given height on opposite ends of an object lying on a flat surface. Another use is that of drawing a line at a given height on an irregularly shaped object, as, for example, a line on an irregularly shaped casting. It also may be used to indicate the accuracy or parallelism of a surface.

Fig. 3-30. Pair of V-Blocks with Clamps Used for Drilling Setup (L. S. Starrett)

Fig. 3-31. V-Block (Brown & Sharpe)

Fig. 3-32. Magnetic V-Block Held Firmly on an Angle Plate Resting on a Magnetic Chuck (Brown & Sharpe)

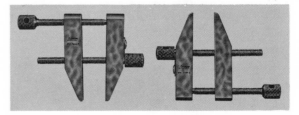

Fig. 3-33. Toolmakers' Clamps

Telescoping Gages

Telescoping gages, Fig. 3-35, are used to gage inside diameters or distances, as shown in Fig. 3-36. The gage is equipped with a plunger which is under spring tension when retracted. When a part is gaged, the tool first is inserted with the plunger retracted; then the knurled nut on the handle is tightened, and the gage is extracted from the part. The distance across the ends of the gage then is measured with a micrometer caliper, Fig. 3-48. The telescoping gage is an important tool for measuring bored holes and the width of slots or grooves. Telescoping gages are available in sizes which measure distances from $5/16''$ to $6''$.

Small-Hole Gage

As the name implies, small-hole gages, Fig. 3-37, are used for gaging the size of small holes. They are available in sizes which measure the diameters of holes or recesses from $1/8''$ to $1/2''$. The ball end always is smaller than the diameter of the hole being measured. In using the gage, select a gage of the proper size,

Fig. 3-36. Using a Telescoping Gage

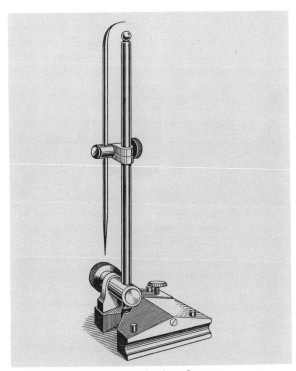

Fig. 3-34. Surface Gage

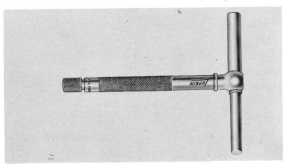

Fig. 3-35. Telescoping Gage

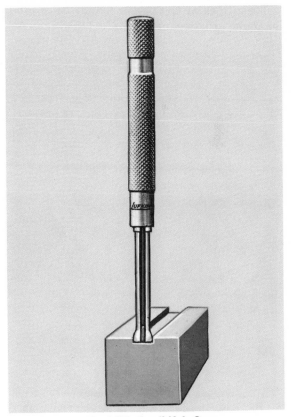

Fig. 3-37. Small-Hole Gage

insert the gage in the hole or recess to be measured, and turn the knurled screw on the handle to expand the ball-shaped end to size. (A very slight pressure or drag will be felt when the screw tension is right.) Then use a micrometer caliper to measure the diameter of the ball end.

Adjustable Parallels

The edges on adjustable parallels, Fig. 3-38, are precision ground and parallel with each other. The parallels are made in various sizes and are adjustable in width within a range for each size. A screw is provided to lock the tool firmly at the adjusted width. Adjustable parallels may be used to gage the width of grooves or slots, Fig. 3-39. The size of the parallel then may be measured with a micrometer to one-thousandth or one ten-thousandth inch.

They may be used as spacers for part location in accurate assembly work, or they may be set at a specific size to serve as gage blocks. They also may be used in machine vises for setting work at the proper height for drilling, shaping, grinding, or milling.

Fig. 3-38. Adjustable Parallels

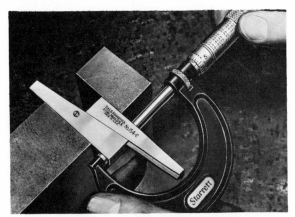

Fig. 3-39. Measuring Width of Slot with Adjustable Parallels and Micrometer (L. S. Starrett)

Master Planer and Shaper Gage

The master planer and shaper gage, Fig. 3-40, has many possible uses in making layouts, machining setups, and precision measurement and inspection work. Tools of this type originally were designed primarily for use in establishing the height of the cutting tool in relation to the workpiece on shapers and planers. The height

Fig. 3-40. Master Planer and Shaper Gage Used to Establish Height of Cutting Tools

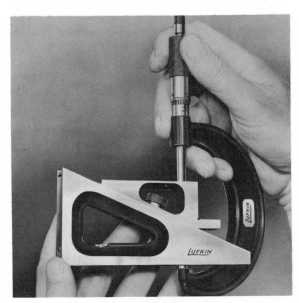

Fig. 3-41. Gage Height or Width Measured to Micrometer Accuracy

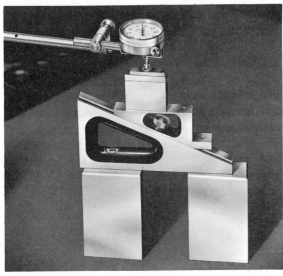

Fig. 3-42. Master Planer and Shaper Gage Used with Gage Blocks for Setting Up Work on Surface Plate

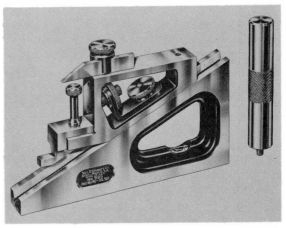

Fig. 3-43. Universal Precision Gage with Extension Bar (L. S. Starrett)

or width of the gage is measured to micrometer accuracy, Fig. 3-41. The cylindrical extension may be screwed into the gage for added length, as shown in Fig. 3-40. The gage is fastened firmly at the desired size with the knurled nut.

Other uses of master planer and shaper gages include the following: use as an adjustable parallel; use in conjunction with gage blocks in building up work on a surface plate, as shown in Fig. 3-42; and use with a dial indicator in transferring measurements.

The gage shown in Fig. 3-43 is a *universal precision gage*. It may be used for the same purposes for which planer and shaper gages are used, and for several other uses as well. It is equipped with a fine-adjustment thumbscrew for ease in making sensitive adjustments required when used with micrometers, vernier height gages, vernier calipers, or gage blocks.

It also is equipped with a scribing attachment for use in layout work or as a height gage. In addition, the screw which holds the beveled scriber may be used to hold a universal indicator (Fig. 3-87) or dial indicator.

Micrometers

Micrometers are precision measuring tools. They are available in a variety of types and sizes, but the most common type is the outside micrometer caliper, Figs. 3-48 and 3-49. A micrometer often is called a *"mike."* Micrometers measure accurately to one-thousandth (0.001) inch. Some micrometers are equipped with a vernier which makes it possible to measure accurately to one ten-thousandth (0.0001) inch. Micrometers also are available which measure in units of the metric system, from 0 to 25 millimeters by hundredths of a millimeter.

Micrometers are equipped with a precision threaded spindle, Fig. 3-49, which makes it possible to measure accurately. Machinists, toolmakers, and mechanics must be familiar with various types of micrometers, and they must know how to read and use them. A micrometer caliper is used to measure a diameter in Fig. 3-50.

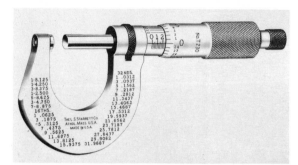

Fig. 3-48. Outside Micrometer Caliper (L. S. Starrett)

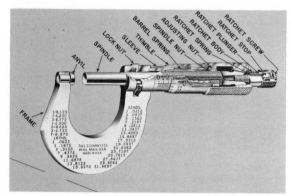

Fig. 3-49. Construction of a Micrometer Caliper
(L. S. Starrett)

Fig. 3-50. Measuring with a Micrometer Caliper

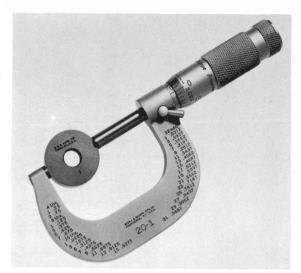

Fig. 3-51. 1"-to-2" Micrometer Caliper with
1" Reference Standard (Brown & Sharpe)

with 25 graduations. The *ratchet* and the *lock nut* are convenient accessories which are available on some micrometers.

The ratchet provides for the application of a uniform pressure on the spindle when making measurement. A uniform pressure is important in making accurate measurements. Without the ratchet, one must develop the right *feel* for accurate measurement. The *lock nut* is used to lock the spindle in position when measurements are made.

Kinds of Micrometers

Many kinds and sizes of micrometers have been developed for various measuring applications. The following are the principal kinds:

Outside Micrometers, which also are called *micrometer calipers*, Fig. 3-48, are used for measuring outside diameters or thicknesses of parts. Outside micrometers are available in various sizes which are limited to 1" measuring ranges, such as 0" to 1", 1" to 2", and so on. A 1"-to-2" micrometer is shown in Fig. 3-51 with a standard 1" round *reference disk*.

The micrometer is set or checked for accuracy by inserting the disk in the micrometer, as shown in Fig. 3-51, with the proper pressure applied. The horizontal *zero* graduation line on the thimble should be in alignment with the horizontal *index* line on the sleeve or barrel. If the two lines are not aligned, they should be

Principal Parts

The parts of a micrometer are shown in Fig. 3-49. The principal parts are the *frame*, the *anvil*, the *spindle* with a precision screw thread, the *sleeve* which is also called a *barrel* or *hub*, and the *thimble* which is numbered

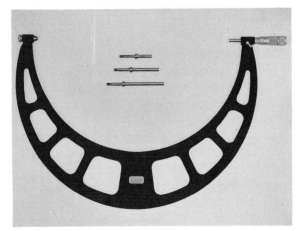

Fig. 3-52. Micrometer with Interchangeable Anvils for 9"-to-12" Range

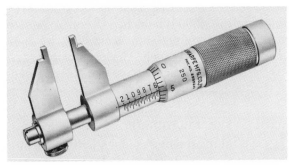

Fig. 3-53. Inside Micrometer Caliper (Brown & Sharpe)

Fig. 3-54. Tubular Inside Micrometer

Fig. 3-55. Measuring with a Tubular Inside Micrometer

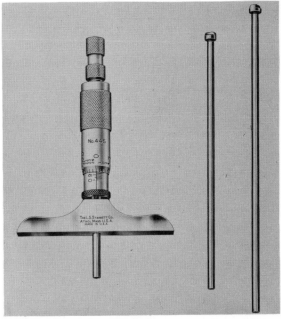

Fig. 3-56. Depth Micrometer with Interchangeable Measuring Rods (L. S. Starrett)

adjusted according to the manufacturer's directions, as supplied with the micrometer. Similarly, larger micrometers must be set or tested with an appropriate reference disk or *standard end measuring rod* before measurements are made.

Large micrometers are available for use in measuring within various 1″ ranges. The micrometer in Fig. 3-52 may be used for measurements in the range from 9″ to 12″ simply by changing and installing the appropriate anvil. Of course, the setting should be checked for accuracy with a standard end measuring rod before use.

Inside Micrometers are used for measuring inside diameters, parallel surfaces, or other inside dimensions. Several types and sizes of inside micrometers are available. The inside micrometer caliper in Fig. 3-53 may be used to measure within the range from 0.200″ to 1.200″. Fig. 3-54 shows a *tubular inside micrometer* which may be used for measuring inside diameters from 1½″ to 12″, in range increments of ½″. Measuring rods are added to either or both ends of the micrometer head to increase its range. A tubular inside micrometer can be used for measuring large diameters, as shown in Fig. 3-55.

Depth Micrometers, Fig. 3-56, are used for measuring the depth of holes, grooves, shoulders, and projections, as shown in Fig. 3-57. The measuring range for depth micrometers

can be increased in multiples of 1″, as desired, by installing interchangeable measuring rods, Fig. 3-56.

Mike Hole Gages, Fig. 3-58, are used for accurately measuring the diameter of holes. Since this tool is equipped with a vernier, it measures directly to 0.0001″. It is available in various size ranges from 0.188″ to 4.005″. The *setting ring*, Fig. 3-59, is available in various sizes and is used for testing and setting the accuracy of the gage.

Threading Micrometers are used to measure the pitch diameter of screw threads, as explained on page 126.

Ten-Thousandth Micrometers are equipped with a vernier, as in Figs. 3-48, 3-60, and may be used for measuring accurately to one ten-thousandth (0.0001) inch. All micrometers may be used to measure accurately to one-thousandth (0.001) inch. The method for reading both types of micrometers will be explained in the next unit.

Light Wave Micrometer

A special micrometer called a light wave micrometer, Fig. 3-60, is designed to measure directly to one one-hundred-thousandth (0.000 01) inch. It has a specially ground and lapped precision screw. The numbered graduations on the large wheel are indicated in thou-

Fig. 3-57. Measuring Depth of a Shoulder with a Depth Micrometer (L. S. Starrett)

Fig. 3-58. Mike Hole Gage

Fig. 3-59. Setting Ring for Testing and Setting Mike Hole Gage

Fig. 3-60. Light Wave Micrometer (Van Keuren)

sandths (0.001) of an inch, and the graduations between the numbers are in ten-thousandths (0.0001). With the use of the vernier and the large wheel, measurements may be read directly to 0.00001″ or 10 millionths inch (0.000 010″).

This micrometer is equipped with a special light wave pressure indicator which is sensitive to less than 0.000 004″. It may be adjusted from a few ounces to 2½ pounds. Thus uniform pressures, as required when measuring to this degree of accuracy, are applied to parts being measured. This is a comparatively expensive measuring instrument, and specific procedures are involved in checking its accuracy and using it properly. Hence the manufacturer's recommendations should be followed carefully when using it. It is used for precision measurement of production parts, plug gages, setting gages, taps, and special gages within its capacity range. It is available in sizes for measurement from 0″ to 3″.

How To Read and Use a Micrometer

The micrometer is a delicate instrument and is easily damaged; therefore, it must not be forced over the work. The various parts of a micrometer and the form of its construction were shown in Fig. 3-49.

The pitch of the screw threads on the inside of the spindle is one-fortieth or twenty-five thousandths of an inch. Notice the fine graduations or divisions on the horizontal *index line* on the sleeve, Fig. 3-48. There are forty of these in an inch. Also notice that every fourth division line is longer than the others and that these are numbered 0, 1, 2, 3, 4, etc. Each of these larger divisions represents one-tenth of an inch.

The beveled edge of the thimble is marked in twenty-five divisions. Every fifth division line is longer and is numbered 0, 5, 10, 15, etc. Rotating the *thimble* through one of these divisions will move the spindle backward or forward (depending upon the direction in which the spindle is turned) one twenty-fifth of twenty-five thousandths, or one-thousandth of an inch; rotating it five divisions will move the spindle five-thousandths of an inch.

Procedure

CAUTION: *When a micrometer is used to measure work, the work must be stationary.*

1. Hold the frame of the micrometer in the left hand. Revolve the thimble until the work just passes between the *anvil* and the tip of the *spindle*.
2. Hold the micrometer perpendicular to the axis of the work, and adjust the spindle until it lightly touches the surface.

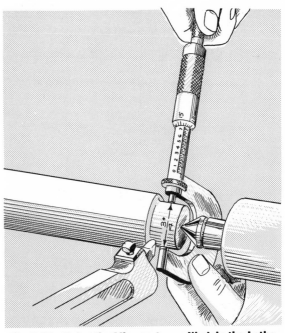

Fig. 3-63. Using the Micrometer on Work in the Lathe

3. With the mike in contact with the work, as in Fig. 3-63, read the number of vertical divisions on the sleeve.

Removal of the micrometer before reading may cause the spindle to revolve slightly and thus cause an error in the final reading.

4. Multiply the number of visible divisions on the sleeve by twenty-five. Add to this product the number of divisions on the bevel of the thimble, from 0 to the line that is even with the horizontal line on the sleeve.

Example: Fig. 3-64 shows 7 divisions visible on the sleeve, and 3 divisions on the thimble, from 0 to the horizontal line on

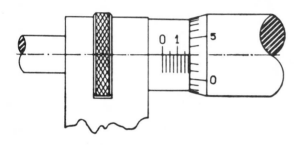

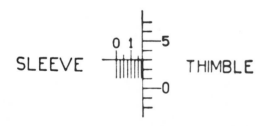

Fig. 3-64. Micrometer Reading of 0.178"
(L. S. Starrett)

the sleeve. Therefore, the distance between the anvil and the tip of the spindle is one hundred seventy-eight thousandths of an inch. This figure is found by multiplying the number of visible divisions on the sleeve by 25, and then adding the divisions on the thimble from 0 to the division mark even with the horizontal line on the sleeve, in this case, 3. Thus: $7 \times 0.025 = 0.175 + 0.003 = 0.178$.

The example in Fig. 3-65 shows a reading of 0.242"; that in Fig. 3-66, 0.359".

Procedure for Ten-Thousandth Graduations

Micrometers with ten-thousandth graduations are used and read in much the same manner as those with thousandth graduations. The only difference is that an additional reading in ten-thousandths is obtained from a vernier and is added to the thousandth reading.

The vernier consists of ten divisions on the sleeve, as shown at B in Fig. 3-67. In reading the ten-thousandth micrometer, first read the measurement to the nearest one-thousandth, as with a one-thousandth micrometer. Then observe which of the lines on the vernier is aligned with a line on the thimble. If the 1 on the vernier is aligned, add one ten-thousandth (0.0001). If the 2 is aligned, 0.0002, and so on.

Example: See Fig. 3-67 (A and B).

The "2" line on the sleeve is visible, representing	0.200
Two additional lines are visible, each representing 0.025	0.050
Line "0" on the thimble is aligned with the index line on the sleeve, representing	0.000

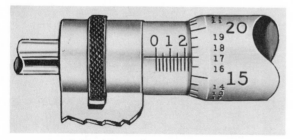

Fig. 3-65. Micrometer Reading of 0.242"
(L. S. Starrett)

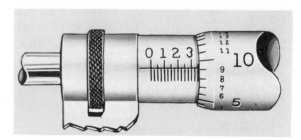

Fig. 3-66. Micrometer Reading of 0.359"
(L. S. Starrett)

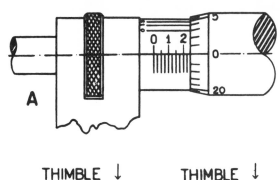

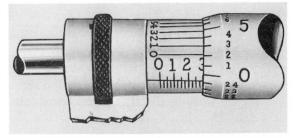

Fig. 3-68. Micrometer Reading of 0.2991"
(L. S. Starrett)

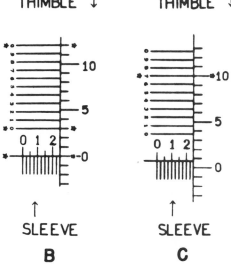

Fig. 3-67. Reading a Micrometer Graduated in Ten-Thousandths (L. S. Starrett)
Readings at A and B are 0.2500";
reading at C is 0.2507".

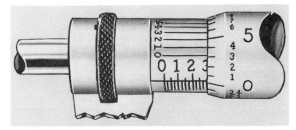

Fig. 3-69. Micrometer Reading of 0.3001"
(L. S. Starrett)

The "0" lines on the vernier are
aligned with lines on the
thimble, representing 0.0000
Adding the total, the reading is 0.2500
The reading at *C*, Fig. 3-67, is 0.2507". The reading in Fig. 3-68 is 0.2991"; that in Fig. 3-69 is 0.3001".

How To Set and Use Calipers

The calipers commonly used by workers in metal are the outside, inside, and hermaphrodite. Outside calipers are used for measuring outside diameters and exterior surfaces. Inside calipers are used for measuring inside diameters and the dimensions of recesses. Hermaphrodite calipers are used principally for locating centers on circular or approximately circular stock. Both outside and inside calipers are made with a spring joint, a firm joint, or a lock joint. The latter has one loose leg and com-

monly is called a transfer caliper. This type, Fig. 3-72, is used for measuring recesses which are wider at the bottom than at the top or for measuring a small object so located that it cannot be measured with an ordinary caliper. Usually calipers are set in one of two ways: first, by adjusting the caliper until the object to be measured will just pass between the extended legs, and second, by setting the caliper to a particular dimension, as described in the following procedure.

Procedure for Setting
the Spring Joint Type

1. Grasp the rule in the left hand and the caliper in the right, as in Fig. 3-73.
2. Place the left leg of the caliper against the left end of the rule; then adjust the right leg by turning the thumbscrew with the right thumb and forefinger until the leg extends the distance desired, Fig. 3-73.
3. Test the setting carefully to see that it is correct. Make adjustment if necessary.

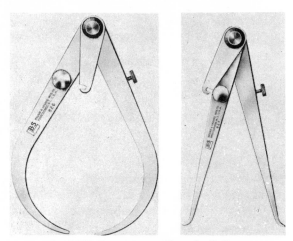

Fig. 3-72. Loose Leg or Transfer Calipers
(Brown & Sharpe)

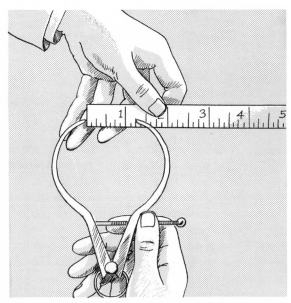

Fig. 3-73. Setting the Outside Caliper

Procedure for Setting
the Tight Joint Type

1. Set by closing or opening the legs with the fingers.
2. Make final adjustment.

    Final adjustments are made by tapping an outer edge of the caliper lightly against a solid surface to decrease the distance between the tips of the legs or by tapping the inside of one leg lightly to increase the distance between the tips.
3. Test and adjust in this manner until the proper setting is achieved.

Procedure for Using
the Outside Caliper

Accuracy in calipering can be achieved only by developing a keen sensitivity to touch. Always hold the caliper very lightly between the tips of the fingers. Continued practice will achieve dexterity.

CAUTION: *The work to be calipered must be stationary.*

1. Set the caliper.
2. With the work stationary, hold the caliper perpendicular to the axis and pass it over the work, Fig. 3-74.

    The piece has been reduced to the size desired when the caliper, of its own weight, just slips over the work. Do not force the caliper. A correct measurement cannot be thus obtained.
3. When turning work to size in the lathe, take a trial cut at the end of the stock, stop the machine, and test with the caliper as in Fig. 3-74.
4. If the work is still too large, take another light cut; then test as before. Continue

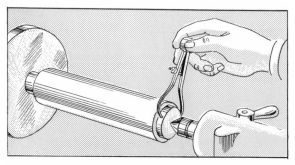

Fig. 3-74. Using the Outside Caliper

cutting and testing until the caliper will just slip over the work.

When calipering work machined in a shaper, milling machine, grinder, or planer, proceed as in steps 3 and 4.

When the work is rotating about a center and the machine is equipped with a micrometer cross-feed dial, measure the diameter of the work and then calculate the amount of material to be removed. Assuming the measurement is found to be $1\frac{3}{8}''$ and the desired dimension is $1\frac{1}{4}''$, advance the micrometer cross-feed one-half the existing difference of $\frac{1}{8}''$, or $\frac{1}{16}''$. Start the cut in the usual manner. When the cut has advanced a short distance, test with the caliper.

Procedure for Using the Inside Caliper

CAUTION: *Never use an inside caliper on work while it is revolving.*

1. Stop the machine.
2. Place the caliper in the opening or recess to be measured, as shown by the dotted line in Fig. 3-75. Then raise the caliper until it is in the position shown by the solid line in the illustration.
3. Adjust the caliper until the points of both legs touch the walls of the recess very lightly.
4. Remove the caliper, and test the measurement with a rule, as in Fig. 3-76.
5. If the recess is not large enough, remove a little more stock at the entrance; then retest with the caliper.

6. Continue this procedure until the opening at the top of the recess is cut to the size required.

Procedure for Setting the Hermaphrodite Caliper

1. Spread the legs of the caliper to the position desired.

   Test the setting by holding the tip of the bent leg against the end of a rule and the tip of the pointed leg on the face of the rule. Then read the distance between the terminals of the legs.
2. Make slight adjustments as in step 2 under "Procedure for Setting the Tight Joint Type."

Procedure for Locating Centers with the Hermaphrodite Caliper

1. Chalk both ends of the stock.
2. Set the caliper to approximately half the diameter of the stock, preferably slightly less than half.
3. Hold the caliper in a vertical position with the bent leg against the outside surface of the stock.
4. Describe four short arcs, as in Fig. 3-77.

Fig. 3-75. Using the Inside Caliper

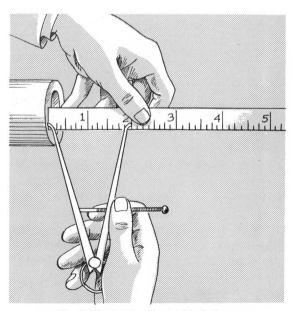

Fig. 3-76. Setting the Inside Caliper

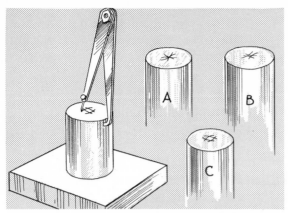

Fig. 3-77. Locating the Center with the Hermaphrodite Caliper

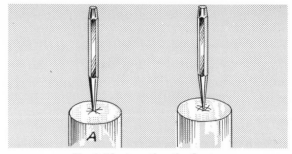

Fig. 3-78. Locating the Center

When the caliper is set at exactly half the diameter of the stock, the arcs will have a form as at *A*, Fig. 3-77. When slightly less than half the diameter, the arcs will have a form as at *B;* when slightly greater, the arcs will appear as at *C*.

5. Make a punch mark in the center of the area formed by the intersection of the arcs, or at the exact point of intersection, as would be the case at *A*, Fig. 3-78.

6. Check the accuracy of the punch mark by placing the point of the straight leg of the caliper in the punch mark and rotating the caliper. Observe if the point of the bent leg remains in contact with the work throughout the course of rotation.

7. If the punch mark is not located at the center of the work, draw the punch mark in the direction desired; then test as in step 6. See Unit 44, following step 10.

Dial Indicating Instruments

Machinists, toolmakers, and parts inspectors use a variety of dial indicating gages or measuring instruments. They must know how to use and care for these instruments.

Dial Indicator

A dial indicator, Fig. 3-80, shows visually the amount of error, in size or alignment, for a part being measured or gaged, as illustrated in Fig. 3-81. The graduations on different gages vary. They may be indicated in thousandths (0.001), ten-thousandths (0.0001), or to the nearest 0.000 05 inch. The dial indicator in Fig. 3-80 has minimum graduations of 0.0001″. The numbered graduations are in thousandths, while the shorter graduations between the numbered lines indicate ten-thousandths.

There are two common types of dial indicators. The *balanced* type has figures in both directions from the zero, as shown in Fig. 3-80. The *continuous-reading* type is numbered clockwise, continuously, starting with the zero, as in Fig. 3-83. The balanced type is the most widely used. The smaller dial indicators may be graduated with a dial range which may vary from 0.010″ to 0.050″.

The indicating hand on the dial is actuated by a plunger and spring. When the contactor point moves, the plunger causes the hand to rotate. The dial may be adjusted to the zero point when the plunger is in any position. Some dial indicators, as in Fig. 3-80, are equipped with a *revolutions counter* which counts the number of revolutions of the hand.

Thus an indicator with a range of 0.010″, which revolves ten times, travels through a total range of 0.100″.

Dial Test Indicator Set

Dial indicators are used on *dial test indicator sets*, such as the set shown in Fig. 3-82. This set has a steel base with T-slots, and it has a column clamped to the base for holding the dial indicator. Dial indicators are also used on a wide variety of other indicating gages and measuring instruments which will be described in this unit.

In using a dial indicator set, the dial indicator first is set at the proper *gaging height;* the gaging height is the basic dimension of the part to be gaged or tested. The gaging height may be established with gage blocks (Fig. 3-133), with a planer gage which is set at the proper height (Figs. 3-41 and 3-42), or with other appropriate gaging devices. The gage blocks should be placed on the T-slot base, under the dial contact point. The dial should be set at *zero*, and it should be under sufficient spring tension to allow the dial hand to rotate in either direction through the desired measur-

ing range. In Fig. 3-81, the gaging height is established between the contact point and the surface of the machine table.

Universal dial indicator sets, as shown in Fig. 3-83, are used widely in many kinds of machine shop and inspection work. With the accessories provided in this set, the dial indicator may be mounted on a surface gage for use on a surface plate or on a machine table. It may be mounted in the tool post of a lathe, as shown in Fig. 3-84. It also may be clamped directly to a machine for special applications.

Fig. 3-81. Checking Height of Machined Part with Dial Test Indicator (L. S. Starrett)

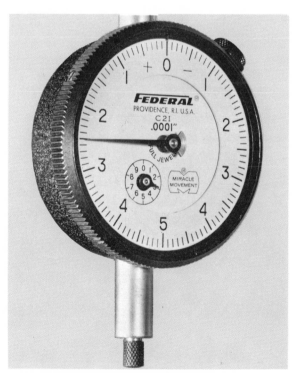

Fig. 3-80. Dial Indicator (Balanced Type)
(Federal Prod.)

Fig. 3-82. Dial Test Indicator Set (L. S. Starrett)

The hole attachment used in Fig. 3-85 is a valuable accessory for use with the dial indicator in testing location or alignment of holes. It is particularly useful for aligning work in a four-jaw chuck. It also may be used for testing the alignment of work in a three-jaw chuck on a lathe, Fig. 3-86.

Universal Indicator

A universal test indicator, as shown in Fig. 3-87, is used for many applications which involve gaging the size of parts, alignment of workpieces in machine setups, or alignment of machine accessories. When the contact point on the indicator touches an object or surface, the indicator hand rotates through its range of 0.010″. The hand swings plus or minus 0.005″ from the zero point at the center.

The indicator is mounted on a standard bar for general use. In this way it may be mounted in a lathe tool post or on a vernier height gage. With the special attachment shown in Fig.

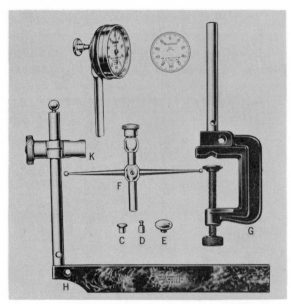

Fig. 3-83. Universal Dial Indicator Set (L. S. Starrett) **C, D, and E are contact points; F is hole attachment; G, clamp; H, tool post holder; K, sleeve.**

Fig. 3-85. Hole Attachment Permits Accurate Internal Tests with Dial Indicator (Brown & Sharpe)

Fig. 3-84. Checking Runout of Work on a Lathe (L. S. Starrett)

Fig. 3-86. Testing Alignment of Work in a Three-Jaw Chuck on a Lathe (L. S. Starrett)

3-87, the indicator may be mounted on a surface gage for use on a surface plate, Fig. 3-88. Also, with this attachment, it may be mounted in a drill chuck, Fig. 3-89, for indicating proper hole alignment.

Dial Indicating Gages

Numerous special gages and measuring instruments are equipped with dial indicators. These gages are used widely for determining whether parts are within required size limits.

Dial indicating depth gages, Fig. 3-90, are used for gaging or testing the depth of holes, slots, shoulders, recesses, and keyways. Extension points increase the measuring depths at which the gage may be used.

Dial indicating hole gages, Fig. 3-91, are used to gage or test holes for size, taper, out-of-roundness, or other irregular conditions. They are available in a wide range of sizes.

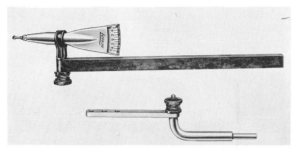

Fig. 3-87. Universal Indicator and Attachment

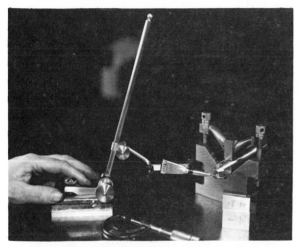

Fig. 3-88. Universal Indicator Used with Surface Gage on Surface Plate

Fig. 3-89. Universal Indicator Used to Test Alignment of Hole for Machining Setup

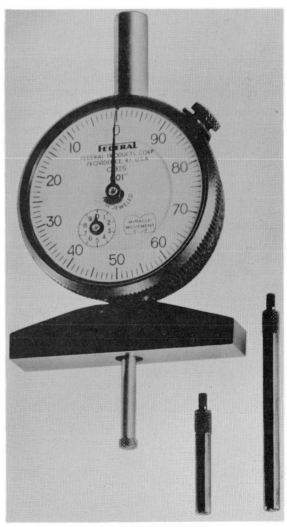

Fig. 3-90. Dial Indicating Depth Gage with Extension Points (Federal Prod.)

Dial indicating snap gages, Fig. 3-92, are used for gaging diameters of parts to determine whether they are within the size limits specified. In use, the gage is snapped over the diameter of the part being gaged. They are efficient for checking parts which are produced in large numbers, and they are available in a wide range of sizes. Each gage may be used for measuring within a 1″ range, such as 0″ to 1″, 1″ to 2″, etc. Size is set by adjusting the frame itself with the knurled wheel near the indicator. The gage may be used at an inspection bench or right at the machine. The snap gage in Fig. 3-93 is used for gaging work mounted in a cylindrical grinder. This gage also may be mounted in a bench stand, as shown in Fig. 3-94.

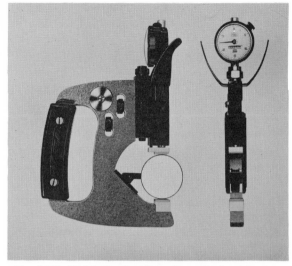

Fig. 3-92. Dial Indicating Snap Gage (Federal Prod.)

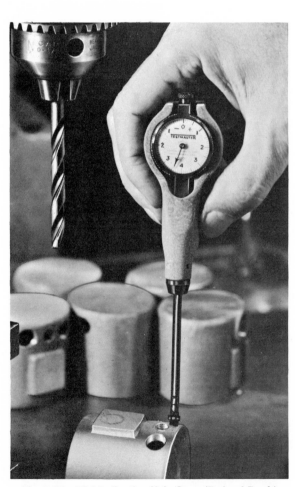

Fig. 3-91. Dial Indicating Hole Gage (Federal Prod.)

Fig. 3-93. Dial Indicating Snap Gage Used to Gage Work in Cylindrical Grinder (Federal Prod.)

A *retractable contact snap gage* is shown in Fig. 3-95. This gage may be used for a wide variety of outside diameter measurements. The contactor point is opened with a button located conveniently for thumb operation. This type of gage is available in sizes which gage, within certain ranges, from 0″ to 4½″.

The *dial indicating micrometer*, Fig. 3-96, may be used as a micrometer or as a snap gage. It has an indicator with ten-thousandth graduations through a range of plus or minus 0.0010″. The lower anvil is the sensitive contact for the built-in dial indicator. A thumb-actuated button on the lower end is used to retract the sensitive contact.

The sensitive indicator eliminates the need for developing the *feel* or *touch* when making measurements to 0.0001″. When used as a micrometer, the thimble is set to the nearest one-thousandth graduation, and the ten-thousandths are read directly on the dial indicator. When used as a snap gage, the spindle is clamped with the clamp ring at the required dimension; the tolerance hands are then set at the desired limits, Fig. 3-97.

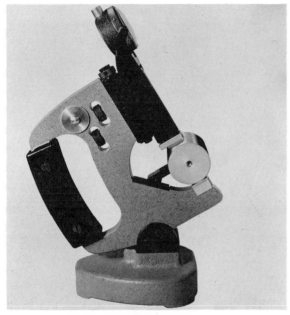

Fig. 3-94. Snap Gage Mounted in Bench Stand
(Federal Prod.)

Fig. 3-96. Dial Indicating Micrometer (Federal Prod.)

Fig. 3-95. Retractable Contact Snap Gage
(Federal Prod.)

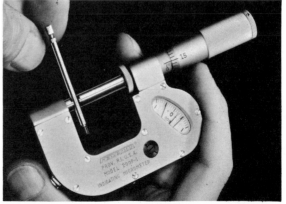

Fig. 3-97. Using Indicating Micrometer as Snap Gage
(Federal Prod.)

75

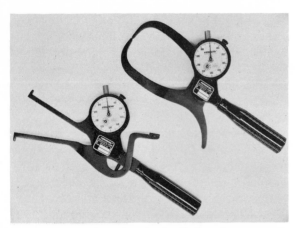

Fig. 3-98. Dial Indicating Caliper Gages
(Federal Prod.)
Inside caliper at left; outside caliper at right.

Fig. 3-99. Setting Disc and Setting Ring
(Federal Prod.)

Dial Indicating Caliper Gages, Fig. 3-98, have minimum 0.010″ dial graduations. The dials also have revolutions counters which make it possible to measure directly through their complete range of 3″. Calipers of this type also are available with 0.001″ graduations, for measuring with greater accuracy.

A *setting disc* and *setting ring*, Fig. 3-99, are used for checking and setting indicating caliper gages, snap gages, hole gages, comparators, and other types of gages. Setting discs and rings are available in various sizes.

Fig. 3-100. Dial Comparator (Federal Prod.)

Comparators

Comparators, as shown in Fig. 3-100, are used primarily for thickness measurement. They may be used for inspection of outside dimensions on many kinds of parts. They also may be used as a gage to determine whether parts are within required size limits. The dial indicator on the illustrated comparator has minimum 0.001″ graduations and is equipped with a revolutions counter. The lifting lever at the top is used to retract the contact point through the full indicator range of 0.250″. The handwheel is used to raise or lower the table to the desired height.

Dial indicating comparators are available in a wide range of models and sizes. The dials may be supplied with minimum 0.001″, 0.0005″, or 0.0001″ graduations. Electronic comparators are available for use in gaging accurately to 0.000 01″ .

Vernier Tools

An accurately graduated steel rule may be used to measure to one thousandth (0.001) inch accuracy when it is equipped with a *vernier scale*. Several common precision measuring tools utilize this type of rule equipped with a vernier.

Vernier Caliper

The *vernier caliper*, Fig. 3-105, is equipped with a 25-division vernier scale. The vernier is in the form of a *vernier plate* mounted on a sliding assembly. The assembly slides on an accurately graduated rule which is called the *beam*. When the *clamp screw* above the fine-adjustment nut is tightened, fine adjustments of the jaws may be made with the *fine-adjusting screw*. The jaws are precision ground and lapped parallel with each other.

The vernier caliper is used for making either outside or inside measurements. When outside measurements such as length, thickness, or outside diameters are made, the size is read on the side of the vernier marked *outside*. When inside measurements are made (such as the width of slots, grooves, shoulders, or inside diameters), the size is read on the side of the vernier marked *inside*. Hence, the *beam* is graduated on both sides, and a vernier plate is located on both sides.

Readings to 0.001″ are taken at the zero line on the vernier, in relation to the graduated lines on the beam. For outside readings, the zero line on the vernier coincides with the zero line on the beam when the jaws are closed.

When outside measurements are made, the end jaw is hooked over the part to be measured, and the sliding assembly is brought in contact with the part, so that both jaws touch the part lightly. The clamp screw above the fine-adjustment nut is then tightened. A fine

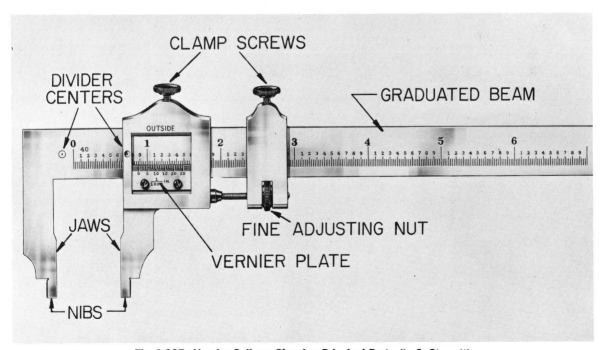

Fig. 3-105. Vernier Caliper, Showing Principal Parts (L. S. Starrett)

adjustment may be made with the fine-adjusting screw, if necessary. Then the clamping screw above the vernier plate is tightened. Finally, the caliper is removed from the workpiece, and the reading is taken, as described later in this unit.

Outside measurements may be made for a range from 0 to the length of the beam in inches. Vernier calipers are available in sizes ranging from 6″ to 48″ in length.

When inside measurements are made, the nibs on the end of the jaws are inserted between the surfaces being measured. Thus, the measuring range for internal measurements varies from the diameter across the nibs in the closed position, to the length of the beam in inches. The distance across the nibs of a 6″ vernier caliper is usually about 0.250″. When making an inside reading with the jaws closed together, the zero line on the vernier will coincide with the graduation line on the beam which indicates the diameter across the nibs.

Vernier Height Gage

The vernier height gage, Fig. 3-106, is a precision tool which has a graduated steel beam mounted upright on a steel base. It is equipped with a vernier plate mounted on a sliding assembly, similar to the vernier caliper. Measurements are read in exactly the same manner as the vernier caliper.

A vernier height gage is used to measure or to mark off vertical distances accurately to 0.001″. A hardened, ground, and lapped scriber may be mounted on the movable jaw, as in Fig. 3-110, for marking off heights. The vernier height gage is being used for layout work in Fig. 3-28.

The vernier height gage also may be used for other purposes. For instance, it may be used on the flat surface of a machine table to measure the height of machined surfaces. A depth gage attachment may be mounted on the movable jaw, Fig. 3-107, for measuring the depth of holes or recesses. An indicator also may be clamped on the movable jaw for inspection work.

The beam may be graduated on one or on both sides (for outside and inside measurements). Readings should be taken from the proper side. Vernier height gages generally are available in sizes ranging from 12″ to 48″.

Fig. 3-106. Vernier Height Gage (L. S. Starrett)

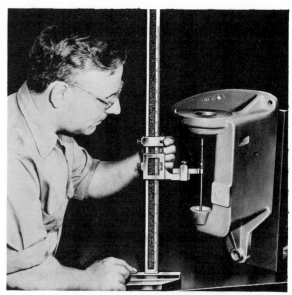

Fig. 3-107. Measuring Depth of Recesses with Vernier Height Gage (L. S. Starrett)

Vernier Depth Gage

The vernier depth gage, Fig. 3-108, is used for measuring depths of holes, slots, and recesses accurately to 0.001″. It commonly is available in sizes from 6″ to 12″ in length. Readings are taken in the same manner as for the vernier calipers and height gages.

Reading a 25-Division Vernier

The vernier found on vernier calipers, height gages, and depth gages permits measuring accurately to 0.001″. Refer to A, Fig. 3-109. The zero graduation line on the vernier plate coincides with a graduation line on the beam indicating the correct dimension or reading. The large numbers on the beam indicate inches. The small numbers indicate tenths (0.100) of an inch; thus ten divisions equal one inch. The small divisions are graduated in 40ths or 0.025″. The vernier plate is graduated into 25 divisions, each representing 0.001″.

To read the vernier, note how many inches, tenths (0.100), and 40ths (0.025) the zero line on the vernier plate is from the zero line on the beam. Then, to this amount, add the thousandths which are indicated by the line on the vernier plate which coincides exactly with a line on the beam.

Examples: Note that in *A*, Fig. 3-109, the zero line on the vernier has passed the large number 1 on the beam, indicating ..... 1.000″
It has passed the small number 4, indicating 4 tenths or .... .400″
It has passed one of the 40th graduations to the right of the 4-tenths graduation, indicating .... .025″
And the 11th line on the vernier ex-

actly coincides with a line on the beam as indicated by the stars ..... .011″
Therefore the reading is 1.436 inches

Total 1.436″

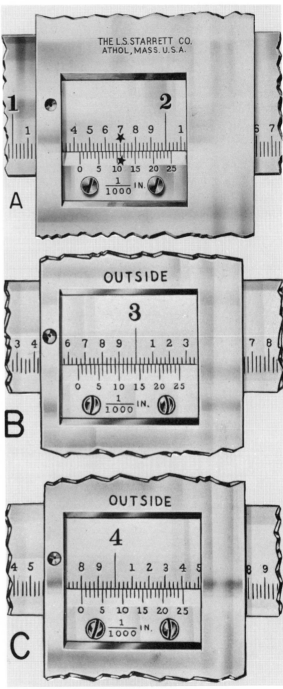

Fig. 3-109. **Readings on a 25-Division Vernier**
(L. S. Starrett)
(A) 1.436″; (B) 2.659″; (C) 3.803″.

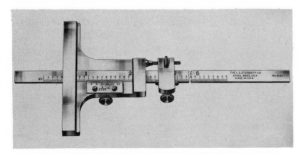

Fig. 3-108. **Vernier Depth Gage** (L. S. Starrett)

The reading at *B*, Fig. 3-109, is 2.659″. The reading at *C*, 3.803″. Since the graduations on a vernier are very fine and rather difficult to see clearly, a magnifying glass may be used for greater ease in making readings.

Reading a 50-Division Vernier

The graduation lines may be seen more easily on a 50-division vernier than on a 25-division vernier. The vernier height gage, Fig. 3-110, has a 50-division vernier.

Measuring tools with a 50-division vernier measure accurately to 0.001″. Readings are made in a manner which is very similar to reading a 25-division vernier. The large numbers on the beam indicate inches; the small numbers, tenths (0.100) of an inch. Each tenth graduation is divided into two parts by the smallest

graduation line on the beam; hence, the smallest division on the beam is one twentieth (0.050) of an inch. The vernier plate is graduated into 50 divisions, each division representing 0.001″.

To read the 50-division vernier, note how many inches, tenths (0.100), and twentieths (0.050) the zero line on the vernier plate is from the zero line on the beam. Then add the thousandths which are represented by the line on the vernier plate which coincides exactly with a line on the beam.

Example: Refer to the outside reading shown in the lower scale of Fig. 3-111: The zero line on the vernier has passed the large number 1 on the beam, indicating .. 1.000″
It has passed the small number 4 on the beam, indicating 4 tenths or ... .400″
It also has passed a midpoint ($\frac{1}{20}$″) division to the right of the 4, thus indicating .... .050″
And the 14th line on the vernier exactly coincides with a line on the beam, indicating thousandths ..... .014″
Thus the reading is 1.464 inches
Total 1.464″

Universal Bevel Protractor

The *universal bevel protractor* equipped with a vernier, Fig. 3-112, measures angles accurately to 5 minutes or one-twelfth of a degree. This tool also is called a *vernier protractor*. It may be used to lay out, measure, or check angles, Fig. 3-113.

The principal parts of the protractor are shown in Fig. 3-112. A 6″ or 12″ blade may be inserted in the graduated dial and is locked

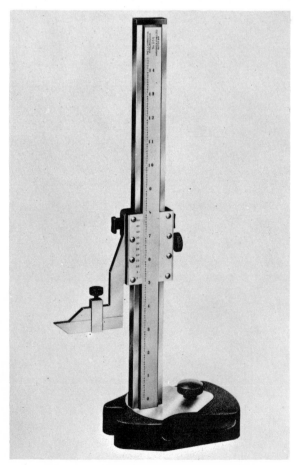

Fig. 3-110. 50-Division Vernier Height Gage
(L. S. Starrett)

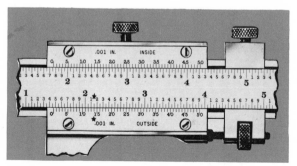

Fig. 3-111. 50-Division Vernier Caliper or Height Gage — Reading of 1.464″ (L. S. Starrett)

in position with the blade clamp nut. The blade and dial are swiveled to the angle desired, and the dial is locked with the dial clamp nut. An acute-angle attachment is provided for use in measuring angles of less than 90°.

The protractor dial is graduated 360°, reading in whole degrees from 0 to 90, 90 to 0, 0 to 90, and 90 to 0. Each 10 degrees is numbered, and a long graduation divides each 5 degrees. The vernier plate is graduated with 12 spaces; thus each line here represents 5 minutes or one-twelfth of a degree. Every third line on the vernier plate is numbered to represent 15, 30, 45, and 60 minutes. Both the protractor dial and the vernier plate have numbers in both directions from zero. Therefore, angles of any size can be measured.

Reading the Vernier: When angles are read in whole degrees, the zero line on the vernier plate coincides with a graduation line on the protractor dial; also the graduation for number 60 will coincide exactly with a graduation on the dial.

When angles are read, which are not in whole degrees, the following procedure should be followed: Note how many degrees can be read from the zero line on the dial up to the zero line on the plate. Then, reading in the *same direction* (and this is important) note the number of minutes indicated by the line on the vernier which coincides exactly with a line on the dial. Add this amount to the number of whole degrees. Remember, each graduation line on the vernier represents 5 minutes.

Example: Refer to Fig. 3-114: The zero line on the vernier has passed line 50 on the dial, indicating 50 degrees .... 50°
Reading in the same direction, the starred 20-minute graduation line coincides exactly with a line on the dial, indicating an additional 20 minutes .... 00° 20′
Therefore, the reading is 50 degrees, 20 minutes .... 50° 20′

A magnifying glass may be used as an aid in reading the fine graduations more accurately.

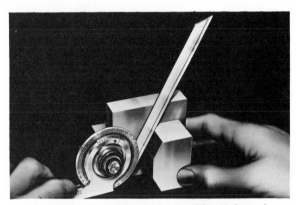

Fig. 3-113. **Measuring an Angle with a Universal Bevel Protractor** (L. S. Starrett)

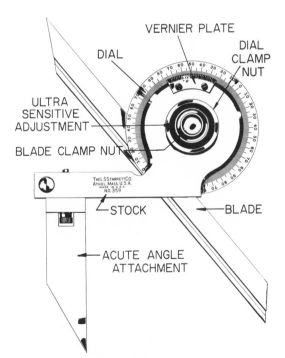

Fig. 3-112. **Universal Bevel Protractor with Vernier** (L. S. Starrett)

Fig. 3-114. **Universal Bevel Protractor Vernier — Reading of 50° 20′** (L. S. Starrett)

Setup Tools

Various tools and accessories are used in making setups for machining operations on machine tools. Setup tools include machine vises, parallels, hold-downs, angle plates, and other assorted work-holding accessories. These tools and accessories are used for mounting workpieces in machine vises or for fastening the workpieces directly to the machine table.

Machine Vises

Various types of machine vises are used for mounting work on drill presses, shapers, milling machines, and other machine tools. Two common types are shown in Fig. 3-117. Ordinarily these vises are mounted on a graduated swivel base so that the face of the jaws may be parallel with, perpendicular to, or at an angle with the line of travel of the tool. The jaws of the machine vise may be made of soft or of hardened steel. Care must be taken to avoid scarring or otherwise damaging them.

Fig. 3-117. Machine Vises (Cincinnati Shaper)

Fig. 3-118. Hardened and Ground Steel Parallels
(Brown & Sharpe)

Parallels

In making setups for machining, as well as setups for layout and inspection work, parallels, Fig. 3-118, often are used. In machining setups, parallels are used to raise the work above the jaws of the vise and to provide a solid seat for it, Figs. 3-119 and 3-121. Parallels are strips of hardened steel which have been machined accurately to the desired size. Ordinarily they are made in pairs and in many different sizes. Parallels which are numbered according to pairs should be used in pairs to insure accuracy of the setup.

For holding workpieces at an angle, *degree parallels* are used, as in *B*, Fig. 3-119. These are similar to *rectangular parallels*, except that one side has been machined at an angle with the base, for example, 15 degrees.

Hold-Downs

Sometimes parallels, or combinations of parallels, of the size required to raise the work

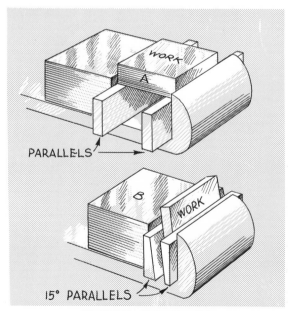

Fig. 3-119. Using Parallels

above the jaws of the vise are not available. This is particularly true when machining thin stock. Hold-downs of the type shown in Figs. 3-119 and 3-120 are used to grip the work and hold it in position, as shown in Figs. 3-119 and 3-121. As may be observed in the illustration, these are wedge-shaped in cross section with the thick edge beveled 2° or 3°. This causes the hold-down to press downward at the thin edge when it is brought against the work. Thus the work is held sufficiently rigid to permit machining with light cuts.

Angle Plates

One common type of angle plate, Fig. 3-122, is L-shaped, with two surfaces accurately finished at 90° to each other and with opposite faces parallel. Work that cannot be held in a vise for machining may be clamped to an angle plate which is bolted to the machine table, as in Fig. 3-122.

In Fig. 3-31, an angle plate is shown resting on a magnetic chuck and supporting a magnetic V-block. An angle plate is also shown in Fig. 3-28 supporting a workpiece for precision layout. Angle plates are used on surface plates for layout work, on magnetic chucks for surface grinding operations, and on machine worktables for machining setups.

Angle plates are precision tools which should be used carefully. They should not be nicked or abused, since nicks, scratches, or rust will affect their accuracy.

Work-Holding Accessories

Workpieces which cannot be mounted in a machine vise often are bolted directly to the worktable with the use of *strap clamps* and parallels, as shown in Fig. 3-123. The parallels are used to support the part, hold it level, or provide a bearing surface for the clamps. Vari-

Fig. 3-120. Hold-Downs

Fig. 3-122. Using Angle Plates for Machining Setups

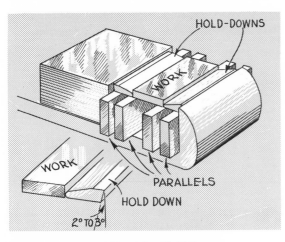

Fig. 3-121. Using Hold-Downs

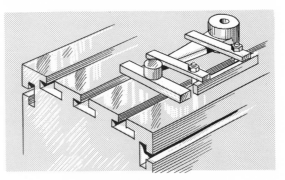

Fig. 3-123. Using Strap Clamps

ous assorted clamps, jacks, and other accessories are used in mounting parts with an irregular shape on machine tables, as illustrated in Fig. 3-124.

T-slot bolts, Fig. 3-125, are used for setting up work on shapers, planers, milling machines, and other similar machines. The bolts are designed so that they will not turn in the T-slot of the worktable when tightened. The bolts, nuts, and washers are heat-treated for strength and durability, and they are available in a variety of sizes.

T-slot clamps of the type shown in Fig. 3-126 are equipped with a T-slot bolt and are used for holding work on all types of machine tables equipped with T-slots. One or more clamps may be used. The clamp is tightened to the table with the T-slot bolt. The work is held down by tightening down on the hand screw.

Machine strap clamps of several kinds are used with T-slot bolts for holding work directly on machine tables. In Fig. 3-127, *A* is called a screw heel clamp; *B*, a goose neck clamp; *C*, a plain clamp; *D*, a U-clamp; *E*, a finger clamp; *F*, a double-finger clamp; and *G*, a universal adjustable clamp.

Planer jacks, Fig. 3-128A, are useful in leveling and supporting castings for setups, as shown in Fig. 3-122. *Vertical jacks*, Fig. 3-128B, also are used to level and support castings. *Bracing jacks*, Fig. 3-128C, are used to prevent the workpiece from sliding, as shown in Fig. 3-124.

Step blocks, Fig. 3-128D, provide support at various heights required for setups. They are useful particularly as support blocks for strap clamps, as shown in Fig. 3-124.

The *wedge*, Fig. 3-128E, is useful in leveling or supporting large castings which are bolted to machine tables.

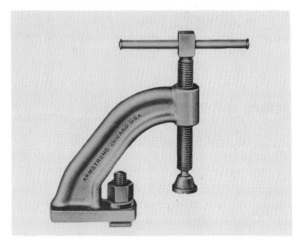

Fig. 3-126. T-Slot Clamp (Armstrong)

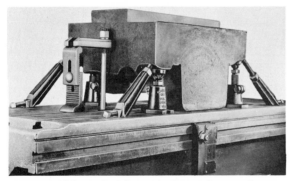

Fig. 3-124. Typical Setup Tools and Accessories
(Armstrong)

Fig. 3-125. T-Slot Bolt, Nut, and Washer (Armstrong)

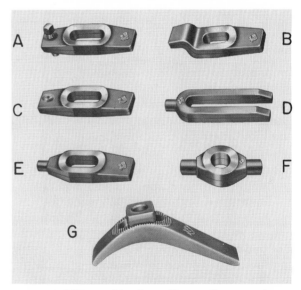

Fig. 3-127. Machine Strap Clamps (Armstrong)
(A) Screw head; (B) Goose neck; (C) Plain; (D) U;
(E) Finger; (F) Double finger; (G) Universal adjustable.

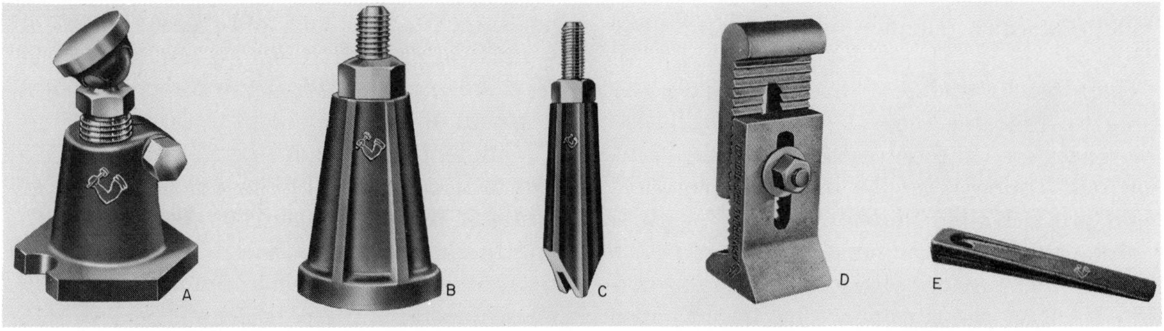

Fig. 3-128. Setup Tools (Armstrong) **(A)** Planer jack; **(B)** Vertical jack; **(C)** Bracing jack; **(D)** Adjustable step block; **(E)** Setup wedge.

Gage Blocks and Gages

Gaging is an operation which involves determining whether parts are produced within specified size limits. The purpose of gaging is not to determine the size of parts, but to determine whether the parts are within specified size limits. The devices or instruments designed for this purpose are called *gages*.

It will be recalled that *tolerance* means the permissible variation in size. The tolerance is the difference between the maximum and the minimum permissible size limits for a given dimension. If a part is gaged and is found to be under the minimum size limit, or above the maximum size limit, it is not acceptable. Either the size limits or the tolerance is specified on the drawing for the part. Parts which are designed for interchangeability must be produced within certain size limits.

Toolmakers, machinists, and inspectors in production plants use gage blocks, gages, and gaging instruments of many types. They must be familiar with these and must know how to use and care for them properly. Many types of gages are very expensive and are not readily available to the machine shop student. Nevertheless, he should be familiar with some of the basic types and their uses.

Gages, such as the snap gage in Fig. 3-93 and the comparator in Fig. 3-100, are designed for measuring large numbers of parts accurately and rapidly. Measurements can be checked more rapidly with gages than with the use of conventional measuring tools, such as micrometers and vernier tools. Gages generally may be used with less training and skill, and there also is less possibility for human error in using them.

Precision gage blocks frequently are used in conjunction with the use of gages. They often are used as *reference standards* for setting the size limits on gages. Also they are used for setting or calibrating measuring tools such as micrometers, snap gages, mechanical comparators, and electrical comparators.

Gage Blocks

Precision gage blocks of the type shown in Fig. 3-131 are rectangular pieces of tool steel $\frac{3}{8}''$ x $1\frac{3}{8}''$ x the specified size. Square gage blocks also are available. Gage blocks are hardened, ground, and finished accurately to tolerances within a few millionths of an inch. Master gage blocks (class AA) have a guaranteed accuracy of plus or minus two-millionths (0.000 002) inch per inch of length, per gage block.

Gage blocks under 1″ in length have the same tolerance as those 1″ in length. These tolerances are valid only at 68°F. — the standardized temperature for precision measurement in the United States.

One can visualize one-millionth (0.000 001) inch by comparison with the thickness of a thin sheet of tissue paper. The tissue paper measures about one-thousandth inch in thickness. If the tissue paper were then divided into 1000 thinner sheets, each sheet would be one-millionth inch in thickness.

Gage blocks are recognized throughout the world as a practical *reference standard* for measuring length. They are used in precision measurement laboratories, inspection departments, toolrooms, and machine shops for calibrating and setting many types of inspection gages, measuring tools, and measuring instruments. Gage blocks, therefore, are the connecting link between the national standard of measurement and measurement in the shop.

Manufacturers produce gage blocks in relation to master gage blocks which must be accurate to plus or minus 0.000 002″ per inch of length; in many cases, their master gage blocks are accurate to within plus or minus 0.000 001″. These master gage blocks are checked periodically for accuracy, with an *interferometer*. This instrument measures gage blocks within a fraction of a millionth of an inch, in units of light wave length. (Light wave length is not significantly affected by changes in temperature and atmospheric conditions.)

Gage blocks may be used together to make up various gage block combinations of greater length. When gage blocks are properly combined, they are said to be *wrung* together. Their surfaces are so flat and smooth that when properly wrung, they stick together as though magnetized, Fig. 3-132. Some have been known to support a weight of over 200 pounds when wrung together.

The reason for the adhesion of gage blocks is not clearly understood, but it is believed to be due to a combination of factors, including at-

Fig. 3-131. 81-Piece Gage Block Set
(Brown & Sharpe)

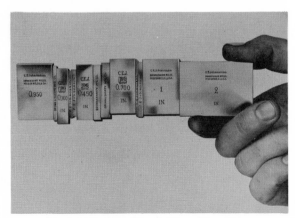

Fig. 3-132. Gage Blocks Wrung Together
(Brown & Sharpe)

Fig. 3-133. Gage Blocks Used to Establish the Height of Dial Indicating Gages (Brown & Sharpe)

mospheric pressure, molecular attraction, and a thin film of moisture or oil. It has been found that thoroughly cleaning the surfaces with certain solutions causes the blocks to fall apart easily. Gage blocks are wrung together by sliding them together under slight pressure. They also should be separated by sliding them apart.

Uses: Gage blocks are used for many purposes involving precision measurement. They are used for establishing the height of dial indicating gages, Fig. 3-133. They are used for establishing the original height setting for precise electronic measuring instruments, as shown in Fig. 3-134. They are used in conjunction with a sine bar for establishing precise angular measurements, as shown in Fig. 3-151. Gage blocks also may be equipped with gage block jaws for determining precision length measurements, as in Fig. 3-135.

Measuring tools lose their original accuracy through wear, warpage, shrinkage, or damage in handling. Therefore, they must be readjusted or recalibrated to gage block standards. Gage blocks are used for this purpose with micrometers, comparators, height and depth measuring tools, parallels, and squares.

Problems in Manufacture: In the manufacture of precision gage blocks, four special production problems had to be solved: (1) *nearly* flat surfaces had to be produced; (it is impossible to produce an absolutely flat surface). (2) *Nearly* parallel surfaces had to be produced; (3) dimensional accuracy within several millionths had to be obtained; and (4) the steel had to be heat-treated for proper hardness and internal stability. (Internal stability is developed through special heat-treatment, seasoning, and aging procedures; it prevents the usual amount of shrinkage, warpage, and dimensional change which takes place in steel through aging.) Solutions to these four basic problems made possible the production of precision gage blocks with tolerances of plus or minus 0.000 001″.

Classifications of Gage Blocks: Gage blocks normally are classified according to three accuracy classifications, AA, A, and B. These are U.S. Federal quality classifications based on permissible tolerances for length, flatness, parallelism, and surface finish. The length tolerances for blocks 1″ or less, at a temperature of 68°F., are as follows:

$$\text{Class AA:} \quad \pm\ 0.000\,002''$$
$$\text{Class A:} \quad +\ 0.000\,006''$$
$$-\ 0.000\,002''$$
$$\text{Class B:} \quad +\ 0.000\,010''$$
$$-\ 0.000\,006''*$$

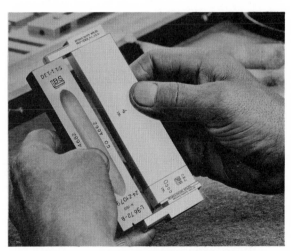

Fig. 3-135. Using Gage Blocks with Jaws to Determine Precise Length Measurements
(Brown & Sharpe)

Fig. 3-134. Using Gage Blocks to Set Precision Electronic Measuring Equipment (Brown & Sharpe)

*U.S. Federal specification GGG-G-15, length tolerance 1 inch and less

Although these are permissible manufacturing tolerances, manufacturers actually produce gage blocks within these classifications to closer tolerances. They usually indicate in their technical literature the tolerances for each classification of their gage blocks.

Some manufacturers produce gage blocks with the special classification, *laboratory master gage blocks*, to tolerances of plus or minus 0.000 001″ per inch of length. These gage blocks, as well as regular *master* gage blocks (class AA), are intended for special purposes in temperature-controlled gaging and measurement laboratories. They are used for experimental work, research work, and as grand master gages for measurement and inspection of other gages.

Class A gage blocks often are called *inspection* gage blocks. They are used primarily for inspection of finished parts and for inspection and setting of working gages. They also may be used as masters in inspection departments and toolrooms.

Class B gage blocks often are called *working* gage blocks. They are used for many applications requiring accurate measurement throughout the shop. They are used on surface plates for accurate layout, on machines for setting cutting tools accurately, and for ordinary inspection work.

Gage Blocks Sets: Gage blocks are available in sets or as individual blocks. Sets are available with from 5 to more than 100 gage blocks. A commonly used standard set, as shown in Fig. 3-131, has 81 blocks. With this set, combinations may be made in sizes from 0.100″ to 0.200″ by 0.001″ steps, and from 0.200″ to over 12″ by 0.0001″ steps. Over 120,000 different gage sizes may be made with this type of set, which has blocks in the following four *series:*

1. *One Ten-thousandth (0.0001″) Series — 9 blocks*
   Sizes 0.1001″ to 0.1009″ by 0.0001″ steps
2. *One thousandth (0.001″) Series — 49 blocks*
   Sizes 0.101″ to 0.149″ by 0.001″ steps
3. *Fifty One-thousandth (0.050″) Series — 19 blocks*
   Sizes 0.050″ to 0.950″ by 0.050″ steps
4. *Inch (1.000″) Series — 4 blocks*
   Sizes 1.000″ to 4.000″ by 1.000″ steps

Gage blocks in the third and fourth series may be combined in steps of 0.050″ for sizes ranging from 0.050″ to 10″. Blocks in the second series may be combined with the third and fourth series for 0.001″ steps. Blocks in the first series may be combined with those from all other series for 0.0001″ steps from 0.200″ to over 12″. Table 1 shows the various sizes for gage blocks in a standard 81-block set.

In contrast with 81-block sets, an inexpensive (equal in cost to a good 1″ mike) 5-block set is available with the following sizes: 0.0625″, 0.125″, 0.250″, 0.500″, and 1.000″. With this set, 31 gage sizes may be made in steps of $\frac{1}{16}$″, from 0.0625″ to 1.9375″.

Gage blocks of greater length also are available individually or in sets. The set in Fig. 3-136 has 8 blocks, which provide for 74 sizes in the range from 5″ to 84″, in even 1″ lengths. Various kinds of fixtures and accessories are available for use in clamping or holding long combinations together. With appropriate accessories, these combinations are used as precision height gages, snap gages, and as gages for other special purposes.

Table 1
Gage Blocks in 81-Piece Set

		First Series		
0.1001	0.1002	0.1003	0.1004	0.1005
0.1006	0.1007	0.1008	0.1009	
		Second Series		
0.101	0.102	0.103	0.104	0.105
0.106	0.107	0.108	0.109	0.110
0.111	0.112	0.113	0.114	0.115
0.116	0.117	0.118	0.119	0.120
0.121	0.122	0.123	0.124	0.125
0.126	0.127	0.128	0.129	0.130
0.131	0.132	0.133	0.134	0.135
0.136	0.137	0.138	0.139	0.140
0.141	0.142	0.143	0.144	0.145
0.146	0.147	0.148	0.149	
		Third Series		
0.050	0.100	0.150	0.200	0.250
0.300	0.350	0.400	0.450	0.500
0.550	0.600	0.650	0.700	0.750
0.800	0.850	0.900	0.950	
		Fourth Series		
1.000	2.000	3.000	4.000	

Procedure for Wringing Gage Blocks

Gage blocks must be clean (free from dirt, dust, corrosion, oil, grease, or nicks) before they can be *wrung* properly, as in Fig. 3-132. Use the following procedure:

1. Clean the gage blocks as necessary by rubbing with a clean, soft, cotton cloth or chamois.
2. Hold the desired gage blocks as shown at *A*, Fig. 3-137.
3. Wipe the contacting surfaces on the wrist or palm of the hand, and place together as at *B*, Fig 3-137.
4. With a slight contact pressure, slide the blocks together, as shown at *C*, Fig. 3-137. If the contact surfaces are clean, the blocks will adhere to each other as though magnetized.
5. Continue the above steps until the proper combination of blocks has been completed.
6. The blocks are self-checking. Equal combinations may be checked against each other or against a single block. At *D* in Fig. 3-137, nine blocks totaling one inch are checked against an inch block.
7. Gage blocks should be disassembled by removing the end blocks with a sliding pressure.

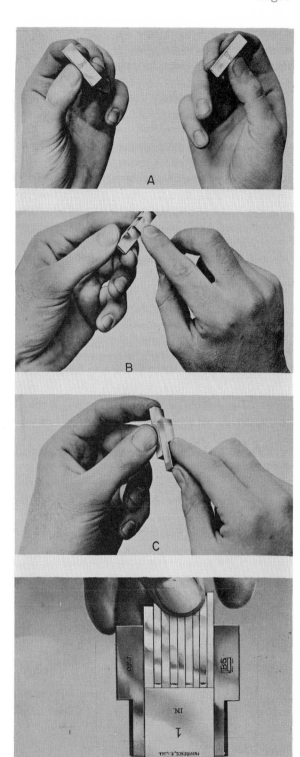

Fig. 3-137. **Building Gage Block Combinations**
(Brown & Sharpe)

Fig. 3-136. **Gage Blocks in Inch Increments**
(Brown & Sharpe)

Precautions in Care and Use of Gage Blocks

1. Do not put gage blocks away while still wrung together. Moisture between the surfaces may cause them to rust.
2. Keep gage blocks free from dust, dirt, or moisture.
3. After use, wipe the gage blocks free of finger marks with a clean cloth or chamois. Then, using a clean cloth or chamois, apply a thin film of white petrolatum, to prevent rusting. Other substances recommended by gage block manufacturers also may be used as a protective film.
4. Nicks may be removed with a very fine deburring stone, which is available from the gage block manufacturer. Examine the block with a magnifying glass, and be careful to remove only the high spots. Do not wear the surface.
5. Gage blocks which are used regularly should be inspected at least once per year. Gage block manufacturers are equipped to inspect gage blocks accurately.

Effect of Temperature Change on Gage Blocks

The accuracy of gage blocks is affected by temperature changes. They are accurate within specified classification tolerances at a temperature of 68°F. The coefficient of expansion for gage blocks is 0.000 0064″ per inch of length per degree Fahrenheit. This means that a 5″ gage block at room temperature of 72°F. would be $5 + (5 \times 4 \times 0.000\,0064'')$ or 5.000 128″ in length. The effect of temperature on gage blocks is about the same as for most kinds of steel.

Expansion or contraction, per degree of temperature variation from 68°F., essentially is the same for both the gage blocks and the steel parts being gaged. Consequently, if the gage blocks are at the same temperature as the steel parts being tested or gaged, size compensations need not be made. The measurements will be essentially equal.

Gage blocks which have raised in temperature due to contact with the hands should be placed flat on a cast-iron surface plate for 15 minutes or more. This will help reduce the difference in temperature between the gage blocks and the parts being inspected or gaged. A soft cloth should be used to insulate gage blocks against heat from the hand while holding them for setting snap gages and other gaging instruments.

The coefficients of expansion for nonferrous metals are different than for steel; therefore, mathematical compensations may be made when nonferrous metal parts are gaged at temperatures which vary significantly from 68°F. Such compensation is required only when the parts must be produced and inspected within gage block tolerances.

Procedure for Building Gage Block Combinations

In building up a specific gage block combination, use as few blocks as possible. You should know the sizes of the gage blocks in the set available. Start by selecting gage blocks which will remove the right-hand figure in the decimal size which you wish to build. Then select blocks which will remove the next right-hand decimal, and so on. Several examples will illustrate the procedure. Refer to Table 1 for gage block sizes in an 81-block set.

Example 1:

Build up 0.9516
Subtract 0.1006 — First block
0.8510
Subtract 0.1010 — Second block
0.750 — Third block

Example 2:

Build up 2.8417
Subtract 0.1007 — First block
2.7410
Subtract 0.141 — Second block
2.600
Subtract 0.600 — Third block
2.000 — Fourth block

Gages

The term *gage* usually refers to devices or instruments used to determine whether the dimensions of parts are within the limits specified for the part. There are many kinds of

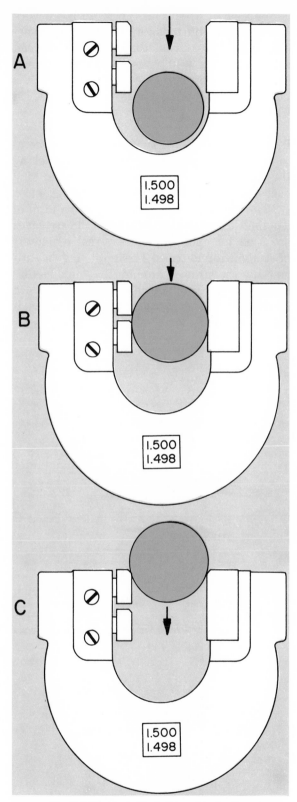

Fig. 3-138. Parts Tested in a Limits Gage
(A) Part is undersize; (B) Part is satisfactory;
(C) Part is too large.

gages designed for many purposes. Some are designed for general use for a number of gaging or measuring applications. Others are designed for special or limited measuring applications within a specific size range.

Adjustable-type gages usually are designed for general use and may be used within various size ranges. Several common gages of this type (described previously in Unit 10) include the following dial indicating instruments: depth gage shown in Fig. 3-90, hole gage in Fig. 3-91, snap gage in Figs. 3-92 and 3-95, micrometer used as a snap gage in Fig. 3-97, caliper gages in Fig. 3-98, and the comparator in Fig. 3-100.

Fixed-type gages usually are designed for special or limited measuring applications, within specific size limits. A few of the more common ones include plug gages, ring gages, snap gages, and thread gages. Gages generally are named after their most distinguishing feature, such as their shape, form, or application. Machinists and inspection workers should be familiar with the principal kinds of gages and their uses.

Reference gages, also called *master gages*, are used for checking other gages. A master gage is an exact duplicate of the part to be made. Inspection gages are tested for accuracy with a reference gage.

Go and No-Go Gages

Go and no-go gages are also called *limits gages*. Because they have two gaging surfaces or points, they sometimes also are called *double gages*. One gaging surface is used for testing the upper size limit; the other, the lower size limit. The common types of limits gages include snap gages, ring gages, and plug gages.

The principles involved in testing parts with go and no-go gages are illustrated in Fig. 3-138. The figure shows how cylindrical parts are checked with a limits *snap gage*. The upper gaging point is the *go* point, while the lower is the *no-go* point. At *A*, the part is too small, since it passed between both the upper and the lower gaging points. At *B*, the part is satisfactory, since it passed the upper point, but hangs on the lower gaging point. At *C*, the part is too large, since it hangs on the upper gaging point. Most such gages are labeled "*go*" and "*not go*", meaning that the part will *go* at the first point, but it will *not go* at the second.

Limits gages never should be forced under high pressures when checking parts. The pressures applied to the gaging surfaces should be slight. Limits gages have contact surfaces which are hardened, precision-ground, and lapped. Although they are designed for accuracy and wear resistance, they should be handled and used carefully.

Snap Gages: One of the most widely used limits gages is the snap gage, Fig. 3-139. This caliper-type gage is used to gage thicknesses, lengths, and outside diameters. Snap gages are available in several styles and sizes. That shown in Fig. 3-139 is an adjustable limits gage. It has one stationary anvil and two button anvils which are adjustable. The outer button is set to the go size, and the inner button to the no-go size. The procedure for using this type of snap gage was described in the preceding paragraphs and is illustrated in Fig. 3-138.

The size limits on a snap gage may be checked with gage blocks, Fig. 3-140. The size limits also may be set or adjusted within specific size ranges with the use of gage blocks. Limits snap gages may be supplied by the manufacturer *set* and *sealed* at specified size limits, or *unset* and *unsealed*. When preset, the adjustment screws usually are sealed with sealing wax and the size limits are stamped on the gage.

Snap gages of special types are fitted with special anvils, buttons, or rolls for gaging special forms or external threads. A *roll thread snap gage*, Fig. 4-40, is used to check the size limits for the pitch diameter of screw threads. Dial indicating snap gages are described in Unit 10.

Ring Gages: Three types of ring gages commonly are used for checking the external diameters of parts — plain ring gages, taper ring gages, and thread ring gages.

Plain ring gages are designed in the form of a cylindrical ring, as in Fig. 3-141. These gages are used for checking the external diameters of straight round parts. The *no-go* ring (identified by the groove around the outside diameter) is used to check the minimum size limit. The *go* ring is used to check the maximum size limit.

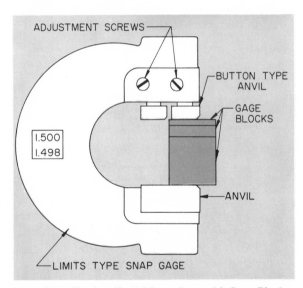

Fig. 3-140. **Testing Size of Snap Gage with Gage Blocks**

Fig. 3-139. **Adjustable Limits Snap Gage (Greenfield)**

Fig. 3-141. **Plain Ring Gages (Greenfield)**

The go ring will pass over a part which is within specified size limits with little or no interference. The no-go ring will not pass over the work. If both rings pass over, the part is undersize. If neither does, the part is oversize.

Taper ring gages are used for checking the size and the amount of external cylindrical taper on parts. The upper three items in Fig. 3-142 are cylindrical taper ring gages. Gages of this type are used for checking the taper shanks on drills, reamers, lathe centers, and other machine accessories.

In using a taper ring gage, first draw three equally spaced chalk lines lengthwise on the external tapered surface which is to be checked. Then slip the ring over the external taper by applying a light pressure for good surface contact. Rotate the ring forward and backward a small amount while continuing to apply light pressure. Remove the gage and observe the external tapered surface. If all three chalk lines have been uniformly rubbed and distributed, the taper is correct. If the chalk lines have been rubbed harder at one end than at the other, then a correction should be made on the taper. The correct amount of taper should be established before the part is machined to finished size. Size may be determined by measuring the small diameter with a micrometer or by noting the distance to which the taper enters the ring gage.

Thread ring gages of the go and no-go type, Fig. 4-39, are used for checking the pitch diameter of external threads. The use of these gages is explained in Unit 23.

Plug Gages: Three basic types of plug gages commonly are used for checking the accuracy of holes — plain cylindrical plug gages, cylindrical taper plug gages, and thread plug gages. Plug gages of special types also are available for use in checking holes of special shape, such as square holes and rectangular holes.

Plain cylindrical plug gages, as shown in Fig. 3-143, are accurate cylinders which are used for checking the size limits of straight cylindrical holes. The gage is provided with a handle for convenient use. The gage may be either the single-end type or the double-end type (which has the go and no-go gages at opposite ends). The go gage is longer than the no-go gage; it should enter the hole with little or no interference. If great pressure is required, the hole is undersize and is not acceptable. The no-go gage should not enter the hole. If it does, the hole is too large.

A *progressive-type plug gage* has both the *go* and the *no-go* gages on the same end of the handle. It is efficient for checking through holes, but it cannot be used for shallow, blind holes.

Tapered cylindrical plug gages, as shown in the lower portion of Fig. 3-142, are used for checking the size and amount of taper in tapered cylindrical holes in drill sleeves, in machine tool spindles, and in adapters for use with taper shank tools.

In using the tapered cylindrical plug gage to check a tapered hole, first draw three equally

Fig. 3-142. Cylindrical Taper Ring Gages
(Brown & Sharpe)

Fig. 3-143. Plain Cylindrical Plug Gages (Greenfield)
(Bottom) Double-end gage; (Above) Single-end gages.

spaced chalk lines lengthwise on the plug gage. Insert the plug in the hole under a slight pressure for firm contact. Still using a slight pressure, turn the gage forward and backward a slight amount. Then remove the gage and observe the chalk lines. If the chalk was rubbed uniformly and there is a uniform distribution of chalk from all three lines, then the tapered hole is satisfactory. If the chalk lines were not rubbed uniformly, the internal taper requires correction. The correct amount of taper should be established before machining the hole to finished size. The hole is finished to size when the gage enters to the end of the plug or to a depth indicated by a mark on the gage.

Thread plug gages, Fig. 4-37, are used for checking the size limits for the pitch diameter of internal screw threads. The use of thread plug gages is explained in Unit 23.

Optical Height Gage

The optical height gage shown in Fig. 3-144 is used for measuring the height of parts accurately to 0.000 005″. This instrument is designed for use on a surface plate only, Fig. 3-145. The optical height gage is basically a stack of gage blocks wrung together to an accuracy of 0.000 005″. The gage is available in several model sizes for use in measuring heights which range from 0 to 85 inches.

The optical height gage measures through a range of 1″. Measurements may start with any desired inch-block setting within the range of the particular gage. Settings on the height gage are made by means of a lever-operated cam and vernier handwheels and are read in the optical eyepiece. Measurements may be taken from the numbered inch-blocks and may be transferred easily to the part being measured on the surface plate.

Angle Gage Blocks

Angle gage blocks are precision tools used for accurate measurement and inspection of angles. A set of sixteen, as illustrated in Fig. 3-146, may be used for measuring 356,400 angles, in steps of 1 second up to 99 degrees. These angle gage blocks may be wrung together in various combinations, just as rectangular gage blocks are. In Fig. 3-147, angle blocks are wrung together for inspection of a

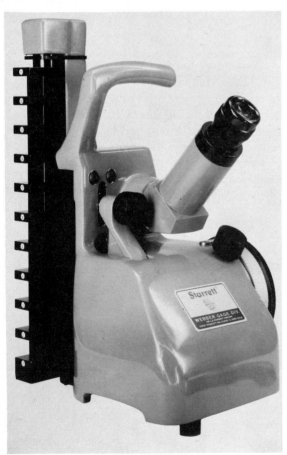

Fig. 3-144. Optical Height Gage
(Webber Div. — L. S. Starrett)

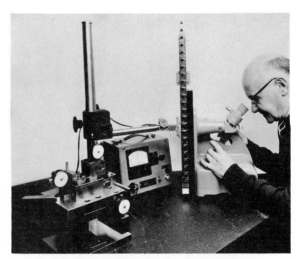

Fig. 3-145. Optical Height Gage Being Used to Check Height of Precision Jigs and Fixtures
(Webber Div. — L. S. Starrett)

Fig. 3-146. Set of One-Second Angle Gage Blocks
(Webber Div. — L. S. Starrett)

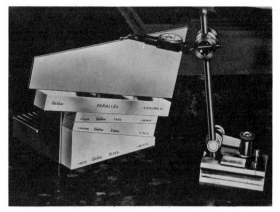

**Fig. 3-147. Inspecting a Simple Angle with
Angle Gage Blocks and Indicator**
(Webber Div. — L. S. Starrett)

simple angle on a part. In Fig. 3-148, they are used to establish the proper grinding angle on a revolving magnetic chuck.

Angle gage blocks are made of hardened tool steel which is ground and lapped to precision tolerances. These blocks are manufactured in two accuracy classifications: *laboratory master angle gage blocks*, which are the most expensive, have an accuracy classification of plus or minus ¼ second. *Toolroom* angle gage blocks have an accuracy of plus or minus 1 second.

Angle gage blocks are so designed that they may be combined in plus or minus positions. One end of each angle block is marked *plus*, while the opposite end is marked *minus*. Several examples will illustrate how the blocks may be combined in either position, thus forming different angles. The plus end of a 15° angle block may be wrung together with the plus end of a 5° block to form a 20° angle. Wringing the plus end of the 15° block together with the minus end of the 5° block forms an angle of 10°. The angle blocks may be wrung together to form angles in steps of degrees, minutes, seconds, or in any combination of these units.

The procedure for setting up or inspecting precision angles with angle gage blocks is less

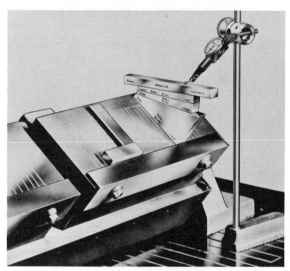

**Fig. 3-148. Setting a Revolving Magnetic Chuck
with Angle Gage Blocks**
(Webber Div. — L. S. Starrett)

complex than the procedure used with a sine bar. The latter method, which is explained in the following unit, involves more complicated mathematical procedures. Also, for many angles, angle blocks are more accurate than the sine bar.

UNIT 14

The Sine Bar and Its Use

The *sine bar*, Fig. 3-151, is a precision tool used for determining angles which must be more accurate than 5 minutes of arc. It may be used to establish or check angles to within one minute of arc. Sine bars must be used in conjunction with some true surface, such as a surface plate, from which accurate measurements may be taken. They are used to establish and check angles for layout work and inspection work. They may be used for making machining setups such as those often required for surface grinding. They also may be used to accurately determine unknown angles.

A sine bar is a hardened and precision-ground steel bar which has two hardened and precision-ground steel rolls of the same diameter attached. The edge of the bar is parallel

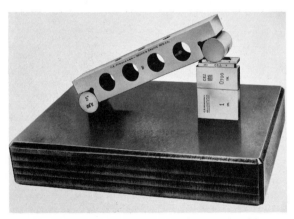

Fig. 3-151. Sine Bar Set at Desired Angle with Gage Blocks (Brown & Sharpe)

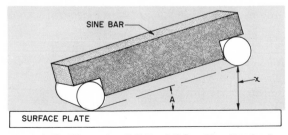

Fig. 3-152. Dimension "x" Establishes Sine Bar Angle

with the center line of the rolls. For convenient mathematical calculation, it is available in lengths which provide a distance of 5″, 10″, or 20″ between the center lines of the rolls.

The sine bar is so named because the *sines* of various angles are used in calculating the altitude (the dimension x, Fig. 3-152) for setting the bar at a desired angle. The dimension x is calculated by multiplying the sine of the desired angle by the length of the bar. The sines for various angles are included in a table of *natural trigonometric functions*, Table 45, appendix. While this brief four-place table is desirable for instruction, the sines should be listed to at least five decimal places for accuracy to 1 minute. Such tables in machinists or mathematics handbooks, for example, indicate that the sine for an angle of 21° 36′ (twenty-one degrees 36 minutes) is 0.368 125. (Table 45, gives the sine of 21° 30′ as 0.3665 and of 21° 40′ as 0.3692, so by interpolation, .6 of the difference places the sine of 21° 36′ at 0.3681.)

An example will illustrate how the distance x for a desired angle of 21° 36′ is calculated for use with a sine bar of 5″ length.

Dimension x = Length of sine bar $\times$
$$\text{sine of angle}$$
$$x = 5 \times \text{sine } 21° \, 36′$$
$$x = 5 \times 0.368\,125$$
$$x = 1.840\,625 \text{ inches}$$

The sine bar also may be used to determine an unknown angle. The bar is aligned carefully with the unknown angle by establishing the distance x with gage blocks which are wrung together to the proper height. The unknown angle may be determined by calculating its sine and then consulting a sine table for the angle. The sine of the unknown angle is equal to the distance x divided by the length of the sine bar.

An example will illustrate how an unknown angle may be determined with a 5″ sine bar when the distance x is known to be 2.3562″.

$$\text{Sine of Angle} = \frac{\text{Distance } x}{\text{Length of Sine Bar}}$$

$$\text{Sine of Angle} = \frac{2.3562}{5}$$

$$\text{Sine of Angle} = 0.47124$$

$$\text{Angle} = 28° \; 7' \text{ (to the nearest whole minute)}$$

A sine bar may be used in conjunction with a master planer gage for setting grinding angles, as shown in Fig. 3-153. The height of the planer gage may be measured with a micrometer or vernier caliper.

Sine Plate

The *sine plate* operates on the same principle as a sine bar and is very similar to a sine bar. The type shown in Fig. 3-154 is called an *inspection sine plate*. It is designed primarily for angular measurement, layout, and inspection work.

The sine plate has hardened precision rolls, hinges, and gage block surfaces. The roll on the right-hand end (Fig. 3-154) is located underneath the sine plate and cannot be seen in the picture. The roll at the left end is hinged to the base with a firm-fitting hinge.

When the sine plate is used, angles are established by wringing gage blocks together and placing them on the smooth gage block surface underneath the right-end roll. The sine plate may be used on a surface plate or it may be mounted on a machine table by clamping the flanged base. Tapped holes are provided on the sides and top of the plate for various clamping arrangements. The end and side holes may be used to fasten end or side plates.

Perma Sine

A perma sine is shown in Fig. 3-155. It is very similar to the sine plate described above, and angles are established in the same manner. It is actually a sine plate equipped with a magnetic chuck for holding workpieces securely, at any desired angle. A perma sine is especially suited for use on surface grinders. The base is equipped with a flange for clamping to the machine table. The holding power of the chuck is turned on or off with a simple lever.

Fig. 3-154. Sine Plate (Brown & Sharpe)

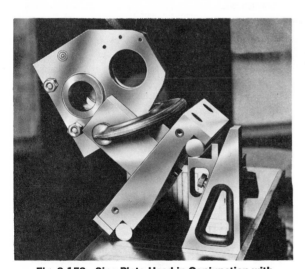

Fig. 3-153. Sine Plate Used in Conjunction with Master Planer Gage for Setting Grinding Angles (Lufkin)

Fig. 3-155. Perma Sine (Brown & Sharpe)

MEASUREMENT:

Test Your Knowledge of Section 3

Unit 5: Principles of Measurement

1. Why is accurate measurement essential in the machine shop?
2. What major nations use the English system of linear measurement?
3. Write decimal fractions for the following: one-tenth, one-hundredth, one-thousandth, one ten-thousandth, and one microinch.
4. What major group of countries uses the metric system of linear measure?
5. List the units into which the meter commonly is divided.
6. Of what significance is the International Prototype Meter bar which is maintained by the International Bureau of Standards?
7. Where does the United States keep its duplicate of the International Prototype Meter bar?
8. What is the length of the meter in terms of light-wave lengths?
9. What is the length of one inch in terms of light-wave lengths?
10. How can the length of one inch be duplicated exactly in any part of the world?
11. What is used as the practical standard of measurement in machine shops throughout the world?
12. Why are parts not produced to absolute size?
13. Define the following terms: (a) actual size; (b) basic size; (c) limits of size.
14. Define the meaning of the term *tolerance*.
15. Define the following terms: (a) fit; (b) clearance fit; (c) interference fit.
16. Define the meaning of the term *allowance*.
17. List several ways in which tolerances may be specified on a drawing.

Unit 6: Measuring and Layout Tools

1. In what lengths are steel rules available?
2. List the types of graduations available on steel rules.
3. To what degree of accuracy can layouts be made with a steel rule?

4. List several uses for a caliper rule.
5. For what purposes is a combination depth and angle gage used?
6. For what purposes are squares used?
7. List four principal parts included in a combination set.
8. List several uses for a combination square.
9. List several uses for a protractor head.
10. For what purpose is a center head used?
11. Describe a precision steel square, and list several uses for it.
12. Explain how a cylindrical square is used.
13. List several uses for the hermaphrodite caliper.
14. For what purposes is a center gage used?
15. Explain how a screw pitch gage is used.
16. Describe a radius gage and its use.
17. Explain what is meant by the term *layout work*.
18. Why do machinists use layout dye for layout work?
19. Explain the difference between dividers and calipers.
20. Explain the difference between a center punch and a prick punch.
21. Describe a surface plate, and list several uses for it.
22. For what purpose is a cast-iron straightedge used?
23. List two kinds of V-blocks, and explain how they are used.
24. Describe a surface gage, and list several uses for it.
25. Describe a telescoping gage, and explain how it is used.
26. Explain how a small-hole gage is used.
27. List several uses for adjustable parallels.
28. List several uses for a master planer and shaper gage.

Unit 7: Micrometers

1. List six principal parts of a micrometer.
2. What purposes does a ratchet serve on a micrometer?
3. What purpose does the lock nut serve on a micrometer?
4. Explain how a 1″-to-2″ micrometer is checked for accuracy.
5. Describe how a single, tubular inside micrometer may be used to measure diameters from 1½″ to 12″.

6. List several uses for a depth micrometer.
7. For what purpose is a mike hole gage used?
8. What purpose does a vernier serve on a micrometer?
9. To what accuracy will a light wave micrometer measure?

Unit 10: Dial Indicating Instruments

1. Explain what a dial indicator is. (Include the kinds of graduations on the dial.)
2. Explain the difference between the balanced dial indicator and the continuous-reading type.
3. How is the revolutions counter on a dial indicator used?
4. Explain how a dial indicator is set to proper gaging height.
5. List several ways in which a universal dial indicator set may be used.
6. List several uses for a hole attachment when used with a dial indicator.
7. List several uses for a universal indicator.
8. Explain several uses for a dial indicating depth gage.
9. Explain several uses for a dial indicating hole gage.
10. What is the principal use and purpose of a dial indicating snap gage?
11. List several advantages of a dial indicating micrometer over a standard micrometer caliper.
12. Explain how dial indicating comparators are used.

Unit 11: Vernier Tools

1. To what degree of accuracy will a vernier-equipped steel rule measure?
2. What kinds of measurements may be made with a vernier caliper?
3. Explain how an outside measurement is made with a vernier caliper.
4. Explain how an inside measurement is made with a vernier caliper.
5. List several uses for a vernier height gage.
6. List several uses for a vernier depth gage.
7. Explain how to read a 25-division vernier caliper.
8. Explain how to read a 50-division vernier caliper.

9. What measuring accuracy ordinarily is possible with a universal bevel protractor?
10. Explain how to read a universal bevel protractor.

Unit 12: Setup Tools

1. Why are machine vises designed so they may be swiveled?
2. List two uses for parallels.
3. Describe how hold-downs are used.
4. List three uses for angle plates.
5. List five work-holding accessories which may be used to mount workpieces on machine tables.

Unit 13: Gage Blocks and Gages

1. What is meant by the term *gaging*?
2. Define the meaning of *tolerance*.
3. List several advantages derived from inspecting large numbers of parts with gages rather than with tools such as micrometers and verniers.
4. How are gage blocks used in conjunction with gages?
5. Describe precision gage blocks.
6. What is the standardized temperature for precision measurement in the United States?
7. What type of measuring instrument measures accurately to within a millionth of an inch in units of light-wave length?
8. List several uses for gage blocks.
9. List several mechanical and metallurgical problems with steel, which were overcome in the manufacture of gage blocks.
10. List the three common accuracy classifications for gage blocks.
11. For what basic purposes are *master* gage blocks often used?
12. For what principal purposes are *working* gage blocks used?
13. Approximately how many gage block combinations may be made with a standard set of 81 blocks?
14. How many gage block combinations may be made with a set of the following five gage blocks: 0.0625″, 0.125″, 0.250″, 0.500″, and 1.000″?

15. Describe the procedure for wringing gage blocks together.
16. Describe how gage blocks are disassembled after being wrung together.
17. List several precautions in caring for and using gage blocks.
18. Explain the effects of temperature change on the accuracy of gage blocks.
19. Explain the procedure involved in building up a gage block combination, such as a combination of 0.7326″ length.
20. Define the meaning of the term *gage*.
21. Give several examples of adjustable gages.
22. For what principal purposes are fixed-type gages used?
23. Explain how a limits-type snap gage is used.
24. How are the size limits for a snap gage checked or set accurately to size?
25. For what purposes are plain ring gages used?
26. Explain how a taper ring gage is used.
27. For what purposes are plain cylindrical plug gages used?

28. Explain how a tapered plug gage is used.
29. Describe an optical height gage.
30. How are angle gage blocks used?
31. What accuracy can normally be obtained with angle gage blocks of the toolroom classification?

Unit 14: The Sine Bar and Its Use

1. For what purpose is a sine bar used?
2. Describe how a sine bar is used.
3. In what lengths are sine bars generally made?
4. Why is a sine bar so named?
5. Where can you secure the sines for various known angles?
6. Give the formula for calculating the altitude (the distance x) for a given angle with a sine bar.
7. Give the formula for determining an unknown angle with a sine bar, when the altitude is known.
8. List several purposes for which a sine plate may be used.
9. Describe a perma sine, and explain how it is used.

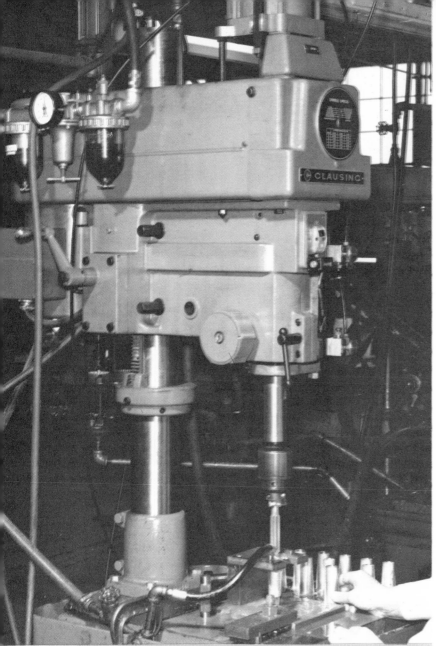

Tapping — Using Precision Fixtures and Automatic Controls
(Atlas Press)

SECTION 4

Threads and Threading

This section includes 13 units concerned with screw threads. The units are arranged in the order in which they usually should be studied. Units 15 through 22 include the information essential for identification of various types of threads. They also include information and procedures for cutting internal and external threads with hand tools. These units normally are considered essential for beginning courses in machine shop. The remaining units include important information necessary for a more complete understanding of screw threads, threading tools, and thread-cutting methods.

Screw Threads and Their Use

A screw thread is a helical or spiral ridge of uniform section on the surface of a cylinder or a cone, either external or internal. Threads on bolts and screws are external threads, Fig. 4-1. Threads on nuts are internal threads, Fig. 4-2. Threads on a cylindrical surface (such as bolts, machine screws, and nuts) are *straight* or *parallel* threads. Threads on a conical surface are *tapered* threads. For example, standard tapered pipe threads are cut on a slightly conical or tapered surface to insure a tight fit. However, most of the threads commonly cut in machine shop practice are straight screw threads.

Threads may be *right-hand* (RH) or *left-hand* (LH). A right-hand thread advances away from the observer when turned clockwise; a left-hand thread advances away from the observer when turned counterclockwise. A grinder with two grinding wheels, one mounted on each end of the arbor, has a right-hand thread and nut on one end and a left-hand thread and nut on the other end. Taps and dies are available for use in cutting right-hand and left-hand threads. Unless a thread is otherwise designated, it is assumed to be right-hand.

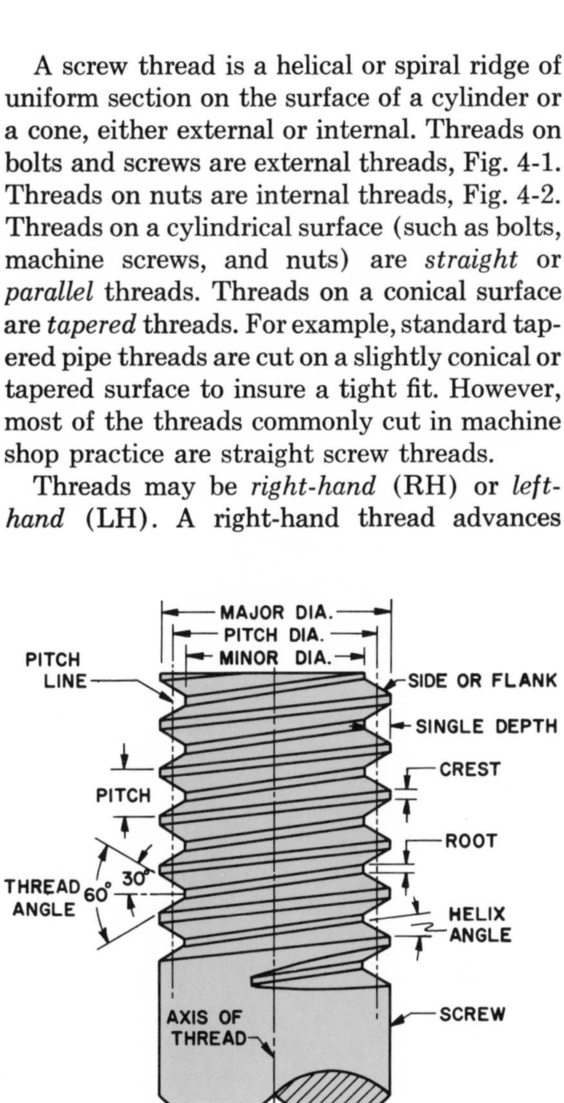

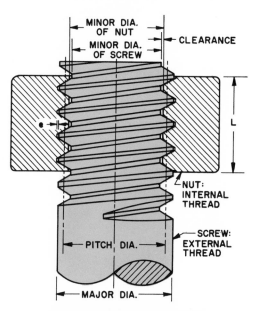

Fig. 4-2. Comparison between the Minor Diameters of a Screw and a Nut, Showing Clearance. External threads and internal threads have the same basic pitch diameters.

EXTERNAL SCREW THREAD

Fig. 4-1. Principal Parts of a Screw Thread

L = LENGTH OF THREAD ENGAGEMENT
e = EXTENDED MAJOR DIAMETER OF TAP FOR CLEARANCE

Uses of Screw Threads

Screw threads have many uses. They may be used to fasten or hold objects (or parts of objects) together, as in the case of bolts, nuts, and screws. Metal parts can be assembled and held together in three common ways: welding, riveting, and the use of screw threads. Screw threads permit easy assembly, dismantling, and reassembly.

Screw threads may be used to transmit motion, transmit power, increase the effect of power, control movement accurately and uniformly, and permit adjustments on machines. The lead screw on a lathe transmits power. The screw on a vise provides for increasing the effect of power. The screw on a micrometer makes possible accurate and uniform control of movement, thus making accurate measurement possible. Screw threads allow for adjustments on many different types of machines. The significance of screw threads may be understood more readily by attempting to answer the following question: Would it be possible to develop an automobile engine or a machine tool such as a lathe or milling machine without the use of various types of screw threads?

How Screw Threads Are Produced

Screw threads may be produced with hand tools and machine tools. Hand taps and dies are used to cut threads by the hand method. Machine tools which may be used to produce screw threads include: lathe, screw machine, turret lathe, tapping machine, milling machine, specialized thread rolling machine, and thread grinding machine. Tapping attachments also are available for use in tapping threads with a drill press or with a portable power drill.

Most of the standard screws, bolts, and nuts used for assembling tools and machines are made by mass-production methods. The setup man on these machines must have a thorough understanding of screw threads. The general machinist and the toolmaker frequently are called upon to make standard or special threads on matching parts. Therefore, it is necessary for the skilled machinist or maintenance worker to have a thorough understanding of screw threads. There are many different types of screw threads, each developed for a specific purpose or use.

Screw Thread Terms

The following terms or definitions are adapted from ASA definitions or are examples of the applications of such definitions. They are used in discussing screw threads and in making the necessary calculations for cutting screw threads:*

Screw thread: A helical ridge of uniform section on the internal or external surface of a cylinder or cone.

External thread: The thread on the external surface of a cylinder or cone, Figs. 4-1 and 4-2.

Internal thread: The thread on the internal surface of a cylinder or cone, Fig. 4-2.

Major diameter: (Formerly known as the outside diameter.) The largest diameter of a straight external or internal threads, Figs. 4-1 and 4-2.

*Unified Screw Threads (ASA B1.1 — 1960), Published by the American Society of Mechanical Engineers, New York, N.Y.

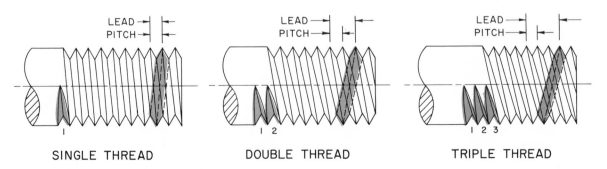

LEAD
PITCH

SINGLE THREAD

LEAD
PITCH

DOUBLE THREAD

LEAD
PITCH

TRIPLE THREAD

Fig. 4-3. Relationship of Pitch and Lead on Multiple Threads

Minor diameter: (Formerly known as the *root diameter* of the thread on a screw, or the *inside diameter* on a nut.) The smallest diameter on a straight external or internal screw thread, Figs. 4-1 and 4-2.

Pitch diameter: On a straight thread, the diameter of an imaginary cylinder which passes through the thread profile at points where the width of the groove and the width of the thread are equal, Figs. 4-1 and 4-2. The pitch diameter may be measured with a thread micrometer, Fig. 4-38. The amount of clearance permitted between two mating threads is controlled by maintaining close tolerances on their pitch diameters.

The pitch diameter on a taper thread, at a given position on the thread axis, is the diameter of the pitch cone at that position.

Pitch: The distance from a point on one screw thread to a corresponding point on the adjacent thread, measured parallel to the thread axis, **Fig. 4-1. The pitch of a thread is a measure of the** size of the thread form. The pitch is equal to 1 divided by the number of threads per inch.

Lead: The distance a thread moves along its axis, with respect to a mating part, in one complete revolution. On a single thread, the lead and the pitch are the same. On a double thread, the lead is equal to twice the pitch. On a triple thread, the lead is equal to three times the pitch. See Fig. 4-3. (A single thread has one groove; a double thread, two grooves; a triple thread, three grooves; and so on, Fig. 4-3.)

Multiple thread: A thread having the same form produced with two or more helical grooves, such as a double, triple, or quadruple thread, Fig. 4-3. A threaded fountain pen cap frequently has multiple threads, usually a quadruple thread with four grooves.

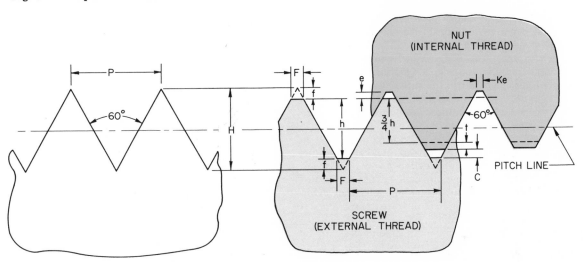

H = Depth of Sharp Vee thread = .866 × Pitch

P = Pitch = $\dfrac{1}{\text{No. Threads Per Inch}} = \dfrac{1}{n}$

n = Number of Threads Per Inch

h = Basic Depth (or Height) = $0.6495\,P = \dfrac{0.6495}{n} = \dfrac{6}{8}\,H$

F = Flat = $0.1250\,P = \dfrac{1}{8}\,P$

f = Truncation = $\dfrac{1}{8}\,H = \dfrac{1}{6}\,h = 0.10825\,P$

e = Extended Major Dia. on Tap for Clearance

Ke = Not Less Than $\dfrac{1}{3}\,F$ or $\dfrac{1}{24}\,P$

t = Tolerance = $\dfrac{1}{12}$ of Basic Depth = $\dfrac{1}{12}\,h$

C = Clearance = $\dfrac{1}{6}$ of Basic Depth = $\dfrac{1}{6}\,h$

$t + C = \dfrac{1}{4}$ of Basic Depth = $\dfrac{1}{4}\,h$

$\dfrac{3}{4}\,h = \dfrac{3}{4}$ of Basic Depth (or $\dfrac{3}{4}$ Full Thread in Nut)

$\dfrac{3}{4}\,h + t = \dfrac{5}{6}\,h = \dfrac{5}{8}\,H = \dfrac{0.54127}{n} = 0.54127\,P$ = Maximum Depth of Thread Engagement, Design Form (Maximum Material Condition)

Minor Dia. of Internal Thread (Design Form) = Major Diameter of Internal Thread — $1.08253\,P$

Fig. 4-4. Sharp V-Thread and Original American (National) Thread Form

Angle of thread: The included angle between the sides or flanks of the thread, measured in an axial plane, Fig. 4-1.

Number of threads: Refers to the number of threads per inch of length.

Lead angle: (Sometimes called helix angle.) Angle made by the helix of a thread at the pitch diameter, measured in a plane perpendicular to the axis of the thread, Fig. 4-1.

Axis of a screw thread: The axis of the pitch cylinder or cone on which the screw thread appears, Fig. 4-1.

Crest: The top surface which joins the two sides of a thread. The crest of an external thread is at its major diameter. The crest of an internal thread is at its minor diameter, Figs. 4-1 and 4-2.

Root: The bottom surface which joins the sides of two adjacent threads. The root of an external thread is at its minor diameter. The root of an internal thread is at its major diameter, Figs. 4-1 and 4-2.

Flank: (Formerly known as the side.) The surface which connects the crest with the root on either side of the thread, Fig. 4-1.

Crest clearance: The distance between the crest of a thread and the root of the mating thread, measured perpendicular to the thread axis, Fig. 4-4.

Depth of engagement: The depth to which one thread is engaged with a mating thread, measured perpendicular to the thread axis.

Length of engagement: The contact distance between an external and internal thread, measured parallel to the axis along the pitch cylinder or cone, Fig. 4-2.

Height of thread: (Sometimes called depth of thread.) The distance between the major and minor cylinders or cones of the thread, measured perpendicular to the axis of the thread.

Form: The profile for a length of one pitch in an axial plane, Fig. 4-4. (See also Fig. 4-6 on page 110.)

Maximum material limits: The maximum limit of size for an external dimension, or the minimum limit of size for an internal dimension.

Minimum material limits: The minimum limit of size for an external dimension, or the maximum limit of size for an internal dimension.

Design form of thread: The form of the thread (either internal or external) under the maximum material condition, *i.e.,* under maximum material limits (Fig. 4-7, page 111). Specified tolerances generally permit the thread roots to be cut deeper than those illustrated in Fig. 4-7.

Terms Related to Thread Classes or Fits

Nominal size: A designation used for general identification purposes.

Actual size: The size of that dimension as measured on the individual part.

Basic size: The theoretical or designated size from which the limits of size are derived through the application of allowances and tolerances.

Allowance: The term *allowance* applies to other machined parts as well as threads. On mating threads or parts, an allowance is the intentional difference in size between the maximum material limits of the parts; the minimum clearance between the parts is called *positive* allowance, and the maximum interference is called *negative* allowance. The allowance on mated threads represents the difference between the largest external thread and the smallest internal thread, thus the tightest possible fit.

The following examples illustrate allowances for external threads mated with internal threads:

Example 1: ⅝"-11 Unified National coarse thread, class 2A external thread and class 2B internal thread with a free fit:

Minimum pitch diameter of nut	0.5660
Maximum pitch diameter of screw	0.5644
Allowance (positive)	0.0016

Example 2: ⅝"-11 Unified National coarse thread, class 3A external thread and class 3B internal thread:

Minimum pitch diameter of nut	0.5660
Maximum pitch diameter of screw	0.5660
Allowance	0.0000

Example 3: ⅝"-11 National coarse thread, old class 4, close fit, on external and internal threads:

Minimum pitch diameter of nut	0.5660
Maximum pitch diameter of screw	0.5665
Allowance (negative)	0.0005

Tolerance: The term *tolerance* applies to other machined parts as well as to screw threads. The tolerance is the total permissible variation between the limits of size for a thread or other part. It may be expressed as plus or minus, or both. The total tolerance is the sum of the plus and minus tolerances. Tolerances on threads may be specified for pitch diameter, major diameter, minor diameter, thread angle, half-thread angle, and lead.

The following is an example of the tolerance or amount of variation permitted on the pitch diameter of a ⅝"-11 UNC thread, class 2A:

Maximum pitch diameter	0.5644
Minimum pitch diameter	0.5589
Tolerance	0.0055

For Unified and American National screw threads, the tolerance is applied *minus* to external threads and *plus* to internal threads.

Limits: The maximum and minimum sizes permissible for a given dimension. The limits for the pitch diameter of a ⅝"-11 UNC thread, class 2A are 0.5644 and 0.5589, as shown in the example above.

Fit: The range of tightness existing between two mating parts as a result of clearance or interference when they are assembled. The fit of threads may range from a loose fit with some play or looseness to an interference fit requiring a screwdriver or wrench for assembly. Where a specific class of thread or fit is designated, it means that certain allowances and tolerances are specified. For all Unified and American (National) threads, the tolerance is applied *plus* to the internal thread and *minus* to the external thread. With this application of tolerances, thread variations from the basic size will tend to fit more freely than tightly.

Classes of threads: One class of thread is distinguished from another by the amount of tolerance (or allowance and tolerance) specified for the thread.

Historical Background of Screw Threads

It is not known who first discovered the use of the screw thread, but it was many centuries ago, probably suggested by Archimedes (278-212 B.C.). He developed a screw which was enclosed in a cylinder for the purpose of drawing water. The lower end of the cylinder was placed in water, and as the screw was turned, the water was raised by the spiral grooves of the screw.

During the Middle Ages, nuts and bolts were used to fasten metal suits of armor together. Such early screws were made by hand tools and were very crude. Before 1800, screws were forged to shape and the threads were layed out and filed by hand. The slots also were cut by hand with a saw. Since there were no standards concerning size or pitch, these early bolts and nuts could not be used interchangeably.

Screw Threads Made by Machine

The era of interchangeability and mass production came about with the invention of the steam engine and power-driven machine tools. Henry Maudslay developed the first power-driven screw-cutting lathe in England in 1797. His lathe was equipped with a master lead screw and several changeable gears which made it possible to cut uniform threads of various size and pitch.

Throughout the 19th Century, improvements were made in the design and development of metalworking hand and machine tools. The turret lathe was developed about 1845.

With improved methods of mass production came a greater demand for a standardized system of screw threads which could provide for some degree of interchangeability.

Screw Threads in Great Britain

In 1841 Sir Joseph Whitworth developed a standard for screw threads in Great Britain. During the next twenty years, his standard was generally adopted in Great Britain, but not in the United States. Whitworth's original standard, with various modifications, formed the basis of the British Standard Whitworth (BSW) thread, which still is used to some extent in Great Britain. The BSW thread has a 55° **V**-form with rounded crests and rounded roots, Fig. 4-5. Three classes of threads are included in the Whitworth Standards; they are designated as close, medium, and free fits.

Screw Threads in the United States

The first progress toward the standardization of screw threads in the United States occurred in 1864. During that year, a committee appointed by the Franklin Institute presented a report recommending proposed screw thread standards, many of which were developed by William Sellers. The report was adopted, and the thread system became known as the *Sellers Standard* (later the United States Standard). Sellers accepted many of the diameter-pitch combinations of the Whitworth system, but omitted some of the sizes over 1½″. He also

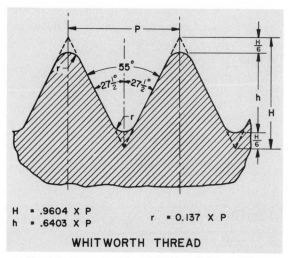

H = .9604 X P
h = .6403 X P   r = 0.137 X P

WHITWORTH THREAD

Fig. 4-5. Cross Section of Whitworth Thread Form

selected 13 threads instead of 12 for the ½″ size. His thread had a 60° included angle, instead of the 55° angle used on the Whitworth thread. Hence, the Sellers thread was not interchangeable with the Whitworth thread. The 60° **V**-form was easier to produce and measure. Sellers modified the sharper **V**-form of thread which was customary at the time by utilizing flats at the crest and roots. The flats were equal to one-eighth of the pitch.

USS Thread

In 1868 the Sellers Standard was adopted by the U.S. Navy and became known as the *United States Standard* (USS) thread. It became widely adopted for government services, railroads, and industry. The USS thread was a system of coarse threads which served the needs of industry in the U.S. at that time.

SAE Thread

With expanding industry and the development of the automobile, the airplane, and other modern equipment, other diameter-pitch combinations with finer threads were needed. This brought forth the adoption of the SAE (Society of Automotive Engineers) thread standard about 1911. The SAE standard included a system of fine threads, which was rather widely adopted in the U.S.

Following the adoption of the USS and SAE thread standards, efforts were made to further

develop and improve these standards. There was a need for the establishment of more specific dimensional limits, tolerances, and classes of thread fits. The established standards were concerned only with thread form, pitches, and external diameters.

Original American (National) Screw Thread Standard (1924)

The National Screw Thread Commission was established by Congress in 1918, for the purpose of adopting new screw thread standards for American industries and government services. Its aim was to eliminate unnecessary sizes and to use predominant existing screw sizes as much as possible. At the same time, industries and engineering societies were interested in the development of new thread standards. Groups cooperating with the Screw Thread Commission included the American Standards Association, the Society of Automobile Engineers, and the American Society of Mechanical Engineers.

As a result of these cooperative efforts, the existing USS and SAE series of threads was used as the basis and was further developed as a new thread standard. The original *American (National) Screw Thread Standard* was approved in 1924. The thread profile was designated as the *American (National) Form* of thread (Fig. 4-4, Unit 15). The external thread is essentially the same basic thread form used on the USS, the SAE, and the former Sellers thread. However, tolerances permitted a fuller minor diameter on the external thread, thus permitting greater tool wear on threading tools. Clearance for the internal thread was provided for through an enlarged minor diameter. Clearance for the major diameter of the nut also was provided by permitting an extended major diameter on the tap.

Two thread series were adopted in the American (National) Screw Thread Standard — the coarse thread and the fine thread. The coarse thread corresponded to the USS thread, and the fine thread corresponded to the SAE thread.

Four *classes of fits* were adopted under the 1924 American (National) Screw Thread Standard — the *loose fit*, the *free fit*, the *medium fit*, and the *close fit*. Tables of tolerances and

American (National) Thread System (1935)

In 1933 the National Screw Thread Commission made several modifications in the American (National) Screw Thread Standard of 1924. The coarse-thread series, previously designated USS, was changed to NC (National Coarse). The fine-thread series, previously designated SAE was changed to NF (National Fine). These modifications were included in the revised American Standard for screw threads approved by the American Standards Association in 1935. Other less commonly used series of threads included the following:

Extra-fine series is designated NEF.

8-thread series is designated 8N. It has 8 threads per inch for all diameters from 1″ to 6″ in diameter.

12-thread series is designated 12N. It has 12 threads per inch for all sizes from ½″ to 6″ in diameter.

16-thread series is designated 16N. It has 16 threads for all sizes from ¾″ to 6″ in diameter.

Special threads are designated NS.

The original American (National) thread profile was retained on all of the thread series classified under the American (National) thread system. The form of the thread profile and the formulas used in calculating the required dimensions are shown in Fig. 4-4.

Classes of Fits: Four regular classes of fits were included under the American National thread system for screws and nuts:

Class 1: loose fit. This fit always provides for some play or looseness between the screw and the mating nut or part. It is used where clearance between mating parts is essential for rapid assembly.

Class 2: free fit. This fit usually has some play or looseness. However, a screw and hole threaded under class 2 specifications may be without looseness and may even have a very slight interference under permissible maximum screw and minimum nut dimensions. The class 2 fit is a high-quality thread fit recommended for the majority of commercial screws, bolts, and interchangeable threaded assembly applications.

Class 3: medium fit. This fit usually provides for some looseness between a screw and a nut. The fit may vary from some looseness to a very slight interference under permissible maximum screw and minimum nut dimensions. The maximum amount of looseness permissible with minimum screw and maximum nut dimensions is approximately 70 percent of that permitted under class 2 specifications. The class 3 fit represents the highest quality fit used for commercially threaded parts requiring interchangeability. It is used where the tolerance of the mating parts demands its use. The cost of production is higher because of the high cost of precise tools and the need for more frequent checking of sizes.

Class 4: close or snug fit. This fit usually requires a wrench or screwdriver to assemble mating threads. A very small clearance may exist with minimum screw and maximum nut dimensions. A small amount of interference *(negative allowance)* may exist between the screw and the nut with the permissible minimum nut and maximum screw dimensions. The class 4 fit is used only where the tolerances of the mating threads are more demanding than the class 3 fit. It is not recommended for quantity-production purposes.

The four classes of fits are obtained through the application of tolerances and allowances. Tables which include the dimensional limits for obtaining each of the fits on screws and nuts are available in standard handbooks.

The 1935 standard for American (National) screw threads, including the four classes of fits, still is being used to a very limited extent by American industry. It has been largely replaced by the *Unified and American (National) Screw Thread Standards* published in 1949 and 1960.* These new Unified Standards include six thread *classes* designed to replace the four classes of *fits* in the 1935 standard.

Unified and American Screw Threads (ASA B1.1-1949) and later edition, *Unified Screw Threads* (ASA B1.1-1960), Published by the American Society of Mechanical Engineers, New York, New York.

17 Unified and American (National) Screw Threads (1948)

Before 1948 screw threads used by the United States, Canada, and Great Britain were not interchangeable. The British Whitworth screw thread used a 55° angle, and the American (National) screw thread, a 60° angle. Three classes of thread fits were used with the Whitworth thread, while four classes of regular fits were used with the American (National) thread. Because of these differences, a unified thread system providing for interchangeability of threads was difficult to develop.

During World Wars I and II, many difficult problems developed because screw threads were not interchangeable on military equipment in various parts of the world. For this reason, efforts were made to develop a unified screw thread system which could be used interchangeably by industries and government services in the United States, Canada, and Great Britain.

Unification of Screw Threads

On December 18, 1948 an agreement was reached on standardization of screw threads by representatives of government and industry bodies of the United States, the United Kingdom, and Canada. The representatives of the cooperating countries were charged with development of standards for screw threads. The following quotation presents the chief features of the agreement:

"The present unification agreement provides a 60° angle and a rounded root for screw threads.

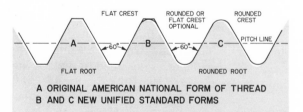

A ORIGINAL AMERICAN NATIONAL FORM OF THREAD
B AND C NEW UNIFIED STANDARD FORMS

Fig. 4-6. Comparison between (A) the American (National) and (B and C) the New Unified Standard Form of Thread

The crest of the external thread may be flat, as preferred in American practice, or rounded, as preferred by the British. The number of threads per inch for the various series of thread diameters has been unified, and the limiting dimensions, for three grades of fit have been agreed upon; thus, interchangeability of screw thread parts, based on the accord, now becomes feasible.

"There is, however, a further degree of interchangeability attained by agreements on the numerical values for allowances and tolerances, thereby setting limits to the least and greatest amounts of looseness between mating parts. Such agreement provides for identity of sizes (or interchangeability of use) of screw thread gauges used in the different countries for controlling the limits of size of the threads. It also standardizes the grade or grades of fits between mating parts."*

The chief differences between the new standards and the American and National Coarse and National Fine threads are the rounded root and the optional rounded or flat crest on the external thread. The rounded root is optional on both the internal and the external threads for most applications; however, for some applications, the root must be rounded. Rounded roots are produced with tools that are purposely rounded, or they may be a result of tool wear. The crest on the internal thread is flat.

Maximum and minimum major diameters, pitch diameters, and minor diameters for both external and internal threads have been agreed upon. A, in Fig. 4-6A shows the old American (National) form of thread, and B and C show the Unified standard form. Producing a thread with a rounded root requires only rounding the point of the tool used for cutting the old form of thread. Further modification of the shape of the tool is required to produce threads with rounded crests. For threads with small pitch, the modification is very slight.

*Technical Report 1315. National Bureau of Standards, U.S. Department of Commerce, Washington, D.C.

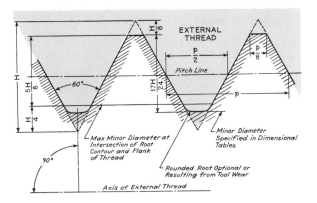
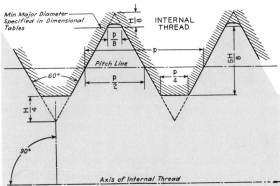

Angle of thread . . . . $2\alpha = 60°$

Half angle of thread . . . . $\alpha = 30°$

Number of threads per inch . . . . $n = \dfrac{1}{p}$

Pitch of thread . . . . $p = \dfrac{1}{n}$

Height of sharp V thread . . . . $H = 0.86603p$
$$= \frac{0.86603}{n}$$

[1]Height of external thread, design form . $h_s = 0.61343p$
$$= \frac{0.61343}{n}$$
$$= \frac{17}{24}H$$

Height of internal thread, design form . $h_n = 0.54127p$
$$= \frac{0.54127}{n}$$
$$= \frac{5}{8}H$$

Depth of thread engagement . . . . $h_e = 0.54127p$
$$= \frac{0.54127}{n}$$

Flat at crest of external thread . . . . $F_{cs} = 0.125p$
$$= \frac{0.125}{n}$$
$$= \frac{p}{8}$$

Truncation of external-thread crest . . . . $f_{cs} = 0.10825p$
$$= \frac{0.10825}{n}$$
$$= \frac{H}{8}$$

[1]Truncation of external-thread rounded
root . . . . $s_{rs} = 0.14434p$
$$= \frac{0.14434}{n}$$
$$= \frac{H}{6}$$

Flat at crest of internal thread,
design form . . . . $F_{cn} = 0.25p$
$$= \frac{0.25}{n}$$
$$= \frac{p}{4}$$

Truncation of internal-thread
crest . . . . $f_{cn} = 0.21651p$
$$= \frac{0.21651}{n}$$
$$= \frac{H}{4}$$

Flat at root of internal thread . . $F_{rn} = 0.125p$
$$= \frac{0.125}{n}$$
$$= \frac{p}{8}$$

Truncation of internal-thread
root . . . . $f_{rn} = 0.10825p$
$$= \frac{0.10825}{n}$$
$$= \frac{H}{8}$$

Addendum of external thread . . . $h_{as} = 0.32476p$
$$= \frac{0.32476}{n}$$
$$= \frac{3}{8}H$$

Major diameter of external
thread . . . . D_s

[2] Pitch diameter of external
thread . . . . $E_s = D_s - 2h_{as}$
$$= D_s - 0.64952p$$
$$= D_s - \frac{0.64952}{n}$$

Minor diameter of external
thread, design form . . . . $K_s = D_s - 2h_s$
$$= D_s - 1.22687p$$
$$= D_s - \frac{1.22687}{n}$$

Major diameter of internal thread . = D_n
Pitch diameter of internal thread . . = E_n
Minor diameter of internal
thread, design form . . . . $K_n = D_n - 2h_n$
$$= D_n - 1.08253p$$
$$= D_n - \frac{1.08253}{n}$$

[1] For calculating minor diameter values in tables.
[2] $2h_{as} = h_b = $ the basic height, h, of the original American National form.

Fig. 4-7. (A) Unified Internal and External Screw Thread (Maximum Material Condition) Design Forms and (B) Thread Formulas, Unified and American National

(Extracted from American Standard Unified Screw Threads (ASA B1.1-1960) with permission of publisher, The American Society of Mechanical Engineers, 29 West 39th Street, New York 18, N. Y.)

Careful study of Figs. 4-5 and 4-6 will reveal that the new Unified standard screw thread profile is a compromise between the British Whitworth thread profile and the American (National) thread profile. With the Unified thread, British practice changed to the 60° thread angle. The root forms are round by design, as preferred by British practice. However, crest clearances permit interchangeability with the optional flat root forms, as preferred by previous American practice. Except for the rounded roots and crests, the Unified thread form is essentially the same as the American (National) thread form.

American (National) standard threads and Unified standard threads of the same diameter and pitch are mechanically interchangeable. The principal differences between the two thread standards occur in the application of allowances, in the variation in tolerances according to size, and in the designation of the thread series.

The basic height or depth of the external Unified thread in the maximum metal condition is slightly less than the height of the American (National) standard thread. The basic height of the external Unified thread is equal to 0.61343 x pitch, Figs. 4-7A and B. The basic height of the American (National) standard thread is 0.64952 x pitch, Fig. 4-4. Because of the application of tolerances and allowances, the two types of threads with the same diameter and pitch are mechanically interchangeable.

The American standard for screw threads, *American Standard Unified Screw Threads* (ASA B1.1-1960)*, includes both systems of screw threads used in the United States — (1) the Unified system of threads and (2) the particular pitch-diameter combinations in the 1935 American (National) standard thread system, which have not been unified. The 1960 standard is an outgrowth of the 1924, 1935, and 1949 standards, and it replaces the earlier standards.

Unified and American Screw Threads (ASA B1.1-1949) and later edition, *Unified Screw Threads* (ASA B1.1-1960), Published by the American Society of Mechanical Engineers, New York, New York.

The transition from the American (National) to the Unified thread standards is essentially completed. The use of standard Unified threads is required on most equipment purchased by the federal government, including military and other equipment. Increased foreign trade has caused wide use of the Unified system in the majority of American industries. Wherever it is possible to do so, Unified threads should be used in the design and development of new products.

Classes of Unified Threads

In the Unified thread system, the term *class of fits*, which referred to the assembly characteristics of mating threaded parts, has been discontinued. The new term used is *class of thread*. It refers to the tolerance and allowance, for one thread component. It does not imply that both the nut and the screw must have the same class of tolerance. In fact, any class of external thread, old or new, may be mated with any class of internal thread, so long as the resulting product meets assembly requirements. Fit is determined by the particular combination of classes of thread selected for the mating parts.

Six thread tolerance classes are included in the Unified thread system — three for screws and three for nuts. The external classes of threads are designated 1A, 2A, and 3A. The internal classes of threads are designated 1B, 2B, and 3B. Associated with these thread classes in the *Unified Screw Thread Standard* (1960) are the old American (National) thread classes 2 and 3 (formerly called fits), for use until complete adoption of the Unified system occurs. The old class 4 has been dropped under the new standard. The old class 2 and class 3 threads are interchangeable with any of the new classes. Thread classes 1A and 1B are intended to replace the old class 1 fit.

The following are the new thread classes for Unified threads:

1A and 1B: Provides a fit with some play or looseness, even for rusty or slightly damaged threads. Some allowance is provided on class 1A.

2A and 2B: Provides a free fit suitable for a large majority of commercially threaded fasteners. Some allowance is provided on class 2A.

3A and 3B: Provides a close fit for applications which require more than the usual accuracy of thread angle and lead. Accurate equipment and frequent inspection are required to maintain consistent production of these thread classes. No allowance is provided on class 3A.

Any combination of the six Unified thread classes may be used with the two old classes in acquiring desired fits for mating threads.

Basic thread dimensions, limits, allowances, and tolerances for Unified and American (National) screw threads are given in the standards, ASA B1.1-1949 and ASA B1.1-1960, footnoted earlier. This information is also available in several of the standard machine shop handbooks.

Designation of Screw Threads

Thread Sizes: The sizes of screw threads are indicated by fraction or by screw gage number. In the coarse-thread series, fine-thread series, and extra-fine-thread series, thread diameters ¼″ and larger are designated by fractional size, such as ¼-20 NC or ¼-20 UNC; thread diameters under ¼″ generally are designated by screw gage number such as 10-24 UNC. A No. 10 machine screw has a diameter of 0.190″. (See Table 35, appendix.) Certain screw threads in the special series, UNS or NS, under ¼″ diameter are designated by fractional size, such as ³⁄₁₆-24 NS or ³⁄₁₆-24 UNS.

Thread Series Included: The following series of screw threads are included in the American standard, *Unified Screw Threads* (ASA B1.1-1960):

UNC — Unified National Coarse
UNF — Unified National Fine
UNEF — Unified National Extra-Fine

The following *constant-pitch* series of threads also are included in the Unified screw thread standard: UN4, UN6, UN8, UN12, UN16, UN20, UN28, and UN32. (See Table 37, appendix.) A constant-pitch thread has the same number of threads per inch for all diameters included. (The UN8 series always has eight threads per inch.) Constant-series threads are used where the coarse, fine, or extra-fine series do not meet specified requirements. When a constant-series thread is selected, preference should be given to the 8-, 12-, or 16-thread series.

Thread Symbols: The following symbols are used in designating Unified and American (National) screw threads on drawings and blueprints:

A indicates external thread.
B indicates internal thread.
U indicates Unified thread, and the particular thread size is recognized as a standard thread in the United Kingdom, Canada and the United States.
N indicates American (National) screw thread.
LH indicates left-hand thread.

When the letter *U* does not appear in the thread designation, but the letter *A* or *B* does appear, it means that all of the thread limits and tolerances conform to the principles involved in the establishment of Unified threads, though the particular thread size is not unified.

When none of the letters *A*, *B*, or *U* appears in the thread designation, the thread conforms to the earlier American (National) thread standard.

Thread Specifications: Unified and American (National) threads are completely specified on drawings with a note. The note always follows the same order: the nominal size is indicated first, followed by the number of threads per inch, thread series designation, thread class, and LH if the thread is left-hand. For example, a thread specified by the note ⅝-18 UNF-3A-LH designates a ⅝″ diameter thread, with 18 threads per inch, the Unified National Fine series, with a class 3A (external) thread, and with left-hand threads. Other examples follow:

⅝-11 UNC-2B
⅝-14 NS-2A
¼-28 UNF-2A

½-28 UNEF-2A-LH
10-24 UNC-2B
10-24 NC-2
⅝-12 N-3

Thread Formulas and Calculations

When threads are cut on a lathe with a single-point tool, it often is necessary to use thread formulas to make the required calcula-tions for such thread elements as external thread height, internal thread height, and internal minor diameter. The formulas required for the calculation of Unified screw threads, according to present standards, are included in Fig. 4-7A and 4-7B. The formulas used for the calculation of the original American (National) screw thread are included in Fig. 4-4. The basic formulas required for other thread forms are included with the figures showing the desired thread.

18   Other Forms of Screw Threads

Sharp Vee Thread

The sharp vee thread is very similar to the American (National) form thread. (See Fig. 4-4.) It was used occasionally by watchmakers and instrument makers, but it is now obsolete. The sharp threads became damaged easily. They also were expensive because of the limited tool life of taps and dies used to produce the sharp vee.

Whitworth Thread

The British Standard Whitworth form of thread is a V-form with a 55° thread angle (Fig. 4-5). The basic thread form is used on the following series of threads: British Standard Whitworth (BSW), British Standard Fine (BSF), and British Standard Pipe (BSP).

Square Thread

The depth, width, and space between square threads are equal; see Fig. 4-8A. The square thread sometimes is used on vise screws, heavy jack screws, and similar items. The square thread cannot be made efficiently with dies, taps, or milling cutters unless the thread form is modified. It must be cut with a single-point tool on a lathe. The use of acme threads large-ly has replaced the use of square threads in machine design and construction.

Acme Thread

Acme threads have a 29° thread angle, as shown in Fig. 4-8B. Originally they were de-signed as a modification of the square thread. They are used to produce traversing move-ments on machine tools, steam valves, vises, and for similar purposes. Although acme threads are not quite as strong as the square thread, they are much easier to machine. They may be cut with dies, taps, milling cutters, grinders, and a single-point tool in a lathe.

There are two basic thread standards for 29° acme threads — the *old standards* and the *new standards* (introduced in 1952). Acme threads produced according to these two standards are not interchangeable. The basic dimensions for old standard general-purpose American (National) acme threads may be determined from the formulas in Fig. 4-8B. The basic dimen-sions, limiting dimensions, and tolerances for these threads may be secured in standard hand-books for the machinist. The machinist, par-ticularly the maintenance machinist, should be familiar with both the old and new acme thread standards.

New *standards* for general-purpose acme threads were established in 1952. The American standard, *Acme Screw Threads* (B1.5-1952)*, gives complete data including basic

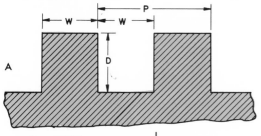

P = PITCH = $\frac{1}{\text{NO. THREADS PER INCH}}$

D = DEPTH = .500 X PITCH

W = .500 X PITCH

WIDTH W OF THREAD GROOVE IN NUT = (.500 X PITCH) + .001 TO .002 INCH CLEARANCE MAKE .001 TO .003 OVERSIZE TO FIT

SQUARE THREAD

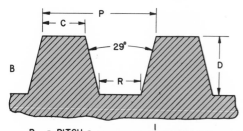

P = PITCH = $\frac{1}{\text{NO. THREADS PER INCH}}$

D = DEPTH = $\frac{1}{2}$ PITCH + .010 INCH

C = FLAT ON TOP OF THREAD = P X .3707

R = FLAT ON BOTTOM = (P X .3707) − .0052

ACME THREAD
(Old Standard Acme General-Purpose)
Thread

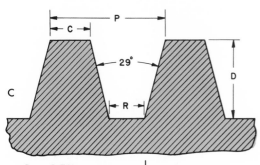

P = PITCH = $\frac{1}{\text{NO. THREADS PER INCH}}$

D = DEPTH = .6866 X PITCH

C = CREST FLAT = .335 X PITCH

R = ROOT FLAT = .310 X PITCH

29° BROWN AND SHARPE WORM THREAD

Fig. 4-8. Cross Sections of Several Forms of Screw Threads

dimensions, limiting dimensions, and tolerances for three classes of general-purpose acme threads. The three classes (designated 2G, 3G, and 4G) are provided with clearances on all diameters for free movement. Class 2G is most widely used for general-purpose work. The other classes are used where backlash or end play must be reduced in the mating threads. Data concerning the new standards for acme threads also are available in standard handbooks for the machinist.

An acme thread gage, Fig. 4-9, is used in grinding an acme threading tool to the correct thread angle and to the correct tool width. The width of the tool point must conform to the numbered notch in the gage. For example, the point of a tool ground to cut five threads per inch must fit in the notch numbered five. The gage also is used to set the tool square with the work.

The number of acme threads per inch for various diameters, recommended by the National Screw Thread Commission (on both the old and the 1952 standards), for standard acme general-purpose threads, is included in Table 2.

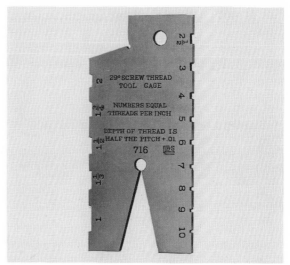

Fig. 4-9. Acme Standard 29° Thread Tool Gage
(Brown & Sharpe)

Acme Screw Threads (ASA B1.5-1952). Published by the American Society of Mechanical Engineers, New York.

Brown and Sharpe Worm Thread

The general form and the basic dimensions for the Brown and Sharpe worm thread are shown in Fig. 4-8C. This thread is similar to the acme thread in thread angle, Fig. 4-8B. Both threads have a 29° included thread angle, but the Brown and Sharpe thread is deeper. The widths of the crests and roots of the thread are also different.

The Brown and Sharpe worm-thread gage in Fig. 4-10 is used to measure the correct tool angle and point width for a single-point tool used in cutting the worm thread. The setting tool also shown in Fig. 4-10 is used to set the tool square with the work.

Pipe Threads

The most commonly used system of pipe threads is the American Standard or *American National* pipe thread. Two types of pipe threads are included in this system — the American Standard taper pipe thread (NPT) and the American Standard straight pipe thread (NPS). A third type which is a variation of the NPT is the American standard Dryseal pipe thread (NPTF).

Pipe Thread Sizes: Pipe diameter designations are different from the actual diameter of the pipe. For example, a ⅛″ pipe has an outside diameter of

.450″; also the actual inside diameter is larger than ⅛″. Tables in standard handbooks for the machinist include the basic pipe thread dimensions, nominal pipe sizes with the number of threads per inch, outside diameters, pitch diameters, and other dimensions.

Tapered Pipe Threads (NPT): The tapered pipe thread is similar to the American National thread. It has a 60° angle between the sides of the threads, and it has flattened crests and roots. However, it differs from the National Form thread in that the threads are tapered ¾″ per foot of length from the small end of the thread toward the large end. Also, the nominal diameter sizes designated are different than the actual outside diameters of the pipe.

Both the external and the internal threads are tapered. This permits drawing the joint up tightly for a rigid joint. However, a pipe compound must be used to seal the clearance space which exists between the crests and roots of the mating threads, thus preventing leakage of liquid or gas under pressure.

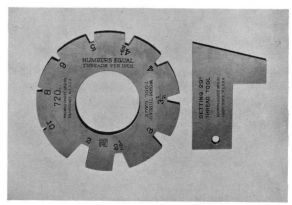

Fig. 4-10. Brown and Sharpe 29° Worm-Thread Gage (Left) and Setting Tool

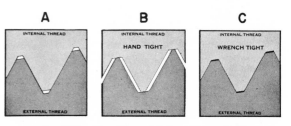

Fig. 4-11. Pipe Thread Joints (Greenfield)
(A) Regular taper pipe joint; (B) Dryseal pipe thread hand-tight; (C) Dryseal pipe thread wrench-tight.

Table 2
Standard General-Purpose Acme Threads

Size	No. of threads per inch	Size	No. of threads per inch
¼	16	1⅜	4
5⁄16	14	1½	4
⅜	12	1¾	4
7⁄16	12	2	4
½	10	2¼	3
⅝	9	2½	3
¾	6	2¾	3
⅞	6	3	2
1	5	3½	2
1⅛	5	4	2
1¼	5	4½	2
		5	2

Straight Pipe Threads (NPS:) The straight and the tapered threads are similar in form and dimensions, but straight threads are not tapered. The straight pipe thread more closely resembles the regular National Form thread in general form, but the pitches and nominal diameter size designations are significantly different.

Straight pipe threads (NPS) sometimes are used in couplings which join pipes having tapered pipe threads (NPT). This type of pipe assembly often is satisfactory for low-pressure lines when a pipe compound is used and when the line is free of vibration.

Dryseal Pipe Threads: American Standard Dryseal pipe threads (NPTF) are used for those pressure joints where the use of a pipe sealing material is objectionable. This type of thread is used on both internal and external threads. On Dryseal threaded pipe joints, the external thread is tapered, while the internal thread may be tapered or straight. Joints with both internal and external threads tapered are superior.

The basic dimensions of most American Standard Dryseal pipe threads are the same as those for the American Standard tapered pipe threads, except that the crests and roots of the Dryseal threads are modified to cause a pressure-tight seal. The crest flats are equal to or less than the root flats of the mating thread, thus causing physical contact between the crests and the roots when turned up hand-tight. When turned wrench-tight, the threads mash together causing a pressure-tight seal, Fig. 4-11C.

Basic Taps and Accessories Used for Hand Tapping

Taps are used to cut internal threads in holes. The process of cutting internal threads is called *tapping*. External threads are cut with a die, and the process is called *threading*.

Taps are made of hardened tool steel, either carbon tool steel or high-speed steel. Carbon steel taps usually are used for hand-tapping operations. High-speed steel taps are used for both hand- and machine-tapping operations.

The flutes on the tap provide for the cutting edges and also provide space for the chips. Standard hand taps usually have four flutes, although some taps have two or three flutes, Fig. 4-12. The square end on the tap is used for holding the tap with a wrench or other holding device. Taps are hard and brittle, and they break quite easily when excessive force is applied to them.

Hand Taps

The three basic types of hand taps are the *taper tap*, the *plug tap*, and the *bottoming tap*, Fig. 4-13. The only basic difference in the three taps is the number of threads which are ground to a taper on the end of the tap. Taps are ground tapered in order to start and cut the threads more easily. Most of the actual cutting of the thread is performed by the chamfered threads on the end of the tap.

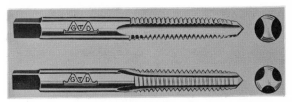

Fig. 4-12. Two-Fluted and Three-Fluted Hand Taps
(Greenfield)

As the name implies, *hand taps* originally were designed for hand-tapping operations. However, in modern industry, hand taps are used widely for machine tapping. The most commonly used tap for production machine tapping is the *plug hand tap*. Generally, when hand taps are used for hand tapping, they are furnished in sets of three, including the *taper*, *plug*, and *bottoming* taps for each thread size and pitch.

Taper Tap: The taper tap has 8 to 10 threads tapered. It is used to tap *open or through* type holes, as in Fig. 4-14A. It also is used as the first step in tapping closed or blind holes in hand-tapping operations, Fig. 4-14B and C. Tool life and breakage largely depend on the length of the tapered threads on the tap. Less power is required and less strain is exerted on a tapered tap than on a plug or bottoming tap. Therefore, the tapered tap should be used whenever possible on hand-tapping operations.

Fig. 4-13. Set of Hand Taps (Greenfield)
(A) Taper tap; (B) Plug tap; (C) Bottoming tap.

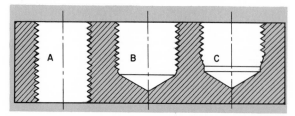

Fig. 4-14. Types of Holes Commonly Tapped
(A) Open or through; (B) Blind bottoming;
(C) Blind but not bottoming.

Plug Tap: The plug tap has 3 to 5 threads tapered. Whenever possible, all three hand taps should be used in tapping closed or blind holes, Fig. 4-14B and C. The tapered tap is used first in tapping to the bottom of the hole, and it is followed with the plug tap and the bottoming tap. When all three taps are not available, the plug tap may be used for open or through holes, if care is taken not to break the tap with excessive force. Plug taps are preferred for machine tapping because the hole can be tapped in one operation when the hole is designed, as in Fig. 4-14C.

Bottoming Tap: The bottoming tap has 1 to 1½ threads tapered. It is used after the plug tap for tapping to the bottom of a hole as in Fig. 4-14B.

Serial Taps: Serial hand taps usually are produced in sets of three (numbered 1, 2, and 3) and are identified with one, two, or three rings on the shank of the tap near the square, Fig. 4-15. Serial taps are used for hand tapping deep holes in tough metals. They are similar to the taper, plug, and bottoming tap in general appearance, but they differ in size of the pitch diameter and major diameter.

Each tap is designed to remove a certain portion of the metal in cutting a thread; this procedure eliminates excessive strain on the tap and aids in preventing tap breakage. The No. 1 tap is used first for cutting a shallow thread. This is followed by the No. 2 tap, which cuts deeper, and finally, the No. 3 tap is used to cut the thread to full depth.

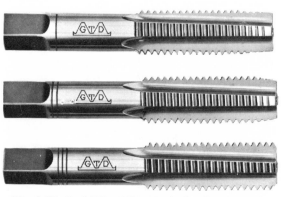

Fig. 4-15. Serial Hand Taps Including No. 1, No. 2, and No. 3 Taps, Identified by Rings in Shanks
(Greenfield)

Tap Size Identification: The size of the tap is stamped on its shank. A tap labeled ½-13 UNC is ½″ diameter, has 13 threads per inch, and is a Unified National Coarse thread. Left-hand taps are identified with the additional letters *LH*, such as ½ - 13 UNC-LH.

Machine Screw Gage Numbers: Machine screw diameters under ¼″ are designated by gage number, such as 0, 6, 8, 10, and 12. A typical designation may be 10-24 UNC. The actual major diameters of machine screw sizes are listed in tables of tap drill sizes, such as Table 35, appendix. The diameters of machine screws can be calculated easily if it is remembered that size 0 is 0.060″ diameter and that each number higher is 0.013″ larger.

Examples:

size   0 = 0.060
size   1 = 0.060 + .013 = 0.073
size   2 = 0.060 + (2 × .013) = .086
size 10 = 0.060 + (10 × .013) = .190

Tap Wrenches

Tap wrenches are used to turn the tap for hand-tapping operations. The wrenches have adjustable jaws which enable the tap to be tightened in the wrench and held firmly. There are two common types of tap wrenches — the *T-handle* tap wrench (Fig. 4-16) and the *straight handle* tap wrench (Fig. 4-17). Both types are available in several sizes. The T-handle tap wrench usually is used for smaller diameter taps than that for which the straight handle tap wrench is used. Taps of a small size may be broken easily with tap wrenches which are too large. Tap wrenches may also be used with reamers, screw extractors, and other tools which are turned by hand.

Screw Plates

Taps, tap wrenches, dies, and die stocks may be purchased in sets called *screw plates*, as shown in Fig. 4-18. Screw plates are available in several sizes and combinations. They may include either a small or large range of thread sizes and either the fine, the coarse, or both series of threads.

Fig. 4-17. Straight Handle Tap Wrench (Greenfield)

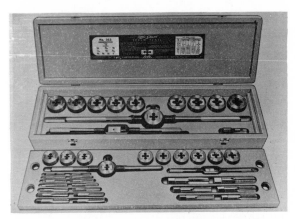

Fig. 4-18. Taps, Dies, and Tap Wrenches Included in Screw Plate (Greenfield)

Fig. 4-16. T-Handle Tap Wrench (Greenfield)

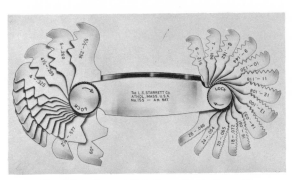

Fig. 4-19. Screw Pitch Gage (L. S. Starrett)

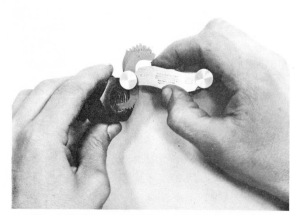

Fig. 4-20. Screw Pitch Gage Used to Determine Pitch of Thread (Brown & Sharpe)

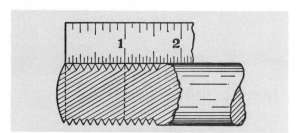

Fig. 4-21. Measuring Shows 8 Threads to the Inch (South Bend Lathe)

Screw Pitch Gage

The pitch of a screw thread may be checked with a screw pitch gage, Fig. 4-19. The gage is made of a series of sheet metal plates into which is cut the form of screw threads of various pitches. Pitch is checked by determining which plate fits accurately into the given thread, as in Fig. 4-20. The gage may be used to determine the pitch or number of threads per inch on screws or nuts. The pitch and number of threads per inch also may be measured with a rule, as shown in Fig. 4-21.

Tap Extractor

If a tap is broken off in a hole so that it cannot be reached with a pliers, it may be re-

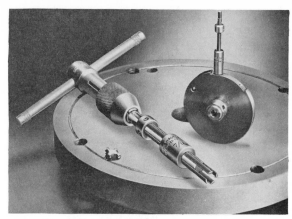

Fig. 4-22. Tap Extractor Used to Remove Broken Taps (Walton)

Fig. 4-23. Screw Extractor (Cleveland Twist Drill)

moved with a tap extractor, Fig. 4-22. In use, the steel prongs of the extractor are pushed down into the flutes of the broken tap. The steel bushing is pushed down toward the end to hold the prongs firmly. A tap wrench is used to turn the extractor in removing the broken tap.

Screw Extractor

A bolt or machine screw which is broken off below the surface, or which is broken off too short to grasp with a pliers, may be removed with a screw extractor, Fig. 4-23. (It also can be used to remove short pieces of pipe which are broken off below the surface of a pipe coupling.) A hole slightly larger than the small end of the extractor must be drilled into the broken screw. The screw extractor is inserted into the hole and turned to the left with the use of a tap wrench. The largest size screw extractor possible for the size of the screw should be used. Screw extractors are available in a full range of sizes.

How To Tap Holes by Hand

1. Determine the size of the thread, and select the tap before drilling the hole.
2. Determine the proper tap drill size by consulting Table 35 or 36, appendix. For example: a $\frac{5}{16}''$ diameter drill is used to drill the hole for a $\frac{3}{8}$-16 UNC thread with approximately 75-percent thread depth. The tap drill size also may be calculated as outlined in Unit 26. Tap drill sizes for threads with less than 75-percent thread depth are shown in Table 40, appendix.
3. Mount the work in a drill vise, and drill the hole.
4. Mount the work in a bench vise so that the hole is in a vertical position.
5. Select the proper tap wrench, and tighten the tap in the wrench.
6. Use the right hand to grasp the tap and tap wrench. Cup your hand over the center of the wrench, as in Fig. 4-25, and place the tap in the hole at a right angle to the hole. Start the tap by turning two or three turns to the right, at the same time keeping a steady pressure downward on the tap. When the tap is started, it may be turned as shown in Fig. 4-26.
7. After the tap is started for several turns, remove the tap wrench without disturbing

the tap. Place the blade of a small square against the solid shank of the tap to check for squareness; check from two positions 90° apart. See Fig. 4-27. If the tap is not square with the work, it will cut too deeply on one side of the hole, will ruin the

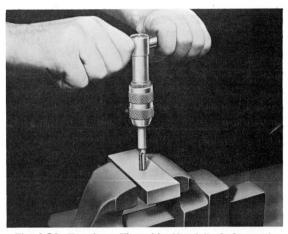

Fig. 4-26. Tapping a Thread by Hand (L. S. Starrett)

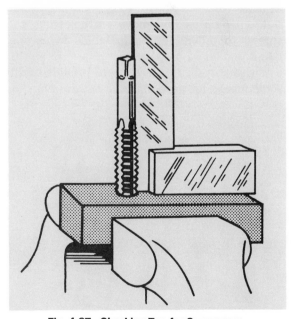

Fig. 4-27. Checking Tap for Squareness

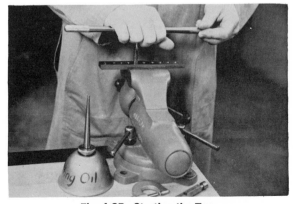

Fig. 4-25. Starting the Tap

thread, and possibly will break in the hole. If the tap is not started square with the work, back it out and restart (as described above).

8. Except on cast iron, always use cutting oil on the tap when cutting threads.

9. Continue tapping the hole as shown in Fig. 4-26. Turn the tap two or three turns; then reverse the tap one turn to break the chips. This aids in chip removal, prevents damage to the threads, and prevents tap breakage.

10. When hand tapping to the bottom of a deep blind hole, it is good practice to back the tap out and clean the chips from the tap and the hole periodically. The taper tap, plug tap, and bottoming tap are used, in that order, to cut the thread to the bottom of deep holes. In shallow blind holes, only the plug tap and bottoming tap are used. Be careful to avoid breaking the tap with excessive force when the bottom of the hole is reached.

11. Clean the chips from the hole, and check the fit of the thread with a thread plug gage. If a gage is not available, check the fit with a bolt or screw of the type to be used in the hole.

21 Hand-Threading Dies

Threading dies are used to cut external threads on round rods or bolts. Dies of various designs are available, usually made of carbon tool steel or high-speed steel. They are designed with internal threads, much like a nut, but with flutes or grooves intersecting the thread to provide space for chips to escape. See Fig. 4-28.

Threading dies generally are provided with some means for adjusting the depth of cut for a snug or free fit. Adjustment of thread depth usually is made with one or more small screws in the die or die holder. The principal types of threading dies are the adjustable *round split die*, the adjustable *two-piece die*, and the *solid bolt thread dies*.

Round Split Die

The round split die is a single-piece, adjustable die, Fig. 4-28. For hand-threading opera-

Fig. 4-28. Adjustable Round Split Die (Greenfield)

Fig. 4-29. Diestocks (Greenfield)
(Above) For round dies; (Below) With Adjustable guide for use with round split die.

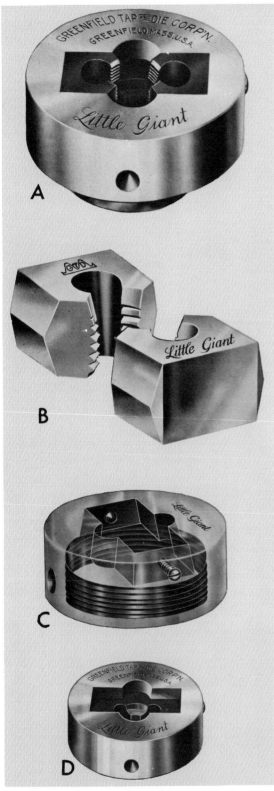

tions, it is mounted in a diestock, Fig. 4-29. When used on a screw machine, it is mounted in a special die holder.

The round split die can be adjusted to cut a thread with a snug or loose fit through use of the small screw in the die. When the screw is turned in, the die opens and a snug-fitting thread results. When a loose-fitting thread is desired, the screw is backed out slightly. For hand-threading purposes, the screw in the die-stock also must be turned in snugly to hold the die closed against the die adjustment screw, so that the thread will cut to the adjusted depth. After the thread is started for several turns, it should be checked for the proper fit. If necessary, further adjustments should be made until the proper fit is achieved. Gages and methods used in measuring threads and determining thread fits are included in Unit 23.

Two-Piece Die

Adjustable two-piece dies must be assembled in collets consisting of a cap and guide. See Fig. 4-30A. The die halves (Fig. 4-30B) are inserted into the beveled cap (Fig. 4-30C) and are held in place by the guide which is screwed into the cap (Fig. 4-30D). The dies may be adjusted for depth of cut with the small screws on either end of the slot, Fig. 4-30C. The dies must be inserted in the cap with the tapered threads downward toward

Fig. 4-30. Two-Piece Die (Greenfield)
(A) Two-piece die assembled; **(B)** Two-piece die blanks; **(C)** Cap; **(D)** Cap with guide inserted.

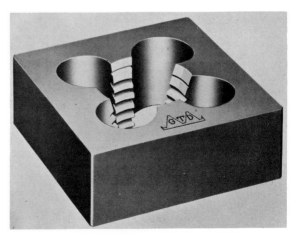

Fig. 4-31. Solid Square Die (Greenfield)

the guide and with the label side of the die toward the top. The guide used on the collet serves as an aid in starting and holding the thread square with the work being threaded.

Solid Bolt Thread Die

The solid square die is designed primarily for dressing or cleaning up bruised or damaged threads, Fig. 4-31. No special holder is used to turn the die. Any wrench of sufficient size may be used.

UNIT

22   How To Cut External Threads with a Die

1. Chamfer the end of the rod to be threaded; this may be done with a file or by grinding. The depth of the chamfer should be about equal to the depth of the thread to be cut, Fig. 4-32.
2. Select the proper threading die, and mount it in the diestock, usually with the labeled side up. The opposite side is tapered for starting and cutting the thread.
3. Mount the rod or workpiece in a bench vise. Short pieces should be mounted in a vertical position; long pieces, usually in a horizontal position.
4. If the guide is adjustable, adjust it to slide freely over the rod.
5. Place the die over the rod, cup the hand over the die, apply pressure evenly, and turn the die to get the thread started. After thread is started, pressure may be applied to both ends of diestock as in Fig. 4-33.
6. Apply cutting oil to the die and workpiece with an oil can. The oil will cause the die to cut more easily, stay sharp longer, and produce a better quality finish on the thread.
7. Check to see that the die is started square with the work, Fig. 4-34. If the die is *out-of-square*, a crooked thread will result; this is called a *drunken thread*.
8. Continue cutting the threads by turning two or three turns forward. After several

Fig. 4-32. End of Rod Chamfered before Threading with a Die

Fig. 4-33. Cup Hand over Die to Start Thread

Fig. 4-34. Threads Being Cut with a Die Mounted in a Diestock (Greenfield)

turns forward, reverse the die about one-half turn to break the chips. When several turns of the thread have been completed, back the die off and check the fit of the thread.

9. Check the thread fit with a thread gage, a thread micrometer, a nut, or the mating part. If the thread is not correct, adjust the screw(s) in the die for the desired fit. (As the die is closed, the thread is cut deeper. As the die is opened, the thread depth is reduced.) Run the die over the thread, and check the fit again. Continue

this adjustment until the proper fit is achieved. Sometimes it is desirable to cut a thread on a practice piece first, until the correct fit is achieved, before cutting on a final workpiece.

10. Continue cutting the thread to the correct length. If the thread must be cut close to a shoulder or close to the head of a bolt, the die may be backed off, inverted, and the last several threads completed while cutting in the inverted position.

Screw Thread Measurement

The size and accuracy of screw threads may be measured with screw thread plug gages, thread micrometers, ring thread gages, roll thread snap gages, thread comparators of various types, and by the three-wire method.

The emphasis in thread measurement is always on the measurement of the pitch diameter. The limits and tolerances on the pitch diameter largely determine the fit of screw threads. Since the pitch diameter of thread ring gages and snap roll gages is difficult to determine accurately by other methods, these gages are set or fitted with the use of accurate plug gages.

Thread Plug Gage

Tapped holes are checked for the correct fit with thread limits plug gages, as illustrated in Fig. 4-37. The gages include a *go* gage (Fig. 4-37A) and a *no-go* gage (Fig. 4-37B). The gage in Fig. 4-37C is a double-end gage, including a go gage on one end and a no-go gage on the opposite end. The go gage is always the longer of the two, and it has a chip

groove for cleaning the threads in the tapped hole being measured.

The thread limits plug gage is used to determine whether the pitch diameter of a tapped thread is within limits for a specified fit or class of thread. The diameter of the go gage is minimum diameter, usually basic, and the no-go gage is maximum diameter.

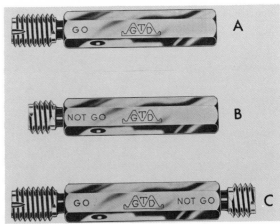

Fig. 4-37. Thread Plug Gages (Greenfield)
(A) Go gage; (B) No-go gage; (C) Double-end gage.

The thread is gaged by having the go gage enter the tapped hole the full length of the gage. The no-go gage may or may not enter; if it does, it should have a snug fit on or before the third thread, thus indicating that the hole is the maximum size permitted for the specified fit. If this gage enters farther, the thread is oversize and will not fit properly.

Thread plug gages are available for each size and class of thread or fit for all standard Unified and American (National) form threads. They also are available for pipe threads.

Thread Micrometer

The pitch diameter of 60° V-threads, including Unified and American (National) form threads, may be measured directly with a thread micrometer. See Fig. 4-38. The spindle of the micrometer has a 60° conical point, and the anvil has a 60° groove. The anvil point swivels for measuring from various angles.

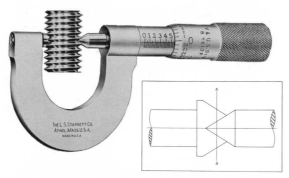

Fig. 4-38. Thread Micrometer Measuring the Pitch Diameter of a Screw Thread Directly (L. S. Starrett) **Inset shows anvil and spindle position at Line AB which corresponds to zero reading.**

Fig. 4-39. Thread Ring Gages — Go and No-Go Gages with Holder (Greenfield)

A given thread micrometer ordinarily is designed to measure a specific range of screw threads, such as 8 to 13 threads per inch or 14 to 20 threads per inch. Care should be taken to select a micrometer with the correct thread range when measuring a specific thread. The micrometer always should be checked for a zero reading before measuring threads. See inset of Fig. 4-38.

Thread Ring Gage

The accuracy of an external thread may be checked with a pair of thread ring gages. The pair includes a go gage and a no-go gage, Fig. 4-39. The *go gage* is designed to check the maximum pitch diameter, flank angle, lead, and the clearance at the minor diameter simultaneously. The *no-go gage* is designed to check only the pitch diameter, to determine whether it is below minimum limits.

To check a thread, both gages are used. If the *go gage* does not turn on freely, one of the thread elements is not accurate, and the thread will not assemble with the mating part. If the *no-go gage* turns on the thread, the pitch diameter of the thread is under the specified minimum limits, and the thread will not fit properly with its mating part.

Roll Thread Snap Gage

External Unified and American (National) form threads may be checked rapidly for accuracy with a roll thread snap gage, Fig. 4-40. The gage illustrated is the open-face type which may be used close to shoulders. Right- and left-hand threads can be checked with the same gage.

The outer or *go rolls* are set to the maximum pitch diameter limits, and they check all thread elements simultaneously. The inner or

Fig. 4-40. Roll Thread Snap Gage (Greenfield)

no-go rolls are set to minimum pitch diameter limits and check only the minimum pitch diameter. Screw threads which are within the correct size limits pass through the go rolls and are stopped by the no-go rolls.

The Three-Wire Method

This is a method of measuring the pitch diameter of external Unified and American (National) form threads, or any thread with a 60° form, such as National pipe threads. The method is recommended by the National Bureau of Standards in Washington, D.C. The three-wire method requires the use of a micrometer and three accurately sized wires to measure the pitch diameter of a thread. A different *best wire size* is recommended for each pitch and diameter combination.

The three-wire method involves the use of several formulas. The *best wire size* must be determined by calculation or by selection from a chart of recommended wire sizes. A measurement across the wires and the thread is made. The pitch diameter is then calculated.

Because the three-wire method is more cumbersome and time consuming to use, many machinists prefer to check the pitch diameter of external threads with a ring gage, thread micrometer, or other instrument. However, the three-wire method is considered to be more ac-curate than the use of many gages designed for this purpose.

The complete procedure with the necessary information for using the three-wire method is included in standard handbooks for machinists.

Special Thread Measuring Devices

Numerous special thread gaging and measuring devices are available for use in measuring thread elements. Some of these devices measure only one element, such as the pitch diameter. Others measure several thread elements simultaneously.

External Thread Comparator: An external thread comparator is used to inspect external threads by means of a single visual reading between indicator tolerance hands. See Fig. 4-41. The comparator checks for errors in lead, thread angle, and pitch diameter; the reading on the indicator dial shows whether the cumulative error of all these elements, combined, falls between the high and low limits for a class-of-fit or class-of-thread tolerance.

The comparator may be used for inspecting many types of threads. Thread anvils for most Unified and American (National) form threads, acme threads, and special threads are available for use with the thread comparator. The comparator is set to a given size with the use of a setting plug thread gage, and the tolerance hands are set for the desired class of fit or class of thread.

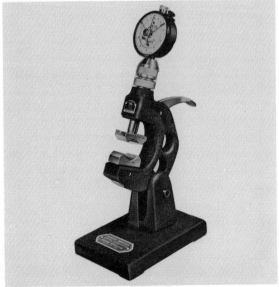

Fig. 4-41. External Thread Comparator
(Hanson-Whitney)

Fig. 4-42. Internal Thread Comparator
(Standard Model) (Hanson-Whitney)

Internal Thread Comparator: The internal thread comparator, Fig. 4-42, works on the same principle as the external comparator. It is used to inspect all classes of internal threads ranging in diameters from ⅜″ to 2″. The comparator is set to a given size with the use of a pitch diameter ring gage, and the tolerance hands are set for the desired class of fit or class of thread.

The comparator is used to check internal threads for assemble-ability by means of a single visual reading between indicator tolerance hands. The single reading represents a composite inspection of accumulated errors of several thread elements, including errors in lead, thread angle, and pitch diameter. The reading on the dial, graduated in 0.0001″ units, indicates whether the accumulated error falls within the high and low limits of class-of-fit tolerance.

<table>
<tr><td>UNIT</td></tr>
<tr><td>24</td></tr>
</table>

Tap Size Limits

Taps are manufactured according to specific size limits and tolerances and are available with either *cut* threads or *ground* threads. Those with ground threads are more expensive, but they generally produce threads with closer size limits and a smoother finish. Both carbon steel taps and high-speed steel taps are available with cut threads. High-speed steel taps also are available with ground threads.

Pitch Diameter Size Limits

The size of the pitch diameter on a tap largely determines the size and fit of the tapped thread produced. If the pitch diameter is oversize, a screw will fit the tapped thread loosely. If the pitch diameter is undersize a slight amount, the thread will fit more tightly. Taps are available with standard pitch diameter size limits, oversize limits, and undersize limits. The size limits of the pitch diameter, therefore, determines the fit of the thread.

Taps with cut threads usually have standard pitch diameter size limits. Taps with ground threads may have standard size, oversize, or undersize pitch diameter size limits, indicated by code letters and numbers on their shank. When ground thread taps are purchased, the limits code number and the class of fit or class of thread should be specified. Otherwise, the

manufacturer generally recommends a tap with pitch diameter size limits appropriate for threads with a class 2 fit for National form threads or a class 2B thread for Unified threads.

Tap standards now include only one classification of ground thread taps — the *ground* thread. Formerly there were several classifications identified as commercial ground (CG), commercial ground high (CGH), and precision ground (PG); these terms are not used on new taps but may be found in toolrooms.

Ground threads with pitch diameter tolerances above basic size are designated as *High* and are identified by the letter *H*. Those ground below basic are designated *Low* and are identified by the letter *L*. Numerals are used to identify the pitch diameter limits of the tap as compared with the basic pitch diameter. The following are pitch diameter limit numbers for taps through 1″ diameter:

L1 — Basic to basic minus .0005″
H1 — Basic to basic plus .0005″
H2 — Basic plus .0005″ to basic plus .0010″
H3 — Basic plus .0010″ to basic plus .0015″
H4 — Basic plus .0015″ to basic plus .0020″
H5 — Basic plus .0020″ to basic plus .0025″
H6 — Basic plus .0025″ to basic plus .0030″

For example, a ½-13 UNC ground thread hand tap selected for a class 3B thread would be identified with the additional label H3. A ½-13 NC ground thread tap selected for a class 2 fit would be identified with the additional label H5. Some manufacturers use the letter *G* with these labels (such as GH3 or GH5), to indicate that the tap is ground.

Tables 38 and 39, appendix, indicate the recommended taps for various classes of threads.

Other Styles of Taps Used for Machine and Hand Tapping

Taps are available in various styles and designs for hand-tapping and machine-tapping operations. While many taps used for machine tapping are called hand taps, some taps are designed with special features which cause them to operate more efficiently for machine tapping on specific materials.

Two- and Three-Fluted Taps

For average hand-tapping operations, taps with the standard number of flutes produce satisfactory results. Larger size standard taps usually have four flutes, while small size standard machine screw taps usually have three flutes, Fig. 4-12. Certain sizes of hand taps in machine screw sizes and in sizes up to ½" also are regularly produced with two or three flutes.

For tapping jobs in deep holes with stringy metal or in blind holes where the chips fall to the bottom of the hole, more flute space is needed for the chips. A tap with three flutes usually has deeper flutes and more chip space than one with four flutes. Similarly, a two-flute tap has deeper flutes and more chip space than a three-flute tap. However, with deeper flutes, the width of the lands* is reduced, and the strength of the tap is reduced. A three-fluted tap generally should be tried first, since it is stronger than a two-fluted tap.

*The term *land* refers to the material left between machined areas or grooves. For example, the lands of a tap are the threaded sections between the flutes.

Gun Taps

The *gun tap* is very similar to the standard hand tap, except that it is designed for machine tapping. It is called a gun tap because the angular design of the cutting point causes the chips to *shoot* ahead of the tap as the thread is cut. See Fig. 4-43. This is a desirable feature when tapping stringy metals, because the chips do not readily clog the flutes, thus preventing tap breakage. The gun tap has fewer flutes than a standard hand tap, but the flutes are not as deep; therefore, the tap is stronger and will withstand the greater strains required in production tapping.

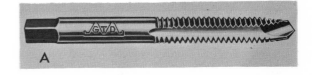

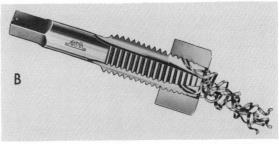

Fig. 4-43. (A) Plug Gun Tap; (B) The Tap in Action
(Greenfield)

129

There are three common types of gun taps—the *plug* gun tap (Fig. 4-43), the *bottoming* gun tap (Fig. 4-44), and the *gun flute only* plug tap (Fig. 4-45). The plug gun tap is designed primarily for tapping open holes. It shoots the chips ahead of the tap and out the hole as in Fig. 4-43B. The bottoming gun tap is designed for blind holes. The point of the bottoming gun tap has a somewhat different design than the plug gun tap. It breaks the chip up finely so that the chips may escape more easily, Fig. 4-44B. The flutes are also deeper and larger for chip removal.

The *gun flute only* plug tap is designed for tapping shallow through holes which are not more than one diameter in depth. Because there are no flutes in the body, the tap is stronger than the plug gun tap. It is recommended for tapping soft, stringy materials.

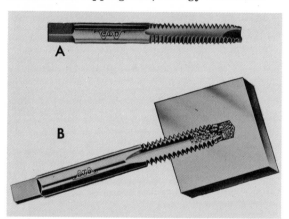

Fig. 4-44. (A) Bottoming Gun Tap; (B) Its Action
(Greenfield)

Fig. 4-45. Gun Flute Only Plug Tap (Greenfield)

Fig. 4-46. Spiral Fluted Taps (Greenfield)
(A) Low-Angle; (B) Hi-Angle

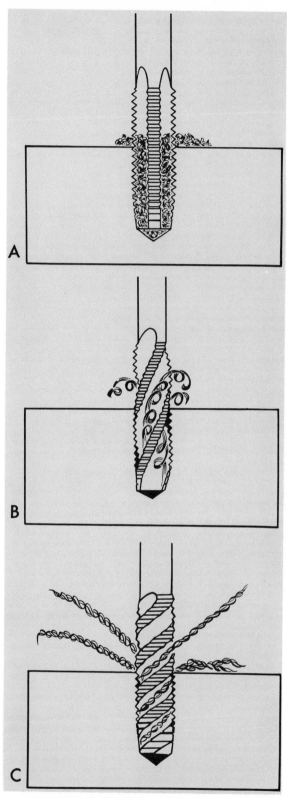

Fig. 4-47. Cutting Action of Taps (Greenfield)
(A) Regular hand tap; (B) Low-angle spiral fluted tap; (C) Hi-angle spiral fluted tap.

Spiral Fluted Taps

Helical fluted taps, commonly called spiral fluted taps, have spiral flutes similar to a drill. The flutes may be the low-angle or hi-angle type, Fig. 4-46. The spiral flutes aid in drawing the chips out of the hole being tapped, as shown in Fig. 4-47. This type of chip removal also aids in preventing tap breakage at high speeds when the tap is backed out of the hole.

Low-angle spiral fluted taps are especially useful in machine-production tapping of stringy materials such as aluminum, copper, magnesium, brass, and die cast metals. Hi-angle spiral fluted taps work well with tough alloy steel in deep blind holes. They also may be used in materials which produce powder or granular chips, such as die castings. Spiral fluted taps also work well in tapping holes where a gap or slot must be bridged in a hole.

Spiral fluted taps generally are available with two, three, or four flutes (depending on the diameter) and in plug and bottoming styles.

Pipe Taps

American standard or *American National* pipe threads are used in coupling and assembling pipes. The following three types of American standard pipe threads commonly are used:

American standard taper pipe thread (NPT)
American standard straight pipe thread (NPS)
American standard Dryseal pipe thread (NPTF)

Further information concerning American standard pipe threads may be found on page x.

Taps are used to cut internal pipe threads in the same manner in which National form threads are tapped. Taper pipe taps are used to tap NPT threads, Fig. 4-48A. Straight pipe taps are used to tap NPS threads, Fig. 4-48B. American standard Dryseal pipe threads are tapped with ground thread taper taps which have the American standard Dryseal pipe form, Fig. 4-11.

Acme Taps

Internal acme threads may be cut with taps, or they may be cut with a single-point threading tool on a lathe. When acme threads are tapped, special consideration must be given to the selection of the proper taps. A specific tap is designed for each type and each class of acme thread. See Unit 18, page 114.

Acme taps often are manufactured in sets of two or three, Fig. 4-49. The roughing tap is used first to remove some of the material, thus cutting the thread to partial depth. The finishing tap then is used to cut the thread to finished depth. In some cases involving open or through holes, one tap of special design may be used to tap the thread to full depth.

Other factors to be considered in the selection of acme taps include the depth of the thread, the hardness and toughness of the material to be tapped, and the depth of the hole. Fine-pitch threads tap more easily than coarse-pitch threads.

In ordering acme taps, one should furnish the manufacturer with complete data concerning the type and class of acme thread, including the following: thread dimensions, hole type, material to be tapped, and type of machine used, if for machine tapping.

Fig. 4-48. (A) Regular Taper Pipe Tap; (B) Straight Pipe Tap (Greenfield)

Fig. 4-49. Acme Taps (Greenfield)
(A) Roughing tap; (B) Finishing tap.

Selection and Calculation of Tap Drill Size

The size of the drill required for a given threaded hole is called the *tap drill size*. Each thread size and pitch has a specific tap drill size to produce the necessary percentage depth of the thread to be cut. The tap drill sizes for average applications are based on threads which are approximately 75 percent of a full-depth thread; thus, the hole is larger than the minor diameter for a full-depth thread. Tap drill sizes for Unified and American (National) screw threads requiring approximately 75 percent thread depth are listed in tables of tap drill sizes, such as Tables 35 and 36, appendix.

If a particular tap drill size is not on hand, such as a number size drill, the next larger size sometimes may be selected. For example, the recommended tap drill for a 10-24 UNC thread is the No. 25 drill, with a diameter of .1495". If the next larger fraction size ($\frac{5}{32}$" or .1562" diameter) is selected, the resulting thread will have a thread depth of approximately 63 percent.

An internal thread with a 75-percent depth has approximately 95 percent of the strength of a full-depth thread. The power required to turn a tap for a thread with 100-percent depth is three times greater than that required for one with 75-percent depth, so excessive tap breakage may result.

For a majority of tapping requirements, a tap drill producing a minor diameter which provides 55- to 75-percent thread depth is adequate. Thread strength tests indicate that a nut made with 50-percent thread depth, according to standard specifications, will break the bolt or screw before the threads strip. These tests also indicate that any increase in the internal thread depth over 60 percent does not increase the strength significantly.

For very tough metals, often it is desirable to use a tap drill which provides less than 75-percent thread depth, but usually not less than 55-percent thread depth. The larger hole size

will reduce tap breakage without significant loss of thread strength. When holes deeper than one-and-one-half times the diameter of the tap are tapped (particularly for small machine screw sizes), a tap drill size larger than the 75-percent type may be used; in such cases, drills which provide for a 55-percent thread depth give satisfactory results. Tap drill sizes for threads of various percentage depths, such as 70, 65, 60, 55, or 50 percent, may be found in Table 40, appendix.

Calculation of Tap Drill Size

The machinist may calculate the tap drill size for Unified and American (National) form threads requiring a 75-percent thread depth by subtracting the pitch from the major diameter. The pitch is equal to 1 divided by the number of threads per inch.

Example 1: Determine the tap drill size for a $\frac{3}{8}$-16 UNC thread of approximately 75-percent thread depth. *Formula:*

Diameter of tap drill = major diameter − pitch
$$= \frac{3}{8} \quad - \frac{1}{16}$$
Diameter of tap drill = $\frac{5}{16}$ inch

The percentage of thread depth obtained by using an alternate size tap drill (a drill close to the size recommended for a 75-percent thread depth) also may be calculated.

Example 2: Determine the percentage of thread depth for a $\frac{3}{8}$-16 NC thread which is drilled with a $\frac{21}{64}$" tap drill.
Where A represents decimal equivalent of drill
Where B represents basic major diameter of thread
Where C represents percentage of thread depth
Where h represents depth of National thread form
Where n represents number of threads per inch

$$h = \frac{.6495}{n} = \frac{.6495}{16} = .0406$$

Formula: $C = \dfrac{B - A}{2\,h}$

$$C = \frac{.3750 - .3281}{2 \times .0406}$$

$$C = \frac{.0469}{.0812} = .5775$$

C = Approximately 58% thread depth

Machine Thread Cutting

Threads may be cut or formed by both hand-threading and machine threading methods. The hand-threading methods include cutting internal threads with hand taps and external threads with threading dies. Hand-threading methods are used regularly by maintenance machinists, repairmen, mechanics, and tool and die makers. Machine-threading methods are used largely in production work which involves many duplicate, threaded parts.

Single-Point Threading Tool

One of the oldest and most versatile machine methods of cutting threads uses a single-point threading tool on a screw-cutting lathe. It is a relatively slow process which frequently must be used by the general machinist or maintenance machinist. Many types of threads may be *chased* (cut) on a lathe, including external and internal threads, single and multiple threads, threads of all sizes and pitches, and threads of any form. A lathe with a precision lead screw will cut threads with very accurate lead. The methods of cutting threads on a lathe are described in Section 9.

Releasing-Type Die Holder

Adjustable round, split dies are mounted in hand diestocks and also in releasing-type die holders on screw machines and turret lathes. Although this type die holder may be used on various threading machines, it is recommended especially for short-run production on hand-operated machines where reversal of the machine is dependent on the operator. The design of most releasing die holders is such that the

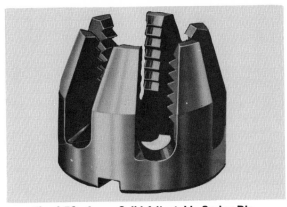

Fig. 4-52. **Acorn Solid Adjustable Spring Die** (Greenfield)

Fig. 4-53. **Acorn Die Mounted in Releasing Die Holder** (Greenfield)

machine spindle must be reversed in order to back the die off after cutting the thread.

An *Acorn** solid-adjustable spring die is shown in Fig. 4-52. It is held in the Acorn releasing die holder in Fig. 4-53. This type of holder functions well on hand-operated turret lathes, screw machines, and drill presses. On a turret lathe or screw machine, the die will thread to a predetermined length, automatically release, and revolve with the work. On a drill press, the die will thread to a predetermined length, release, and remain stationary while the die holder revolves with the spindle. The operator then reverses the spindle of the machine, and the die holder again engages the die, thus causing it to back off from the thread. Care must be taken to apply very light tension when retracting the die from the thread, in order to avoid damaging the first thread on the end of the workpiece.

Adapters are available for holding Acorn dies of various sizes in an Acorn die holder. These dies may be adjusted for thread depth by turning the adjusting cap which holds the die in place. Each of the threaded sections pulls in evenly because of the spring taper design.

Fig. 4-54. Stationary Die Head
(H & G Sales — Eastern Machine Screw)

Threading with Die Heads

A large percentage of external threads in modern production are produced with die heads on various machines used to cut threads. Die heads are of two basic types — the *stationary* or hand-operated type and the *revolving* type. Both must have retractable dies, called *chasers*. The chasers are closed before cutting the thread, and they must be retracted or opened upon completion of the thread.

Stationary Die Head A stationary die head which is used frequently on turret lathes and hand screw machines is shown in Fig. 4-54. It is equipped with a handle which is used to open or close the chasers. The chasers are closed manually before starting the thread, and they are *pulled off* or retracted upon completion without the use of an external mechanism. The die head is returned and indexed for the next cycle through the use of the lathe turret mechanism.

Stationary die heads which are used on automatic screw machines are closed by an automatic mechanism and are totally automatic in operation. Stationary die heads are not used on machines where they are required to revolve about their axis in operation.

Fig. 4-55. Revolving Die Head
(H & G Sales — Eastern Machine Screw)

*Trade name used by the Greenfield Tap and Die Corporation.

134

Revolving Die Head: Revolving die heads (Fig. 4-55) are used on drill presses and automatic screw machines which have revolving spindles and which require the die head to revolve about its axis. This type of die head is equipped with a yoke, or other mechanism, which is actuated by the machine itself and which causes the chasers to retract and close automatically for each threading cycle.

Die heads are selected on a basis of the type of machine, whether the chasers are to be opened manually or automatically, and whether the head remains stationary or revolves. The clearance on the machine must be considered, since die heads are available in both small and large diameters. Die heads also are available in varying weights, depending on the size and coarseness of the thread to be cut and the toughness of the material to be threaded.

Various diameter and pitch combinations may be cut with a given die head. The chasers are of the insert type and are available in sets of a given diameter and pitch. Die heads also are provided with a means for adjustment of thread depth to conform to required limits and tolerances.

Machine Tapping

Tapping operations may be performed on drill presses, turret lathes, hand screw machines, automatic screw machines, specialized tapping machines, and portable drilling machines. For tapping operations, these machines must be equipped with tapping attachments or accessories. The tapping device must hold the tap securely while it is turned into the hole and while it is reversed for extraction from the hole. Some common tapping accessories used for machine tapping include *tapping attachments*, *tap drivers*, and *tap holders*.

Tapping accessories vary considerably in design, depending on the operating characteristics desired. Skilled machine operators can perform tapping operations on a drill press or turret lathe with nothing more than a chuck or solid tap holder to hold the tap; as the hole is tapped through, the spindle is reversed immediately to extract the tap. Extreme care must be taken to avoid tap breakage when a tap is held in a solid chuck or tap holder.

Tapping attachments or devices are available with one or more features designed to provide for improved operation and minimum tap breakage. Machines equipped with reversing spindles may utilize a *reversing* tap driver which extracts the tap by reversal of the spindle. Machines not equipped with a reversing spindle must be provided with a *non-reversing* tap driver; this type of driver causes the tap to rotate in a direction opposite to spindle rotation while the tap is being extracted from the hole. The tapping attachment mounted on a drill press in Fig. 4-56 is a non-reversing tapper. When the thrust is down, into the work, the forward clutch engages to drive the tap in. When the forward pressure is released, torque on the tap is released, and tap rotation stops. When the drill press lever is raised, the reversing gear in the tapping attachment is engaged, and the tap backs out easily.

Some types of tap drivers or holders are provided with friction clutch mechanisms, which aid in preventing tap breakage. A pre-selective

Fig. 4-56. Non-Reversing Tapper Mounted on Drill Press (Supreme Prod. — Rigid Tool)

135

torque-setting device (available on some tap drivers) provides for setting the torque to coincide with the strength of the tap being used. If the pre-selected torque is exceeded, due to the accumulation of chips in the flutes of the tap or due to striking the bottom of a hole, a clutch mechanism releases the tap, thus preventing tap breakage; the tap is extracted by reversing the spindle.

An *adjustable* tap holder of the *releasing* type, which commonly is used on turret lathes and hand screw machines, is shown in Fig. 4-57. This type is designed for machines which do not require the tap holder to rotate about its axis. The adjustable feature permits accurate alignment of the tap between the turret and the work spindle. The releasing feature causes the tap to be released from the holder mechanism when the hole is tapped to a predetermined depth, thus permitting the tap to float freely with the workpiece. When the machine spindle is reversed, the tap is again engaged, and it backs out.

The type of tapping attachment selected is determined, basically, by the design of the machine on which it will be used and by the operating features desired. Other factors which should be considered are the skill of the machine operator and initial cost of the attachment.

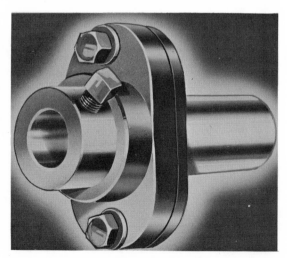

Fig. 4-57. Adjustable Tap Holder, Releasing Type
(Boyar-Schultz)

Test Your Knowledge of Section 4

Unit 15: Screw Threads and Their Use

1. Explain the difference between straight threads and tapered threads.
2. Give an example of the use of a left-hand thread.
3. List four uses of screw threads.
4. What tools are used to cut threads by hand?
5. List five machine tools which may be used to cut threads.
6. Why should the machinist have a thorough understanding of threads?
7. Explain the difference between the major diameter and the minor diameter of a screw thread.
8. How is the amount of clearance between two mating threads controlled?
9. Explain the difference between the pitch and the lead of a screw thread.
10. What is meant by the *angle* of a thread?
11. What is the axis of a screw thread?
12. Explain the meaning of crest clearance on a screw thread.
13. What is meant by the design form of a thread?
14. What is meant by the basic size of a screw thread?
15. Explain the meaning of allowance, as used with screw threads or other machine parts.
16. Explain the meaning of positive allowance.
17. Explain the meaning of negative allowance.
18. Explain the meaning of tolerance, as used with screw threads or other machined parts.
19. List three thread factors which may have tolerances specified.
20. Explain how the tolerance is applied to external threads.
21. Define the meaning of limits, as used with threads or other machined parts.
22. Explain the meaning of fit, as used with assembled threads or other machined parts.
23. What is meant by class of thread?

Unit 16: Historical Background of Screw Threads

1. How were early screw threads produced?
2. What machine was first used to produce screw threads?
3. Describe the general form of the British Standard Whitworth thread.
4. Who developed the first screw thread standards used in the United States?
5. Explain the basic differences between the first standardized thread system used in Great Britain and that used in the United States.
6. What is the basic difference between the USS and the SAE thread series?
7. When was the original American (National) Screw Thread Standard approved?
8. What was the basic difference between the original American (National) form thread and the USS thread form?
9. Explain the thread designations used for coarse- and fine-thread series under the American (National) thread standard adopted in 1935.
10. List several less commonly used thread series included under the 1935 standard.
11. Describe the four classes of thread fits included under the American (National) screw thread standard of 1935.
12. What class of fit was used for the majority of commercial screws, bolts, and interchangeable threads produced under the American (National) thread standard of 1935?
13. How are the classes of fits on screw threads obtained?
14. To what extent is the 1935 standard for American (National) screw threads used today?
15. Of what significance are the Unified and American (National) screw thread standards adopted in 1949 and 1960?

Unit 17: Unified and American (National) Screw Threads (1948)

1. Why were British and American screw threads not interchangeable before 1948?
2. What countries cooperated in the development of the Unified screw thread system of 1948?
3. Describe the general form of the Unified screw thread? How does it differ from the British Whitworth thread?
4. Are American (National) standard threads and Unified standard threads interchangeable? Explain.
5. What are the principal differences between the American (National) and the Unified thread standards?
6. What screw thread system is most widely used in American industry today?
7. For what applications should Unified threads be used today?
8. What is meant by the term *class of thread*, as used in the Unified thread system? How does it differ from the term *class of fit*, as used in the American (National) thread system of 1935?
9. Explain the six thread tolerance classes used in the Unified thread system.
10. Which of the older American (National) thread classes, formerly called fits, are still included for limited use in the 1960 *Unified Screw Thread Standard?*
11. Explain the type of thread fit which results from the use of class 2A and 2B threads.
12. Where may one secure the basic dimensions, limits, allowances, and tolerances for Unified and American (National) screw threads?
13. Explain how screw threads are designated on drawings or blueprints.
14. What series of threads are included under the American standard, *Unified Screw Threads* (ASA B1.1-1960)?
15. When is it necessary for the machinist to use thread formulas in making thread calculations?

Unit 18: Other Forms of Screw Threads

1. Describe the sharp vee form of screw thread.
2. Describe the British Standard Whitworth form of thread.
3. How are square threads cut?
4. List several uses of acme threads.
5. How may acme threads be produced?

6. Explain how an acme thread gage is used.
7. How many standard acme threads per inch usually are recommended for a 1″ diameter acme screw?
8. Describe the tapered pipe thread, NPT, and explain its use.
9. Describe the characteristics of the straight pipe thread, NPS.
10. Describe the features of the Dryseal pipe thread.

Unit 19: Basic Taps and Accessories Used for Hand Tapping
1. Of what materials are hand taps made?
2. Describe the three basic types of hand taps and their characteristics.
3. Are hand taps used only for hand-tapping operations? Explain.
4. What taps should be used in tapping closed or blind holes?
5. Describe several taps and explain how each is used.
6. Describe how tap sizes are identified and labeled.
7. Explain how the diameter of a No. 10 machine screw may be calculated.
8. Describe two types of tap wrenches.
9. Describe a screw plate.
10. Explain how a screw pitch gate is used.
11. Explain how a tap extractor is used.
12. Explain how a screw extractor is used.

Unit 21: Hand-Threading Dies
1. Of what materials are hand-threading dies made?
2. Why must threading dies be provided with some means of adjusting the depth of cut?
3. Describe the characteristics of the round split die.
4. Describe the characteristics of the adjustable, two-piece threading die.
5. For what purpose is the solid bolt thread die used?

Unit 23: Screw Thread Measurement
1. Why is measurement of the pitch diameter of screw threads always important?
2. Explain what a thread limits plug gage is and how it is used.
3. Describe the characteristics of a thread micrometer, and explain how it is used.
4. Explain how ring thread gages are used.
5. Explain how a roll thread snap gage is used.
6. Explain how an external thread comparator is used to inspect external threads.
7. Explain how an internal thread comparator is used to inspect threads.

Unit 24: Tap Size Limits
1. What advantages are gained in using ground thread taps rather than cut thread taps?
2. Why are the size limits of the pitch diameter of a tap important?
3. How are pitch diameter size limits designated on ground thread taps?
4. If the limits code number or class of thread fit is not specified when ordering a ground tap, what pitch diameter size limits will the manufacturer usually provide?

Unit 25: Other Styles of Taps Used for Machine and Hand Tapping
1. For what tapping applications are taps with two or three flutes used?
2. For what tapping applications are gun taps used?
3. Describe the characteristics and uses of spiral fluted taps.
4. What types of pipe taps are available for use in tapping pipe threads?
5. What special factors must be considered in selecting taps for cutting acme threads?

Unit 26: Selection and Calculation of Tap Drill Size
1. Why are internal threads usually tapped only 75 percent of full depth for most thread applications?
2. For what tapping applications should tap drill sizes be increased to produce less than 75-percent thread depth?

3. Is an internal thread of 75-percent thread depth significantly stronger than one of 60-percent depth?

4. How can the tap drill size for a thread of 60-percent thread depth be determined?

5. Calculate the tap drill size for a ½-13 UNC thread with approximately 75-percent thread depth.

6. Calculate the percentage of thread depth for a ½-13 NC thread which is tap drilled with a diameter tap drill.

Unit 27: Machine Thread Cutting

1. What types of workers must cut threads frequently with hand taps and dies?

2. For what types of work are machine-threading methods frequently used?

3. What kinds of threads may be chased on a lathe with a single-point cutting tool?

4. On what types of threading applications are releasing die holders generally recommended?

5. Explain how an Acorn die holder functions on a turret lathe or on a drill press.

6. Explain how a stationary die head operates on a turret lathe or hand screw machine.

7. Explain the operation of a revolving die head used on a drill press.

8. On what types of machines may tapping operations be performed?

9. Explain the difference between a reversing and a non-reversing tap driver.

10. What is the advantage in having a preselective torque setting device on a tap driver?

11. Explain how a releasing adjustable tapper functions on a turret lathe or screw machine.

Proper Tool Form — Demands a True Wheel
(Desmond-Stephan)

The Tool Grinder and Its Operation

The Tool Grinder

Grinders, either hand or power-driven, are used for keeping cutting tools sharp and for shaping metals. Because of its greater cutting speed and its capacity for grinding harder metals, the grinding wheel of today has displaced the old-fashioned grindstone.

Types of Grinders

Although there are many types of grinders, including pedestal grinders, bench grinders, surface grinders, cylindrical grinders, centerless grinders, and others, only tool grinders are considered in this unit. See Figs. 5-1 and 5-2.

Tool grinders are divided into two distinct classes: (1) dry grinders and (2) wet grinders. The dry wheel usually has a coarse grain and is used for rough grinding. The coarse grain cuts the metal easily and prevents overheating. The wet grinder is used principally for grinding tools. Generally the wheel has a finer grain than that for dry grinding, but because the fine grain does not cut the metal rapidly, it is necessary to use a water solution on the wheel to prevent the metal from becoming overheated. A soluble oil solution, described in Unit 139, often is used for this purpose. Some power grinders are equipped with a pumping device, to keep a constant stream of water or other coolant playing on the wheel.

The grinder shown in Fig. 5-1 is a standard, pedestal tool grinder. It is used for grinding many kinds of hand tools and cutting tools, including chisels, punches, lathe tool bits, and shaper tool bits. Grinding operations performed on this type of tool grinder are called *offhand* grinding operations.

The tool grinder shown in Fig. 5-2 is equipped with a tilting table which may be adjusted to any desired angle. This type grinder is used for grinding cutting tool bits for ma-

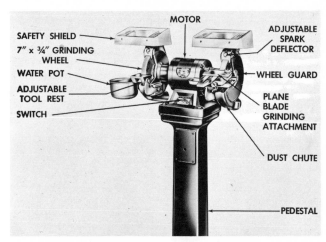

Fig. 5-1. **Standard Tool Grinder** (Rockwell)

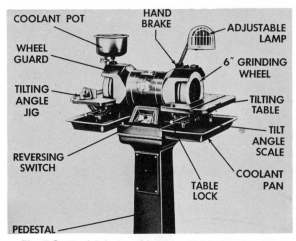

Fig. 5-2. **Tool Grinder with Tilting Table** (Rockwell)

Fig. 5-3. Loaded Grinding Wheel, before Dressing
(Desmond-Stephan)

Fig. 5-4. Grinding Wheel after Dressing
(Desmond-Stephan)

chines such as lathes, shapers, and planers. The table also is equipped with a tilting angle jig, or miter gage, which is used for grinding edge or end angles accurately. This grinder usually is equipped with a silicon-carbide wheel or a diamond wheel for grinding tungsten-carbide cutting tools; see Fig 9-46. It also has an aluminum-oxide wheel for grinding all types of steel, including high-speed steels.

Operating the Tool Grinder

The tool grinder is a simple machine to use, but care must be taken in order to operate it effectively, efficiently and safely. When the grinder is in operation, the tool rests should be as close to the wheel as possible, in order to prevent the work from becoming wedged between the rest and the wheel. After adjusting the rest, it is good practice to rotate the wheel by hand before turning on the power, to determine if the wheel will clear the rest. If the tool rest is too close to an out-of-round wheel, the high spot may strike the rest.

If too much pressure is used when grinding, the tool or metal being ground will become overheated. The pressure or heat may cause the face of the wheel to wear away more rapidly at some points than at others and thus become out of round. In order to distribute the wear evenly on the face of the wheel, the work should be moved back and forth alternately.

The harder the stock being ground, the more quickly the grains of the wheel become dull; thus, the harder the material, the softer should be the wheel. This is not true, however, when grinding very soft metals such as brass, copper, or aluminum. In this case, a medium-soft wheel having coarse grains should be used. If the wheel becomes glazed because the cutting particles have become dull or because the pores between the cutting particles have become clogged or loaded with the material being ground, or if the wheel becomes out of round, it should be dressed and trued with a wheel dresser.

Grinding Wheel Dressing Tools

A loaded grinding wheel is shown in Fig. 5-3. After the wheel is dressed and trued with a wheel dressing tool, the wheel appears as shown in Fig. 5-4.

Grinding wheel dressers are used for dressing and truing grinding wheels. *Dressing* removes the ground particles in the pores of the wheel. It also causes the dull abrasive grains on the surface of the wheel to fracture away, thus exposing sharp new abrasive grains. The clean, sharp abrasive surface improves the cutting action of the wheel.

Truing a grinding wheel restores the original shape to the wheel. In some cases, truing involves forming a new shape on the surface of the wheel for the purpose of grinding a surface of special shape.

Grinding wheel dressers often are classified as *mechanical* dressers, *abrasive* dressers, or *diamond* dressers. A widely used mechanical dresser is the *Huntington* type shown in Fig. 5-5. When dressing a wheel with this tool, place the tool on the grinder tool rest and press it firmly against the revolving wheel. Move the tool across the wheel evenly in both directions until the wheel is dressed and true. Care should be taken to avoid running off the edge of the wheel, since this will cause the corner of the wheel to wear off unevenly.

An abrasive wheel dresser is shown in Fig. 5-6. This type usually has a silicon-carbide abrasive wheel; this wheel is installed with its axis at a 15° to 30° angle with the axis of the wheel which is to be dressed. The abrasive tool dresses and trues grinding wheels with a shearing action when pressed against the wheel.

The abrasive stick wheel dressing tool in Fig. 5-7 consists of a steel tube filled with hard abrasive. This tool works well on the smaller sizes of medium- and soft-grade grinding wheels. In using the dressing tool, place it on the tool rest, as in Fig. 5-8. Apply pressure to the tool while *rolling* it across the face of the grinding wheel, thus dressing and truing the wheel. As the abrasive is worn off on the end, the steel tube is ground back, thus exposing new abrasive.

Diamond-point wheel dressing tools, Fig. 5-9, are used for dressing and truing grinding wheels where an extremely accurate finish is required. They are used for dressing and truing wheels on surface grinders, cylindrical grinders, and tool grinders. On these machines, a short diamond-point *nib* is mounted in a guide or holding device at a drag angle of about 15°. See Fig. 5-10.

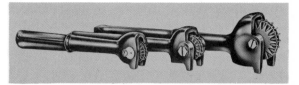
Fig. 5-5. Huntington Wheel Dressers
(Desmond-Stephan)

Fig. 5-6. Abrasive Wheel Dresser (Desmond-Stephan)

Fig. 5-7. Abrasive Stick Wheel Dressing Tool
(Desmond-Stephan)

Fig. 5-8. Correct Use of Abrasive Stick Wheel Dressing Tool (Desmond-Stephan)

A diamond-point dressing tool with a handle, Fig. 5-9, often is held manually for truing or shaping small, tool grinding wheels. The depth of cut should be limited to about 0.001″, and the tool should be fed slowly and uniformly across the surface of the wheel. The tool should be held at a *drag* angle of about 15° in relation to the center line of the wheel, Fig. 5-10. If there is doubt as to the location of this center line, the point should be lowered about 1/8″ below the line for safety. The tool also should be held at a *lead* angle of about 30° in relation to the face of the grinding wheel. This procedure will aid in preventing chatter and will help keep the diamond point sharp.

Grinding Wheel Selection

Complete information concerning both abrasives and grinding wheels is included in Section 12. Information concerning the classification and selection of grinding wheels is included in Unit 111. Table 15 in Section 12 may be used as an aid in selecting the proper wheel. A list of ten precautions for using grinding wheels also is included in Unit 111, and these precautions should be studied at this time, in addition to those given below.

Safety Precautions for Grinding

The following safety precautions should be followed when using the tool grinder:

1. Always wear approved safety goggles when grinding, even though the grinder is equipped with safety glass shields.
2. Avoid grinding on the side of the wheel. Always grind on the face of the wheel.
3. Keep the tool rest adjusted to within 1/16″ from the face of the wheel.
4. Hold the workpiece securely while grinding.
5. The wheel must be kept true and balanced at all times.
6. Be sure that the grinding wheel is not operated at a speed in excess of the rpm marked on the wheel label.
7. See that all safety guards or hoods are secure and in the proper place.
8. Avoid personal contact with the grinding wheel.
9. Wear safe clothing while grinding. Avoid loose neckties or shirt sleeves hanging loosely.
10. Do not force work heavily against a cold wheel. Allow the wheel to warm up slightly before heavy grinding.
11. If the grinder appears to be unsafe, report it to the person in charge.

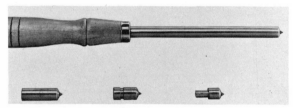

Fig. 5-9. Diamond-Point Wheel Dressing Tool and Diamond Nibs (Desmond-Stephan)

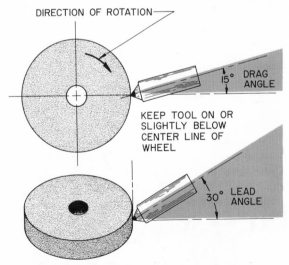

DIRECTION OF ROTATION

15° DRAG ANGLE

KEEP TOOL ON OR SLIGHTLY BELOW CENTER LINE OF WHEEL

30° LEAD ANGLE

Fig. 5-10. Angle of Diamond-Point Tool when Dressing or Truing a Grinding Wheel

Test Your Knowledge of Section 5

Unit 28: The Tool Grinder
1. For what purposes is a tool grinder used?
2. List several types of grinders, other than tool grinders.
3. What is the principal use for wet tool grinders?
4. What type of coolant solution commonly is used for wet grinding?

5. Define the meaning of *offhand* grinding operations.

6. For what basic purpose is a tilting-table tool grinder used?

7. What kind of grinding wheel is used for grinding most types of steel?

8. What kinds of grinding wheels are used for grinding tungsten-carbide cutting tools?

9. How close should the tool rest be to the grinding wheel on a tool grinder?

10. Explain the principal difference between *dressing* and *truing* a grinding wheel.

11. List three common classifications for grinding wheel dressing tools.

12. Explain how the *Huntington* wheel dresser is used to true a grinding wheel.

13. Explain the position at which a diamond-point wheel dresser usually should be held for truing or dressing a wheel.

14. In which unit of this book can you find information concerning grinding wheel selection?

15. List several precautions which should be observed in using grinding wheels.

16. List several safety precautions which should be observed when using a tool grinder.

Functional Power — Straightforward Engineering
(Racine Hydraulics and Machinery)

SECTION 6

The Power Hacksaw and Its Operation

The Power Hacksaw

Power hacksaws are used primarily for cutting to length metal of various kinds, sizes, and shapes. Some machines are equipped with a vise that can be swiveled through 45°. With such machines, stock can be cut square or at any angle within the capacity of the machine and vise.

Types of Power Hacksaws

In general, there are two types of power hacksaws — wet- and dry-cutting machines. Both operate on the principle of a reciprocating stroke. On the cutting stroke, the saw blade engages the metal, and as it progresses, each tooth removes a small chip. At the end of the stroke, the saw blade is raised slightly and moves back to a point where the direction of stroke is reversed; then it again moves forward, and another cut is made. The wet-cutting machine runs at high speeds and has a cabinet base which houses a coolant reservoir and a pump to circulate the coolant. A dry-cutting machine is illustrated in Fig. 6-1. Its rated capacity is 6″ x 6″. Actually it will take stock a little larger than 6″ square or 6″ in diameter. Fig. 6-2 represents a wet-cutting machine. It has the same capacity as the dry-cutting machine. Both are classified as *utility machines*, which means that either will cut a variety of metals ranging from soft aluminum through hard alloys in the form of tubing, bars, or shapes.

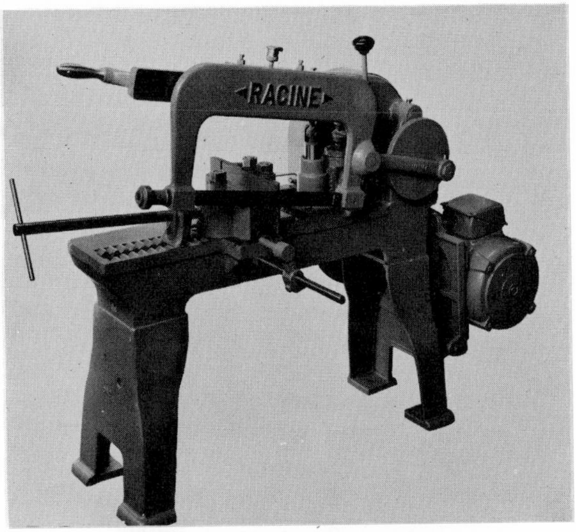

Fig. 6-1. Dry-Cutting Power Hacksaw
(Racine Hydraulics and Machinery)

Fig. 6-2. Wet-Cutting Power Hacksaw
(Racine Hydraulics and Machinery)

151

Feed and Cutting Speed

Both of the machines just described are equipped with oil hydraulic feed. This provides accurate feed and pressure control throughout the cut regardless of the type of material. When the cut has been completed, a knockout disengages the clutch; this activates the saw, and the saw frame automatically rises to its highest inactive position. The dry-cutting machine has two cutting speeds — 70 and 100 strokes per minute. The wet-cutting machine is available with two or four cutting speeds. The two-speed type has 100 to 140 strokes per minute. The four-speed type operates at speeds of 35, 70, 100, and 140 strokes per minute. Typical uses of some speeds are as follows: 140 strokes for cutting mild and cold rolled steel, 90-100 for tool steel and cast iron, and 60-70 for high-speed steel, stainless steel, and hard alloys. On machines equipped with four speeds, a four-speed drive motor is used. Changes in cutting speed are made by moving the change speed lever to the position recommended on the feed speed chart. Feed on these machines is controlled automatically, as is the downward pressure on the saw blade during the cutting stroke. At the end of the stroke, the blade is raised automatically to clear the work and is carried back to the starting point of the cutting stroke. This prevents unnecessary wear on the back of the teeth, which would greatly shorten the life of the blade.

Vises

On utility machines, the vises are of the swivel type and have a rated capacity of 4″. The movable jaw can be positioned quickly by means of a toothed (serrated) rack, Fig. 6-3, which is part of the table plate. Notice in Fig. 6-2, the movable jaw of the vise has been advanced along the toothed rack until it is close to the fixed jaw, thus requiring little advance of the clamping screw to close the jaws completely. The machines illustrated in Figs. 6-1 and 6-2 have adjustable stops which, when set to a particular dimension, enable the operator to cut a number of pieces identical in length without having to measure each piece. In Fig. 6-1 the stop is plainly visible on the near side.

Saw Blades and Their Selection

The blades recommended for the saws shown in Figs. 6-1 and 6-2 are 14″ in length, 1¼″ wide, and normally are available with 4, 6, or 10 teeth per inch. Blades with more teeth per inch can be used when necessary, for example, when cutting thin-walled tubing. The blades are held in position against the aligning surfaces of the blade holder with socket head screws, and they are tensioned by means of hardened bolts. The blades may be selected as recommended in Table 3.

The following general principles apply to the selection of power hacksaw blades:
1. A minimum of two teeth should be kept in contact with the workpiece at all times.
2. Large cross sections require coarse teeth for adequate chip clearance.

Table 3
Tooth Selection for Power Hacksaw Blades

Material Being Cut	Machinability Group*	Teeth Per Inch (Pitch) Minimum Material Thickness				
		¼″	½″	¾″	1″	2″ or over
Easily machined	1 (above 70%)	10	6	6	4	4
Moderately difficult to machine	2 (50%-70%)	10	10	6	6	4
Difficult to machine	3 (40%-50%)	10	10	10	6	6

*For general machinability ratings of metals, see Cutting Fluid Selection Table 43. Also see Table 30, appendix.

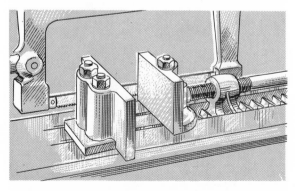

Fig. 6-3. Positioning the Vise on the Power Hacksaw Table

3. Small sections and thin-walled sections require fine teeth.
4. Soft and easily machined materials require coarse teeth to provide adequate chip clearance.
5. Hard materials which are difficult to machine require finer teeth, thus providing more cutting edges per inch.

Drive

Both wet- and dry-cutting utility saws can be purchased with either belt drive or direct motor drive. The saws illustrated in this unit have direct motor drive.

Figs. 6-4 and 6-5 are heavy-duty production saws with accurately controlled blade feed. The saw blade is fed into the work progressively throughout the cutting stroke to remove long, thin, curled chips. A single lever is used to control the feed, clutch, rapid traverse, and neutral operating positions. Most all metals from low-carbon steels to high-temperature alloys can be cut with these saws.

Fig. 6-6 is another heavy-duty hydraulic saw. The machine illustrated has been loaded with long bars from which pieces of a certain length are being cut. With this type of machine, the stock to be cut is loaded on a carriage which, at the completion of a cut, automatically moves forward the distance required. Hydraulic pressure automatically operates the vise jaws, gages the material, and raises and lowers the saw blade. Once the machine has been set up for cutting stock to a given length, it will operate automatically without the attention of an operator, until all stock loaded on the carriage has been cut. This machine is available with a swivel base for cutting angles and with a capacity as high as 12" x 16".

Safety Precautions for the Power Hacksaw

1. Mount work in the saw only when the saw is stopped.
2. Support protruding ends of long pieces so they will not fall and cause injury.

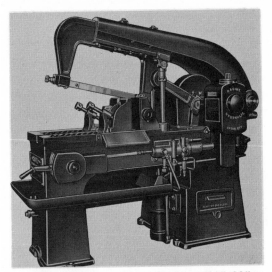

Fig. 6-5. Heavy-Duty Power Hacksaw (10"x10" to 24"x24" Capacity) (Racine Hydraulics and Machinery)

Fig. 6-4. Heavy-Duty 6"x6" Power Hacksaw
(Racine Hydraulics and Machinery)

Fig. 6-6. Heavy-Duty Automatic Hydraulic Saw
(Racine Hydraulics and Machinery)

3. Hang a cloth over protruding ends of long pieces, and see that others do not run into these ends.

4. Be sure that saw blades are in good condition.

5. When raising the saw frame, always use the handle provided.

6. Do not bend over the saw frame while the machine is running.

7. Avoid getting the hands in the area of the saw blade while the saw is running.

8. Be careful to avoid cutting the hands on the burrs at ends of parts which are cut off. The burrs may be removed with a file.

9. Wear approved safety goggles at all times in the shop.

30   How To Cut Metal with a Power Hacksaw

Power metal-cutting saws cut most effectively when the recommended cutting speed is used for a particular material. For information concerning cutting speeds, see Unit 29. Most of the metal cut in a school shop is of the soft variety and can be cut at high speed, at speeds of 100 to 140 strokes per minute. When it is necessary to cut high-speed steel, hard alloys, or cast iron, the machine should be adjusted to run at slower speeds — 35 to 100 strokes per minute.

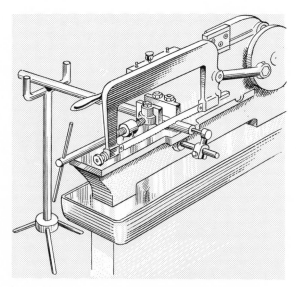

Fig. 6-7. Using a Support to Cut Long Stock

Only when cutting thin-walled material such as tubing or hard metal is it necessary or advisable to use a saw with more than 4 or 6 teeth per inch.

Procedure for Square Cutting

1. If necessary, set the machine at the speed recommended for the material to be cut.

   If the machine is of the transmission type, adjust the speed change lever to the position desired: high, medium, or low. If belt driven, shift the belts in a manner that will produce the speed desired.

   If a change of blade appears necessary, consult the instructor.

2. Secure the stock to be cut.

3. Measure and mark the point on the stock where the cut is to be made, or set the stop so that the distance from the outside of the saw to the stop equals the length of stock required.

4. Place the stock between the jaws of the vise in position to make the cut; the end should be against the stop, if one is used. If the stock is long, use a support as shown in Fig. 6-7.

5. When the stock has been correctly positioned, draw the movable jaw of the vise against the stock with the clamping screw.

6. When the workpiece has been fastened securely, start the machine, open the coolant valve, and direct the flow of coolant into the saw cut.

7. At the end of the cut, shut off the power. This step is unnecessary if the machine is equipped with an automatic knockout.

8. Measure the cut piece to determine if it is the correct length. If not, make the necessary adjustment of the stop.

9. Loosen the vise and adjust the stock for the next cut, if any; then proceed as in steps 6 and 7.

Procedure for Angular Cutting

1. Loosen the clamping bolts on the vise jaws; then adjust the jaws to the angle desired, for example, 45°. See Fig. 6-8.

2. Tighten the clamping bolts, and proceed as when making a square cut.

CAUTION: *If a stop is used, be sure to recheck it for the required length of material.*

Test Your Knowledge of Section 6

Unit 29: The Power Hacksaw

1. Through what angles can the vise be swiveled on a power hacksaw?

Fig. 6-8. Vise in Position to Make a Cut at a 45° Angle (Racine Hydraulics and Machinery)

2. What is the purpose of the hydraulic feed mechanism on a power hacksaw?

3. List the suggested cutting speeds for mild steel, cast iron, and high-speed steel, to be used with the wet-cutting power hacksaw.

4. List the general principles which apply to the tooth selection of power hacksaw blades.

5. How many teeth per inch should a power hacksaw blade have for cutting ¼″ diameter steel?

6. List several safety precautions which should be observed when operating the power hacksaw.

Heat — Another Force Precisely Controlled to do Work
(DoAll)

Metal-Cutting Band Saws and Their Operation

Metal-Cutting Band Saws

Two general types of band saws are available for cutting metals — the *horizontal* type and the conventional or *vertical* type. On the horizontal type, Fig. 7-1, the blade travels in a horizontal plane or in a plane slightly inclined from the horizontal. On the vertical type, Fig. 7-3, the blade travels in the traditional manner, approaching the work in a vertical plane. Some light-duty, metal-cutting band saws are so designed that they may be changed easily from either a horizontal or vertical position. On both types of band saws, the saw blade travels around saw-carrier wheels which usually have a heavy layer of hard rubber cemented to their surface to protect the saw teeth.

Horizontally Operated Cutoff Band Saws

The horizontal saw illustrated in Fig. 7-1 can be adjusted to cut stock square or at an angle. Its maximum capacity is 12″ x 9″ stock. Although the horizontal band saw is used primarily for cutting off stock to the desired length, within its capacity, it can be used to cut a variety of irregular shapes. The feed is hydraulically controlled; consequently, so long as the hydraulic system is working properly, the danger of too rapid feeding is eliminated. Other features include an adjustable vise, an adjustable stock stop, and a means of varying the cutting speed.

Horizontal band saws may be operated as *dry-cutting* or *wet-cutting* machines. For wet-cutting operation, the machine must be equipped with a circulating coolant pump system or with a spray mist system which will di-

rect cutting fluid at the saw teeth. Saw blades for this type of band saw may be either high-quality carbon steel or high-speed steel. The carbon-steel blades have a hard cutting edge and a flexible back. The latter facilitates continual bending.

Horizontal band saws are available in a wide variety of sizes. Some models are manually operated, while others operate automatically. A large machine, although not the largest available, is the automatically operated machine illustrated in Fig. 7-2. This type is equipped with an automatic stock-feeding mechanism and will cut off multiple pieces automatically. It has capacity for 12″ x 16″ stock.

Conventional Metal-Cutting Band Saws

The conventional or vertical band saw is available in a number of sizes ranging in work

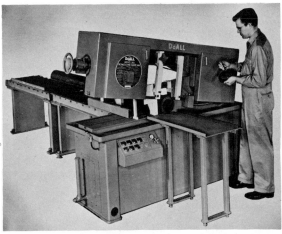

Fig. 7-1. Horizontal Metal-Cutting Band Saw (DoALL)

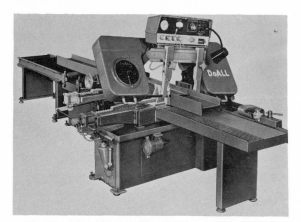

Fig. 7-2. Automatic Horizontal Power Saw (DoALL)

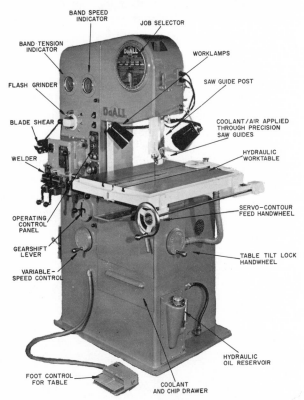

BAND SPEED
INDICATOR

JOB SELECTOR

BAND TENSION
INDICATOR

WORKLAMPS

FLASH GRINDER

SAW GUIDE POST

BLADE SHEAR

COOLANT/AIR APPLIED
THROUGH PRECISION
SAW GUIDES

WELDER

HYDRAULIC
WORKTABLE

OPERATING
CONTROL
PANEL

SERVO-CONTOUR
FEED HANDWHEEL

GEARSHIFT
LEVER

VARIABLE-
SPEED CONTROL

TABLE TILT LOCK
HANDWHEEL

HYDRAULIC
OIL RESERVOIR

FOOT CONTROL
FOR TABLE

COOLANT
AND CHIP DRAWER

Fig. 7-3. Conventional (Vertical) Heavy-Duty
Band Saw (DoALL)

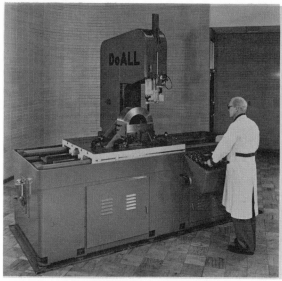

Fig. 7-4. Band Milling with 2″ Width Blade (DoALL)

capacity from 8″ to 24″ in thickness and in throat capacity from 16″ to 60″. A heavy-duty type is shown in Fig. 7-3. This machine has a throat capacity of 16″ and a work-thickness capacity of 12″.

Vertical band saws frequently are called *contour machines*. They are used widely for sawing, filing, and polishing contours of either regular or irregular shape. See Figs. 7-18, 7-26, and 7-27. A large, production sawing machine, which is called a *band mill*, is shown in Fig. 7-4. This machine is using a 2″ width blade for cutting large-diameter work.

Vertical band saws are available with either fixed or variable speeds. The fixed speeds usually may be adjusted in certain increments in terms of feet per minute of saw travel. The variable-speed feature permits easy adaptation to various operating conditions and the peculiar characteristics of a wide range of materials.

Variable-Speed Band Saws: Variable-speed machines are equipped with a job selector, Fig. 7-5. This is a circular chart that gives recommended saw travel and other data pertinent for cutting a large number of commonly used materials. Reference to the chart is a ready means of quickly determining correct cutting speed for a particular material or an operating condition, such as hardness and thickness of the material. Many of these machines are equipped with a variable-speed unit (Fig. 7-6) through which a desired speed can be obtained by merely turning a hand crank located at the left side of the machine. A gear shift, also located at the side, provides easy shifting of the gears to produce either high or low speeds.

Some saws are equipped with a tachometer or speed indicator, Fig. 7-3. This instrument gives the speed the blade is traveling in feet per minute.

The table on most of these machines can be tilted 45° to the right and 10° to the left, front, and rear. On a few machines, it can be tilted only 45° to the right and 5° to the left.

Some machines are equipped with power feed. The power-feed mechanism shown on the machine in Fig. 7-7 is actuated by an adjustable weight. A power-feed control handwheel, located at the front end of the machine, regulates the pull on the work. When occasion requires, pressure applied to the power-feed pedal instantly releases all pressure on the work. The feed mechanism is at the rear of the machine as illustrated.

The machine illustrated in Fig. 7-3 is equipped with an infinitely variable hydraulic-feed mechanism which has a feed range from 0″ to 12″ per minute. The feeding force also may be adjusted within an infinitely variable range from 0 to 350 lbs. The hydraulic system which operates the feed mechanism also is shown in Fig. 7-6.

Metal-cutting band saws of the conventional type are used both for cutting off stock and for contour machining—internal and external. When used for internal sawing, as in Fig. 7-17, the saw blade must be cut, threaded through a

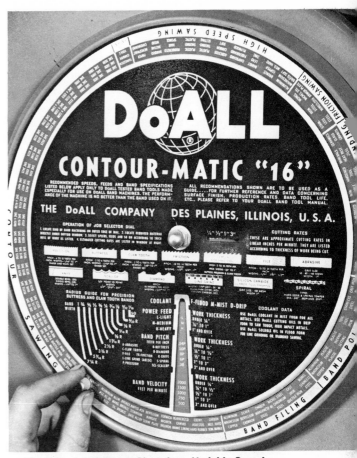

Fig. 7-5. Job Selector Chart for a Variable-Speed Band Saw (DoALL)

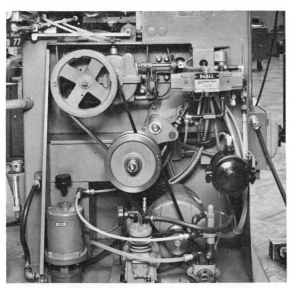

Fig. 7-6. "Speed Master" Variable-Speed Drive System (DoALL)

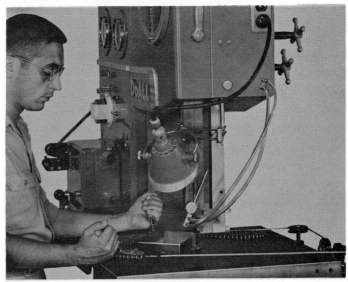

Fig. 7-7. Band Saw Equipped with Power Feed (DoALL)

161

pilot hole drilled in the material, and then butt welded. To perform this, an attached shear to cut the blade, and a butt-welding and annealing unit can be used. Such a unit is shown in Fig. 7-8, combined with a flash grinder and saw-thickness gage built in the machine. However, it is available as a separate unit. Thus the blade is welded, annealed, reduced to uniform thickness and ready for service with a minimum of effort and interruption of production.

Many metal-cutting band saws, particularly those which run at high speed, are equipped with safety brakes. Such brakes are automatically set and the driving power cut off

Fig. 7-8. Butt-Welding and Annealing Unit with Grinder for Joining and Dressing Saw Blade (DoALL)

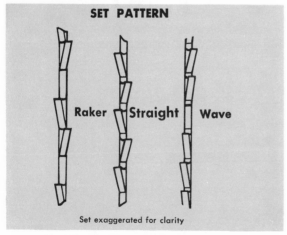

SET PATTERN

Raker | Straight | Wave

Set exaggerated for clarity

Fig. 7-9. The Three Set Patterns (DoALL) Straight set is no longer used for metalworking.

should the blade happen to break. On some machines, the blades are fully guarded except at the point of work.

Saw Blades

Band saw blades may be manufactured from high-quality carbon steel, high-speed steel, or tungsten carbide. Carbon-steel blades are the most widely used for general applications requiring moderate cutting speeds and a moderate production rate. High-speed steel blades (which stay sharp longer) may be used at higher cutting speeds and are recommended where higher rates of production are required. The cutting rate with high-speed steel blades may double the rate possible with carbon-steel blades; however, they are more expensive.

Tungsten-carbide blades generally are recommended for work thicknesses greater than 3″. These blades have tungsten-carbide teeth brazed to a steel band. They usually have a coarse pitch — $1\frac{1}{2}$ to $2\frac{1}{2}$ teeth per inch. They are recommended only for heavy-duty saws where the cutting speed and rate of production must be greater than for either carbon-steel or high-speed steel blades. The carbide blades may be operated at higher cutting speeds than high-speed steel blades, but they are also more expensive.

Carbon steel blades for metal cutting have hardened teeth and a flexible back. The latter feature resists fatigue and facilitates continuous bending. Blades are available in various widths, lengths, and pitches (teeth per inch). Common pitches are 6, 8, 10, 14, and 18; common widths are $\frac{1}{4}″$, $\frac{3}{8}″$, $\frac{1}{2}″$, $\frac{5}{8}″$, $\frac{3}{4}″$, and 1″. The length of saw blade required for a particular machine is determined by the construction of the machine and its blade capacity. The life of the saw blade is affected in no small degree by the manner in which the operator uses it. Improper speed, feed, or tension will shorten the life of a blade; consequently, it is the responsibility of an operator to see that these factors are correct for each job. The vertical band saws illustrated in this unit are equipped with a blade tension indicator, which shows proper tension for each width of blade. On saws not so equipped, the manufacturer's recommendation should be followed concerning proper blade tension. Manufacturers usually supply an operator's manual which includes this type of information, with each machine delivered.

Blade Set: The teeth of band saw blades are bent or offset slightly to the right and to the left to provide clearance for the blade while cutting. This offsetting is called *set*, Fig. 7-9. The distance from the outside of one tooth to the outside of the tooth on the opposite side of the blade is the set dimension. The set on a band saw enables the blade to cut contours. With a small-width blade and a wide set, small-radius contours may be cut.

The common types of set on metal-cutting band saw blades are the *raker* set and the *wave* set, Fig. 7-9. The raker set has one straight tooth at the center, one offset to the right, and one offset to the left, continuing in that order. The wave set gradually weaves from left to right and back again. A third type of set, the *straight* set which has teeth alternating left and right, no longer is used for metalworking.

The raker set is recommended for cutting most contours. It also is recommended for a majority of horizontal cutting operations where the thickness and the shape of the stock being cut do not vary. The wave set is recommended wherever the work has a varying cross-sectional thickness and wherever one band saw blade must be used for a wide range of material sizes and shapes. It is recommended for cutting pipe, angle iron, and other irregular structural shapes.

Filing and Polishing

Both filing and polishing can be performed effectively on metal-cutting band saws by means of endless filing and polishing bands. Excellent work can be done with filing bands and in much shorter time than by hand filing (Fig. 7-26). This is also true of polishing bands (Fig. 7-27). File bands are available in various styles and cuts: flats, half-round, and oval. Common sizes are $\frac{1}{4}''$ to $\frac{1}{2}''$ widths. Length is determined by the blade capacity of the machine.

Applications

Metal-cutting band saws can be used to cut or shape a great variety of materials and products, including practically all metals, pipe, punches, dies, plastics, and woods.

A *diamond-tooth blade* makes possible cutting even such refractory materials as glass, tile, marble, granite, china, porcelain, and silicon carbide. This is a comparatively new development in saw blades. The blade is constructed of highly fatigue-resistant steel, and hundreds of small rods ($\frac{1}{16}'' \times \frac{3}{8}''$) consisting of natural or synthetic diamond particles bonded with a patented tungsten alloy and electronically brazed to the steel band. Because the tungsten-alloy matrix wears away very slowly, such blades have a long life. A cutting compound or lubricant always should be used with these blades.

Friction Sawing

Friction sawing is a relatively recent development in metal cutting. Although this process will not work satisfactorily with metals which melt or become soft and sticky at low temperatures (such as aluminum, brass, bronze, and copper), it is much faster than conventional methods of cutting and will cut metal that can be machined in other ways only with great difficulty, if at all. Cutting is accomplished by momentary contact between the material and a rapidly moving saw blade, which produces sufficient friction to heat the metal immediately ahead of the saw to its softening point.

A third advantage of this method of cutting is the small amount of heat penetration into the side walls of the cut. Thus, the characteristics of the material are preserved. In addition, only a very small burr is produced, which can be removed quickly by means of a band filing machine.

This method is adapted to both straight and contour cutting, even contours involving radii as short as $\frac{5}{8}''$, using a $\frac{1}{4}''$ saw. Only saw blades recommended for friction sawing should be used. The blade need not be sharp,

Table 4
Job Selector for Friction Cutting

STEELS — SAE	SAW VELOCITY			SAW PITCH		
	Thickness 1/16"–1/8"	Thickness 1/8"–1/4"	Thickness 1/4"–1/2"	Thickness 1/16"–1/8"	Thickness 1/8"–1/4"	Thickness 1/4"–1/2"
Carbon steel #1010–#1095	3,000	5,000	12,000	18	14	10
Manganese steel #T1330–#1350	3,000	5,000	12,000	18	14	10
Free machining #X1112–#X1340	3,000	5,000	12,000	18	14	10
Nickel steels #2015–#2515	3,000	6,000	13,000	18	14	10
Nickel chromium #3115–#3415	3,000	6,000	13,000	18	14	10
Molybdenum steel #4023–#4820	3,000	6,000	13,000	18	14	10
Chromium steels #5120–#5150	3,000	6,000	12,000	18	14	10
Chromium steels #51210–#52100	5,000	10,000	14,000	18	14	10
Chromium vanadium #6115–#6195	5,000	12,000	15,000	18	14	10
Tungsten steel #7260–#71360	5,000	12,000	15,000	18	14	10
N.E. steels #8024–#8949	5,000	12,000	15,000	18	14	10
Silicon manganese #9255–#9260	5,000	12,000	15,000	18	14	10
OTHER STEELS						
Armor plate	3,000	9,000	13,000	18	14	10
Stainless steel 18-8	3,000	9,000	14,000	18	14	10
Illium	4,000	12,000	15,000	18	14	10
Cast steel	3,000	9,000	12,000	18	14	10
CAST IRONS						
Gray cast iron	3,000	5,000	7,000	18	14	10
Malleable cast iron	3,000	5,000	7,000	18	14	10
Meehanite castings	3,000	5,000	7,000	18	14	10

(Courtesy, The DoALL Company)

as a dull blade increases friction, thus producing higher heat and higher cutting speed.

Armor plate as thick as 1/2" can be friction cut successfully. Thicker material can be cut by using a rocking technique. In this procedure, the rear end of the material is raised, thus presenting the top edge of the material to the saw. When the saw starts to cut, the rear is lowered to the table, and then raised and lowered alternately throughout the cut.

Friction cutting employs speeds ranging from 3,000 to 15,000 feet per minute, depending upon the composition and thickness of the material. The job selector chart in Table 4 gives recommended saw velocity and saw pitch according to thickness and kind of material.

Safety Precautions for the Band Saw

1. Always be sure that the saw guide is set to within 3/8" to 1/2" above the thickest portion of the workpiece to be cut.

2. When starting the saw, stand to one side of the saw frame; then adjust the speed as desired.

3. Support protruding ends of long pieces so they will not fall and cause injury.

4. Hang a cloth over protruding ends of long pieces, and see that others do not run into them.

5. Be sure that the saw blade is in good condition.

6. Avoid getting the hands too close to the blade.

7. Use a stick to remove short pieces of work from the area close to the blade.

8. Be careful in handling parts with sharp burrs on the ends. The burrs may be removed with a file.

9. Wear approved safety goggles at all times in the shop.

How To Saw Metal with a Horizontal Band Saw

With a horizontal band saw, stock may be cut square, or at any angle desired between 0° and 45°.

Procedure for Square Cutting

1. Determine that the saw is set to make a square cut. Make a trial cut, and test with a square. Make adjustments, if necessary.
2. Secure a piece of stock. Then measure and mark the point at which the cut is to be made.
3. Place the stock or workpiece in the vise of the machine. Observe the methods used for clamping workpieces in the vise. Flat structural stock is clamped as shown in Fig. 7-11, round stock as in Fig. 7-12, and multiple pieces of angle iron as in Fig. 7-13. Adjust it under the saw blade in

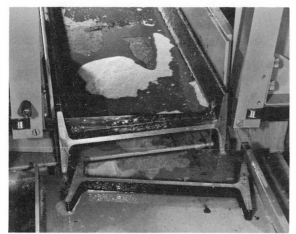

Fig. 7-11. Cutting Structural Member with Horizontal Band Saw (DoALL)

Fig. 7-13. Angles Nested in Vise for Cutting Multiple Pieces of Identical Length (DoALL)

Fig. 7-12. Cutting Round Stock with Horizontal Band Saw (DoALL)

Fig. 7-14. Cutting at an Angle with Horizontal Band Saw (DoALL)

a manner that will assure a cut at the point desired. Be sure that the work is so positioned that the cut will be made in the waste stock.

4. When the workpiece has been positioned correctly, clamp it securely by means of the vise-adjusting handwheel. If more than one piece is to be cut, set the stop against the end of the piece.

5. Start the machine, and make a very slight kerf; then stop the machine, and measure the workpiece to determine if it is the length required. Make adjustment, if necessary.

6. Again start the machine, turn on the cutting lubricant, and make the cut. Be sure the lubricant is directed against the teeth of the saw in the saw kerf.

7. Adjust the stock for the next cut, if any; then proceed in the usual manner.

Procedure for Angular Cutting

1. Determine the angle at which to set the saw.
2. Release the clamping device, and swing the saw frame to the required angle. See Fig. 7-14.
3. Secure a piece of stock, and mark the point at which the cut is to be made.
4. Place the stock in the vise of the machine, and position it so that the cut will be made where marked.
5. When the work has been positioned correctly, clamp it securely by means of the vise-adjusting handwheel.

   If more than one piece is to be cut, set the stop against the end of the stock.
6. Start the machine, and make a very light saw kerf; then stop the machine, and measure the workpiece to determine if it is the length required and angled as needed. Make adjustment, if necessary.
7. Again start the machine, turn on the cutting fluid, and make the cut in the usual manner.

UNIT

33 How To Saw Metal with a Vertical Band Saw

Vertical band saws are used for straight, angular, and contour cutting, both external and internal. As internal sawing involves an operation other than sawing, it is included in a separate unit.

Procedure for Cutting with Table Horizontal

1. Secure the material to be cut.
2. Locate the position on the work at which the cut is to be made; then, if necessary, draw guidelines or use appropriate machine guides, as in Fig. 7-15. The attach-

ment illustrated can be used for cutting off, ripping, or mitering operations.
3. Determine kind and size of saw blade required by consulting the job selector chart, Fig. 7-5. If necessary, change the saw blade.
4. Determine the cutting speed required; consult the job selector chart.
5. Protect the eyes by wearing properly fitted goggles.

   CAUTION: *When handling metals on which cutting produces a burr or sharp edges, protect the hands by wearing properly fitted leather gloves.*

6. Lower the saw guide until it is within ⅜″ to ½″ of the thickest or highest part of the work surface; then clamp the guide in position.

7. Start the saw. When the machine is running at full speed, bring the stock slowly into contact with the traveling blade. Advance the work by exerting a light, but steady, pressure. Do not crowd the saw; allow it time to remove the metal, but keep the work advancing steadily. When the machine is so equipped, power feed should be used for cutting heavy pieces. See Fig. 7-7.

Round or irregularly shaped pieces should be held in a vise, jig, or fixture. This then should be held against a suitable guide. See Fig. 7-15.

The use of a cutting compound or fluid is recommended when cutting steel. When used, it should be directed at the teeth of the saw where they contact the workpiece (or slightly above).

CAUTION: *In placing the hands on the material, be sure they will not come in contact with the traveling saw blade.*

8. At the end of the cut, stop the machine and remove the workpiece. Remove the waste stock and clean the machine, unless other pieces are to be machined.

CAUTION: *Use a piece of wood or other suitable material to remove short workpieces or waste stock from the vicinity of the saw blade. Use a brush to remove metal chips from the saw table. Never use the bare hands to perform either of these tasks.*

Procedure for Cutting with Table at an Angle

1. Proceed as when making a straight cut, steps 1 through 4 inclusive.
2. Tilt the table to the angle desired, and clamp it in position. When cutting a heavy piece of material, use a guide or fixture such as shown in Fig. 7-16.
3. Place the work on the saw table, and move it close to the saw blade. Then adjust the saw guide, bringing it as close to the work surface as practicable.
4. Start the machine, move the work against the saw, and make the cut in the usual manner.

NOTE: If a guide is used, move the workpiece forward until the teeth of the saw just touch the foremost edge of the work. Then examine the position of the work to make certain the cut will be made where desired.

Procedure for Cutting External Contours

1. Secure the material to be cut.
2. Lay out the required shape on the surface of the workpiece.

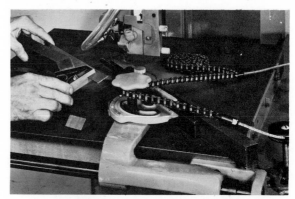

Fig. 7-15. Cutoff and Mitering Attachment Used to Cut Stock at Any Angle (DoALL) Manual or power feed may be used.

Fig. 7-16. Making Cut with Table Tilted (DoALL)

3. Determine the size and kind of saw blade required to perform the operation; consult the job selector chart, Fig. 7-5. When the shape involves sharp curves, a narrow saw should be used.
4. Determine the cutting speed required; consult the job selector chart.
5. Protect the eyes by wearing properly fitted goggles. Use leather gloves when necessary.
6. Lower the saw guide to within $\frac{3}{8}''$ or $\frac{1}{2}''$ of the thickest or highest part of the work; then clamp it in position.
7. Start the saw. When the machine is running at full speed, bring the stock slowly into contact with the traveling saw blade. Advance the work steadily, and follow the outline. Do not crowd the saw. Power feed may be used to advantage when cutting long sweeping curves. Round or irregularly shaped pieces should be held in a vise or jig.

When it is necessary to cut a very sharp curve, it may be advisable to bypass it temporarily; then, when the waste material has been removed from other parts of the work, the cut can be made in the usual manner.

Use of a cutting compound or fluid is recommended when cutting steel.

8. At the end of the cut, stop the machine and remove the workpiece. Remove the waste stock by means of a piece of wood or other suitable material; then clean the machine, unless other pieces are to be machined. Use a brush to remove waste material or chips from the saw table; do not use the bare hands.

UNIT 34   How To Saw Internal Contours with a Band Saw

Rectangular, circular, or irregular internal contours may be cut with a band saw.

Procedure

1. Secure the material to be cut.
2. Lay out the required contour or outline on the surface of the workpiece, Fig. 7-17.
3. Drill a pilot hole near one edge of the contour or outline. Be sure to make the hole large enough to permit free entry of the saw blade. See Figs. 7-17 and 7-18.

When the enclosure is rectangular, a pilot hole should be drilled at each corner. Drilling a pilot hole wherever a contour changes its direction sharply, involving an acute angle on a very short radius, will facilitate turning or reversing the direction of the cut.

4. Determine the size and kind of saw blade required to perform the operation; consult the job selector chart.
5. Cut the saw blade. Then draw one end through the pilot hole in the workpiece, place the ends of the blade in the automatic butt welder, and turn on the current. See Fig. 7-8. This will instantly weld the ends together.
6. Place the welded joint in the flash grinder, just above the automatic welder, and grind the joint smooth and even.

On machines not equipped with a welder, the operation must be performed with a separate welder or brazed with a torch, and the joint annealed and filed smooth.

7. Place the welded blade on the wheels of the machine, and tension it correctly.

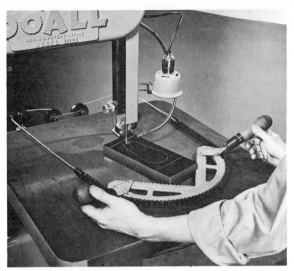

Fig. 7-17. **Band Saw Inserted through Drilled Hole for Internal Contour Sawing (DoALL)**

Fig. 7-18. **Internal Contour Sawed Out (DoALL)**

8. Determine the cutting speed required; consult the job selector chart, Fig. 7-5.
9. Adjust the speed-control mechanism by revolving the speed-control hand crank to the position desired.

On machines not equipped with a variable-speed mechanism, change of speed is achieved by changing the drive belt to the position desired on the step pulley. Shift to high or low speed is achieved by means of a gear shift on machines so equipped.

10. Protect the eyes by wearing properly fitted goggles. Use leather gloves when necessary.
11. Start the saw; then when the machine is running at full speed, bring the workpiece slowly into contact with the traveling saw blade. Advance the work steadily, and follow the outline. Be careful not to crowd the saw.

When it is necessary to cut a very sharp curve, it may be advisable to bypass it temporarily; then after waste material has been removed, the cut can be made in the usual manner. Use of a cutting compound or lubricant is recommended.

12. When the cut has been completed, stop the machine, cut the saw blade, and remove it.

Saw blades that have been cut to remove them from an enclosure often are set aside for use on a similar operation.

13. With a brush, remove waste stock and metal chips from the saw table. Do not use the bare hands.

How To Friction Cut Metal with a Band Saw

Straight or contour sawing can be done by friction sawing. Care must be taken that the recommended saws and cutting speeds are used; see Table 4, Unit 31.

Most conventional methods of cutting metals employ a cutter with a keen edge. When cutting by friction, a keen edge is not required; in fact, a dull edge is more effective, because it creates more friction and, consequently, more heat. (See Fig. 7-19.) This softens the metal immediately ahead of the blade and thus increases cutting efficiency.

Procedure

1. Secure a workpiece.
2. Locate the position on the workpiece at which the cut is to be made; then draw appropriate guidelines or use appropriate machine guides.
3. Determine size and kind of saw required; consult Table 4, Unit 31. Change the saw if necessary.
4. Determine cutting speed required; consult Table 4.
5. Adjust the speed-control mechanism by revolving the speed-control hand crank to the position desired.
6. Protect the eyes, hands, and clothing by wearing properly fitted glasses, leather gloves, and appropriate coveralls.
7. Start the machine; then when it has attained full speed, bring the work gently into contact with the blade, as in Figs. 7-20 and 7-21. Advance the work steadily. Use the rocking technique, if necessary; that is, alternately slightly raise and lower the rear end of the work.
8. At the completion of the cut, stop the machine, remove the work, and clean the worktable.

Fig. 7-19. Dull Edge for Friction Sawing (DoALL)

Fig. 7-20. Friction Sawing Hardened Coil Springs (DoALL)

Fig. 7-21. Friction Sawing Hardened Steel Milling Cutter (DoALL)

How To Cut Refractory Materials with a Band Saw

A variety of refractory materials (such as glass, porcelain, china, marble, granite, and silicon carbides) can be cut with a diamond-tooth band saw.

Procedure

1. Secure the workpiece, Fig. 7-22.
2. Lay out the design on the workpiece or otherwise indicate where the cut is to be made.
3. Secure a diamond-tooth saw blade, Fig. 7-23. Mount it on the saw, and tension it properly.
4. Set the machine for a cutting speed of 2000 to 4000 feet per minute.
5. Protect the eyes by wearing goggles.
6. Start the machine, turn on the cutting compound or fluid, and direct it at the teeth of the blade where they contact the workpiece. A spray lubricator is recommended. Fig. 7-24 shows the spray tubes.

   NOTE: When sawing circular pieces, hold them in a vise, a jig, or other suitable fixture. The same applies when sawing irregular shapes.

7. Bring the workpiece gently against the traveling blade, and feed it steadily forward. (See Fig. 7-24.) Do not crowd the saw.
8. At the completion of the cut, stop the machine, remove the work, and clean the machine.

Fig. 7-23. Diamond-Tooth Band Saw Blade (DoALL)

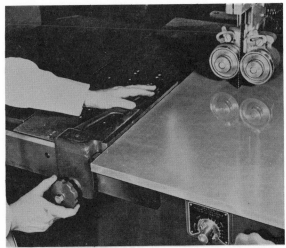

Fig. 7-22. Cutting Glass with a Diamond-Tooth Blade (DoALL)

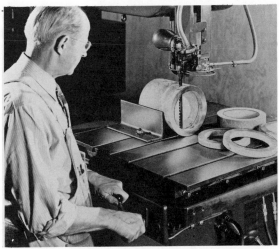

Fig. 7-24. A Spray Lubricant Is Recommended for Refractory Material (DoALL)

171

How To File and Polish Work with a Band Saw

Endless filing and polishing bands are available for use with metal-cutting band saws. When properly handled, an endless file will do accurate work, much more rapidly than can be done by hand. (The same applies to an endless polishing band.) An endless file band is fitted with a special joint which permits its use for internal filing, Figs. 7-25 and 7-26.

Procedure for Filing External Contours

1. Select a file band of appropriate grade and shape. Also select a suitable band guide.
2. Mount the guide on the guidepost.
3. Mount the band on the wheels of the saw, and tension it properly, usually about one-quarter turn of the handwheel after the band comes under tension.
4. Protect the eyes by wearing properly fitted goggles.

5. Start the machine, and bring the workpiece gently against the traveling file band, Fig. 7-26. Move the work in a manner that will cause the file to remove the excess stock the entire length of the surface to be filed.
6. When filing has been completed, remove the filing band and guide; then clean the machine.

Procedure for Filing Internal Contours

1. Select a file band of appropriate grade and shape, and a suitable band guide.
2. Mount the saw guide on the guidepost.
3. Uncouple the file band, Fig. 7-25, and insert one end through the opening in the

Fig. 7-25. Uncoupling the File Band (DoALL)

Fig. 7-26. Band Filing Application (DoALL)

172

workpiece. Then couple the ends of the band, and mount it on the wheels of the saw. Properly tension the band.

4. Proceed as in steps 4 through 6 inclusive, "Procedure for Filing External Contours."

Procedure for Polishing

1. Select a suitable polishing band and guide.
2. Mount the guide on the guidepost and the band on the wheels of the saw.
3. Protect the eyes by wearing properly fitted goggles.
4. Start the machine; then bring the workpiece gently against the traveling band, Fig. 7-27. Progressively move the work in a manner that will bring the polishing band into contact with all parts of the surface to be polished, Fig. 7-27.
5. When the operation has been completed, remove the polishing band and clean the machine.

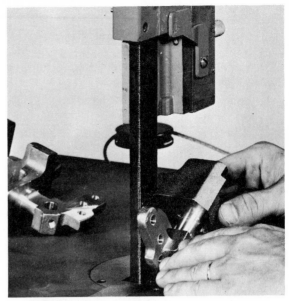

Fig. 7-27. Polishing with an Abrasive Band on the Band Saw (DoALL)

Test Your Knowledge of Section 7

Unit 31: Metal-Cutting Band Saws

NOTE: Additional information concerning these questions may be found in Units 32 through 37, which include the procedures used for various band sawing operations.

1. List two general types of band sawing machines.
2. For what basic type of work is a horizontal band saw generally used?
3. What advantages are obtained in wet-cutting, rather than dry-cutting, with a band saw?
4. What size stock may be cut in the largest horizontal saw illustrated in this unit?
5. What information is provided by a job selector chart for vertical band saws?
6. To what angles may the table on a band saw be tilted?
7. On a vertical band saw, what purpose does the foot pedal on the power-feed mechanism serve?

8. Explain how the saw blade is inserted through the workpiece for internal contour cutting with a vertical band saw.
9. List three types of material from which saw blades may be made.
10. What type of band saw blades are most widely used for general applications at moderate cutting speeds and moderate production rates?
11. What advantages result in using high-speed steel band saw blades, as compared with carbon-steel blades?
12. For what purposes are tungsten-carbide band saw blades recommended?
13. In what pitches and in what widths are carbon-steel band saw blades usually available?
14. What operational factors will shorten the life of a band saw blade?
15. How does one determine proper blade tension on a vertical band saw?

173

16. What are the two types of set commonly used on the teeth of band saw blades?
17. For what basic purposes are band saw blades with the raker set generally recommended?
18. For what purposes are band saw blades with the wave set generally recommended.
19. How are filing operations performed on a band sawing machine?
20. How are polishing operations performed on a band sawing machine?

21. List several different kinds of materials which can be cut on metal-cutting band saws.
22. What materials can be cut with a diamond-tooth band saw blade?
23. Explain how friction sawing is done; indicate what cutting-speed range is used for friction sawing.
24. What type of metals is not recommended for friction sawing?
25. List several safety precautions which should be observed when using the band saw.

Rhythmic Undulations — Poetry in Machining
(Johansson)

Drills and Drilling

The Drill Press

The drill press, Fig. 8-1, is one of the most important machine tools in the industrial shop or school. It is one of several types of machine tools used for drilling holes in metal. The drill press also is widely used for hole-machining operations such as reaming, boring, counter- boring, countersinking, and tapping. See Fig. 8-2. In addition to these operations, the drill press also may be used for honing or lapping, as well as for spot-finishing as shown in Fig. 8-75.

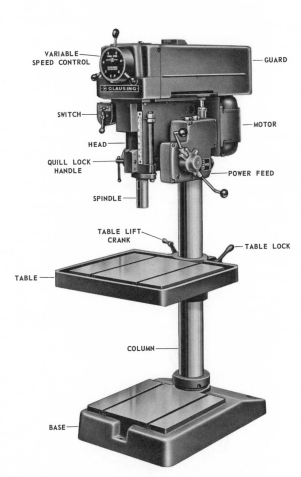

Fig. 8-1. Floor-Model Sensitive Drill Press
(Clausing Div. — Atlas Press)

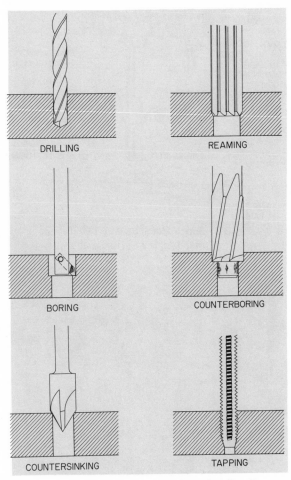

Fig. 8-2. Six Common Operations that Can Be Performed on a Drill Press

The six operations illustrated in Fig. 8-2 also commonly are performed on metalworking lathes, turret lathes, hand and automatic screw machines, and vertical milling machines, as well as on modern numerically controlled *drilling-milling-boring* machines of the type shown in Fig. 8-19.

The principles involved in performing these six operations are essentially the same, whether they are done on a drill press or on other basic or specialized production machine tools. Thus the drill press, which is relatively inexpensive, is one of the most important tools in the shop.

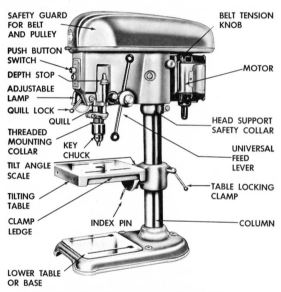

SAFETY GUARD FOR BELT AND PULLEY
BELT TENSION KNOB
PUSH BUTTON SWITCH
DEPTH STOP
ADJUSTABLE LAMP
QUILL LOCK
QUILL
THREADED MOUNTING COLLAR
KEY
CHUCK
TILT ANGLE SCALE
TILTING TABLE
CLAMP LEDGE
INDEX PIN
LOWER TABLE OR BASE
MOTOR
HEAD SUPPORT SAFETY COLLAR
UNIVERSAL FEED LEVER
TABLE LOCKING CLAMP
COLUMN

Fig. 8-3. Bench-Model Sensitive Drill Press
(Power Tool Div. — Rockwell)

Sensitive Drilling Machines

Sensitive drilling machines are equipped with a hand feed which enables the operator to *feel* the progress of the machine cut. The floor-model drill press in Fig. 8-1 and the bench model in Fig. 8-3 are sensitive drilling machines. This type machine also may be equipped with power feed, as shown in Fig. 8-1. These machines generally are used for light-duty drilling operations in tool and die shops, maintenance shops, and school shops. They are available with drilling capacities ranging up to about 1½″ in diameter. Often they are arranged in a line to make up a *gang drilling* machine as shown in Fig. 8-15.

Principal Parts and Characteristics

The principal parts of a drilling machine, as shown in Fig. 8-1, include the following: base and column, spindle, motor and head, table, feed mechanism, and quill. Other important parts include a drill chuck, on-off switch, table-raising crank, table lock or clamp, and a depth stop as identified in Fig. 8-3.

Speed Variation: Variation of spindle speed is accomplished through several types of drive systems. One common method involves the *step-pulley drive* with a V-belt, as shown in Fig. 8-4. With this system, spindle speed is increased by stepping the V-belt up to a larger diameter on the motor pulley. Similarly, spindle speed is decreased by stepping the belt down to a smaller diameter on the motor pulley. When changing speeds

Fig. 8-4. Step-Pulley Countershaft Drive
(Clausing Div. — Atlas Press)

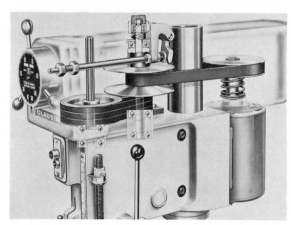

Fig. 8-5. Variable-Speed Countershaft Drive
(Clausing Div. — Atlas Press)

either way, begin at the stepped pulley (either at the motor or the one at the center) which will put its belt onto a smaller pulley; then move the opposite end to the correspondingly larger step. (The belt must not run diagonally, nor be stretched.)

A second drive system is the *variable-speed drive*. With this system, the speed is infinitely variable throughout the total speed range of the drilling machine. The drill press in Fig. 8-1 has a variable-speed countershaft drive of the type shown in Fig. 8-5. Usually the speed must be changed *only* while the machine is running.

A third method for variation of spindle speed involves a *gear drive system*. Here speed-selector handles are used to shift the gears for the desired spindle rpm. Usually the machine must be stopped while speed changes are made. This type of drive system generally is included on heavy-duty drilling machines.

A two-speed motor may be used in conjunction with any of the above drive systems. This type motor generally provides both *low-* and *high-*speed ranges for the spindle.

The speed ranges on drill presses may vary from about 30 to 5000 rpm. The spindle speed should be determined by the nature of the work and the size of drill used.

Feed: All drill presses are equipped with a *hand feed*. In addition, many are equipped with an *automatic feed*. The drill press illustrated in Fig. 8-1 has a mechanical automatic-feed mechanism. *Mechanical* automatic feeds usually are set at a certain feed per revolution of the drill press spindle, such as 0.004″ per revolution. The range of feeds varies from 0.002″ to 0.025″ per revolution.

An *air-hydraulic* feed mechanism is shown in Fig. 8-6. This type may be set at infinitely variable feeds from ½″ to 60″ per minute. It operates from air pressure and may be used in conjunction with either automatic or semi-automatic operation. *Liquid-hydraulic* feed mechanisms also are widely used on large production drill presses.

Attachments: Several special attachments are available for use on drill presses. The *universal compound vise*, Fig. 8-7, is useful in clamping work securely for many drilling operations. The vise normally is bolted to the drill press table. With compound slides

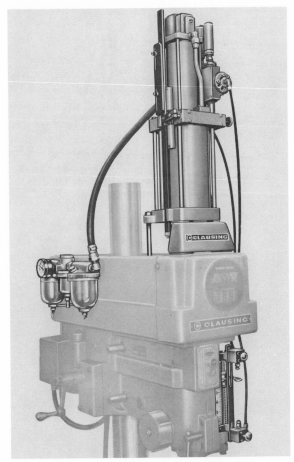

Fig. 8-6. Air-Hydraulic Feed on Drill Press
(Clausing Div. — Atlas Press)

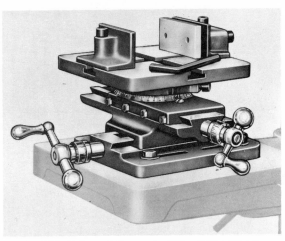

Fig. 8-7. Universal Compound Vise (Atlas Press)

in both directions, workpieces may be easily aligned. A less complex drilling vise is shown in Fig. 3-117. A *tapping attachment* is shown in Fig. 8-8, and a second type is shown in Fig. 4-56.

A *multiple-spindle drilling head*, Fig. 8-9, may be mounted on the drill press spindle for drilling several holes at the same time. A drilling jig or fixture generally is used in conjunction with this type drilling head. A *horizontal drilling head*, Fig. 8-9, may also be used for drilling holes simultaneously while vertical holes are being drilled. A larger multiple-spindle drill head is being used on the drill press in Fig. 8-10.

A mortising attachment, Fig. 8-11, is attached to the drill press spindle for making mortises in wood. A shaping attachment for shaping wood is shown in Fig. 8-12.

Size and Capacity: Usually, the size of a drill press is given in terms of the distance from the column to the point of the drill. A 16″ drill press will drill a hole in the center of a circle 16″ in diameter. The vertical capacity of the machine is determined by the distance from the table (in its lowest position) to the bottom of the jaws of the chuck when fully elevated, less the amount the drill projects. Other factors determining capacity include the distance of spindle travel and the size of drill which the quill or chuck will accommodate. Drill presses are made in many sizes and for a number of special purposes.

Fig. 8-9. **Multiple-Spindle Drill Head Mounted on Single-Spindle Drill Press** (Zagar)

Fig. 8-10. **Multiple-Spindle Drill Head Mounted on Floor-Model Drill Press** (Zager)

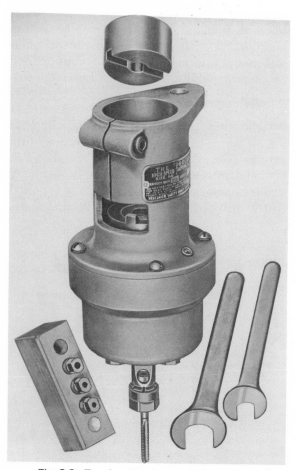

Fig. 8-8. **Tapping Attachment** (Atlas Press)

180

Fig. 8-11. **Mortising Attachment** (Atlas Press)

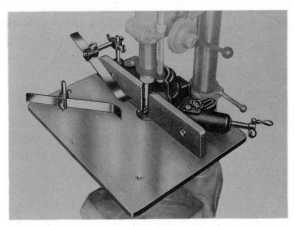

Fig. 8-12. **Shaping Attachment** (Atlas Press)

Safety with Drilling Operations

1. Always wear appropriate safety goggles.
2. Never leave the chuck key in the drill chuck.
3. Mount the work securely before drilling. Do not hold thin or small pieces in the hands.
4. Remove chips with a brush or piece of wood; never use the hands.
5. Ease up on the feed pressure as the drill begins to break through a hole. This will prevent the drill from breaking or pulling the work loose.
6. Do not attempt to stop the spindle with the hands after turning the machine off.
7. Apply a few drops of cutting oil to the drill with a small brush. Excess oil in the area or on the floor is a safety hazard.
8. Never drill copper alloys, including brass and bronze, with a drill which is ground for steel. Request the instructor to show you how to grind the drill for this purpose. A drill ground for steel may dig in, break, ruin your work, or cause injury.
9. Keep long sleeves, other loose clothing, or long hair away from the revolving spindle or belts.
10. Do not operate the drill with the covers or guards removed.

UNIT
39

Types of Drilling Machines in Industry

Several basic types of drilling machines are in common use. Some are designed for general use, while others are designed for mass production. *Sensitive* drilling machines were explained in the previous unit.

Upright Drilling Machine

The upright drilling machine, Fig. 8-14, is designed for general-purpose and heavy-duty work on small parts which may be mounted on the table. It can be used with drills of larger diameter than those normally used on standard bench- and floor-model drill presses. Upright drilling machines are available in various sizes and with various drilling capacities (ranging up to 3" diameter drills on the largest machines). Machines of this type often have a gear-driven mechanism for changing spindle speeds and feeds. Wide ranges of speeds and feeds generally are available.

Gang Drilling Machine

The gang drilling machine, Fig. 8-15, basically is a series of single-spindle drilling heads

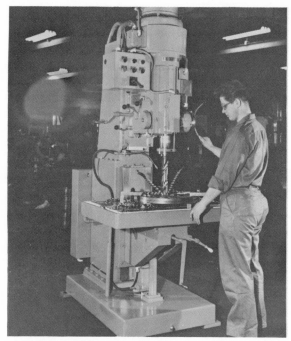

Fig. 8-14. Upright Drilling Machine with Power Feed
(Johansson)

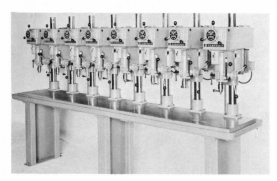

Fig. 8-15. Gang Drill (Atlas Press)

on a long table. It is designed for mass-production purposes where a number of drilling operations must be performed in a certain sequence. Each drilling head may be equipped with a different tool (such as a center drill, drill, reamer, countersink, boring tool, counterbore, tap, etc.), and the part being machined is moved from one drilling head to the next. Several operators generally work at the same machine. These machines may be equipped with from two to ten or more spindles.

Radial Drilling Machine

The radial drilling machine, Fig. 8-16, is the most versatile of all drilling machines. It is designed primarily for use on parts which are too large for the operator to move and handle for each drilling operation. The drilling head slides along a large radial arm, thus providing for adjustment of the drilling distance from the column. The arm also swings about the column for locating the drill horizontally. The arm is raised or lowered with power by means of a lead screw. These machines are provided with a wide range of spindle speeds and automatic feeds.

Radial drilling machines are available in various sizes and capacities. Arm lengths range up to about 14', column diameters up to 30" or more, and drilling capacity for drills up to 5" in diameter. The machine illustrated

Fig. 8-16. Two-Station Radial Drilling Machine
(Carlton Machine Tool)
The machine is equipped with revolving indexing fixtures and jigs for drilling a typical job.

in Fig. 8-16 is the two-station type. It is equipped with revolving indexing fixtures and jigs for drilling a typical job.

Multiple-Drill-Head Machine

Various machines with multiple drills in a single drilling head are available. A multiple-drill-head machine is shown in Fig. 8-17. For light-duty work, a multiple-drill-head attachment may be mounted on the spindle of a standard floor-model drill press, as shown in Fig. 8-10. Multiple-drill-head machines are designed for drilling a number of holes at the same time for mass-production purposes. They are used for drilling parts such as engine blocks or parts with bolt circles. Besides saving time, such machines insure accurate spacing between holes.

Drills in the drill head may be located randomly, as desired, within the range of the drilling head and the machine table. Drilling jigs or fixtures generally are used in conjunction with this type drilling head to maintain accurate hole location. Machines of this type have been produced with from 2 to more than 200 spindles. They range in horsepower from $\frac{1}{2}$ hp to more than 100 hp. Most of these machines are designed for drilling in the vertical position, but some drill horizontally.

Turret Drilling Machine

The turret drilling machine has a multisided spindle turret with 6, 8, or 10 spindles. See Figs. 8-18 and 8-19. The turret may be indexed to the desired tool in the sequence necessary. That shown in Fig. 8-18 is a small hand-operated machine with a six-spindle turret. It has capacity for drilling $\frac{1}{2}''$ diameter in steel. A smaller model of this type machine also is available. The turret head may be tooled with six tools in any desired order, for operations such as centerdrilling, drilling, counterboring, reaming, boring, or tapping. Turret drilling machines provide for increased production by eliminating time for tool changes or by reducing the number of standard drilling machines required.

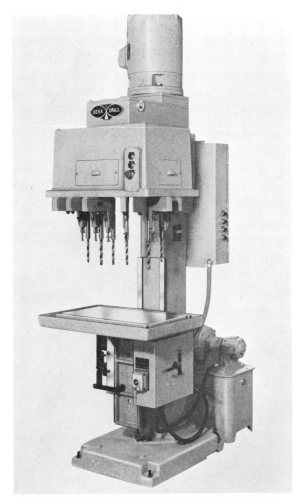

Fig. 8-17. Multiple-Drill-Head Drilling Machine Drills Several Holes at the Same Time (Precision Tool)

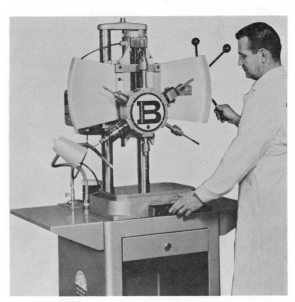

Fig. 8-18. Small Turret Drilling Machine (Burgmaster)

Turret drilling machines are available in a variety of sizes. They may take the place of several conventional drilling machines and milling machines. The large turret drilling machine in Fig. 8-19 has an 8-spindle turret. It is capable of performing all common drilling operations, as well as tapping and several face-milling and end-milling operations (such as face milling flat surfaces or end milling shoulders and slots). This type of machine may be operated either manually through the use of the electrical controls or automatically through the use of a tape-control system known as *numerical control*.

Numerical Control

A numerically controlled machine tool, such as the large turret drilling machine in Fig. 8-19, will cycle automatically through all of the hole-machining and end-milling operations required on one surface of a part. When the required operations are completed on one surface, the part may be turned and other surfaces may be machined in similar fashion with a second setup. Machines of this general type often are referred to as *drilling-milling-boring machines*. The machine will perform automatically all of the operations within its tooling capacity.

A turret drilling machine with an eight-station turret, tooled with eight different tools, can machine any specified number of operations for each tool. It will do this in accordance with instructions which are fed into the machine's electronic control system from a standard paper or plastic numerical control tape.

Programming: Before a part may be machined by a numerically controlled machine, a *program* of instructions must be prepared. The program identifies and

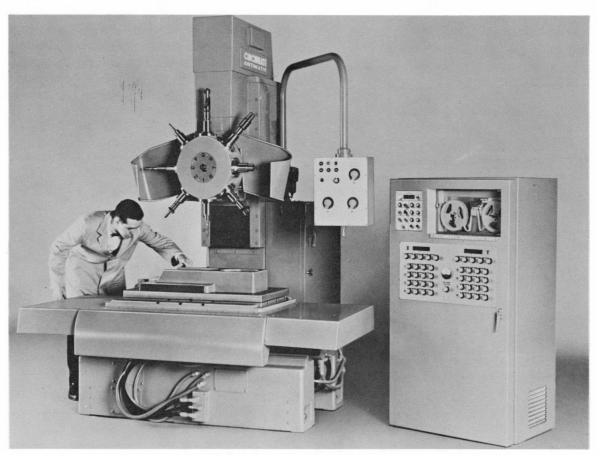

Fig. 8-19. Numerically Controlled Turret Drilling Machine (Cincinnati Lathe & Tool)

includes the following necessary machining instructions: sequence of each operation, type of operation, dimensional location for each operation, depth of cut, cutting speed, feed rate, spindle speed, and tool number. Other information also may be included. The program of instructions is prepared in the form of a code composed of letters and numerals in special arrangements and a specific sequence.

The coded instructions are then punched into a standard tape used for numerical control systems. Each letter or number is represented by a different arrangement of perforated holes. These are punched with a perforating machine, which has a keyboard very similar to a standard typewriter.

The punched tape then is inserted into the electronic numerical control system which controls the machine tool. The control system accurately interprets the punched tape and causes the machine tool to perform all operations in the proper sequence. The operations are performed to tolerances within 0.001″. After the initial setting up of fixtures or holding devices, the only work required of the operator is to change workpieces after each part has been machined. Of course, he must see that the cutting tools, such as drills, ream-

ers, and taps, are sharp and in good condition. If a tool breaks, he must replace the tool and get the machine back into operation.

Operator Training: Before a worker is permitted to operate an expensive numerically controlled machine tool, such as a turret drilling machine, he generally is required to know and understand all of the basic operations which the machine is capable of performing. These operations can be learned through study of and experience with basic machine tools, such as the drill press and the milling machine in the school.

Many modern industrial plants have programs for training workers to operate numerically controlled machine tools. For these programs, they generally select employees who have a good understanding of basic machining operations.

The use of numerically controlled machine tools is increasing rapidly. The outlook for workers who are capable of becoming *parts programmers* or who can operate numerically controlled machine tools is very good for the decade ahead.

Twist Drills and Boring Tools

Drills are used for piercing or cutting circular holes into or through material. There are many kinds of drills used for this purpose; however, twist drills are by far the most commonly used.

Parts of a Drill

Generally speaking, a drill has three principal parts: the point, or dead center, the

body, and the shank, Fig. 8-22. The spiral grooves that wind around the body of the drill are called *flutes*. They provide a means whereby (1) a suitable lip or cutting edge may be formed on the point of the bit; (2) the chip removed by the cutting lip may be carried by a channel to the surface; and (3) a lubricant can be carried easily to the cutting edge. The body surface between the flutes is known as the *land*. The narrow strip of metal, labeled

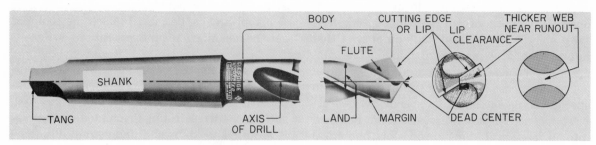

Fig. 8-22. Parts of a Drill (Cleveland Twist Drill)

Fig. 8-23. Types of Drill Shanks (Cleveland Twist Drill)

Fig. 8-24. Sleeve or Shell Socket
(Cleveland Twist Drill)

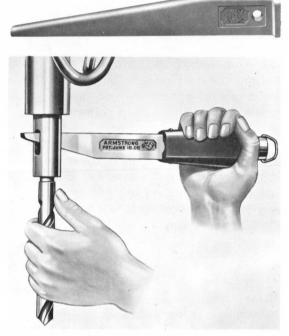

Fig. 8-25. (Above) Plain Drill Drift; (Below) Safety Drill Drift (Armstrong; Cleveland Twist Drill)

margin, Fig. 8-22, is formed by grinding away some of the land, to give the drill body clearance.

The thin wall between the flutes is called the *web.* It is this part that gives rigidity and strength to the drill. As the web approaches the shank, it thickens. This is accomplished by cutting the flutes somewhat shallower but slightly wider. Widening the flutes permits free passage of the chips.

The shank (that part of the drill which fits the spindle or chuck of the drill press or the jaws of a brace) varies in shape according to its size or the purpose for which it was designed. *A* in Fig. 8-23 is a square shank intended for use with a bit brace; *B* is an ordinary straight shank, found on drills up to ½″ diameter, and is intended for use with a chuck; *C* represents a taper-shank drill. Taper-shank drills have standard Morse tapers and will fit the spindles of standard drill presses or auxiliary sleeves. The tang on shank *C* fits a slot in the spindle, to prevent the drill from slipping or turning in the spindle.

Fitting Taper-Shank Drills: *Morse-taper shanks* are standard on taper-shank drills.

They also are used on a variety of other tools such as reamers, milling cutters, counterbores, and spot-facing tools. Morse tapers are made in various sizes ranging from Nos. 0 through 7. The No. 2, 3, and 4 tapers are used most commonly on drills from ⅜″ to 1½″ diameter.

Table 5
Causes of Drill Breakage, Damage, or Inaccuracy

Symptoms	Probable Cause	Remedy
Breaking of drill.	Spring or back lash in press or work. Too little lip clearance. Too low speed in proportion to the feed. Dull drill.	Test press and work for rigidity and alignment. Regrind properly. Increase speed or decrease feed. Sharpen drill.
Breaking down of outer corners of cutting edges.	Material being drilled has hard spots, scale or sand inclusions. Too much speed. Improper cutting compound. No lubricant at point of drill.	Reduce speed. Use proper cutting compound and correct application.
Breaking of drill when drilling brass or wood.	Chips clog up flutes.	Increase speed. Use drills designed for these materials.
Broken tang.	Imperfect fit of taper shank in the socket — due to nicks, dirt, burrs, or worn out socket.	Get a new socket or ream old one to prevent recurrence.
Chipping of margin.	Oversize jig bushing.	Use proper size bushing.
Chipping of lip or cutting edges.	Too much feed. Too much lip clearance.	Reduce feed. Regrind properly.
Chipping or checking of a high speed drill.	Heated and cooled too quickly while grinding or while drilling. Too much feed.	Warm slowly before using. Do not throw cold water on hot drill while grinding or drilling. Reduce feed.
Change in character of chips while drilling.	Change in condition of the drill such as chipping of cutting edge, dulling, etc.	Regrind drill properly.
Hole too large.	Unequal angle or length of the cutting edges, or both. Loose spindle.	Regrind properly. Test spindle for rigidity.
Only one lip cutting.	Unequal length or angle of cutting lips or both.	Regrind drill properly.
Splitting up center.	Too little lip clearance. Too much feed.	Regrind with proper lip clearance. Reduce feed.
Rough hole.	Dull or improperly ground drill. Lack of lubricant or wrong lubricant. Improper set-up. Too much feed.	Regrind properly. Lubricate or change lubricant. Reduce feed.

Since a ½″ drill with a No. 2 Morse-taper shank will not fit a drill press spindle with a larger No. 3 or 4 taper hole, a reducing fitting called a *sleeve* or *shell socket* must be used, Fig. 8-24. These sleeves are available in several standard sizes. The sleeve is placed over the drill shank and tapped lightly with a hammer. It fits the taper shank securely because of a close friction fit. The drill together with its sleeve then is mounted in the drill press spindle by tapping the end of the drill lightly with a lead hammer for a snug fit.

To remove the drill from the spindle or from the sleeve, a drill drift is used, Fig. 8-25. The drift is inserted in the hole in the sleeve and tapped lightly with a hammer, thus causing the taper shank to slide from the taper hole.

The safety drill drift in Fig. 8-25 also works well in removing drills from the spindle. The handle, which is attached permanently to the drift, operates with a sliding action. It is used to drive the drift into the spindle hole, thus loosening the drill which can be held with the free hand.

187

Fitted sockets, Fig. 8-26, are used to adapt tools having a different size of tapered shank to the Morse-taper hole in the spindle of drill presses, milling machines, engine lathes, turret lathes, or other machines. Fitted sockets are available with a variety of standard ex-

Fig. 8-26. Fitted Socket (Cleveland Twist Drill)

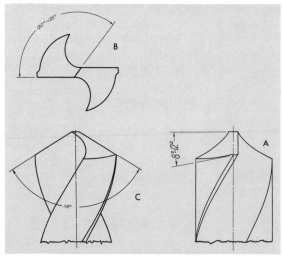

Fig. 8-27. Correct Angles for Standard General-Purpose Drills (Cleveland Twist Drill)
(A) Lip clearance; (B) Location of the point; (C) Lip angle.

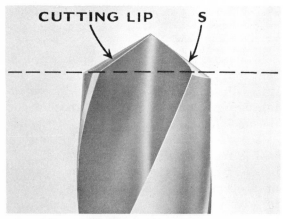

Fig. 8-28. Drill Without Lip Clearance Will Not Cut
(Cleveland Twist Drill)

ternal and internal tapers so that a large shank may be adapted to a small hole or vice versa. (They also can be used simply to extend the reach of a drill.) For example, an adapter with a No. 2 hole and a No. 3 shank may be used to adapt the shank of a drill or other tool having a No. 2 taper to a spindle having No. 3 internal taper. Similarly, an adapter with No. 3 hole and No. 2 shank may be used to adapt a tool with a No. 3 taper to a machine spindle having a No. 2 internal taper. A socket with a No. 3 hole and a No. 3 shank is used as an extension.

Drill Sizes

Drill sizes are indicated in three ways: (1) by number; (2) by letter; and (3) by fractional parts of an inch. Drill sizes by number are given in terms of wire gage, and they range from No. 80, which has a diameter of .0135″, up to No. 1 with a diameter of .2280″. The series continues with lettered sizes from *A* up to *Z*. An *A* drill has a diameter of .2340″ and *Z*, a diameter of .4130″. Drill sizes given in fractional parts of an inch are available as small as $\frac{1}{64}$″ in diameter to $3\frac{1}{2}$″ or even larger on request. Drill sizes designated in fractions of an inch increase in size by $\frac{1}{64}$″ up to 3″, after which stock drills increase by $\frac{1}{32}$″ or $\frac{1}{16}$″. Drills are also available in fractional parts of a millimeter. The decimal equivalents for letter, number, and fractional sizes of twist drills are listed in Table 47, appendix.

Grinding Drills

Most of the difficulties encountered in drilling may be attributed to improper grinding. When grinding, three factors are important: (1) correct *lip clearance* as at *A*, Fig. 8-27; (2) correct *lip angle* as at *B*; (3) correct *point location* with respect to the center of the drill, as at *C*. Correct lip clearance for standard general-purpose drills used for drilling most steels is 8° to 12°. This means that the heel of the lip should be ground away that much. Lip clearance permits the cutting edge of the lip to engage the work.

A drill with no lip clearance will not cut. Note in Fig. 8-28 that the cutting lip and the heel are at the same level horizontally. Thus this drill cannot possibly cut. It will just go around and around, thereby causing excess heat which will damage the drill. A drill with proper lip clearance is shown in Fig. 8-27. Note that the cutting lip at *A* is above the level of the heel, thus providing for a proper clearance angle of from 8° to 12°.

The correct lip angle for general-purpose drills used for drilling most machine steels, and many other metals, is 59° to a line through the center axis of the drill, *B*, Fig. 8-27. Thus the total included angle of the drill point is 118°. To check the lip angle, use a *drill point gage*, Fig. 8-29. An angle of 59° is recommended because it has been found that drills ground at that angle cut more rapidly and with less exertion of power than when ground at any other angle. The point of a drill should have an angle of 120° to 135° and be centered exactly in line with the center of the drill, *C*, Fig. 8-27.

When grinding drills for drilling manganese steel, the lip angle should be 75°; total point angle of 150°. This material is very hard and tough; consequently, the shorter lip secured when ground at the flatter angle takes less power to operate and does not cause quite so great a strain on the drill.

When grinding drills for use in drilling softer materials such as bakelite, hard rubber, molded plastics, fiber, and wood, the lip angle should be ground to an angle of 45°, a total angle of 90°. More information concerning drill grinding and the procedures used in grinding drills is included in Unit 43.

A drill with a standard 118° point is used for drilling brass and bronze. However, the drill point should be faced as shown in Fig. 8-30. The front of the cutting lip is ground parallel to the axis of the drill, thus producing a neutral *rake* or helix angle at the cutting edge. This type of point will prevent the drill from *digging in* and breaking. This procedure also is recommended for drilling very hard steel, because it reduces the angle of the cutting edge of the drill. This increases the strength of the cutting edge, thus preventing chipping.

Spiral-Point Drill

A spiral point, as shown in Fig. 8-31, may be ground on a standard twist drill with a drill-

grinding machine of special design. The spiral-point drill offers many operating advantages not available with the conventional chisel-point drill.

With the conventional drill, a center punch mark is required to start the drill. Without the punch mark, the drill has a tendency to *walk*

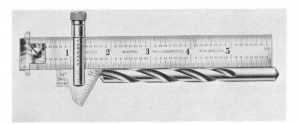

Fig. 8-29. Drill Point Gage (L.S. Starrett)

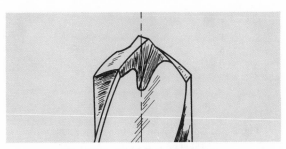

Fig. 8-30. 118° Point for Brass

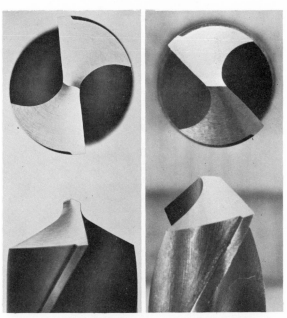

Fig. 8-31. Comparison of Spiral-Point Drill (Left) and Chisel-Point Drill (Right) (Cincinnati Lathe & Tool)

189

to one side or another, thus drilling a slanted hole or a hole in the wrong location. The spiral-point drill has a sharp point on the end, rather than a wide chisel point, Fig. 8-31. This eliminates the need for center punching or center-drilling to start the drill accurately.

With the conventional chisel-point drill, jigs and drill bushings normally are required to start and guide the drill most accurately for production setups. In most instances, the spiral-point drill will start accurately and drill a true hole without jigs and fixtures.

Most *two-lipped* drills produce holes several thousandths of an inch oversize, depending on the material being drilled, the accuracy of the

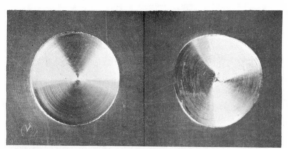

Fig. 8-32. Comparison of Hole Roundness with Spiral-Point Drill (Left) and Chisel-Point Drill (Right)
(Cincinnati Lathe & Tool)

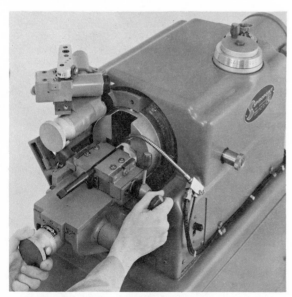

Fig. 8-33. Spiral Point Being Ground by a Special Spiral-Point Drill-Grinding Machine
(Cincinnati Lathe & Tool)

ground point, the rigidness of the setup, and whether or not fixtures with bushings are used to guide the drill. With the use of spiral-point drills, the average range of *hole oversize* is reduced by more than 50 percent.

Spiral-point drills also produce holes which are more accurate in roundness. See Fig. 8-32. Where accurate size and shape are required for holes drilled with chisel-point drills, it is common practice to drill the hole slightly undersize, followed by reaming or boring. In many instances, spiral-point drills hold size and shape sufficiently to eliminate the need for reaming and boring.

The use of the spiral-point drill is particularly desirable on numerically controlled drilling machines, Fig. 8-19. The spiral points generally eliminate the need for hole-spotting operations. They also largely eliminate the need for drilling fixtures.

The spiral point is ground on a conventional twist drill with a drill-grinding machine designed especially for this purpose, Fig. 8-33. Directions for grinding spiral points on drills are supplied by the manufacturer of this drill-grinding machine. These directions should be followed carefully. Once the proper settings are made for the diameter of the drill and for the clearance angle, the grinder will produce the spiral point automatically.

Using Drills

For best results, a drill should be used at the correct speed and feed. The speed of a drill refers to the rate at which it travels at the circumference. This is called peripheral or outside speed and is given in terms of *surface feet* traveled per minute. The feed is the rate at which the drill advances into the work per revolution, measured in thousandths of an inch or fractions of a millimeter. For correct speeds and feeds, see Unit 42.

Types of Drills

Numerous styles and types of drills are used on standard drill presses and on other machine tools such as lathes, jig borers, screw machines, and special production machines. Each type of drill is designed for certain applications. Those types of drills used most in schools, maintenance shops and tool and die shops are the *straight-shank drill* and the *taper-shank drill*, Fig. 8-23. These are general-purpose two-flute drills which produce good results in drilling most ordinary metals.

Several other less-common types of drills (illustrated in Fig. 8-34) include:

A. *Drills with ½″ shank* are designed for use either in portable electric drills or in drill chucks on smaller drill presses. Care should be exercised in drilling over ¾″ diameter, since the shanks may not be strong enough for heavy feeds on tough materials. A pilot hole should be drilled first.

B. *Straight-shank drills with carbide tips* are recommended for high-production drilling of cast iron, cast steel, and nonferrous materials. They are not recommended for drilling steel.

C. *Carbide-tipped die drills* of the straight-shank type are recommended for use in drilling hardened steel in the range from 48 to 65 Rockwell-C hardness. Holes may be drilled without annealing the metal. A steady hand feed with a good flow of cutting fluid should be used at a cutting speed from 75 to 100 rpm.

D. *Three-fluted core drills* are used for enlarging cored holes or previously punched or drilled holes. Because of their wide use in drilling cored holes in castings, they are known as *core drills*. This type of core drill will enlarge holes of approximately 60 percent of the drill diameter. The advantages of a multi-flute drill include increased rate of metal removal, increased accuracy in hole size and location, and improved finish.

E. *Four-fluted core drills* are used for essentially the same purposes for which three-fluted core drills are used. The three-fluted drill has more chip-clearing ability. However, many users prefer the four-fluted type because they find it easier to measure and resharpen.

F. *Sub-land drills* are special multicut drills which can drill several diameters in one operation. Drilling operations of this type are called *step-drilling* operations. Many variations of step-drilling operations are possible with multicut drills, Fig. 8-35.

The sub-land drill has two distinct lands which run nearly the entire length of the drill. When the cutting edges of the large diameter are resharpened, it is not necessary to touch the margins of the small diameter. Sub-land drills are available in more than two diameters. They also are available with four flutes.

G. *Oil hole drills* are used on high-production screw machines. Oil is forced through the machine spindle and through the oil holes to the cutting edges. The oil not only serves as a lubricant and coolant, but it also tends to force the chips out of the drilled hole.

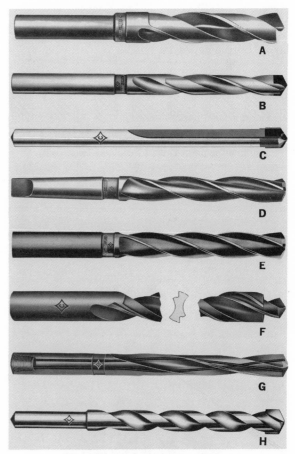

Fig. 8-34. Several Types of Drills
(Cleveland Twist Drill)
(A) Drill with ½″ shank; (B) Straight-shank drill with carbide tip; (C) Carbide-tipped die drill; (D) Three-fluted core drill; (E) Four-fluted core drill; (F) Sub-land drill; (G) Oil hole drill; (H) Carbide-tipped masonry drill.

H. *Carbide-tipped masonry drills*, as the name implies, are used for drilling all types of concrete or masonry. They may be used for drilling materials such as brick, slate, wallboard, plaster, and marble.

Boring Tools

When a drill of a particular dimension is not available, or when a very straight, accurate hole is desired, a boring tool may be used. See Fig. 8-36. In such cases, a hole large enough to permit entry of the boring tool is drilled with a standard drill.

The boring head in Fig. 8-37 is adjustable to within 0.0005″ or less. This type is available in a wide range of sizes. Boring capacity may range from ¾″ to 2″ offset from center (or a hole capacity of over 4″). Similar types of boring heads are available with a much larger boring capacity.

The boring head may be equipped with either a taper shank or a straight shank, depending on the type of machine in which it is used. A standard Morse taper shank is most frequently used on drill presses. Either the straight or the taper shank can be adapted to turret lathes, screw machines, milling machines, or jig boring machines, depending on the type of machine spindle. Either straight boring bars with insert type tool bits or solid boring bars of the type shown in Fig. 8-36 may be used.

Adjustable boring heads eliminate the need for a complete inventory of expensive, large-size drills in the school shop, small job shop, or maintenance shop. When used with care on rigid setups, extremely accurate holes may be machined with this type of tool.

Counterboring Tools

The counterboring tool, Fig. 8-38, is used to spot-face or counterbore for bolts and screws, to enlarge holes to receive the head of fillister-head screws, and for similar purposes. It has a pilot or guide on the point which frequently

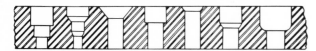

Fig. 8-35. Types of Single Operations Possible with Multiple-Diameter Drills (Cleveland Twist Drill)

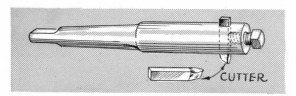

Fig. 8-36. Boring Tool

Fig. 8-37. Adjustable Boring Head and Boring Tools
(I.S.U. Photographic Ser.)

Fig. 8-38. Counterboring Tool

Fig. 8-39. Counterbore and Spot-Facing Tools
(Cleveland Twist Drill)
(Above) High-speed steel; (Below) Carbide-tipped.

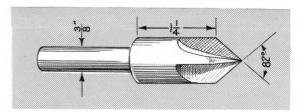

Fig. 8-40. 82° Countersink

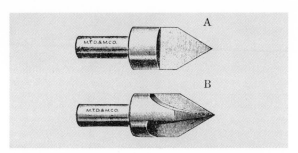

Fig. 8-41. 60° Countersink (South Bend Lathe)

Fig. 8-42. Combined Drill and Countersinks — (Above) Plain; (Below) Bell (Cleveland Twist Drill)

is interchangeable. Ordinarily, the pilot has a diameter about 0.002″ smaller than that of the drilled hole.

Pilots of various diameters, but with a shank size to fit the counterbore, may be used with a given counterboring tool. Counterboring tools should be run at lower cutting speeds than a drill of corresponding diameter. A cutting fluid should be used freely.

Counterboring tools are available in many sizes. They also are available in high-speed steel (above, Fig. 8-39) and with carbide insert teeth (below, Fig. 8-39). The former type is designed for counterboring steel, while the latter is recommended for use with cast iron.

Countersinks

A countersink with an included angle of 82° (Fig. 8-40) is used to enlarge the end of a hole in conical form to receive a flat-head machine screw. A and B, Fig. 8-41, illustrate two types of countersinks used for drilling center holes in stock which is to be turned while being held between centers. The inclusive angle at the point of these tools is 60°. The 82° countersink never should be used for countersinking centers, nor the 60° for countersinking for screw heads.

The combination drill and countersinks shown in Fig. 8-42 also are used for drilling and countersinking centers in stock to be held in a lathe. These tools drill and countersink in one operation. The bell drill and countersink (below, Fig. 8-42) produces a hole which has a secondary bevel near the surface. This type of hole is desirable because it prevents the edges of the center holes from becoming marred or nicked when parts are handled frequently for a number of machining operations.

Reamers

41

Reaming is an operation performed to enlarge and finish a drilled hole to exact dimension and smoothness, Fig. 8-2. The cutting tool used for reaming is called a *reamer*. Drilled holes usually have a rough finish and are considered to be inaccurate in size and roundness. Although, as previously mentioned, drilled holes generally are several thousandths of an inch oversize, they usually are satisfactory for bolts and screws. However, where accurately sized holes with a smooth finish are required for use with bushings or bearings, the holes often are reamed, either by hand or by machine.

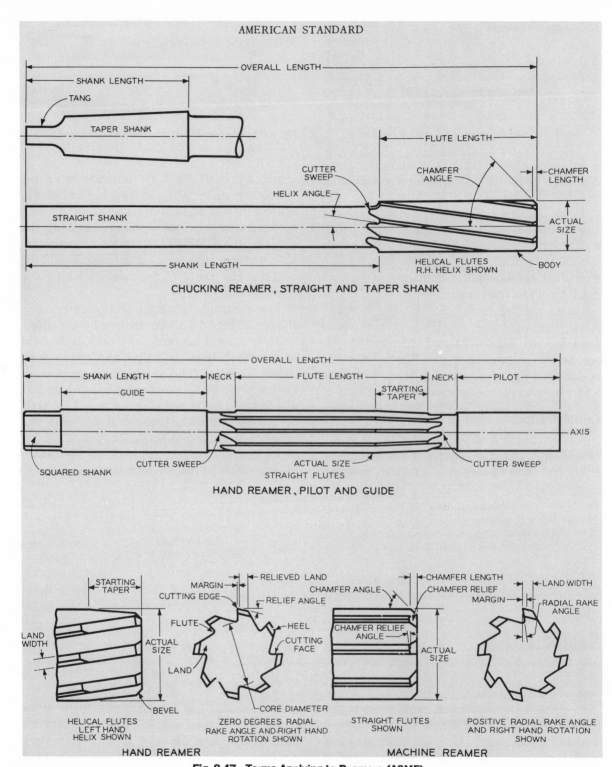

AMERICAN STANDARD

CHUCKING REAMER, STRAIGHT AND TAPER SHANK

HAND REAMER, PILOT AND GUIDE

HAND REAMER

MACHINE REAMER

Fig. 8-47. Terms Applying to Reamers (ASME)

Extracted from American Standard Reamers, ASA B94.2 — 1964, with the permission of the publisher, The American Society of Mechanical Engineers, United Engineering Center, 345 East 47th Street, New York, N.Y. 10017.

Allowance for Reaming

The usual procedure for producing a reamed hole is to produce an *undersize* hole first, followed by reaming. The undersize hole provides a material allowance for reaming. The hole for reaming may be produced by one of three ways — drilling, boring, or both drilling and boring. The method employed depends on the material allowance which is to be left for reaming. Very little material allowance is made for hand reaming, while more material may be allowed for machine reaming. Irregardless, the material allowance for reaming is relatively small in comparison with that left for boring or drilling operations.

Holes for machine reaming should be produced undersize an amount which will provide the following maximum material allowances:

¼″ holes	0.010″
½″ holes	0.016″
1″ holes	0.020″
2″ holes	0.032″
3″ holes	0.047″

For *one-step* machine reaming, it is common practice to drill holes ¹⁄₆₄″ (0.0156″) undersize, followed by reaming with a fluted reamer. Reamers designed for machine reaming generally retain their sharpness longer when the cut is not too light.

Where extreme accuracy is required, hand reaming often is recommended. *Hand reaming* is done with reamers specifically designed for such operations. Light cuts which remove from 0.002″ to 0.005″ are made. A cut of 0.002″ usually is recommended. *Never leave over 0.005″ of material for hand reaming.* The usual procedure for hand reaming is to drill and bore (or drill and rough ream) the hole to 0.002″ undersize and then ream the hole by hand with a hand reamer. Reamers used for rough reaming to undersize dimensions are intentionally designed or ground undersize several thousandths of an inch for this purpose.

An alternate *two-step* machine reaming procedure often is used to produce reamed holes to closer tolerances and with a better finish than those resulting from the one-step method. The procedure involves rough reaming the hole to about 0.002″ to 0.005″ undersize, followed by finish reaming with a fluted machine reamer.

General Classification of Reamers

Reamers are multiple-cutting-edge tools which may be made of carbon tool steel or high-speed steel. They may or may not have carbide-tipped cutting edges. They are available in a wide variety of types and sizes.

Reamers may be classified into two general groups — hand reamers (Fig. 8-49, page 197) and chucking (machine) reamers (Fig. 8-48, page 196). *Hand reamers* are designed for hand operation with light cuts. They are equipped with a square shank which is turned with a tap wrench, Fig. 4-17. Usually they are made of either carbon tool steel or high-speed steel.

Chucking reamers, or machine reamers, are designed for machine reaming operations on drill presses, engine lathes, turret lathes, vertical milling machines, and other special production machines. They usually are made of high-speed steel, or they have cemented carbide cutting tips.

Chucking reamers are available with either standard Morse taper shanks or straight shanks, depending on the type of machine on which they are used, Fig. 8-47. They include both rose reamers and fluted reamers, which will be discussed shortly.

Cutting Action: *Chucking reamers* have a bevel of from 40° to 50° (usually 45°) on the cutting end, Fig. 8-47. They cut differently than hand reamers. Chucking reamers are *end-cutting* reamers which cut on the beveled end in the same manner as a drill cuts as it enters a hole. When the reamer becomes dull, it is resharpened on the 45° beveled end only. It cannot be sharpened by hand grinding. It must be sharpened on a tool-and-cutter grinder so that all cutting edges are exactly even.

Hand reamers, on the other hand, cut on the *periphery* of the reamer. The flutes are ground straight for the whole length, except near the cutting end which is ground with a *starting taper,* Fig. 8-47. This taper, which is about equal in length to the diameter of the reamer, permits the reamer to enter the hole easily. Thus, hand reamers are essentially scraping tools. They cut with a scraping action, and

195

nearly all cutting takes place along the starting taper at the cutting end of the reamer. Hence, the hand reamer is designed for removing only very small amounts of material. When the hand reamer becomes dull, it must be resharpened on the starting taper portion only. Like the chucking reamer, it must be sharpened on a tool-and-cutter grinder. *Never attempt to sharpen a reamer by off-hand grinding on a bench-model tool grinder.*

Types of Chucking Reamers

Rose Reamers: Rose reamers are rough chucking (machine) reamers intentionally designed to rough-ream cored or drilled holes 0.003″ to 0.010″ undersize. Therefore, the basic diameter of a rose reamer always is ground undersize the desired amount. It is designed for two-step reaming operations. After rough reaming, the hole is finish-reamed to final size with a fluted reamer.

Rose reamers have a 45° end-cutting angle which does all of the cutting and which is capable of cutting rapidly. The reamer also has

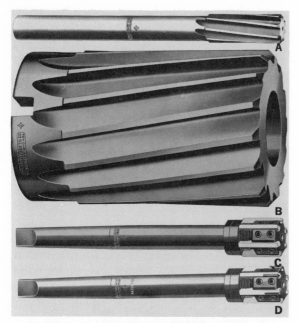

Fig. 8-48. Types of Chucking (Machine) Reamers
(Cleveland Twist Drill)
(A) Straight-shank; (B) Helical-fluted shell;
(C) Adjustable; (D) Carbide-tipped adjustable.

a *back taper, i.e.,* it is tapered a maximum of 0.001″ per inch of length for the length of the flutes. The back taper prevents binding in deep holes with heavy cuts. The outside diameter of the reamer is ground cylindrically, thus leaving a wide circular margin. There are no cutting edges along the flutes, which merely provide space for cutting fluid and chip ejection.

Fluted Reamers: As implied by their name, fluted chucking (machine) reamers generally have more flutes than rose reamers and are designed for reaming holes to finish size. They may be used for one-step reaming operations, or they may be used after a rose reamer in two-step operations.

The cutting action takes place at the 45° beveled cutting end. A narrow circular margin, from 0.005″ to 0.020″ in width, runs along the entire length of the flute. The lands are backed off along the length of the flute to provide a body clearance angle. The reamer is not provided with significant back taper.

Several common types of chucking reamers are shown in Fig. 8-48. That at *A* is a *helical fluted* chucking reamer with a straight shank. This type also is available with a taper shank. These reamers are designed for reaming materials which ordinarily are considered difficult to ream. The helical (spiral) flutes provide a free-cutting action which aids in producing smooth, accurate holes.

Straight fluted chucking reamers are designed for use with materials which possess average reaming properties. They are available with either straight or taper shanks.

Shell reamers are available with helical flutes (as shown at *B* in Fig. 8-48) or with straight flutes. They also are available in the rose type or the fluted type. Except for the presence of the hole, shell reamers do not differ significantly from ordinary solid chucking reamers, and they are used for the same purposes. Shell reamers are designed with the hole for economy reasons. The hole is tapered to fit snugly and accurately on a special arbor, which is available with either a straight or taper shank. Several sizes of shell reamers may fit the same arbor. When the reamer is worn out, it may be discarded, and a new reamer may be used on the old arbor.

Adjustable chucking reamers, as shown at *C* and *D* in Fig. 8-48, are available with either high-speed steel blades or carbide-tipped high-speed steel blades. They also are available with either straight or taper shanks. These reamers are easily adjusted for size within a range of $\frac{1}{32}''$ diameter. As the blades become dull, they can be expanded and reground several times. When worn out, the blades may be replaced.

As well as being more abrasion resistant, carbide-tipped reamers can withstand higher temperatures and higher cutting speeds than high-speed steel reamers. They are particularly well adapted for reaming castings, both ferrous and nonferrous, which have sand or scale inclusions. For more information concerning high-speed steel and cemented carbides, see Unit 140 concerning cutting tool materials.

Carbide-tipped adjustable chucking reamers of the shell type also are available. They may be used with either straight or tapered shell reamer arbors.

Special machine reamers of many types and sizes are available for special purposes. An important type of special reamer is the *combination drill and reamer*, which has a drill at the end and a reamer farther back. This design makes it possible to drill and ream a hole in one operation. Machine reamers of this type are available with straight or taper shanks.

Types of Hand Reamers

Numerous hand reamers are available for hand reaming operations. A tap wrench is placed over the square shank for hand reaming. Several basic types of hand reamers, including those shown in Fig. 8-49, are described below.

Straight-fluted hand reamers of the solid type are shown at *A*, Fig. 8-49. They are available in either carbon tool steel or high-speed steel. The cutting end is ground with a starting taper for easy entry into a hole. This type reamer is recommended for general-purpose reaming of holes to finish size. It produces accurate holes with a smooth finish.

Helical-fluted hand reamers are solid reamers similar to the straight-fluted hand reamer. The only difference is the helical or spiral flute, which is left-handed. This type reamer is rec-

ommended for reaming holes with interruptions or keyways. The helical flute produces a smooth cutting action with minimum chatter.

Expansion hand reamers may be of the straight-flute type (as shown at *B*, Fig. 8-49) or the helical-fluted type (as at *C*). Expansion reamers may be expanded slightly in size to produce an oversize hole with a desirable fit. The amount of expansion possible depends on the diameter of the reamer. It may vary from about 0.006″ for a $\frac{1}{4}''$ reamer to about 0.012″ for a $1\frac{1}{2}''$ reamer. These reamers are provided with an adjusting screw for expansion only. An undersize pilot is provided on the end to aid in alignment. The left-hand helical-fluted, right-hand cut expansion reamer at *C*, Fig. 8-49, is recommended for reaming holes with interruptions or keyways. Except for the helix, it is similar to the straight-fluted expansion hand reamer.

Adjustable hand reamers, *D*, Fig. 8-49, may be adjusted infinitely for any size, above or below basic size, within the range of the reamer. These reamers are available in standard sizes which are capable of reaming holes of any size from $\frac{1}{4}''$ to about $3\frac{11}{32}''$ diameter. Each reamer may be expanded to the smallest size of the next-size reamer.

Blades are available in carbon steel or high-speed steel. They slide in accurately tapered slots and may be adjusted by loosening one nut

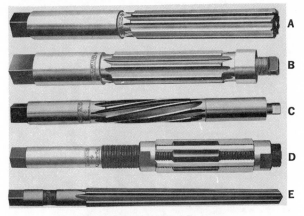

Fig. 8-49. Types of Hand Reamers
(Cleveland Twist Drill)
(A) Straight-fluted; (B) Expansion, straight flute;
(C) Expansion, LH helical flute; (D) Adjustable;
(E) Taper pin.

197

and tightening the other, thus moving the blades in the slots. When the blades become dull, new blades may be replaced in the shop without regrinding them. This is probably the most efficient type of reamer for school shops, maintenance shops, and many small machine shops.

Taper pin reamers, E, Fig. 8-49, have a taper of $\frac{1}{4}''$ per foot. They are used for reaming holes for standard taper pins. Best results are achieved when the drilled hole is slightly smaller than the small end of the taper pin. These reamers are available with straight- or left-hand helical flutes, and in carbon steel or high-speed steel. They are available in a complete range of sizes for all standard taper pins.

Taper socket reamers of the solid type are available for reaming standard Morse or Brown and Sharpe taper holes. Square-shank hand reamers are intended for maintenance of taper holes in machine tools and accessories. Taper-shank roughing reamers and finishing reamers are designed for production use in producing standard taper holes.

Burring reamers, Fig. 8-50, are used for removing burrs from cut pipe and conduit. They also may be used for enlarging holes in thin materials. The straight-shank reamer may be used in drill presses or portable electric drills. The bit-stock shank is used with a hand brace.

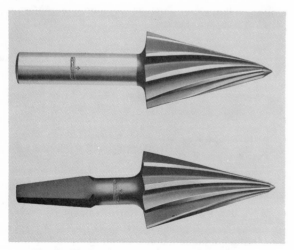

Fig. 8-50. Burring Reamers with Spiral Flutes
(Cleveland Twist Drill)

Reaming Practices

Reaming speeds may vary considerably, depending on the type of material to be reamed, the type of machine used, the type of finish required, and the accuracy required. As a general rule, machine reaming is done at about two-thirds the speed used for drilling the same material. (Drilling speeds are shown for various materials in Table 6.)

Reaming feeds are much higher than for drilling, usually two to three times higher. If the feed is too low, excessive reamer wear will result. If the feed is too fast, the hole will be inaccurate. The feed should be sufficient to cause each flute to cut a chip rather than burnish or rub the material. One generally should use the highest feed possible while still producing an accurate hole with the required finish. A good starting point is to use a feed from 0.0015″ to 0.004″ per flute per revolution. Then the feed can be adjusted as required for desired results.

Reamer alignment is one of the most important factors in reaming accuracy. When reaming, the spindle, reamer, reamer bushing, and the hole to be reamed should be in perfect alignment. Any variation in these factors detracts from reaming accuracy and results in excessive reamer wear. The effects of reamer

Table 6 Cutting Speeds (sfpm) for High-Speed Drills	
Low-carbon mild steel (.05-.30% carbon)	80-110
Medium-carbon steel (.30-.60%, annealed)	70- 80
High-carbon tool steel (.60-1.70%, annealed)	50- 60
Steel forgings	50- 60
Alloy steel	50- 70
Stainless steel	30- 40
Cast iron, soft gray	100-150
Cast iron, hard-chilled	70-100
Cast iron, malleable	80- 90
Ordinary brass and bronze	200-300
High-tensile bronze	70-150
Monel metal	40- 50
Aluminum and its alloys	200-300
Magnesium and its alloys	250-400
Slate, marble, and stone	15- 25
Bakelite and similar plastics	100-150
Wood	300-400

Carbon-steel drills should be run at speeds of from 40% to 50% of those given above.

(Courtesy The Cleveland Twist Drill Co.)

misalignment may be reduced through the use of a *floating* reamer holder. When possible, holes should be drilled and reamed in the same setup, with the work and the spindle in the same location.

Chatter can affect the accuracy and finish of reamed holes. The following are possible causes for chatter:

1. Excessive speed.
2. Too light a feed.
3. Setup not rigid.
4. Spindle too loose.
5. Excessive clearance on reamer.
6. Excessive looseness in floating holder.

Chatter can be prevented or reduced by removing the cause.

Cutting fluids aid in producing good results when reaming. Mineral-lard oils and sulfurized oils are desirable for most reaming applications. See Table 43, appendix, for specific cutting fluid recommendations. Grey cast iron generally should be reamed dry, or the reamer may be cooled with a jet of compressed air.

Care of reamers affects the accuracy of reamed holes. Reamers should be handled without bumping, nicking, or otherwise abusing them. They should be stored in containers or holders which will prevent nicks along the cutting edges or ends.

Hints for Reaming

1. See that the reamer is free from nicks.
2. Utilize a setup and procedures which will prevent the causes of chatter.
3. Never reverse a reamer or the workpiece when reaming. To do so will cause chips to damage the margins of the reamer, thus causing an inaccurate hole with a poor-quality finish.
4. Avoid starting a reamer on a slanted or uneven surface. To do so will cause the reamer to drift out of alignment.
5. Follow the procedure outlined in Unit 46 when reaming.

UNIT

Cutting Speeds and Feeds for Drilling

42

The cutting speed and the feed at which metal should be drilled vary for different metals. The feed also varies according to the size of the drill. The terms *cutting speed* and *rpm* (revolutions per minute) are interrelated.

Cutting Speed

Cutting speed for drilling is the circumferential speed of the drill, and it is expressed in terms of *surface feet per minute* (sfpm). It is the distance that a point on the circumference of the drill will travel in one minute. (Or it may be visualized as the distance in feet at which the drill would roll on the floor in one minute.) If the cutting speed for drilling is too

high, the drill will become overheated and will dull easily. If the cutting speed is too low, the production rate will be low and the drill may break easily.

Cutting speed has a different meaning than *revolutions* per minute (rpm). These terms should not be confused. A ¼″ diameter drill turning at 1222 rpm has a cutting speed of 80 sfpm. A ½″ diameter drill at 80 sfpm would turn at only 611 rpm. Consequently, the drill press spindle must be set at the proper rpm in order to obtain the correct cutting speed in surface feet per minute.

There is no one correct speed for drilling all materials. It is common practice to select an *average* cutting speed for each type of material. The cutting speed selected may then be increased or decreased according to conditions which affect the particular job setup and the material drilled. The following factors affect the cutting speed selected for drilling operations:

1. The kind of material being drilled. Softer materials generally are drilled at higher cutting speeds than harder materials. See Table 6.
2. The kind of cutting tool material. Carbon-steel drills are used with cutting speeds which are about one-half those used with high-speed steel drills. Tungsten-carbide drills generally are run at higher speeds and lighter feeds than high-speed steel drills.
3. Whether or not a cutting fluid is used.
4. The size and the type of drilling machine used, and the rigidness of the work setup.
5. The quality of finish desired in the hole.

The following are general guides covering the average cutting speed in surface feet per minute for drilling the more common metals with high-speed steel drills:

Low-carbon steel	100 sfpm
Medium-carbon steel, annealed	80 sfpm
High-carbon tool steel, annealed	50 sfpm
Stainless steel	40 sfpm
Soft gray cast iron	100 sfpm
Aluminum and its alloys	250 sfpm
Ordinary brass and bronze	250 sfpm

For carbon-steel drills, these speeds should be reduced by about 50 percent. For more complete listing of cutting speed ranges for various materials, see Table 6.

Calculating rpm: The rpm for a given cutting speed may be calculated with the following formula:

$$rpm = \frac{CS' \times 12}{D'' \times \pi}$$

Where: CS = Cutting speed in surface feet per minute

D = Diameter in inches for drills or other cylindrical cutting tools

π = Pi or 3.1416 (a constant)

rpm = Revolutions per minute

Example: Calculate the rpm for a ¼″ diameter drill which is to drill at a cutting speed of 100 sfpm.

$$rpm = \frac{100 \times 12}{0.250 \times 3.1416}$$

$$rpm = \frac{1200}{.7854}$$

$$rpm = 1528$$

The figure 3 may be substituted for 3.1416 when calculating the *approximate* rpm. This procedure is satisfactory in most applications, giving 1600 rpm in the above example without involved calculations.

Calculating Cutting Speed: The cutting speed for drilling may be calculated when the diameter of the drill and the rpm are known, by using the following formula:

$$CS = \frac{D'' \times \pi \times rpm}{12}$$

Example: Calculate the cutting speed for drilling with a ⅜″ diameter drill at 815 rpm:

$$CS = \frac{0.375 \times 3.1416 \times 815}{12}$$

$$CS = \frac{960}{12}$$

$$CS = 80 \text{ sfpm}$$

The figure 3 may be substituted for 3.1416 when calculating the *approximate* cutting speed. This procedure is satisfactory in most applications, giving a little over 76 sfpm in this example.

When the diameter of the drill and the cutting speed are known, the rpm may be determined simply by referring to a *table of cutting speeds* (Table 41, appendix). Tables of this type very often are posted in machine shops. However, the competent machinist or machine operator also should be able to calculate rpm and cutting speeds when necessary.

The above two formulas also can be used to calculate the cutting speed and rpm for all types of cylindrical cutting tools, including taps, reamers, counterboring tools, and milling cutters. In addition, they may be used to calculate cutting speeds for turning or boring on a lathe; however, in this case, the *diameter* (*D*) refers to the diameter of the workpiece being turned (or the diameter of the hole being bored).

Feeds

The *feed* for a drill refers to the rate at which the drill advances into the work in one revolution. Hence, with a feed setting of 0.004″, the drill advances into the work 0.004″ deeper each revolution.

Feeds are governed by the size of the drill and the material to be drilled. The general rule when drilling mild steel is to use a feed of .001″ to .002″ per revolution for drills smaller than ⅛″; .002″ to .004″ for drills ⅛″ to ¼″; .004″ to .007″ for drills ¼″ to ½″; .007″ to .015″ for drills ½″ to 1″; .015″ to .025″ for drills larger than 1″. Alloy and hard steels should be drilled with a lighter feed than given, while cast iron, brass, and aluminum usually may be drilled with a heavier feed.

Extreme speed or feed will cause drills to chip or break at the cutting edges or to split the web; similar damage also may be a result of improper grinding. Rapid wearing at the outer corners of the cutting edges usually is an indication of too much speed.

Cutting Fluids

To maintain the feeds and speeds recommended, it is necessary to use a good cutting fluid. The following are recommended for drilling operations:

Hard refractory steel — turpentine, kerosene, emulsifiable oils (soluble oils), mineral-lard oils.

Soft steel and wrought iron — emulsifiable oils (soluble oils), sulfurized oils, mineral-lard oils.

Malleable iron — emulsifiable oils, mineral-lard oils.

Brass and bronze — emulsifiable oils, or dry.

Aluminum and aluminum alloys — mineral oils, emulsifiable oils, mineral-lard oils.

Grey cast iron — Dry or with a jet of compressed air.

The selection of cutting fluid also varies with the *machinability* of the material and the *severity* of the operation being performed. For more specific recommendations concerning these factors in relation to cutting fluid selection, see Table 43, appendix.

How To Grind Metalworking Drills

Drills are used for producing round holes in metal. They are effective tools for this purpose when properly sharpened. Three things are important when grinding a drill: (1) *lip clearance*, (2) *length* and *angle* of the *cutting lip*, and (3) *location* of the *point*.

Lip clearance is produced by grinding away the surface back of the cutting edge or lip, Fig. 8-52. If lip clearance were not given the drill, it would be impossible for it to enter the metal. Correct lip clearance for ordinary work is 12° (*A*, Fig. 8-27). Clearance greater than this weakens the cutting edge.

By experimentation and experience, it has been found that the most effective lip angle for metalworking drills is 59° with the axis (*B*, Fig. 8-27). The length of the lips must be equal, as must the lip angle. Otherwise, one lip will do most of the cutting, and an oversize hole will be produced, Fig. 8-53. Furthermore, the point will be off-center, which may cause the drill to chip or break.

DRILLS:

To produce accurate work and to avoid undue strain on the spindle and bearings of the drill press, locate the point in the center of the drill. Fig. 8-53 shows the effect of the point being located off-center, even though the lip angles are equal. To insure correct length of lip and correct lip angle, test with a drill point gage, Fig. 8-29.

Some grinders are equipped with a drill-grinding attachment, Fig. 8-54. The V-block holder on this device centers the drill and holds it in place. A special lip stop and micrometer feed insure accurate grinding of both lips.

Procedure

1. *Put on goggles.* This should be done even when the wheel is protected with a shield.
2. Examine the grinding wheel to make sure the face is straight and true. If it is not, dress it with a wheel dresser.
3. If a coolant is used, see that there is sufficient liquid in the reservoir; then start the machine.
4. Examine the angle at which the drill was last ground. Check with a drill point gage.
5. Assuming the angle is correct, hold the cutting edge or lip of the drill parallel with the face of the wheel and perpendicular to the side, Fig. 8-55. Then bring the drill lightly into contact with the wheel; at the same time, draw it slowly upward with a slight rotary motion or stroke. Repeat the operation until the cutting edge is sharp

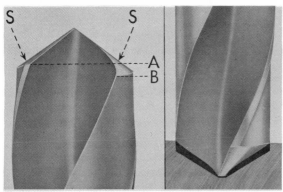

Fig. 8-52. Proper Lip Clearance (Cleveland Twist Drill) Note how much lower heel line B is than cutting line A.

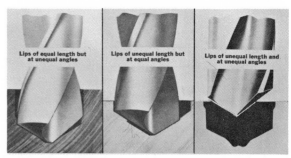

Fig. 8-53. Incorrect Points (Cleveland Twist Drill)

Lips of equal length but at unequal angles

Lips of unequal length but at equal angles

Lips of unequal length and at unequal angles

Fig. 8-54. Drill-Grinding Attachment (Atlas Press)

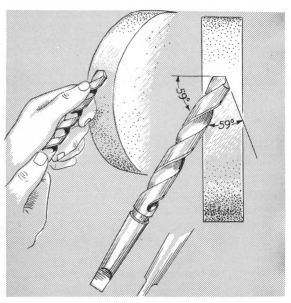

Fig. 8-55. Grinding a Drill

and the correct lip clearance is achieved. The rotary motion gives the bit the required clearance.

Be sure to hold the drill at the correct angle throughout the operation and hold it lightly against the face of the wheel. Otherwise, there is danger of drawing the temper by overheating, thus damaging the cutting qualities of the drill.

6. Give the drill a half turn, and grind the other cutting edge in a similar manner. Maintain the same angle on both edges.
7. Test the drill with a bit gage. Be sure that both cutting edges are the same length and are ground at the correct angle. Correct if necessary.

How To Drill a Hole

Holes may be drilled in most metals with an ordinary twist drill, providing it is correctly ground and a suitable cutting fluid is applied during the operation. For selection of the proper cutting fluid for various materials, see Table 43, appendix. Cast iron, brass, copper, lead or other soft metals require no lubricant when drilling.

Procedure for Drilling Work Clamped Flat on the Table

1. Locate the position of the hole with short, light lines drawn at right angles (A, Fig. 8-57).

2. With a center punch, make a distinct impression at the intersection of the lines (B, Fig. 8-57).

If extreme accuracy is desired, rub the surface of the piece with chalk or layout dye, mark the center with a prick punch, and then lay out the size of the hole with a pair of dividers, Fig. 8-58. With a prick

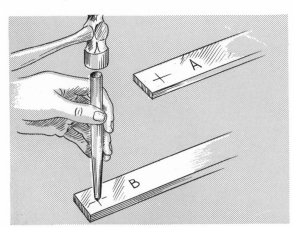

Fig. 8-57. Center Punching

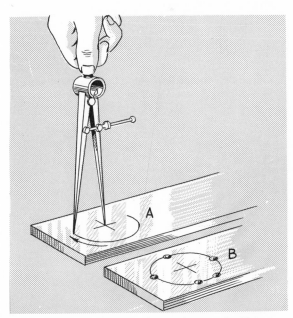

Fig. 8-58. Scribing the Circumference of a Hole

203

punch, make four or more marks along the circumference line, as shown in B, Fig. 8-58. These marks will enable the operator to see if the hole is being drilled at the position desired, even though the circumference line becomes erased. When a high degree of accuracy is required, a concentric circle $\frac{1}{32}''$ to $\frac{1}{16}''$ larger in diameter sometimes is drawn and punch marked, Fig. 8-59. The second circle serves as a check in case the drill should happen to lead off-center and eliminate some of the punch marks on the first concentric circle.

3. Examine the impression to see that the center is located at the intersection of the lines and is large enough to receive the point of the drill.

4. Select a drill of the size desired, insert it in the spindle or chuck, and fasten securely.

5. Determine the speed at which the drill should run to produce the best result (Table 6 or 41). Then adjust the drive so as to produce the rpm desired by changing the belt, speed differential, or variable-speed drive.

Caution: *With a variable-speed drive, the speed usually must be changed only while the machine is running.*

6. Place the workpiece on a block of wood on the drill press table. Round stock should be placed in a V-block, Fig. 8-60. Always make sure that the work is firmly supported so that there will be no spring when pressure is applied to the drill.

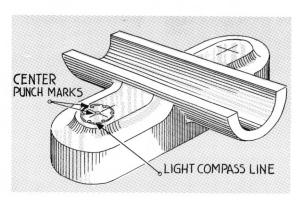

Fig. 8-59. **Second Concentric Circle Scribed and Punched**

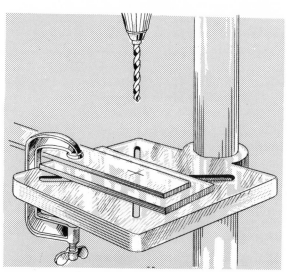

Fig. 8-61. **C-Clamp Used to Hold Work**

Fig. 8-60. **Round Stock Supported in a V-Block**

Fig. 8-62. **Vise Used to Hold Work**

7. Adjust the stock so that the punch mark is under the point of the drill.

8. Clamp or otherwise hold the work securely on the table, Fig. 8-61. A vise, such as shown in Fig. 8-62, is recommended, if available.

9. Start the machine, draw the drill down until the point is in contact with the work, and slowly advance the drill until a *distinct impression* has been made.

10. Raise the drill and examine the impression to be sure that the hole has been started at the position desired.

    If the impression is not in the center, as in *A*, Fig. 8-63, make a prick punch mark on the side of the impression toward which the hole is to be drawn, *B*, Fig. 8-63. The punch mark should be made far enough from the center of the impression to draw the drill over the amount desired, Fig. 8-64.

    If preferred or necessary, the center may be drawn over by cutting one or more small grooves in the waste stock on the side toward which the center is to be drawn, *D*, Fig. 8-63.

11. If needed, pour a few drops of oil or other suitable cutting fluid into the impression made by the drill.

12. Draw the drill down and feed it into the work slowly.

    If the machine is equipped with a power feed, engage the automatic feed. See Unit 42 for selection of the proper feed.

    Fig. 8-65 shows how the chip should appear when mild steel is drilled with a correctly sharpened drill.

13. As the drill advances, pour a little more oil on the revolving drill about half an inch above the work.

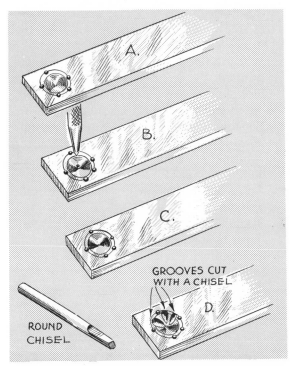

Fig. 8-63. Moving the Center of a Partially Drilled Hole

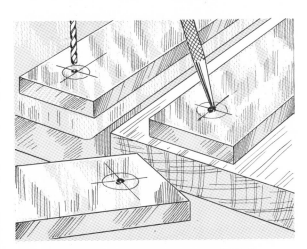

Fig. 8-64. Corrected Center Punch Mark

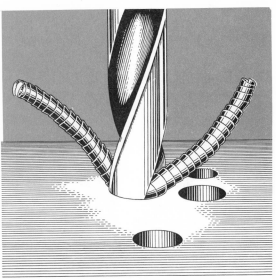

Fig. 8-65. Drilling Mild Steel

14. When hand feeding and the point of the drill breaks through the metal, decrease the pressure on the feed mechanism; then continue to feed forward slowly until the hole is completed.

CAUTION: *Be sure the stock is held securely throughout the operation, particularly when the point breaks through on the underside. Otherwise the piece is likely to spin around with the drill and damage the drill or the work, or injure the operator.*

When it is necessary to drill a hole to a certain depth, draw the feed lever down as far as it will go; adjust the table until the top of the work is just even with the point of the drill, and return the feed lever. Then raise the table an amount equal to the desired depth of the hole. When the machine is adjusted for depth, drill the hole in the usual manner. Some machines are equipped with a feed lever stop. In such cases, one may control the depth of the hole by setting the stop at the position desired.

15. When the operation is completed, stop the machine, and remove the clamp, work, and drill. Return them to the place where they are kept when not in use.

Procedure for Drilling Work Clamped in a V-Block

1. With a center punch, mark the position on the stock at which the hole is to be drilled.
2. Select a suitable sharp drill, and insert it in the spindle or chuck.
3. Place the stock in a V-block, and adjust until the center of the punch mark is exactly under the point of the drill.

   If necessary, test the accuracy of the setting by testing the center from both sides with a surface gage, as in Fig. 8-66, or by measuring with a rule and try square as indicated.
4. When the center has been located correctly under the point of the drill, clamp the piece in position on the table of the drill press with a strap clamp as in Fig. 8-67. Be sure the clamp is approximately parallel with the table.
5. Adjust the machine for the correct speed and feed, Unit 42.
6. Apply a suitable cutting fluid, Table 43, appendix.
7. Start the machine; then draw the drill down against the stock and continue feeding it forward until the hole is drilled to the depth desired. Use the automatic feed if the machine is so equipped.
8. When the operation is completed, stop the machine, and remove the clamp, stock, and drill. Return them to the place where kept when not in use.

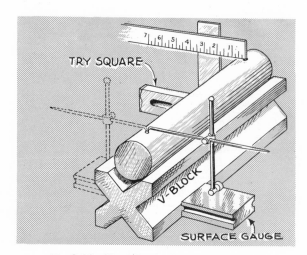

Fig. 8-66. Checking the Center Punch Mark

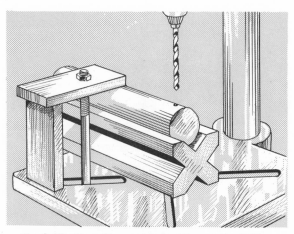

Fig. 8-67. Work Clamped in Position on the Table

Fig. 8-68. Work Held Against an Angle Plate

Procedure for Drilling Work Held Against an Angle Plate

1. Accurately locate the point at which the hole is to be drilled, and mark it distinctly with a center punch.

2. Secure a sharp drill of the size desired, and insert it securely in the spindle or chuck.

3. Bolt an angle plate on the table of the drill press in such position that when the work to be drilled is clamped against it, a hole may be drilled in the work at the position desired, Fig. 8-68.

4. Clamp the work securely to the angle plate.

5. With the hand feed, advance the drill until the point is exactly over the center of the punch mark.

6. If necessary, adjust the table or the work until the point of the drill is centered over the punch mark.

7. If a cutting fluid is necessary, pour a few drops into the impression made by the punch.

8. Start the machine, and draw the drill down against the work. Use the power

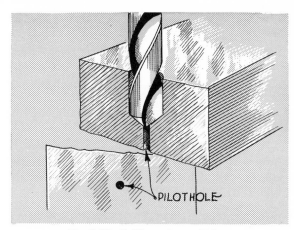

Fig. 8-69. Drilling a Large Hole

feed if the machine is so equipped. Continue advancing the drill until the hole is drilled the depth desired.

9. When the operation is completed, stop the machine, and remove the clamp, drill, and work. Return them to the place where kept when not in use.

Procedure for Drilling a Large Hole

1. Prepare the stock in the usual manner, and fasten it securely on the table of the drill press.

2. Select a drill of the size required; also select a small drill having a diameter comparable to the thickness of the web of the large drill.

3. Insert the small drill in the spindle or chuck.

4. Start the machine, and drill the pilot hole, Fig. 8-69.

5. Remove the small drill, and insert the large drill in the spindle.

6. Start the machine, and drill the hole as in Fig. 8-69.

207

How To Bore a Hole with a Drill Press

When it is necessary to produce a very straight hole, frequently it is accomplished by first drilling an undersize hole and then finishing with a boring tool. See Fig. 8-72. Boring also is resorted to when a drill of the size desired is not available. For ordinary boring, the hole is drilled from $\frac{1}{16}''$ to $\frac{1}{8}''$ undersize.

Procedure

1. Clamp the stock on the drill press, and in the usual manner, drill an undersize hole of the dimension desired.

    CAUTION: *Do not loosen the clamps or change the position of the stock on the*

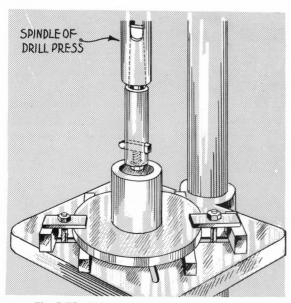

Fig. 8-72. Using a Boring Tool in a Drill Press

table of the drill press, except for correcting any error made in drilling.

2. Select a boring bar of suitable size, and insert it in the spindle of the drill press. Tap the protruding end of the boring bar with a lead hammer, thus seating it firmly in the socket or spindle.

3. Examine the cutter to make sure it is sharp. Grind it if necessary.

4. Adjust the cutter in the boring bar so that it will make a cut of the depth necessary to produce a hole of the size desired. For greater accuracy, a roughing cut should be made first, followed by a light finishing cut, 0.005'' to 0.010'' depth. Be sure the bit is fastened securely.

5. Set the machine at the speed recommended for drilling a hole of similar size, Table 6 or 41.

6. Start the machine, and feed the tool into the hole, Fig. 8-72.

7. When the tool has entered the stock to the point where a full cut is being made, stop the machine, and caliper or measure the diameter of the hole accurately.

8. If the hole is not being bored the diameter desired, make the necessary adjustment, and then continue boring until the job is completed. If the machine is equipped with a power feed, its use is recommended.

    CAUTION: *When using a light boring tool, be sure to take a light cut and feed.*

9. When the operation is completed, remove the clamps, work, and boring tool and return them to the place where kept when not in use.

How To Ream a Hole by Hand or with a Machine

A reamer is used when it is necessary to produce a hole in metal which is both accurate and smooth. A hole may be machine reamed or hand reamed (or both). A hand reamer is more commonly used in schools.

Procedure for Hand Reaming

1. Drill or bore a hole about .002″ undersize. Allow from .002″ to .005″ when the work is to be both machine and hand reamed.
2. Grip the piece to be reamed in a vise.
3. Select a reamer and a tap wrench of the sizes desired.

    CAUTION: *Before using a reamer, examine the cutting edges to make sure they are smooth. A burr on a cutting edge will ruin the work.*
4. Fit the wrench on the end of the reamer.
5. Insert the point of the reamer in the hole, Fig. 8-73. Then accurately align it with the axis of the hole, and slowly turn it to-

ward the right (clockwise). Continue advancing the reamer in this manner until the hole is reamed its full length.

Be sure to use a lubricant, preferably mineral-lard oil, when reaming steel.

When the hole has been drilled or bored in either a drill press or a lathe, the hole may be reamed with a hand reamer before the work is removed from the machine. If the work has been drilled or bored on *a drill press*, remove the drill and insert a lathe center in the spindle. Fit the wrench on the shank of the reamer; then place the point of the reamer in the hole. Draw the center in the spindle down into the center hole in the shank of the reamer, Fig. 8-74, and then start turning the reamer with the wrench. Continue turning the reamer and advancing the center until the reamer has been advanced into the work far

Fig. 8-73. Starting a Hand Reamer

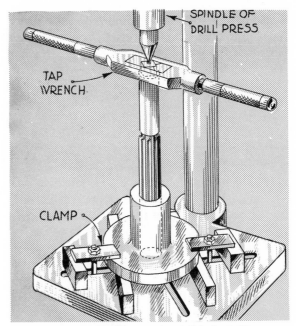

Fig. 8-74. Using the Drill Press Spindle to Keep Reamer Aligned

enough to insure a straight hole. (An inch or so is sufficient.)

If the work has been drilled or bored on *a lathe*, place the reamer in the hole and draw the dead center against the center hole in the shank of the reamer. Turn the reamer with a tap wrench, and at the same time, advance it by advancing the dead center.

Either of these methods will insure starting the reamer parallel with the axis of the hole. However, be sure *not to crowd the reamer by advancing the center too rapidly*.

6. When the hole has been reamed its full length, continue turning the reamer for-

ward (clockwise), and at the same time, pull upward on the wrench. Continue thus until the reamer clears the hole. Never turn a reamer backward; doing so will damage the cutting edges and tear the work.

Procedure for Machine Reaming

Machine reaming always should be performed before the work is removed from the machine. It should be done at about two-thirds the speed used for drilling the same material; see Table 6 for drilling speeds. A slower speed may be used if desired. The feed should be from 0.0015″ to 0.004″ per flute, per revolution. Use the highest feed which will produce an accurate hole with the desired finish.

UNIT

47 How To Spot-Finish Metal with a Drill Press

Sometimes steel is given what is called a spot-finish. This process consists of making a series of small circular spots on the surface of the metal with a suitable device. The spots may be made so that they are merely adjacent, or with a certain amount of overlapping, usually the latter. See *A*, Fig. 8-75.

Procedure

1. Machine or hand work the object to size.
2. Polish the surfaces to be spot-finished with fine aluminum oxide or with emery cloth and polishing oil. A heavy machine oil may be used for this purpose.
3. Cut or make a short piece of dowel of the size needed to make the spots on the finished surface. Use a hard wood.

   The chuck on most drill presses in schools will not take a dowel larger in diameter than ½″. If a larger dowel is

needed, turn it with a shank that will fit the chuck on the drill press (*B*, Fig. 8-75).
4. Mount the dowel securely in the chuck.
5. Start the drill press; then square the end of the dowel by drawing it down against a sheet of abrasive cloth placed on the table of the press.
6. Prepare a pasty mixture of fine abrasive and lard oil. Coat the surface to be spot-finished with abrasive and oil. Valve grinding compound may be used instead.
7. Clamp a straightedge on the table of the drill press in such a position that when the dowel is drawn down on the surface of the work, a spot will be made near one edge.
8. Place the work against the straightedge, and adjust it so that the first spot will be made at one corner, Fig. 8-76.
9. Bring the revolving dowel into contact with the surface of the work, and hold it

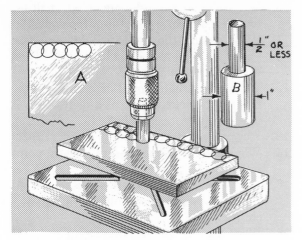

Fig. 8-75. Spot-Finishing with a Drill Press

Fig. 8-76. Beginning the Spot-Finishing

there for about 10 seconds. Then raise the dowel and move the piece over the width of one spot, or, if overlapping, about two-thirds of this width.

10. Again bring the dowel into contact with the surface, and make a second spot. Continue thus to the end of the work.

11. Move the straightedge back the width of the spot, or, if overlapping, two-thirds of this width; proceed as in steps 9 and 10.

12. Repeat the above steps until the whole surface is spot-finished.

13. Remove the dowel and straightedge; then thoroughly clean the drill press with an old rag or waste.

14. With clean waste or a soft cloth, remove remaining emery and oil from the finished surface of the object; then apply a coat of commercial antirust compound. Unless protected, steel rapidly oxidizes or rusts. The presence of moisture, even in small quantities, hastens oxidization.

Test Your Knowledge of Section 8

Unit 38: The Drill Press

1. List six hole-machining operations which can be performed on a drill press.
2. Name three machine tools, other than drill presses, on which hole-machining operations may be performed.
3. Describe sensitive drilling machines, and list their basic uses.
4. Name three types of drive systems which make it possible to vary the speed of a drill press spindle.
5. What two types of feed mechanisms are used on drilling machines?
6. What is the purpose of a multiple-spindle drilling head on a drill press?
7. How is the size of a drill press designated?
8. List several safety precautions which should be observed in operating a drill press.

Unit 39: Types of Drilling Machines in Industry

1. Describe an upright drilling machine, and explain the purpose for which it usually is designed.
2. What is the drilling capacity of upright drilling machines?
3. Describe a gang drilling machine, and explain its principal uses.
4. Describe a radial drilling machine.

211

5. For what principal type of work is a radial drilling machine designed?
6. With what capacities are radial drilling machines available?
7. For what purpose are multiple-spindle drilling machines designed?
8. What purpose does a drilling jig or fixture serve on a multiple-spindle drilling machine?
9. Describe a turret drilling machine.
10. What advantages are derived from a turret drilling machine?
11. What types of milling operations may be performed on a large turret drilling machine?
12. Describe in a brief and general way how a numerically controlled drilling machine functions.
13. What kinds of information are included in a program of instructions which is to be placed on a tape for a numerically controlled drilling machine?
14. What knowledge and experience must one generally possess before he is permitted to operate an expensive numerically controlled machine tool? Where can this knowledge and experience be acquired?

Unit 40: Twist Drills and Boring Tools

1. Name the three principal parts of a drill.
2. List three types of shanks used on drills.
3. Describe Morse taper shanks, and list several types of tools on which they are used.
4. Describe how sleeves or shell sockets are used.
5. Describe how a taper shank drill is removed from a drill press spindle.
6. Describe how you could mount a drill with a No. 3 Morse taper shank in a drill press with a No. 2 Morse taper hole.
7. List three ways in which drill sizes may be indicated.
8. List three factors which are important in grinding a drill properly.
9. What should the lip-clearance angle be for a general-purpose drill for drilling most steels?

10. What should the total included angle be for the point of a general-purpose drill?
11. What should the total included angle be for a drill used to drill molded plastics and fibrous materials?
12. What rake angle should be ground on the front of the cutting lip of a drill which is used to drill brass? Why?
13. How is a spiral point produced on a drill?
14. What are the advantages of a spiral point on a drill?
15. Why are spiral-point drills recommended for numerically controlled drilling machines?
16. What are the two most common styles or types of drills used in the school or in a maintenance shop?
17. List several materials which may be drilled with carbide-tipped drills.
18. For what purposes are three- or four-fluted core drills used?
19. What are the advantages derived from drilling with drills which have more than two flutes?
20. For what principal purpose are subland drills used?
21. What is the principal use for drills with oil holes?
22. What materials may be drilled with masonry drills?
23. For what purposes are boring tools used?
24. Describe how an adjustable boring head is used.
25. List several common machine tools on which an adjustable boring head may be used.
26. For what purpose are counterboring tools used?
27. For what purpose are holes countersunk at an angle of 82°?
28. For what purpose is a 60° combination drill and countersink used?

Unit 41: Reamers

1. What is reaming, and what is its principal purpose?
2. What is the usual procedure involved in producing a reamed hole?
3. List three ways in which holes are produced before they are reamed.

4. What determines the method used to produce a hole for reaming?

5. What is the maximum reaming allowance for holes up to 2″ diameter which are to be machine reamed?

6. What depth of cut generally is recommended for hand reaming?

7. What procedure generally is employed to produce the hole for hand reaming?

8. Describe the two-step machine reaming procedure.

9. Of what materials are reamers generally made?

10. What are the two general classifications into which reamers may be grouped?

11. List four types of machine tools on which chucking (machine) reamers may be used.

12. What types of shanks are generally used on chucking reamers?

13. Explain the cutting action of machine reamers.

14. How is a chucking reamer resharpened?

15. Explain how cutting takes place with a hand reamer.

16. What portion of a hand reamer is resharpened when the reamer becomes dull?

17. Describe rose reamers, and indicate their principal use.

18. Describe fluted chucking reamers, and indicate their principal use.

19. List several fluted chucking reamers, and indicate their principal uses.

20. For what purpose is a combination drill and reamer used?

21. For what kinds of reaming operations are solid hand reamers recommended?

22. For what kinds of reaming operations are expansion hand reamers used?

23. What are the advantages of adjustable hand reamers?

24. What is the general procedure used for reaming a hole for a taper pin?

25. For what purposes are taper socket reamers used?

26. For what purposes are burring reamers used?

27. What factors determine reaming speeds for machine-reaming operations?

28. What general rule may be applied in the selection of reaming speeds, in comparison with drilling speeds?

29. How do reaming feeds generally compare with drilling feeds?

30. Why is reamer alignment important when reaming?

31. List several factors which cause chatter while reaming.

32. What cutting fluid should be used for reaming steel?

33. List several precautions to be observed in caring for reamers.

34. Why should one avoid reversing a reamer?

Unit 42: Cutting Speeds and Feeds for Drilling

1. Describe the meaning of cutting speed as it relates to drilling operations.

2. Describe the difference between cutting speed and rpm (revolutions per minute).

3. List several factors which affect the cutting speed selected for drilling operations.

4. Name suggested cutting speeds for some of the more common metals drilled in machine shops.

5. Give the formula which may be used for calculating the rpm for a drill press when the cutting speed is known.

6. Give the formula which may be used to calculate the cutting speed for drilling when the rpm is known.

7. Define the meaning of feed as related to drilling operations.

8. List suggested feeds for drilling mild steel with drills $\frac{3}{16}$″, $\frac{3}{8}$″, and $\frac{3}{4}$″ in diameter.

9. What damage can result from excess speed and feed in drilling operations?

10. List several cutting fluids which may be used for drilling soft steel.

11. In what source in this book can one secure information concerning the selection of cutting fluids for all types of drilling and other machining operations?

Heat — Another Force Precisely Controlled to do Work

SECTION 9

The Lathe and Its Operation

Fig. 9-1. Operator Turning Work Mounted in a Chuck on a Lathe (South Bend Lathe)

The Metalworking Lathe

The metalworking lathe, as shown in Fig. 9-1*, is a basic machine tool which performs many different basic machining operations. The above illustration shows metal being *turned*, *i.e.*, metal chips are being removed from the outside diameter of the workpiece. The lathe performs many kinds of *cylindrical* metal-machining operations.

External cylindrical machining operations performed on the lathe include straight turning, taper turning, turning shoulders, turning grooves, facing flat surfaces on the end of stock, threading, knurling, and cutting off stock. Some of these operations and the types of cutting tools used to perform them are shown in Fig. 9-28.

Internal cylindrical machining operations which can be performed on a lathe include all common hole-machining operations, such as drilling, boring, reaming, counterboring, countersinking, tapping, and threading with a single-point tool (Fig. 8-2). Hence, all of the common operations performed on a drill press also can be performed on a lathe. Because the lathe is the most versatile of all machine tools, it often is referred to as the "grandfather of all machine tools."

The lathe is one of the most important of the basic machine tools. When you have learned how to perform the basic operations which may be performed on a lathe, you can apply the principles involved to other specialized produc-

*Many of the illustrations in this section are reprinted by arrangement with South Bend Lathe, Inc., from *How To Run A Lathe,* copyrighted, all rights reserved.

tion machines which are modifications or adaptations of the lathe.

Specialized production machines which are adapted from the lathe include turret lathes, hand screw machines, automatic screw machines, chucking machines, boring machines, and vertical turret lathes. A basic understanding of the metalworking lathe and its operation is fundamental in the development of a broad knowledge of machine shop theory and practice.

Historical Background

The lathe is thought to be one of the first machines invented by man. By whom or when the first lathe was built no one knows. One of the earliest-known illustrations of a lathe is shown in Fig. 9-2. It is what is known as a tree lathe. This machine was intended for turning wood, and, as may be seen, consisted of two centers, a tool rest (the board in the rear), and a means of rotating the work. Several things

Fig. 9-2. Primitive Lathe

in this crude machine are common in modern woodworking or metalworking lathes: centers, headstock, tailstock, and legs.

From the time of this first invention until 1797 when an Englishman, Henry Maudslay, designed and built the screw-cutting engine lathe shown in Fig. 9-3, there doubtless were many improvements in lathe construction, but none which were strikingly outstanding or efficient. The outstanding feature of Maudslay's lathe is a lead screw geared to the spindle of the lathe. This invention made possible the advancement of the tool at a constant rate of speed and distance of travel.

In the older forms, various means were used to rotate the work, the most common being ropes, foot treadles, hand cranks, and belts. The latter were used principally in connection with water, steam, and electrically operated devices. The term *engine lathe* seems to have originated from the practice of driving lathes by means of a steam engine; the lathe was connected by means of a belt to a line shaft, which derived its rotating motion from the steam engine.

Modern Lathes

Modern lathes are highly efficient, accurate, and complex devices, capable of doing a great quantity and variety of work. A well-constructed engine lathe, when properly operated, will produce work accurate within .001″ or even less. Fig. 9-4 gives an idea of the complexity of a modern lathe and shows many of its principal parts.

Power for driving a lathe comes from an individual motor. On some machines, the motor

Fig. 9-3. Lathe of 1797 (South Bend Lathe)

Fig. 9-4. Parts of a Modern Lathe (South Bend Lathe)

is direct mounted, while on others, it is connected by means of a short belt, usually of the V-type. Fig. 9-5 illustrates a type of lathe in which the motor is mounted under the head in the hollow leg.

The size or capacity of a lathe is given in terms of swing and length of bed. The *swing* refers to the diameter of work that can be rotated in the lathe. Thus a 16″ lathe will swing work as large as 16″ in diameter. The length of a lathe bed should not be confused with the maximum distance between centers when the tailstock is moved to the far end of the lathe bed. For example, a five-foot bed may take only 36″ between centers. This maximum distance between centers, usually, determines the length of stock that can be machined. Stock which is somewhat longer than this maximum length may be machined by holding the left-hand end in a chuck and supporting the free end with a steady rest.

Lathes are made in a wide variety of types and sizes, from the small precision lathe found in watch repair shops to the immense machine used in manufacturing big guns or mill rolls. A modern heavy-duty lathe with a geared-head drive is shown in Fig. 9-9.

Modern lathes perform basically the same operations which were performed on lathes at the turn of this century. However, because of improved design features and improved cutting tools, they accomplish these operations more accurately and efficiently today. Without the metalworking lathe, modern industrial machines and equipment could not be produced.

How a Modern Lathe Operates

Before attempting to operate a lathe, you should become familiar with its principal parts, controls, and accessories. The principal component parts of a metalworking lathe are shown in Fig. 9-6. By studying this figure carefully you will understand the function of each basic part of a lathe and its relationship to other parts. The principles which apply to the component parts of the lathe in Fig. 9-6 also apply to other metalworking lathes.

The principal controls on a modern lathe are indicated in Fig. 9-4. Although the controls are not identical on all lathes, most lathes are equipped with similar controls.

Changing Spindle Speeds: With a *flat-belt drive* (on the type lathe shown in Fig. 9-4), spindle speeds are changed by first loosening the belt with the belt tension handle and then stepping the flat belt to the desired step on the step pulley. See Fig. 9-5. The lathe always must be stopped when making speed changes.

The pulley has four steps which provide four higher speeds while in direct drive. The lathe is also equipped with a *back-gear* mechanism which provides for four lower speeds in back gear. Hence, this lathe has eight speeds available, ranging from about 40 to 940 rpm, with a single-speed motor. When equipped with a two-speed motor, 16 speeds are available. The speeds may then range up to 1600 rpm.

Lathes such as shown in Figs. 9-4 and 9-6 are equipped with a lock pin in the *bull gear*, which is located on the headstock spindle. For direct drive, the pin is pushed in and the back-gear lever is placed in the released position. For back-geared drive, the pin is pulled out to the released position and the back-gear lever is engaged.

Lathes of the type shown in Fig. 9-6 may be equipped with several types of V-belt drive

Fig. 9-5. Lathe with Flat-Belt Drive (South Bend Lathe)

Fig. 9-6. How a Modern Lathe Operates (Sheldon)

To understand the lathe it is important to remember that its only purpose is to change the shape of metal. No matter how complicated a lathe appears, it is just a means for machining metal by rotating a workpiece against a moveable cutting tool.

All lathe parts, controls and accessories are designed to perform this one purpose. All lathes have the same basic design and have component parts which serve one of these three primary functions.

(1) Driving the lathe — Line of Power
(2) Holding and Rotating Work
(3) Holding and Moving Tool

Once these primary functional divisions have been learned, their parts and their purposes, as well as the operation of the lathe will be easy to understand.

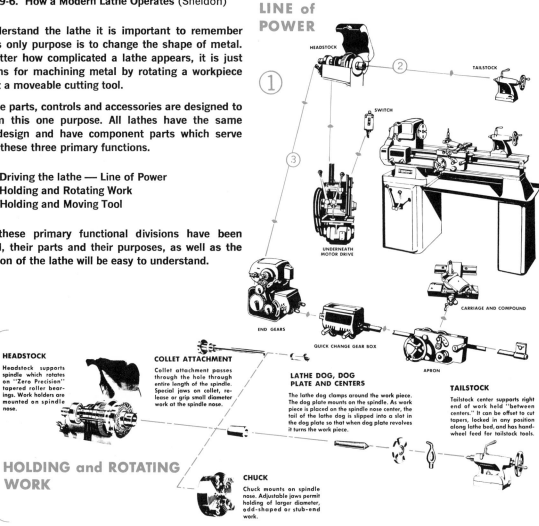

LINE of POWER

① HEADSTOCK
② TAILSTOCK
③ SWITCH
UNDERNEATH MOTOR DRIVE
END GEARS
QUICK CHANGE GEAR BOX
APRON
CARRIAGE AND COMPOUND

② HOLDING and ROTATING WORK

HEADSTOCK
Headstock supports spindle which rotates on "Zero Precision" tapered roller bearings. Work holders are mounted on spindle nose.

COLLET ATTACHMENT
Collet attachment passes through the hole through entire length of the spindle. Special jaws on collet, release or grip small diameter work at the spindle nose.

LATHE DOG, DOG PLATE AND CENTERS
The lathe dog clamps around the work piece. The dog plate mounts on the spindle. As work piece is placed on the spindle nose center, the tail of the lathe dog is slipped into a slot in the dog plate so that when dog plate revolves it turns the work piece.

TAILSTOCK
Tailstock center supports right end of work held "between centers." It can be offset to cut tapers, locked in any position along lathe bed, and has handwheel feed for tailstock tools.

CHUCK
Chuck mounts on spindle nose. Adjustable jaws permit holding of larger diameter, odd-shaped or stub-end work.

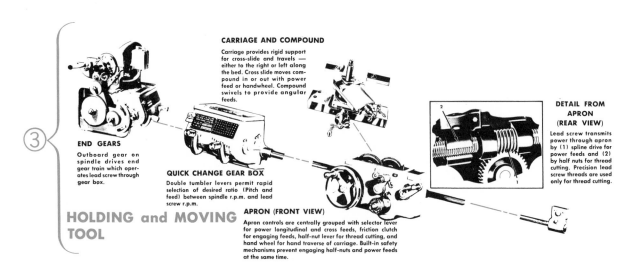

③ HOLDING and MOVING TOOL

CARRIAGE AND COMPOUND
Carriage provides rigid support for cross-slide and travels — either to the right or left along the bed. Cross slide moves compound in or out with power feed or handwheel. Compound swivels to provide angular feeds.

END GEARS
Outboard gear on spindle drives end gear train which operates lead screw through gear box.

QUICK CHANGE GEAR BOX
Double tumbler levers permit rapid selection of desired ratio (Pitch and feed) between spindle r.p.m. and lead screw r.p.m.

APRON (FRONT VIEW)
Apron controls are centrally grouped with selector lever for power longitudinal and cross feeds, friction clutch for engaging feeds, half-nut lever for thread cutting, and hand wheel for hand traverse of carriage. Built-in safety mechanisms prevent engaging half-nuts and power feeds at the same time.

DETAIL FROM APRON (REAR VIEW)
Lead screw transmits power through apron by (1) spline drive for power feeds and (2) by half nuts for thread cutting. Precision lead screw threads are used only for thread cutting.

systems for changing spindle speeds. With the *manual-shift* system, as shown in Fig. 9-7, the belt tension is released with a lever provided for this purpose, and the V-belt is shifted manually to the position desired on the step-type V-pulley.

With the *lever-shift* V-belt drive system shown in Fig. 9-8, speed changes are made by shifting the two-speed change levers to any of four different positions. With this arrange-

ment, four speeds are available in direct drive and four speeds in back-geared drive.

With a *geared-head drive*, as on the lathe shown in Fig. 9-9, it is not necessary to shift belts for making changes in spindle speeds. Speed changes are made by shifting speed-change levers, Fig. 9-10.

Speed changes on most geared-head lathes may be made only while the machine is stopped. To shift the gears while the machine is running could cause serious damage to the speed-change gears. With a two-speed motor, eighteen spindle speeds ranging from 30 to 1580 rpm are available.

Some lathes are equipped with a *variable-speed drive* system. One type system is similar to that used on many drill presses and band

Fig. 9-7. Manual-Shift V-Belt Drive (Sheldon)

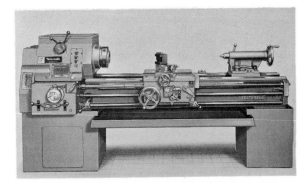

Fig. 9-9. Modern Geared-Head Lathe
(South Bend Lathe)

Fig. 9-8. Lever-Shift V-Belt Drive (Sheldon)

Fig. 9-10. Headstock with All-Geared Drive
(South Bend Lathe)

saws. This drive usually is limited to small- or medium-duty lathes. With this system, the motor usually must be running while speed changes are made. Lathes of this type also are equipped with a back-gear mechanism, thus providing for low- and high-speed ranges. Several other variable-speed drive systems are available on modern lathes of various sizes.

Feeding and Threading Mechanism: Lathes are so equipped that the cutting tool may be fed manually or automatically along the work which is being turned or faced. The feed is called *longitudinal feed* when the tool travels along the work, parallel to the lathe bed. It is called *cross feed* when the tool travels across the end of the workpiece, or in and out. Thus the cross feed is used for facing the end of a workpiece.

The amount of *longitudinal feed* is the distance that the tool advances along the workpiece during one revolution of the work. The amount of *cross feed* refers to the distance the tool travels across the end of the workpiece (in or out) during one revolution.

The amount of feed, both longitudinal and cross feed, is controlled through the use of the feeding and threading mechanism. This mechanism includes the following three basic components: the end-gear train (Fig. 9-11),

the quick-change gear box (Figs. 9-12 and 9-13), and the carriage and apron assembly (Fig. 9-14).

The *end gears* transmit power from the lathe spindle to the lead screw, through the gear box. The levers on the *quick-change gear box* make the selection of different feeds possible. These levers determine the ratio between spindle speed and the speed of the lead screw to the carriage.

The controls on the carriage and apron assembly control all carriage and tool movements. The apron *handwheel* is used to move or feed the carriage along the lathe bed manually. The *cross-feed knob* is used to move or feed the tool crosswise (in and out) manually. The *compound-rest knob* is used to feed the compound rest manually.

The compound rest may be set at any angle required. Unless necessary for special operations, it normally is turned at an angle of about 30° from the crosswise position, as shown in

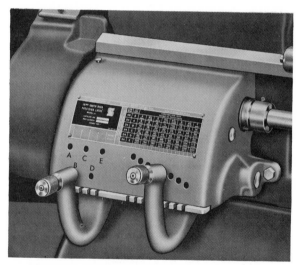

Fig. 9-12. Quick-Change Gear Box with chart (South Bend Lathe)

	STUD GEAR	LEFT HAND TUMBLER	THREADS PER INCH FEEDS IN THOUSANDTHS							
POWER CROSS FEED .375 TIMES LONGITUDINAL FEED	48	A	4 .0841	4½ .0748	5 .0673	5½ .0612	5¾ .0585	6 .0561	6½ .0518	7 .0481
	24	A	8 .0421	9 .0374	10 .0337	11 .0306	11½ .0293	12 .0280	13 .0259	14 .0240
	24	B	16 .0210	18 .0187	20 .0168	22 .0153	23 .0146	24 .0140	26 .0129	28 .0120
	24	C	32 .0105	36 .0093	40 .0084	44 .0076	46 .0073	48 .0070	52 .0065	56 .0060
	24	D	64 .0053	72 .0047	80 .0042	88 .0038	92 .0037	96 .0035	104 .0032	112 .0030
	24	E	128 .0026	144 .0023	160 .0021	176 .0019	184 .0018	192 .0017	208 .0016	224 .0015

Fig. 9-13. Index Chart for Quick-Change Gear Lathe (South Bend Lathe)

Fig. 9-11. End-Gear Train (South Bend Lathe)

Fig. 9-14. The lock screw is used to lock the carriage in position for operations such as facing.

The *feed-change lever* is used to select either of the following three types of feed: longitudinal feed, cross feed, or threading feed. While threading, the feed-change lever is left in the center position as shown; the feed is then engaged with the *half-nut lever* (which is used only for threading operations).

For longitudinal feed or cross feed, the feed-change lever is located in either the upper or lower position, as desired. The *automatic feed clutch* then is used to engage or disengage the feed for automatic operation.

When it is necessary to reverse either the longitudinal or the cross feed, the lead screw must be reversed. This is done with the *feed-reverse lever*, which was labeled in Fig. 9-4.

It should be noted that there are large numbers and also small decimal numbers located on the index plate on the quick-change gear box, Figs. 9-12 and 9-13. The *large* numbers indicate the pitch or number of threads per inch selected for threading operations only. Thus, if the large number 32 were selected, the lathe feed would be $1/32''$ per revolution of the spindle while threading; or, the carriage would travel $1''$ longitudinally, while the headstock spindle made 32 revolutions. The threading feed will function only while the feed-change lever is in the center position.

Fig. 9-14. Parts of Lathe Carriage and Apron Assembly
(South Bend Lathe)

Fig. 9-15. Lathe Center with 60° Point
(Cleveland Twist Drill)

On the other hand, the *small* decimal numbers indicate the amount of feed for automatic longitudinal feed and cross feed; however, the cross feed does not always equal the longitudinal feed indicated. On the lathe in Figs. 9-4 and 9-13, the cross feed is equal to 0.375 times the longitudinal feed.

For example, if the feed selected were indicated by the small decimal number 0.0105, the longitudinal feed would be 0.0105″ per revolution of the work. But the cross feed would be only 0.375 x 0.0105″, or 0.004″ per revolution of the lathe spindle. The ratio of cross feed to longitudinal feed varies for different lathes, and it usually is indicated on an index plate on the quick-change gear box.

Lathe Accessories

Numerous accessories are required for various machining operations on a lathe. Several standard accessories needed for beginning lathe operations are described in this unit. Other accessories are described in those units dealing with lathe operations for which they commonly are used.

Lathe Centers: Two lathe centers (similar to the one shown in Fig. 9-15) are required for turning work between centers on a lathe. Fig. 9-78 shows work being turned between centers. Thus the lathe centers are considered as holding devices. The centers have a Morse-taper shank which fits into the tapered hole in the tailstock and the tapered hole in the spindle sleeve. The spindle sleeve is an adapter which makes it possible to adapt the center (which has a smaller-sized taper) to the lathe spindle (which has a tapered hole of larger size).

The center in the headstock rotates with the spindle and the work, and, therefore, is called the *live* center; that in the tailstock is stationary and is called the *dead* center. The center in the tailstock must be made always of hardened steel or carbide; that in the headstock may be either hardened or unhardened steel. Hard lathe centers are made of either carbon tool steel or high-speed steel, or they may be equipped with carbide tips which are highly wear- and heat-resistant.

Center holes are drilled into the workpiece, thus permitting the workpiece to be supported between the centers. The center hole in which the dead center is inserted must be lubricated to prevent it from becoming overheated and scored or burned. A mixture of white lead or red lead and oil is a satisfactory lubricant.

Some manufacturers make *rotating live* centers for the tailstock. Such centers are equipped with ball bearings or tapered roller bearings which permit the center to rotate with the work. It is not necessary to lubricate the center holes when mounting work on centers of this type.

For accurate work, lathe centers must be free from nicks or chips. The holes in the tailstock and headstock spindle must be cleaned each time the center is replaced in the hole.

When hard lathe centers become scored, nicked, or damaged, they must be resharpened by grinding, as shown in Fig. 9-16. They are ground with a tool post grinder mounted on the compound rest on a lathe. The point angle of the lathe center is 60° and is checked with a *center gage*, as shown in Fig. 9-17.

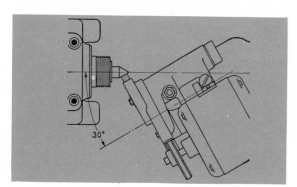

Fig. 9-16. Truing 60° Lathe Center Point
(South Bend Lathe)

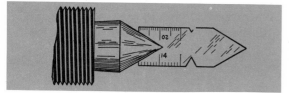

Fig. 9-17. Testing Angle of Lathe Center
(South Bend Lathe)

Lathe Dogs: When a workpiece is mounted between centers on a lathe, it is driven with a bent-tail lathe dog. Several lathe dogs of this type are shown in Fig. 9-18. The clamp dog may be used on work of many diameters within its size range. The dogs with the square-head screw or the recessed safety screw are available in various sizes with work capacities ranging from ⅜″ to 6″ diameter.

Other Accessories: The following lathe accessories are described in conjunction with lathe units which present the procedures for performing various lathe operations: toolholders, cutting tools, steady rest, follower rest, knurling tools, chucks, faceplates, types of spindle noses, boring tools and toolholders, mandrels, taper attachments, and milling attachments.

Safety Precautions for the Lathe

General Turning
1. Wear approved safety goggles.
2. Examine the belt lacing for loose hooks or ends, and have them corrected.
3. See that all guards are in place.
4. Before starting the lathe, turn the spindle by hand, to insure that it turns freely. If the spindle is locked in a stationary position with the back-gear lever as well as the bull-gear pin, release one of these devices for the desired kind of drive and speed.
5. Stop the machine to make all adjustments.
6. Stop the machine for all measurements.

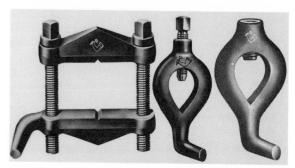

Fig. 9-18. Lathe Dogs (Armstrong)
(Left) Clamp type; (Center) With square-head screw;
(Right) With safety screw.

7. Stop the machine to remove chips. Do not remove them with the hands — always use a brush or stick.

8. Stop the machine for oiling.

9. Always stop the machine when adjusting the tool in the tool post.

10. While making adjustments of the work, always remove the tool from the holder, or remove or swing the holder, so that your hand will not slip against the sharp tool.

11. Keep the machine clear of long chips, rags, and unnecessary hand tools.

12. Use the right type of cutting tool for the job.

13. Adjust the feed, speed, and depth of cut according to the size and type of metal.

Turning Between Centers

14. For work held between centers, be sure that the tailstock is tight to the bed.

15. Be sure that the tailstock spindle is locked securely.

16. When available, use a safety dog to drive the workpiece. Select the smallest dog which will do the job, and clamp it tightly.

17. Lubricate the tailstock center properly and frequently.

18. Always cut in the direction toward the headstock when possible.

19. Before starting the power feed, make certain that the carriage has sufficient free travel to complete the cut.

Turning Work in a Chuck

20. Place a board under the chuck when mounting it or removing it from the spindle. Keep the fingers clear.

21. Be sure that the chuck is mounted tightly to the spindle.

22. Be sure that the work is mounted tightly in the chuck.

23. Always remove the chuck wrench or key from the chuck immediately after using it.

24. Turn the chuck one complete revolution by hand after the work is mounted, to see that it clears the carriage and the ways.

25. Stop the power feed before the tool reaches the jaws of the chuck.

Turning Work on a Faceplate

26. Be sure the faceplate is secured tightly to the lathe spindle.

27. Use the shortest bolts and clamps possible for clamping work to the faceplate, and clamp the work securely. The clamps should be supported at the outer ends and should be parallel to the faceplate.

28. Use a counterweight, if necessary, to reduce vibration of the faceplate.

29. Before starting the machine, turn the work one complete revolution by hand to see that it clears the carriage and the ways.

30. Stand to one side of the revolving faceplate.

Cutting Speeds for Lathe Work

UNIT
52

For lathe work, cutting speed refers to the rate in surface feet per minute (sfpm) at which the tool removes the stock from the surface. The sfpm indicates the periphery (surface) speed of the revolving work at the point of the tool; that is, the diameter of the work at the bottom of the cut. Conditions that affect cutting speed include: kind of material, machinability of material, kind of tool used (*e.g.*, carbon or high-speed steel), rigidity of work, rigidity of machine, type of cut, and kind of cutting fluid used.

Table 7
Cutting Speeds (sfpm) for the Lathe Using High-Speed Tool Bits Without Coolant

Material	Turning and Boring		Cutting Screw Threads
	Heavy Cut	Finishing Cut	
Low-carbon mild steel	90	100	35
Tool steel, annealed	50	70	20
Cast iron, soft gray	50	80	25
Brass	150	300	50
Aluminum	200	300	50
Bronze	90	100	25

The cutting speeds in Table 7 are recommended when using high-speed tool bits without coolant.

Additional general cutting-speed recommendations for other metals and materials are included in Table 8. Further data concerning cutting speeds for specific metals and for specific machining applications are included in standard handbooks for machinists.

When using cast-alloy tools, the cutting speeds may be increased by 50 to 75 percent. When using tungsten-carbide tipped tools, the cutting speed should be increased markedly — ordinarily, from two to four times the speed recommended for high-speed tool bits.

Calculating Cutting Speed

To find the cutting speed, multiply the diameter of the work in inches by 3.1416. Multiply this product by the number of revolutions per minute of the headstock spindle. Divide this final product by 12. This will give the cutting speed in surface feet per minute.

Formula for Cutting Speed

$$CS = \frac{D'' \times \pi \times rpm}{12}$$

Table 8
Average Tool Angles and Cutting Speeds for Single-Point High-Speed Tools

Material	Side[1] Relief	End[2] Relief	Side[3,4] Rake	True Back[4] Rake	Suggested Cutting Speeds sfpm[5]
Free-machining steel	10°	10°	10°-22°	16°	160-350
Low-carbon steel (.05%-.30%)	10°	10°	10°-14°	16°	90-100
Medium-carbon steel (.30%-.60%)	10°	10°	10°-14°	12°	70-90
High carbon tool steel (.60-1.70%)	8°	8°	8°-12°	8°	50-70
Tough alloy steel	8°	8°	8°-12°	8°	50-70
Stainless steel	8°	8°	5°-10°	8°	40-70
Stainless steel, free-machining	10°	10°	5°-10°	16°	80-140
Cast iron, soft	8°	8°	10°	8°	50-80
Cast iron, hard	8°	8°	8°	5°	30-50
Cast iron, malleable	8°	8°	10°	8°	80-100
Aluminum	10°	10°	10°-20°	35°	200-1500
Copper	10°	10°	10°-20°	16°	100-120
Brass	10°	8°	0°	0°	150-300
Bronze	10°	8°	0°	0°	90-100
Molded plastics	10°	12°	0°	0°	150-300
Plastics, acrylics	15°	15°	0°	0°	60-70
Fiber	15°	15°	0°	0°	80-100

[1] End- and side-relief angles from 3° to 5° generally are recommended for shaper and planer tools.

[2] End-relief and side-relief angles averaging 8° to 10° are fairly standard for turning most metals. For general machining operations, both side- and end-relief angles often are equal.

[3] Use the lower angle when no chip breaker is used. Use the higher angle with a chip breaker.

[4] Rake angles are true angles measured from horizontal and vertical planes.

[5] Use the lower speeds on roughing cuts and when machining dry. Use higher speeds when using cutting fluids and on finishing cuts. See Table 42, appendix for selection of cutting fluids. (Use speeds 50% to 70% higher with cast alloy tools, and 2 to 4 times higher with cemented-carbide tools.)

Where:

CS = Cutting speed in surface feet per minute

D = Diameter of work in inches

π = Pi or 3.1416

rpm = Revolutions per minute

Example: What is the cutting speed in surface feet per minute of a piece of cast iron, 1½ inches in diameter, revolving at 150 revolutions per minute?

$$\frac{1.5 \times \overset{.2618}{\cancel{3.1416}} \times 150}{\cancel{12}} = \text{surface feet per minute (sfpm)}$$

or

1.5 × .2618 × 150 = 58.9, approx. 59 sfpm

A second formula can be used to find the number of revolutions per minute (rpm) the headstock spindle should make to produce a cutting speed of a given rate. Simply multiply the cutting speed in surface feet per minute by 12; then divide this product by the product of the diameter of the piece in inches multiplied by 3.1416.

Formula for rpm:

$$\text{rpm} = \frac{\text{CS} \times 12}{\text{D} \times \pi}$$

Example: How many revolutions per minute should a piece of mild machinery steel, 1¼ inches in diameter, make to produce a heavy cutting speed of 90 sfpm? (Refer to Table 7 to find recommended cutting speed.)

$$\frac{\overset{18}{\cancel{90}} \times \overset{1}{\cancel{12}}}{\underset{.25}{\cancel{1.25}} \times \underset{.2618}{\cancel{3.1416}}} = \frac{18}{.065450} = 275 \text{ rpm approx.}$$

or

$$\frac{90}{1.25 \times .2618} = \frac{90}{.32725} = 275 \text{ rpm approx.}$$

The figure 3 may be substituted for 3.1416 for calculating approximate cutting speeds or approximate rpm.

With the diameter of the work and the cutting speed known, one can determine the approximate rpm from a *Table of Cutting Speeds*, such as Table 41, appendix. Tables of this type are often posted in machine shops. The competent machinist, however, also must know how to calculate the correct cutting speed and rpm, since tables of cutting speeds usually are limited to small diameters only.

Lathe Cutting Tools and Toolholders

For efficient machining on a metalworking lathe, the correct type of cutting tool, called a *tool bit*, must be used. A tool bit is a *single-point* cutting tool. A variety of lathe cutting tools and their applications are shown in Fig. 9-28.

For machining applications, the tool bit is mounted in a toolholder as shown in Fig. 9-29. A tool bit must be sharp and the cutting edge must be well supported. It must be the correct type for the job, and it must be set in the right position in relation to the work being ma-chined. The cutting angles must be ground correctly in order to cut efficiently.

Tool Bits

Tool bits may be designed and ground with many different shapes for special purposes. The principles involved in cutting metals with a single-point cutting tool, however, apply to nearly all lathe, shaper, and planer tool bits, regardless of the particular design or shape. The terms which apply to all single-point cutting tools have essentially the same meaning, and these must be understood in order to select, grind, and set a cutting tool properly for a given application.

Some of the most popular types and shapes of lathe cutting tools, particularly those made of high-speed steel, are shown in Fig. 9-28. Note that the types of tool bits include right- and left-hand *turning* tools, *facing* tools, *cutoff* tools, *threading* tools, and *boring* tools.

The turning tools have a round nose with a comparatively large nose radius. This type of tool is designed primarily for finish turning with relatively light cuts. For rough turning with heavier cuts, a tool with a very small nose radius is used. A rough-turning tool also is designed with a wider nose angle for additional support of the cutting edge. Hence, there are many possible ways of grinding tool bits for particular applications.

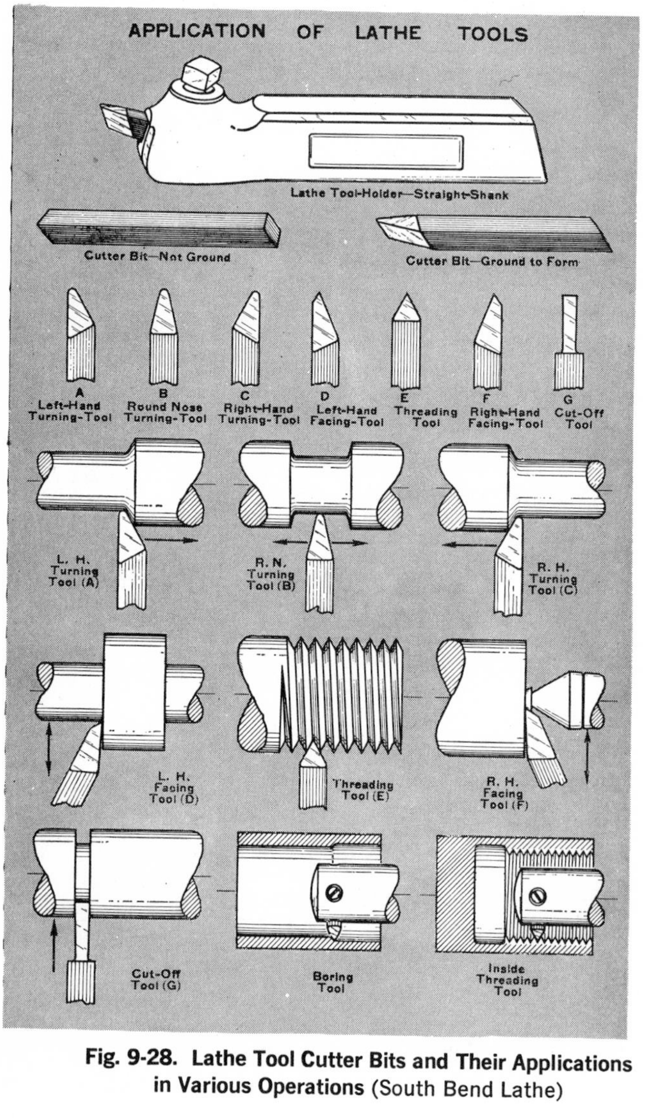

Toolholders

Various toolholders are available for holding single-point cutting tools on lathes, shapers, and planers. Some are standard types which may be used for many standard applications. See Figs. 9-29 and 9-30. Numerous toolholders are designed for special lathe applications. Some of the standard types of toolholders are explained briefly in this unit.

Shank Angle: Toolholders for turning and cutoff tools are available with three standard types of shanks: *straight*, *right-hand*, and *left-hand*, Fig. 9-30. The type is determined by holding the end with the screw in

Fig. 9-28. Lathe Tool Cutter Bits and Their Applications in Various Operations (South Bend Lathe)

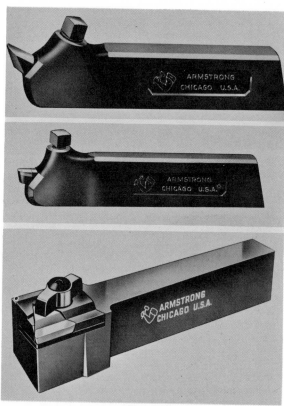

Fig. 9-29. Lathe Toolholders (Armstrong) (Top) Straight-shank 16½° turning type; (Center) Straight-shank carbide type for carbide-tipped cutters; (Bottom) Carbide insert type with carbide insert tool and chip breaker.

the right hand and observing the direction in which the shank is bent. If the shank is bent to the right, the toolholder is a right-hand holder; if bent to the left, it is a left-hand holder.

Left-hand toolholders permit machining operations close to the lathe chuck or faceplate. Right-hand ones sometimes are used for machining operations which are very close to the tailstock of the lathe. Straight-shank toolholders usually work best for general machining applications on long workpieces.

Toolholders: The angle at which a turning tool bit is held in a toolholder, in relation to the base of the toolholder shank, is important. A standard turning toolholder (of the type shown at the top of Fig. 9-29) generally holds the tool bit at an angle of about 16½°. This type of toolholder is intended for use with tool bits made of high-speed steel. It is called a *16½° toolholder* in this book.

The toolholder shown at the center of Fig. 9-29 holds the tool bit parallel to the base of the toolholder shank. This type is intended for holding carbide-tipped tool bits, but it also may be used for holding cast-alloy bits. In this book, it is called a *zero-degree toolholder*.

The toolholder shown at the bottom of Fig. 9-29 is a *carbide insert toolholder*. It is used to hold a carbide insert cutting tool and chip breaker. The carbide chip breaker has a beveled edge and is clamped on the top of the cutting tool. The cutting edge of the tool may be rotated when it becomes dull. When all cutting edges are dull or worn, the tool may be replaced. The chip breaker also may be replaced when badly worn.

Boring toolholders, Fig. 9-30, are used for boring operations on a lathe. Other typical types are shown in Unit 69.

Cutoff toolholders, Fig. 9-30, are used for holding cutoff tools in a lathe. Cutoff tools are used for cutting grooves (Fig. 9-28), cutting to a shoulder, or for cutting off stock. Cutoff operations normally are performed with the workpiece mounted in a lathe chuck.

Threading toolholders are used for holding commercially produced threading tools of the type shown in Fig. 9-30. Standard lathe tool bits also may be ground for thread cutting and are used in standard turning toolholders. More

information concerning threading tools and how to grind them is included in Units 54 and 55.

Knurling tools, Fig. 9-30, are used for performing knurling operations. Information concerning knurling tools and knurling operations is included in Unit 63.

Special toolholders of many kinds are available for use in performing various lathe, turret lathe, and screw machine operations.

Cutting Tool Materials

Cutting tools for metalworking, including both single-point and multiple-point tools, commonly are made of *high-speed steel*, *cast alloys*, and *cemented carbide*. They also may be made of *ceramics* for special purposes. Cutting tools must be made of materials which possess special properties — (1) they must

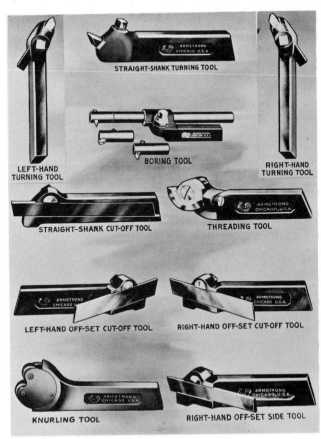

Fig. 9-30. Commonly Used Lathe Toolholders and Cutting Tools (Armstrong)

229

have sufficient hardness to cut other materials; (2) they must be capable of retaining hardness at the high temperatures which are produced at the cutting edge; (3) they must rank high in wear resistance; and (4) they must possess sufficient toughness (impact strength) to prevent chipping or fracturing.

High-Speed Steel: High-speed steel tools are the most commonly used ones in schools. They retain their hardness up to a dull-red temperature, about 1000° F. They generally rank higher in toughness, but lower in wear resistance than cast-alloy or cemented-carbide tools. All basic types of single-point tools, drilling tools, and milling cutters are available in high-speed steel from most supply sources. Suggested cutting speeds for high-speed steel, single-point cutting tools are listed for various materials in Table 8.

Cast Alloys: Cast alloys are used in the manufacture of solid tool bits, brazed tips on tool shanks, and as inserts in toolholders and milling cutters. Some common brand names for cast alloys include Stellite, Rexalloy, Armaloy, and Tantung. Cast alloys can withstand higher temperatures and higher cutting speeds than high-speed steel, but generally they are not as tough. They do not lose significant hardness at temperatures below 1400° F. They may be used at cutting speeds 50 to 70 percent higher than for high-speed steel tools, Table 8.

Cemented Carbide: Cemented carbide is used for brazed tips on single-point tools, as shown at the center of Fig. 9-29. It is used for insert tools and chip breakers which are clamped in a toolholder, as shown at the bottom of Fig. 9-29. It also is used for tips brazed on drills, reamers, or milling cutters. Cemented carbide is so named because the tiny particles used in its manufacture (usually tungsten carbide) are cemented together with cobalt.

Cemented carbide retains its hardness at temperatures higher than those for either high-speed steel or cast alloys. It does not lose significant hardness at temperatures below 1700° F. Therefore, cutting speeds from two to four times greater than for high-speed steel may be used, Table 8. However, cemented carbides are much more brittle than high-speed steel, and, for this reason, they should be rigidly supported in the toolholder or other holding device. The machine and the work setup should be free from vibration. Zero-degree toolholders, as shown at the center, Fig. 9-29, should be used. Interrupted cuts should be avoided when possible. Because of the pressure-welding characteristics of carbide tools, they should be used at recommended cutting speeds.

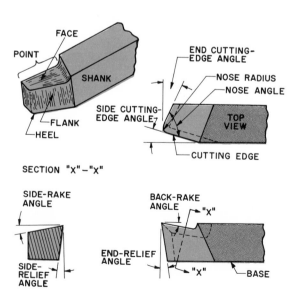

Fig. 9-31. Cutting-Tool Angles and Terms for Lathe, Shaper, or Planer Tools

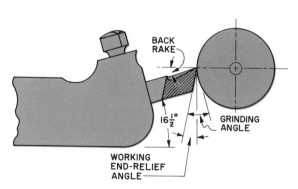

Fig. 9-32. Cutting Edge Set on Center with 16½° Toolholder

Further information concerning the above cutting-tool materials, as well as ceramic and diamond cutting-tool materials, is included in Unit 140, "Cutting-Tool Materials."

Single-Point Cutting-Tool Terms

The following are some of the most important terms, definitions and angles which apply to all single-point cutting tools, including those used on lathes, shapers, and planers. Unless otherwise indicated, refer to Fig. 9-31 for illustrations of each term.

The term *tool bit* commonly is applied to relatively small pieces of cutting-tool material, which are inserted in a toolholder or tool shank in a manner which permits easy removal for regrinding or replacement. (See Figs. 9-28 and 9-29.)

The *cutting edge* is the part of the tool bit that does the actual cutting.

The *face* is the top surface of the tool upon which the chips bear as they are removed from the workpiece and slide away.

The *flank* of the tool is the surface adjacent to and just below the cutting edge.

The *nose* is the corner or arc which joins the side cutting edge and the end-cutting edge.

The *nose radius* is the dimension of the round arc which forms the nose of the tool bit. For rough turning, a small nose radius (usually about $1/64''$) is used. For finish turning, a radius from $1/16''$ to $1/8''$ is used. A turning tool with a nose radius of $1/32''$ will produce satisfactory finish for general rough or finish turning.

The *shank* is the body portion of the tool, one end of which has a point which is ground, shaped, or supported.

The *point* of the tool includes all of that portion of the tool which is shaped to produce the face and the cutting edges.

The *base* of the tool is that portion of the tool which bears against the supporting toolholder or supporting tool block.

A lathe *tool bit* is designated right-hand or left-hand, depending on the direction in which it cuts; see Fig. 9-28. A *right-hand* tool has its cutting edge on the left, and it cuts from right toward left. A *left-hand* tool has its cutting edge on the right, and it cuts from left toward right.

Tool Angles

Toolholder Angle: The toolholder angle is measured between the bottom of the tool bit slot and the base of the toolholder shank. Toolholders are designed to hold tool bits at either fixed or variable angles. A standard $16\frac{1}{2}°$ toolholder, commonly used for high-speed steel bits, is shown in Figs. 9-32 and 9-33. A zero-degree toolholder, commonly used for cast-alloy and cemented-carbide tool bits, is shown in Fig. 9-34. Shaper and planer toolholders usually support the tool at a zero-degree angle, that is, parallel to the base of the toolholder. For example, see Fig. 10-13. The angle at which the tool bit is held in the toolholder must be considered before grinding a tool bit.

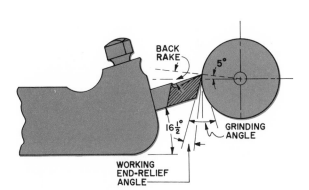

Fig. 9-33. Cutting Edge Set 5° Above Center with $16\frac{1}{2}°$ Toolholder

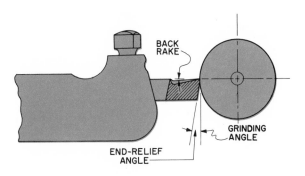

Fig. 9-34. Cutting Edge Set on Center with Zero-Degree Toolholder

Side-Relief Angle: Formerly called side clearance, the side-relief angle is ground back below the cutting edge. It is measured between the ground flank below the cutting edge and a line passing through the cutting edge perpendicular to the base of the tool or the toolholder, Fig. 9-31. The side-relief angle permits free cutting by preventing the side flank of the tool from rubbing against the work.

End-Relief Angle: Formerly called front clearance, the end-relief angle is ground back below the nose of the tool. It is measured between the flank ground below the nose and a line passing through the nose cutting edge perpendicular to the base of the tool bit or the toolholder, Figs. 9-31 and 9-34. The end-relief angle permits free cutting by preventing the flank below the nose cutting edge from rubbing against the work.

Working Angles: Working angles are located between the tool and the work. In addition to the shape of the tool, these angles depend upon the location of the tool in relation to the work. They formerly were called *effective angles*.

Working Relief Angle: The *working* relief angle formerly was called the *effective* relief angle. It is the angle formed between the ground flank of the tool and a line passing through the active cutting edge tangent to the machined surface, Figs. 9-32 and 9-33.

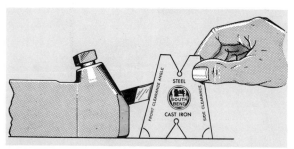

Fig. 9-35. Checking Relief (Clearance) Angles on Tool Bit (South Bend Lathe)

Comparison of the *normal* end-relief angle (grinding angle) and the *working* end-relief angle in Figs. 9-32 and 9-34 makes their differences apparent. The *normal* end-relief angle equals the total *grinding angle*; it is the angle which must be ground on the tool bit in order to produce the proper *working* end-relief angle.

End-relief angles may be measured with a tool-angle gage of the type shown in Fig. 9-35. In this figure, the *working* end-relief angle of the tool is being checked, since the tool is mounted at an angle in the toolholder. The *normal* end-relief angle may be measured with the same gage; however, the base of the tool then must be placed parallel to the base of the gage. For this, the tool bit may be placed on a flat surface against the gage, or it may be placed in a zero-degree toolholder and held against the gage. A simple tool-angle gage with the desired end-relief angles can be made from a piece of sheet metal or a thin, flat steel bar.

When a tool bit is placed in a zero-degree toolholder in a lathe, and when the tool is mounted on the center line of the work (Fig. 9-34), the end-relief angle, the *working* end-relief angle, and the grinding angle are equal. This also is true for shaper and planer tool bits which are mounted with the base of the tool bit parallel to the base of the toolholder, Fig. 10-15.

Amount of Relief Angle: The purpose of the end- and side-relief angles is to permit free cutting by preventing the flanks below the cutting edge from rubbing against the work. For different metals, the working relief angles vary from about 3° to 15°. The *amount* of relief angle depends on the following factors:

1. Kind of material being cut.
2. Hardness of the material being cut.
3. Kind of cutting-tool material.
4. Position of the tool in relation to the work.
5. The nature of the cut.

Only the required amount of end or side relief should be used. Excess relief angle reduces the support under the cutting edge and weakens the tool, thus reducing tool life. Hard materials such as high-carbon steel or hard cast iron require smaller relief angles than soft and more ductile materials. Also, smaller relief angles are used with the harder and more brittle cast-alloy or tungsten-carbide tools than with the tougher high-speed steel tools. Since the working relief angle is reduced when a lathe tool is positioned above the center line of the work (Fig. 9-33), an increased end-relief grinding angle is required, in order to provide adequate clearance. Also, a larger end-relief grinding angle must be provided for a tool mounted in a 16½° toolholder than for a zero-degree toolholder, so as to provide an adequate working relief angle. See Figs. 9-32 and 9-34.

The nature of the cut also determines the amount of end and side relief used. For interrupted cuts, such as those required for turning shafts with keyways or irregularly shaped objects, small relief angles are used. Shaper and planer tools, therefore, should be provided with end- and side-relief angles of 3° to 5°.

Thus, it is evident that the end- and side-relief angles may vary considerably, depending on a number of factors. The suggested working end-relief and side-relief angles for single-point, high-speed steel cutting tools, for average uses, are given in Table 8. End- and side-relief angles from 8° to 10° are fairly standard for turning many common metals with high-speed steel tools. In many shops, it is the practice to grind both the end and side relief at the same angle.

For general-purpose turning applications in schools and maintenance shops, the following working end- and side-relief angles may be used: 10° for high-speed steel, 7° for cast-alloy, and 7° for tungsten-carbide tools.

Further information concerning all cutting-tool angles for single-point cutting tools for various applications is included in standard handbooks for machinists.

Back-Rake Angle: The back-rake angle is found between the face of the tool bit and a line perpendicular to the work at the cutting edge. This angle depends largely on the position at which the tool is held. In the case of a tool bit held in a zero-degree toolholder, with the tool parallel to the base of the holder, the back-rake angle is measured between the face of the tool and a line parallel to the top of the tool, Figs. 9-31 and 9-34.

When the tool is in an angular toolholder, such as a 16½° toolholder, the back rake is established largely by the toolholder. The back rake then is measured between the face of the tool and a line perpendicular to the work at the cutting edge, Figs. 9-32 and 9-33.

An increase in rake angle increases the shear angle at the chip, thereby reducing the cutting force and power required. However, the increase in rake also reduces the cutting angle of the tool and thereby reduces the amount of material which supports the cutting edge.

Generally, small rake angles are used for machining hard materials, while steeper rake angles are used for more ductile materials. Exceptions to this rule include tools for brass, bronze, certain plastics and nonmetals.

Back-rake angles may vary from 0° to 35° for various applications. Suggested rake angles for single-point, high-speed steel tool bits are included in Table 8.

For a majority of the general machining applications encountered in the school shop, the back-rake angle established by a 16½° toolholder will produce satisfactory results with high-speed steel tools, Fig. 9-32. When little or no back-rake angle is desired with high-speed steel tools, a zero-degree toolholder should be used, Fig. 9-34. This type toolholder also is used for cast-alloy and carbide tools which generally must be used with smaller rake angles. Further recommendations for specific rake angles are included in standard handbooks for machinists.

Side-Rake Angle: *Side rake* is the slope found *across* the top of the tool face and is the angle between the tool face and a line which represents the top of the unground tool as it is viewed from the end, Fig. 9-31. By providing a shearing action for chip removal, this angle enables the tool to cut more freely.

For side-cutting tools, the side-rake angle is much more important than the back-rake angle. It weakens the tool less than a steep back-rake angle. The side-rake angle largely determines the type of chip produced and the direction at which the chip leaves the tool face.

A steep side-rake angle causes long wire-like chips on ductile materials. This type of chip is a safety hazard. A decreased side-rake angle causes the chip to curl up and break off more readily.

Side-rake angles may range from 0° to 22° or more for various applications. Suggested averages for machining various materials with high-speed tools are shown in Table 8.

These side-rake angles are listed within a range, such as 10° to 22° for free-machining steel. For steels of highest machinability, the ideal angle in this case would approach 22°. However, with the steeper angle, a chip breaker generally is required to cause the chips to curl up and break off readily. (Chip breakers are described later in this unit.) If a chip breaker is not used, the lower angle (in this case 10°) generally should be used.

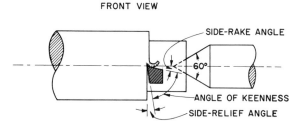

FRONT VIEW

Fig. 9-36. Application of Side-Relief and Side-Rake Angles on Lathe Tool Bit

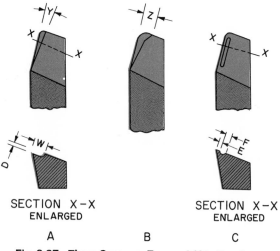

SECTION X–X
ENLARGED

SECTION X–X
ENLARGED

A   B   C

Fig. 9-37. Three Common Types of Chip Breakers

Angle of Keenness: The angle of keenness is the included angle of the tool between the face of the tool and the ground flank adjacent to the side-cutting edge, Fig. 9-36.

Side Cutting-Edge Angle: The side cutting-edge angle is formed by the straight side-cutting edge and a line representing the side of the tool shank before grinding, Fig. 9-31. This angle may vary from 0° to 30° for machining various materials. Angles of more than 30° tend to cause tool chatter. An angle of 15° generally is used for rough turning, while one of 20° produces good results for general machining applications.

End Cutting-Edge Angle: The end cutting-edge angle is formed by the end cutting edge of the tool and a line at right angles to the straight side of the tool shank. This angle may vary from 7° to 30°.

An average angle of 15° is used for rough turning. An angle of 30° produces good results for general turning applications. The 30° angle also permits the toolholder to be swiveled when turning close to shoulders or when turning close to the lathe dog or faceplate. Increased end cutting-edge angles decrease the material which supports the nose and the end cutting edge of the tool, thus reducing tool life when heavy cuts are made.

Nose Angle: The nose angle is the included angle between the side cutting edge and the end cutting edge of the tool bit, Fig. 9-31.

Chip Breakers

When relatively steep side-rake angles are used on single-point cutting tools, ductile materials are cut more freely. However, as previously mentioned, with the steep angles, long continuous chips are formed. This type of chip is a safety hazard to the machine operator, and the chips are more difficult to remove from the machining area.

A *chip breaker* causes the chip to coil up tightly and break off readily, thus removing the safety hazard. The short, broken chips occupy less space, and also permit better flow of cutting fluid to the tool point.

Three common types of chip breakers used on cutting tools are shown in Fig. 9-37. In order to grind chip breakers of this type accurately, a cutter and tool grinder is used. A surface grinder with a special compound-angle tool-holding fixture also may be used for this purpose.

With the *angular-shoulder chip breaker* shown at *A*, the angle *Y* may vary from about 5° to 15°, with 7° or 8° being the average. The width *W* and depth *D* depend on the feed, speed, depth of cut, and kind of material. The width *W* at the end of the tool usually varies from $\frac{1}{16}''$ to $\frac{3}{16}''$, and the depth, from $\frac{1}{64}''$ to $\frac{1}{16}''$. Tools with a large nose radius have a secondary angle as shown at *B*. The width *Z*

should be about one-and-one-half times the nose radius.

The *groove chip breaker* (*C*, Fig. 9-37) has a groove ground parallel to the side-cutting edge of the tool. For average applications, the following dimensions may be used: *E*, $\frac{1}{32}''$; *F*, $\frac{1}{16}''$; and depth of groove, $\frac{1}{32}''$.

A removable *tungsten-carbide chip breaker* with a beveled edge is shown at the bottom of Fig. 9-29. The chip breaker is clamped above the cutting face of the tungsten-carbide, inserted cutting tip. When the chip breaker becomes badly worn, it may be replaced with a new one. This type also may be used with cast-alloy inserted cutting tools.

Grinding Lathe Cutter Bits

Lathe tool bits are ground at various angles to give them keenness and strength. Grinding a tool so as to produce excessive side or end relief will produce a keen, but weak, cutting edge. Such an edge breaks easily because the supporting metal has been ground away.

Lathe tool bits may be ground to many different shapes for special applications. They also may be ground with a variety of different relief angles, rake angles, and cutting-edge angles. For optimum cutting efficiency in modern production, a particular type of tool bit should be selected, and it should be ground according to the shape recommended for the specific application (including recommended relief, rake, and cutting-edge angles, Table 8). Appropriate cutting fluids also should be used.

As a start for the beginning machine shop student or lathe operator, however, several general-purpose tools may be ground with angles which will produce reasonably good results on most common metals. Although cutting fluids improve their efficiency, the tools may be used for dry cutting operations where necessary. The following recommendations may be followed in grinding general-purpose lathe tools.

R.H. Turning Tool

A right-hand general-purpose turning tool is shown in Figs. 9-47 and 9-48 (in the next unit). It should be ground according to the specifications in Fig. 9-48. The nose radius depends on the depth of cut and finish desired: $\frac{1}{64}''$ for rough cuts, $\frac{1}{32}''$ for general turning with moderate or light cuts, and $\frac{1}{16}''$ or larger for light cuts requiring a smoother finish. The procedure for grinding this tool bit is included in Unit 55.

R.H. Side-Facing Tool

A right-hand side-facing tool is necessary for facing ends of stock or for facing shoulders, Fig. 9-38. When facing the ends of stock mounted between the centers of the lathe, the nose angle must be less than 60°, usually about 55°. Thus an angle of 5° will be provided for clearance along the cutting edge, as shown in Figs. 9-38.

The point of the facing tool should be set at the height of the center line of the work, as shown in Fig. 9-32. The general-purpose side-facing tool should be ground according to the following specifications:

Side-relief angle 8°-10°.

Working end-relief angle 8°-10°.

Side-rake angle 8°-10°.

Back-rake angle 0°-16½° (may be established by the toolholder angle).

If desired, the sharp point may be ground back several thousandths of an inch (maximum 1/64″), to prevent fracture. By grinding the general-purpose R.H. facing tool on the end opposite from the general-purpose R.H. turning tool, the two most frequently used tools may be provided on one tool bit.

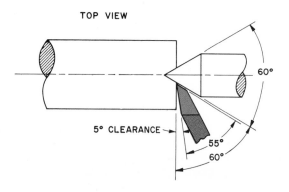

TOP VIEW

60°

5° CLEARANCE

55°
60°

Fig. 9-38. R.H. Side-Facing Tool, Facing End of Work Between Centers of Lathe

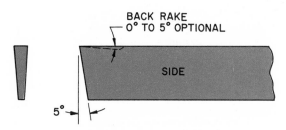

BACK RAKE
0° TO 5° OPTIONAL

SIDE

5°

Fig. 9-39. Cutoff Tool Blade

Cutoff Tool

The cutoff tool (Fig. 9-28) sometimes is called a *parting* tool. It is used for cutting grooves or for cutting off stock. Cutoff tool blades which are mounted in special cutoff toolholders (Fig. 9-30) are widely used.

Cutoff tool blades are designed with beveled sides which provide several degrees of side relief on each side, Fig. 9-39. The blade is ground on the front and top only, never on the sides. An end-relief angle from 3° to 10° may be used; an angle of 5° produces good results for general-purpose cutoff work.

No side rake is used for general-purpose cutoff work. No back rake is required, but an angle of from 0° to 5° sometimes is used.

A cutoff tool may be ground from a standard lathe tool bit, as shown in Fig. 9-40. The angles X and Y should be very small — just enough to clear the sides of the groove which is being cut. If the tool bit does not have a ground finish on its surfaces, the cutting face should be ground smooth.

Cutoff operations may be performed only on work which is mounted in the chuck. Never attempt to cut off stock which is mounted between centers. To do so will cause the work to bend, bind on the sides of the tool, and fly out of the lathe before the piece is cut off.

For cutoff operations, the work and the tool must be mounted rigidly. The tool should extend from the toolholder as little as possible. Likewise, the toolholder should extend from the tool post as little as possible. The cutting edge of the tool should be mounted at the height of the center line of the work.

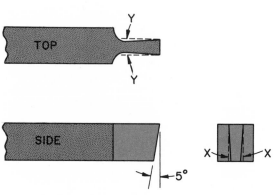

Y

TOP

Y

SIDE

5°

X   X

Fig. 9-40. Cutoff Tool Ground on Tool Bit

Cutting speeds used should be about one-third less than those used for turning. If tool chatter develops, usually it may be reduced or eliminated by reducing the cutting speed. The tool should be fed by hand until experience is acquired. Power cross feed may be used later.

Threading Tools

Threading tools for Unified or American (National) form threads are ground V-shaped with an inclusive angle of 60°. The tool bit is given from 8° to 10° end relief and from 8° to 10° side relief on each side, Fig. 9-41. The point of the bit generally is flattened about one-eighth of the *pitch* for Unified and American (National) form threads. The cutting edge of the tool is set at the height of the center line of the work, with no working back-rake angle required, Fig. 9-41.

A threading toolholder with a formed threading tool for sharp V-threads is shown in Fig. 9-42. This type threading tool may be used for cutting Unified or National form threads of any pitch, but without the flat provided at the root of the thread. Threading tools with the flat provided on the point are available in pitches from 4 to 32 threads per inch.

Threading tools used in the threading toolholder shown in Fig. 9-42 are designed and provided with the proper front and side relief when the tool is ground and set in the toolholder properly. The tool is ground across the top only, without side rake, in line with line A-A. The point of the tool is set at the height of the center line of the work.

For internal threading, a threading tool bit is mounted in a boring bar as shown in Fig. 9-43. This particular boring bar holds the tool at a 30° angle. Boring bars which hold the tool at a 90° angle also are used; with this type, the threading tool is ground in the same manner in which threading tool bits are ground for external thread cutting, Fig. 9-41.

Grinding the Tool

Grinding high-speed steel lathe bits presents no special problem other than to observe that the correct angles are produced for respective metals and that each ground face is as nearly a straight plane as possible (never convex). Ordinarily, the nose of round-nose tools should be ground slightly elliptical rather than round. After grinding, whetting on an abrasive stone will produce a bit that will cut smoother and retain its edge longer. See Unit 55 for **grinding single-point cutting tools.**

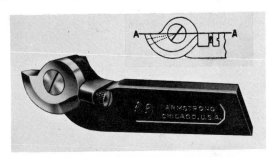

Fig. 9-42. Threading Tool (Armstrong)

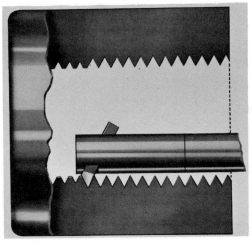

Fig. 9-43. Threading Tool for Internal Threading (Armstrong)

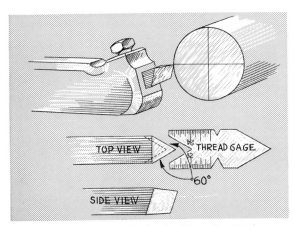

Fig. 9-41. Cutting Angles for Threading Tools

UNIT 55

How To Grind and Whet Cutting Tools for Lathe or Shaper

Accurate work with a good finish cannot be done on the lathe or shaper unless the cutters are sharp and are ground at the correct angle. The angle at which the cutters are ground generally is the same, regardless of whether the cutter is a forged tool or a high-speed steel bit. Carbide-tipped and alloy bits are ground with a little less front and side relief than that recommended for high-speed steel bits.

A soft or medium-soft grinding wheel is recommended for grinding high-speed steel cutting tools; see Table 15. A standard bench- or floor-model tool grinder of the type shown in Fig. 5-1 may be used. Or, a tool grinder with a tilting table may be used, Fig. 5-2.

For grinding either solid or tipped cast-alloy tool bits, a tool grinder with a tilting table, as shown in Fig. 9-46, should be used. The grinder should be equipped with an aluminum-oxide grinding wheel. The tool may be ground wet or dry, but it should not be quenched after grinding dry.

For grinding tools with cemented-carbide tips, a grinder of the type shown in Fig. 9-46 also should be used; however, it should be equipped with either a silicon-carbide or diamond grinding wheel. Aluminum-oxide grinding wheels are too soft for grinding carbide tools. More information concerning the selection of grinding wheels for grinding carbide tools is included in Units 111 and 140.

The two most-used high-speed steel tool bits for lathes are the *R.H. turning tool* and the *R.H. side-facing tool*. The suggested shape and the suggested grinding angles for these two tools for general-purpose work, as described in Unit 54, are shown in Figs. 9-47 and 9-48. Variations of the turning tool are indicated in Fig. 9-49. The angles may be altered for special machining applications, as suggested in Table 8.

Fig. 9-46. Table of Tool Grinder Tilted to Correct Grinding Angle (Stellite Div. — Union Carbide)

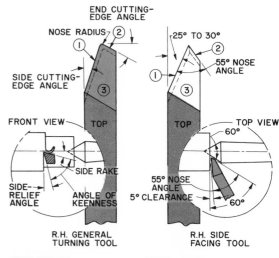

NOSE RADIUS:

$\frac{1}{64}$" ROUGH TURNING

$\frac{1}{32}$" GENERAL TURNING

$\frac{1}{16}$" FINISH TURNING

STEPS:

① GRIND SIDE CUTTING-EDGE ANGLE WITH SIDE RELIEF

② GRIND END CUTTING-EDGE ANGLE AND NOSE RADIUS WITH END RELIEF

③ GRIND SIDE-RAKE AND BACK-RAKE ANGLE

Fig. 9-47. Grinding the Two Most-Used Tool Bits

238

Procedure for Grinding Lathe Cutters

1. Select a suitable wheel.
2. Examine the faces of the wheel for trueness and freedom from grooves.
3. If necessary, dress all of the surface to be used until all ridges or grooves have been removed and the wheel is running true, with the face of the wheel perpendicular to the sides.
4. Protect the eyes against flying particles of loosened abrasive by using a shield and goggles.

   On some grinders, a coolant is used. When this is the case, be sure there is sufficient in the container. Turn on the coolant, and allow it to run on the face of the wheel for a minute before grinding.
5. For previously shaped tools, examine the angles at which the tool was last ground, and compare these with the suggestions offered in Unit 54 or with Table 8. If the angles of side relief, end relief, side rake, and back rake are not correct, they should be corrected.

   For a new tool bit which has not been ground previously, determine the shape and angles which should be ground. For general-purpose turning, the R.H. turn-

ing tool in Figs. 9-47 and 9-48 is suggested. For facing between centers, the R.H. side-facing tool in Fig. 9-47 is suggested.

The angles generally should be ground in the order suggested in Fig. 9-47, as follows:

a. Grind the side cutting-edge angle with side relief.
b. Grind the end cutting-edge angle and nose radius with end relief.
c. Grind the side-rake and back-rake angles.

6. If a grinding holder (Fig. 9-50) is available, mount the tool bit in the holder. This procedure is much safer than holding the tool with your fingers.
7. Grind the side cutting-edge angle, being sure to provide the proper side-relief angle. Check the angle with a tool-angle gage of a type similar to that shown in Fig. 9-35.

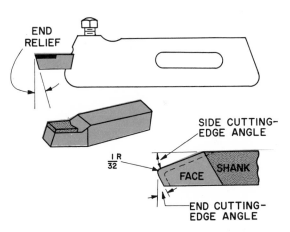

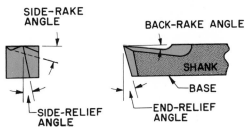

Fig. 9-49. (Top) Zero-Degree Toolholder; (Below) L.H. General-Purpose Turning Tool
(Note that grinding angles are the same as the relief angles.)

Fig. 9-48. (Top) Standard 16½° Toolholder for High-Speed Steel Tool Bits; (Below) R.H. General-Purpose Turning Tool with Angles Given
(Note that end-grinding angle is larger than end-relief angle.)

If such a gage is not at hand, it may be made easily by cutting the desired angles on the ends of a strip of sheet metal. When the tool is to be used in a $16\frac{1}{2}°$ toolholder, the actual or working side-relief angle is measured with the tool in the toolholder.

8. In grinding the end cutting-edge angle and nose radius, be sure to provide the proper end-relief angle. The tool angle will be checked with a tool-angle gage.

   If the tool is to be used in a $16\frac{1}{2}°$ toolholder, the actual or working end-relief angle is measured with the tool in the toolholder. Note in Fig. 9-48 that the normal end-relief angle (actual grinding angle) is considerably greater than the working end-relief angle.

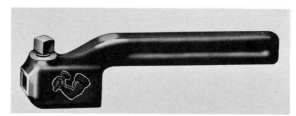

Fig. 9-50. Grinding Holder for Holding Tool Bits While Grinding (Armstrong)

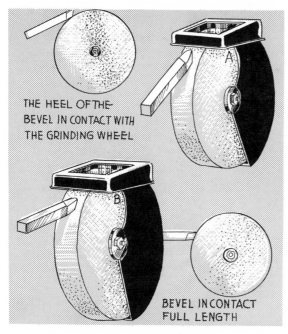

THE HEEL OF THE BEVEL IN CONTACT WITH THE GRINDING WHEEL

BEVEL IN CONTACT FULL LENGTH

Fig. 9-51. Grinding Cutter Bits

Proceed to grind the end cutting-edge angle with end relief. Bring the heel of the tool bit into contact with the wheel (A, Fig. 9-51). Raise the rear of the tool until the flank being ground rests its full length on the surface of the wheel (B, Fig. 9-51). Holding the cutter at this angle, move it back and forth across the wheel. The nose radius is ground by rolling the tool from right to left across the wheel while maintaining the same angle. Check the angles with a tool-angle gage.

When available, a grinder with an adjustable tool rest is recommended (Fig. 9-46). Set the adjustable rest or table at the angle desired, the relief angle required, and clamp it in position. Place the cutter on the table, and then bring it against the face of the wheel. Proceed as in steps 9 and 10.

9. Continue grinding until all parts of the cutting edge have been brought into contact with the wheel. Be sure to maintain the correct shape and angle.

10. Remove the tool from the grinder, and carefully examine the *cutting edge*. If any previously worn bright spots are visible, again bring the part or parts of the cutter into contact with the grinding wheel. Continue grinding until all spots have been removed.

11. If necessary, grind the top of the cutter to give it the amount of rake recommended, Unit 54 or Table 8. Ordinarily, grinding on the top of a previously shaped tool bit should be kept at a minimum.

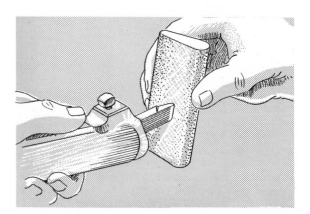

Fig. 9-52. Whetting a Lathe Tool Bit

Procedure for Whetting Lathe Tools

1. Secure a medium-soft oilstone, and apply a little machine oil to one surface.
2. Hold the oilstone flat on the ground surface, Fig. 9-52. Then move the stone up and down until the whole cutting edge has been whetted. Bear heavily on the downward stroke and very lightly on the return stroke.

Procedure for Grinding Shaper Tools

1. Proceed as under "Grinding Lathe Cutters," steps 1 through 4 inclusive.

2. Examine the angles of clearance at which the cutter was last ground, and compare these with the recommendations made in Unit 54 and Table 8. Then make the necessary corrections.
3. Proceed as under "Grinding Lathe Cutters," steps 5 through 11 inclusive.

Procedure for Whetting Shaper Tools

1. Proceed as when whetting lathe tool bits.

How To Locate, Test, Drill and Countersink Centers for Turning

The approximate center of round and irregular pieces of stock may be found in a number of ways. The most commonly used of these are discussed in the following paragraphs.

Procedure with a Center Head

1. Secure stock of the size desired.
2. Apply layout dye or chalk to the ends of the piece.
3. Set the stock on its end on a bench, or grip it in a vise.
4. Place the center head across one end of the piece, as shown in A, Fig. 9-56. Then carefully scribe a line across the chalked surface.
5. Give the square a third of a turn, and scribe a second line.
6. Give the square another third turn, and scribe a third line (B, Fig. 9-56).
7. Repeat steps 3 through 6 on the other end of the piece.
8. Place the point of a sharp center punch at the center of the intersection of the lines on one end of the stock.
9. Holding the center punch in a vertical position, strike it a light blow with a hammer.
10. Repeat steps 8 and 9 on the other end of the piece.

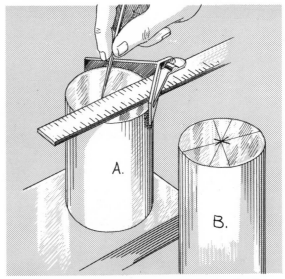

Fig. 9-56. Finding the Center with Center Head

11. Examine the position of the punch marks. If each seems to be located in the center, punch them a little deeper.

    If the punch marks are not in the center of the piece, correct them as in the paragraph following step 10, Unit 44.

Procedure with Dividers

1. Select and cut the stock to length.
2. Apply layout dye or chalk to both ends of the piece.
3. Set a pair of dividers so that the distance between the points is slightly less than half the diameter of the piece.
4. Lay the work on a flat surface, preferably a metal surface plate, and hold it in position with the left hand.
5. Place one leg of the dividers on the plate at the position where the work lies, Fig. 9-57. Make a short arc on the chalked surface of the work.
6. Give the piece a quarter turn, and repeat the operation.
7. Continue this until the short arcs form a four-sided figure (A, Fig. 9-57).

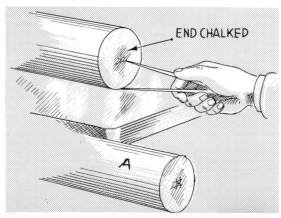

Fig. 9-57. Finding the Center with Dividers

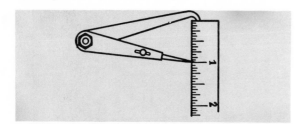

Fig. 9-58. Setting the Hermaphrodite Caliper

8. Place the point of a center punch at the center of this figure; then with the punch held parallel to the piece, strike it a light blow with a hammer.
9. Find the center of the opposite end in a similar manner.
10. Examine the position of the punch mark at each end of the piece. If both seem to be located in the center of the four-sided figure, punch them to the depth desired.

    Location of center may be checked with a pair of dividers set to a distance equal to the radius of the stock. Place the point of one leg in the punch mark. Then rotate the point of the other leg around the circumference of the stock, observing how accurately the point follows the circumference.

    If correction of position of punch marks is necessary, then proceed as in the paragraph following step 10, Unit 44.

Procedure with Hermaphrodite Caliper

1. Secure stock of the size desired.
2. Chalk or apply layout dye to the ends of the piece.
3. Set the stock on its end on a bench, or grip it in a vise.
4. Set the hermaphrodite caliper so that the distance between the point of the bent leg and that of the straight leg is about $\frac{1}{32}''$ greater than half the diameter of the stock at the end where the center is to be located. See Fig. 9-58.

Fig. 9-59. Finding the Center with Hermaphrodite Caliper

5. Place the bent leg against the side (circumference) of the stock *near the top edge*. Hold it firmly in this position with the left hand, and, with the straight leg of the caliper, draw a short arc on the chalked end of the stock, Fig. 9-59.

6. Move the bent leg of the caliper half of the distance around the circumference of the stock, and draw a second short arc. Then move the bent leg one-fourth of the distance and draw a third short arc. Continue thus until four short arcs have been drawn, Fig. 9-59.

7. Place the point of a sharp center punch at the center of the small enclosure made by the four arcs.

8. Holding the center punch in a vertical position, strike it a light blow.

9. With the hermaphrodite caliper, check the location of the center punch mark, as described in the paragraph following step 10 under "Finding the Center with Dividers."

   If the punch mark is not in the center of the piece, correct the position as described in the paragraph following step 10, Unit 44.

10. When the punch mark has been correctly located, punch it a little deeper.

11. Locate the center at the other end of the piece, if necessary.

Procedure with a Bell Centering Cup

1. Select and cut stock to size. Be sure the ends are cut square with the axis of the stock.

2. With a file, remove any burrs or projections on the circumference of the stock at the end or ends to be centered.

3. Place the stock on its end on a flat solid surface, preferably a heavy surface plate.

4. Place the bell centering cup over the end of the work, as in Fig. 9-60. Be sure the barrel of the cup is held in a plane *parallel* with the *axis of the work*.

5. Strike the center punch or plunger a sharp blow with a hammer, thus locating the center. When necessary to increase the depth of the punch mark, do so with an ordinary center punch.

6. Locate the center at the other end in a similar manner, if necessary.

Procedures with a Surface Gage

1. Apply layout dye or chalk to the ends of the piece.

2. Mount the stock in a V-block or V-blocks on a surface plate, Fig. 9-61.

3. Set a surface gage, and draw a line near the approximate center of the piece (A, Fig. 9-61).

4. Move the surface gage to the opposite end, and draw a corresponding line there.

5. Turn the piece a quarter of a turn or as far as its shape will permit without raising center. Draw a second line on each end.

6. Repeat steps 4 and 5 until a four-sided figure has been described on each end (B, Fig. 9-61).

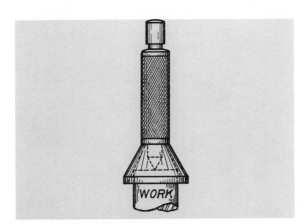

Fig. 9-60. **Bell Centering Cup** (South Bend Lathe)

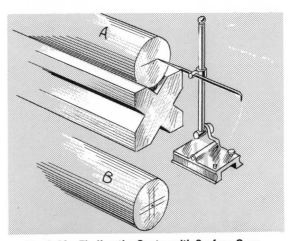

Fig. 9-61. **Finding the Center with Surface Gage**

243

7. Place the point of a center punch in the center of this figure, and strike the punch a light blow with a hammer. Sink the punch mark to the depth desired with repeated blows.

8. Repeat step 7 on the other end.

Procedure for Testing Centers

1. Place the work between the lathe centers, Fig. 9-62. Then draw the tailstock center tight enough to support the work.

2. Hold a piece of chalk close to the work at one end, Fig. 9-62. The hand holding the chalk should be supported by resting the arm on the compound rest or other suitable support.

3. With the left hand, revolve the work, and, at the same time, advance the chalk until it just touches the revolving piece. The chalk will make a mark on the high side, or the point farthest from the center.

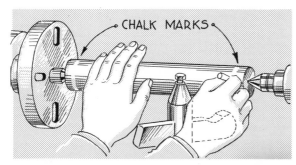

Fig. 9-62. Testing Centers with Chalk

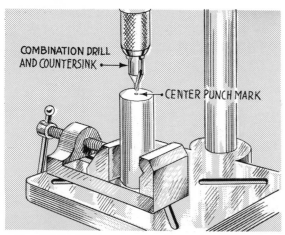

Fig. 9-63. Drilling Centers with Combination Drill and Countersink

This test may be made with the lathe running at slow speed.

4. Repeat the operation on the other end of the piece.

If the stock is accurately centered, the chalk will make a complete line around the piece. When the centers are not true, make necessary corrections as described in the paragraph following step 10, Unit 44.

Procedure for Drilling Centers on the Drill Press

There are two common methods of drilling and countersinking holes for centers — in a lathe and on a drill press.

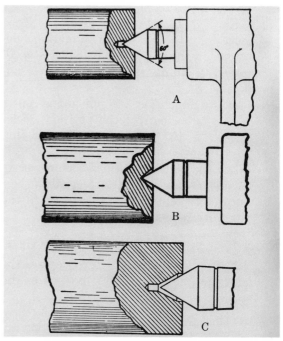

Fig. 9-64. Good and Poor Center Holes
(South Bend Lathe)

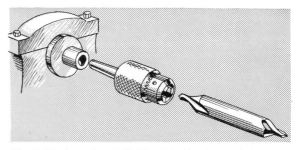

Fig. 9-65. Inserting Drill Chuck in Headstock Spindle

When drilling in the lathe, if the work is accurately centered and securely held in a chuck, and the drill held in the tailstock, it is not necessary to locate the center in the work before starting to drill.

1. Secure stock of proper length. Be sure the ends are square with the side of the piece.
2. Locate the center of the work at each end of the stock and mark with a center punch. Test the location of centers as described under "Procedure for Testing Centers."
3. Insert a combination drill and countersink in the drill press chuck, Fig. 9-63.

   For small or light work, a No. 2 combination drill and countersink is suitable. One of this size has a body diameter of about $5/16$".
4. Place the work in position on the drill press table and start the machine.

   If available, a cup center accurately centered under the spindle of the drill should be used under the work. This will largely offset irregularities on the end of the work.
5. Draw the point of the drill into the impression made by the center punch (Fig. 9-63), and drill until the tapered part of the drill has entered about *three-quarters of its full length*. If drilling steel, keep the drill well lubricated.

   A, Fig. 9-64, shows a correctly drilled and countersunk hole. Notice that the lathe center fits the tapered hole accurately with clearance at the point. *B* is not countersunk at the correct angle, and *C* is drilled too deep to fit the center. When center drilled and countersunk as at either

B or *C*, the lathe center will be damaged.
6. Drill the other end in a similar manner.

Procedure for Drilling on the Lathe

1. Secure stock of proper length.
2. Locate the center of the work at each end of the stock, and mark with a center punch.
3. Remove the lathe center in the headstock.
4. Insert the shank of the drill chuck in the headstock spindle, Fig. 9-65.
5. Select a combination drill and countersink. A No. 2 or No. 3 is suitable for light or medium work.
6. Insert the combination drill and countersink into the jaws of the drill chuck, and fasten it securely with a chuck wrench.
7. Hold the center mark against the point of the drill; then draw the tailstock up to within $3/8$" of the other end of the work.
8. Tighten the nut that holds the tailstock to the ways of the lathe.
9. Loosen the tailstock binding lever. This will allow the dead (tailstock) center to advance freely.
10. Place a little lubricant on the drill, and then start the lathe on medium or slow speed, about 700 rpm.
11. Hold the work against the point of the dead center with the left hand, palm up, as in Fig. 9-66.
12. Feed the work forward slowly, by turning the handwheel at the rear of the tailstock until the point of the drill enters the marked center.

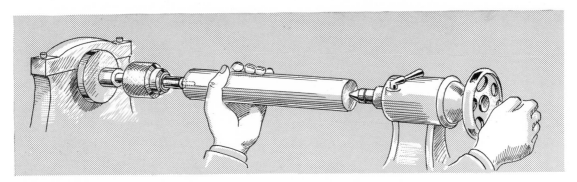

Fig. 9-66. Drilling Center Hole on the Lathe

13. Continue advancing the combination drill slowly and carefully, until the tapered part has entered the work about three-quarters of the length of the taper.

14. When drilled to depth, draw the tailstock spindle and work back until the drill clears the hole; then stop the lathe.

15. Reverse the piece and drill the other end.

How To Set a Lathe Tool for Turning Metal

The height at which a lathe tool should be set depends upon the metal to be turned and, to some extent, upon the operation being performed. As a general rule, the point of a high-speed steel tool bit may be set up to about 5° above the center (Fig. 9-33), except when turning brass or copper or when turning a taper, cutting a thread, boring, or cutting off stock. In all of these exceptions, the point of the tool should be at exactly the same level as the axis of the work, Fig 9-32.

Fig. 9-69. Cutter Bit Inserted into 16½° Toolholder
(South Bend Lathe)

When turning steel or cast iron of small diameter, the point of the tool should be set on or only very slightly above the axis of the work. For turning aluminum, a tool especially ground and sharpened for that purpose often is recommended, with the point of the tool set considerably higher above the axis of the work than when turning steel.

The point of cast-alloy tools or cemented-carbide tools should be set exactly at the height of the center line of the work, Fig. 9-34.

Regardless of the operation to be performed or the kind of metal being turned, always set the cutter well back into the toolholder, and the holder itself so that it projects but slightly beyond the edge of the compound rest. Also make certain that the toolholder is fastened

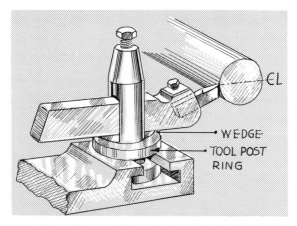

Fig. 9-70. Adjusting Toolholder in Tool Post

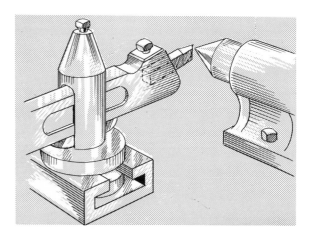

Fig. 9-71. Testing Height of Tool

securely in the tool post and the cutter in the holder. A loose cutter or toolholder may cause an accident or damage the machine or the work.

Procedure

1. Select a sharp tool of the shape and kind desired.

   Select a turning tool for straight, longitudinal cuts or facing cuts in faceplate turning; a right- or left-hand side-facing tool for sharp shoulders; a roundnose tool or a right- or left-hand turning tool for cutting shoulders with a fillet; a boring tool for boring recesses; a parting or cutoff tool for cutting narrow grooves or cutting off pieces of stock; and a threading tool for cutting threads, Fig. 9-28. For general turning on most metals, a left- or right-hand turning tool is used.

2. Insert the cutter in the toolholder, allowing it to project about ½″, as in Fig. 9-69. Then tighten the setscrew that holds the cutter. Do not allow the cutter to project more than the recommended amount, unless conditions *absolutely* necessitate this.

3. Insert the toolholder in the tool post, and adjust the point of the cutter to the height desired by sliding the wedge backward or forward in the tool post ring. See Fig. 9-70.

4. Clamp the toolholder in position by tightening the setscrew at the top of the tool post.

5. Test the height of the tool by running in the cross slide until the point of the tool is as close as possible to the point of the dead center, Fig. 9-71.

How To Mount Work Between Lathe Centers

Mounting work between centers is a very common method of holding work while it is being machined. To rotate the work, a faceplate having an open slot on one side is mounted on the spindle. A lathe dog with a bent tail is mounted on the stock and the tail engaged in the slot in the faceplate.

Procedure

1. Remove the chuck if one is mounted on the lathe spindle.
2. Clean the threads on the lathe spindle with a piece of cloth or a small handful of waste. Remove any remaining lint or threads; then apply a few drops of lubricating oil.
3. Test the points of the lathe centers for alignment, as in Fig. 9-72. Both points

should be in the same horizontal and vertical planes.

4. Select a faceplate of suitable size. Clean the threads with a piece of cloth or waste, and apply a few drops of lubricating oil.

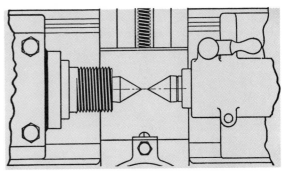

Fig. 9-72. Testing Lathe Centers for Alignment
(South Bend Lathe)

5. Disengage the back gear, if any.

6. Hold the hub of the faceplate squarely against the nose of the spindle with the right hand; then rotate the cone pulley with the left, as in Fig. 9-73. Continue rotating the pulley until the faceplate comes firmly against the shoulder of the spindle. If the spindle cannot be rotated, then rotate the faceplate by hand, clockwise.

CAUTION: *Do not allow the hub of the faceplate to strike hard against the shoulder of the spindle, as this may make it very difficult to remove the faceplate.*

7. Thoroughly clean the openings in the headstock and tailstock spindles with a piece of cloth wrapped about a small stick. Remove any remaining lint or threads.

CAUTION: *Never put your finger in the hole of the lathe spindle while it is revolving.*

8. Wipe centers with a piece of cloth or waste.

9. Insert the soft center in the headstock spindle and the hardened one in the tailstock. The hardened center usually has a groove cut near the cone end, Fig. 9-72.

10. Fasten the lathe dog (Fig. 9-74) on one end of the work, with the bent tail pointing outward.

If the work where the dog is attached is a finished surface, insert a small piece of sheet copper or brass between the end of the screw in the dog and the work; this will prevent marring.

11. Place center lubricant, such as white lead and oil, in the center to be engaged by the dead (tailstock) center.

12. Engage the center hole in the work with the point of the live (headstock) center, and with the tail of the lathe dog in the slot in the faceplate, Fig. 9-75. Hold the work in this position with the left hand.

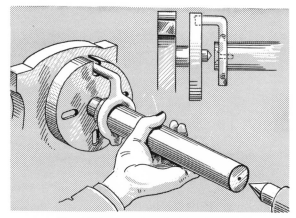

Fig. 9-75. Engaging the Live Center

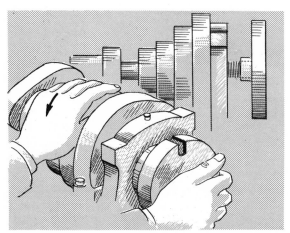

Fig. 9-73. Mounting the Faceplate

Fig. 9-76. Engaging the Dead Center

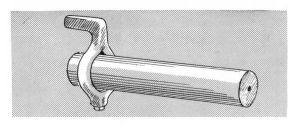

Fig. 9-74. Lathe Dog in Position

CAUTION: *Be sure the tail of the dog does not rest on the bottom of the slot in the faceplate, as that will prevent the center from entering the countersunk hole in the work correctly.*

13. Grasp the tailstock with the right hand, and move it forward until the point of the dead center enters the center hole in the stock.

14. Fasten the tailstock in position by tightening nut *A*, Fig. 9-76.

CAUTION: *Before clamping the tailstock in position, be sure there is sufficient room for the saddle and tool block to operate.*

15. Advance the tailstock spindle by turning the handwheel at the rear of the tailstock clockwise, Fig. 9-76, until the point of the dead center enters the countersunk hole in the end of the work and all motion endwise is eliminated.

16. Turn the handwheel back very slightly. Then move the tail of the dog back and forth, and, at the same time, adjust the handwheel until only a slight resistance is felt. Tighten the tailstock binding lever, *B*, Fig. 9-76.

How To Make Roughing and Finishing Cuts on a Lathe

A *roughing cut*, as the name indicates, is a cut taken to remove the rough stock on the surface. Usually it is a heavy cut, depending somewhat upon the amount of material to be removed and the capacity of the tool to withstand the strain of removing a large amount of metal as quickly as possible. Naturally, this leaves the turned surface in a somewhat rough condition. In rough turning, the work should be machined to nearly the finished size, in preparation for the finishing cut. Whenever possible, the cut should be fed toward the headstock, especially when turning between centers. Experienced workmen frequently finish the work to the size desired with a single cut.

When taking a rough cut on cast iron, cast steel or other metals that have a hard scale on the surface, be sure to set the tool deep enough to cut under the scale. Otherwise, the hard scale will wear away the cutting edge.

Before mounting stock between centers, be sure the centers are in line. Test by moving the tailstock close to the headstock center, Fig. 9-72. This is a very rough check and must not be relied upon when accurate work is required.

A more accurate test may be made by turning a section at each end of the piece and then testing for accuracy with a micrometer or a caliper. To make such a test, mount a piece of stock between centers, and feed the tool in at *A*, Fig. 9-77, with the cross feed, until the work has been reduced about $\frac{1}{16}''$ in diameter. Then with the longitudinal feed, advance the tool until a straight cut about $\frac{1}{2}''$ long has been made. Stop the lathe and withdraw the dead center far enough to permit swinging the right-hand end of the stock to the rear, to permit running the carriage to the right until the tool clears the right-hand end of the stock.

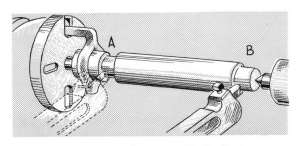

Fig. 9-77. Testing Accuracy of Lathe Centers

When moving the carriage, be sure that you do not change the position of the tool by moving the cross feed. Replace the stock on the dead center, and adjust for tension. Then, without changing the cross feed, make a short longitudinal cut, as at B, Fig. 9-77. With a micrometer, measure the turned sections at A and B. If the lathe centers are in line with each other, there should be no difference in the diameter of the two sections. In most cases, a difference of .002″ or less may be disregarded.

If a difference in diameter greater than .002″ is found, the centers should be brought into alignment by setting the tailstock over, in the direction desired, one-half the difference in diameter, for example, one-half of .003″, or .0015″. For procedure in setting the tailstock over, see Unit 71.

After one is familiar with operating lathe feeds manually, he may use the automatic feeds for making long cuts.

Procedure for Stock on Centers

1. Mount the work in the lathe. See Unit 58.
2. Select a sharp cutting tool of the size and shape desired.

    For roughing cuts, select a tool strong enough to take a heavy cut. If the stock to be machined is cast iron or steel and the tool travels toward the headstock, the usual practice is to select a right-hand turning tool, Fig. 9-28 and 9-48. A left-hand tool is used when the tool travels toward the tailstock. For turning brass, a roundnose tool should be used, Fig. 9-28.

3. Insert the tool in the holder, with the point of the bit projecting about ½″, Fig. 9-69.
4. For turning steel or cast iron, set the toolholder in the tool post with the point from 0° to 5° above the center of the work. See Figs. 9-32 and 9-33. The nose of the holder should project very slightly beyond the edge of the compound rest.
5. Swing the toolholder so that it is inclined about 4° or 5° to the right or left, depending upon the direction of travel. Swing to the right when the line of travel is toward the left, Fig. 9-78; then tighten the setscrew holding the holder in the tool post and also the setscrew holding the bit in the holder.

    This cannot be done when it is necessary to work close to the dog. In that case, set the toolholder in the tool post so that any rotation of the toolholder, which will cause the tool to dig, will be prevented by the toolholder being in contact with the sides of the slot in the tool post.

6. With the cross-feed crank, draw the tool back until it clears the work. Start the lathe, and carefully advance the tool until it just touches the work. Then set the micrometer collar on the cross-feed screw at zero, Fig. 9-79, and lock it in this position

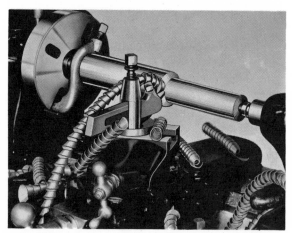

Fig. 9-78. Turning a Steel Shaft Mounted Between Centers (South Bend Lathe)

Fig. 9-79. Micrometer Collar on Cross-Feed Screw (South Bend Lathe)

with screw *A*. Advance the tool to the desired depth, which should cut well below the scale on the surface of the work. The depth of cut is read directly in thousandths of an inch. Remember that the diameter of the workpiece is reduced by an amount equal to twice the depth of the cut; thus with a $\frac{1}{8}''$ depth cut, the diameter is reduced by $\frac{1}{4}''$.

7. When the tool is in position to make the cut, advance it lengthwise of the work by turning the apron handwheel.

8. When about $\frac{1}{8}''$ of the piece has been machined, draw the tool back. Test the piece for size with a pair of calipers, as in Fig. 9-80.

9. If the piece is undersize or oversize, make the necessary adjustment. Be sure to allow about $\frac{1}{32}''$ for the finishing cut.

10. After making adjustments, proceed with the roughing cut, feeding the tool forward at the rate of about 0.010'' per revolution. With experience, a heavier cut may be taken. Either hand feed or automatic feed may be used.

11. Continue until the tool is within about an inch of the dog, or, if the tool is set toward the right side of the compound rest, until the left side of the compound rest is within $\frac{1}{2}''$ of the dog. Stop the lathe, and run the saddle back until the point of the tool is back beyond the turned end of the piece.

12. Remove the piece from between the centers; then remove the dog, and place it on the turned end. Again mount the stock in the lathe and proceed as before, turning the remaining portion of the stock to diameter.

Procedure for Finishing Cut

1. Adjust the tool for the finishing cut.
2. Machine a short section of the piece, and test for size.

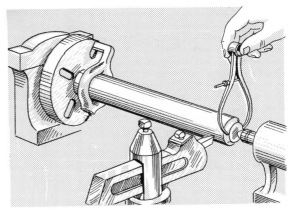

Fig. 9-80. Testing the Piece with Calipers

3. Make adjustments if necessary; then test again. When the stock is to be machined within very close tolerance limits, test the size of the work with a micrometer.

4. When the tool has been set so as to machine the piece to the dimension desired, proceed as when making a roughing cut.

Procedure for Cylindrical Stock Mounted in a Chuck

1. Mount the stock in a chuck. See Unit 66. Use a three-jaw chuck if possible and convenient.

   If a four-jaw chuck is used, take care in rechucking the work; otherwise it will not run true.

2. Rough turn as when mounted between centers. Be sure to stop the lathe when the edge of the compound rest or the point of the tool comes within 1'' of the jaws of the chuck.

3. Stop the lathe; then turn the piece around and chuck it again. Finish rough turning as before.

4. Make the finishing cut in the same manner.

How To Face Work Mounted Between Centers in a Lathe

Procedure for Facing Work

1. Mount the work between centers. See Unit 58.
2. Select a facing tool of the kind and shape desired, and mount it in the toolholder, as in *A*, Fig. 9-83, with the point of the tool on a level with the point of the tailstock center.

3. Start the machine, and advance the tool until the point is almost in contact with the center, Fig. 9-83. Then, with longitudinal feed, advance the tool so that it takes a light cut.
4. With the cross-feed crank or knob (Fig. 9-14), draw the tool toward the outer surface.

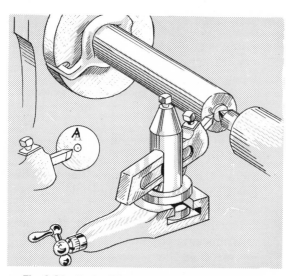

Fig. 9-83. Facing Work Mounted Between Centers

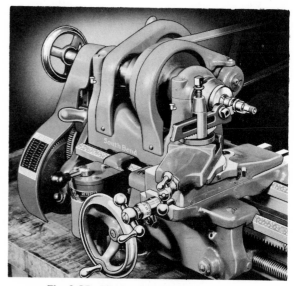

Fig. 9-85. Making Cut with Parting Tool
(South Bend Lathe)

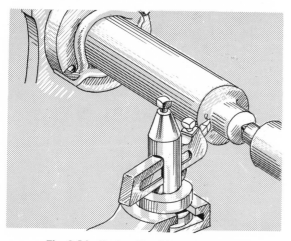

Fig. 9-84. Facing Shoulders with a Fillet

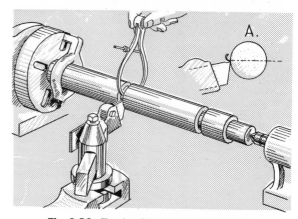

Fig. 9-86. Testing Diameter with Calipers

5. When other cuts are necessary, make them in a similar manner.

6. If the other end is to be faced, turn the piece end for end, and face as before.

Procedure for Filleted Shoulders

1. When the shoulder has a *fillet* (a rounded surface at the bottom of the shoulder, Fig. 9-84), select a roundnose tool and mount it in the tool post, with the point at the same height as the point of the dead center.

2. Machine the curved surface of the fillet with light cuts.

3. Starting at the root of the fillet and working toward the outer edge, face the shoulder.

Procedure for Square Shoulders

When a square shoulder is to be machined, the first cut often is made with a parting tool, Fig. 9-85. This provides clearance at the end of the part to be machined and permits more rapid machining, as one needs only to approach the end of the cut with care to avoid advancing the cut too far.

1. Select a suitable parting tool.

2. Securely mount the toolholder in the post, with the point of the tool on the same level as the point of the dead center (*A*, Fig. 9-86).

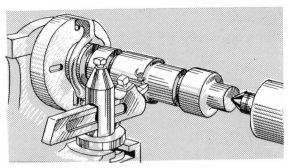

Fig. 9-87. Removing Stock Between Square Shoulders

3. With the apron handwheel, advance the carriage and tool to the position where the shoulder is to be cut on the work.

4. Test the setting for accuracy by measuring with a rule.

5. Set the caliper for the desired diameter of stock at the shoulder.

6. Start the machine; then with the cross-feed screw, advance the tool into the work, Fig. 9-86. Be sure to make the cut in the *waste stock*.

7. Hold the caliper lightly against the work in the cut, Fig. 9-86. When it passes over the work, stop the cut immediately.

8. If necessary to produce a wider groove at the shoulder, make a second cut as in steps 5 through 7 inclusive.

9. Remove remaining stock as when turning between centers. See Unit 59 as well as Fig. 9-87.

How To Use a Steady Rest and Follower Rest on a Lathe

The steady rest (sometimes called a center rest), *A*, Fig. 9-88, is a device used to support long shafts or spindles of small diameter while they are being turned, bored, or threaded. When in use, the rest is mounted on the lathe bed and held in position with a clamp. A follower rest, *B*, Fig. 9-88, is a supporting device which, when correctly attached to the saddle of the lathe with the supporting jaws adjusted to the work, follows along the finished face of the work and holds it steady against the cutting tool.

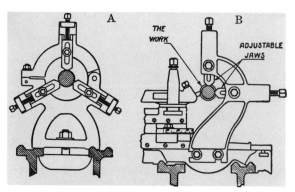

Fig. 9-88. (A) Steady Rest; (B) Follower Rest
(South Bend Lathe)

Fig. 9-91. Using Steady Rest for Boring or Internal
Threading (South Bend Lathe)

Fig. 9-89. Using Both Steady Rest and Follower Rest
for Turning (South Bend Lathe)

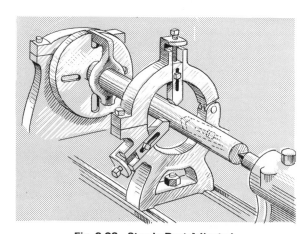

Fig. 9-92. Steady Rest Adjusted

Fig. 9-90. Using Both Steady Rest and Follower Rest
for Cutting Threads (South Bend Lathe)

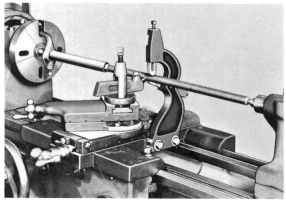

Fig. 9-93. Follower Rest in Position (South Bend Lathe)

When turning very long rods, shafts, or spindles, it sometimes is necessary to use both a steady and a follower rest in combination, Fig. 9-89. Both the steady rest and the follower rest are being used for cutting threads in Fig. 9-90. The steady rest may be used with work mounted in the chuck for boring and internal threading as shown in Fig. 9-91.

Procedure for the Steady Rest

1. Mount the rest on the bed of the lathe, and fasten it loosely.
2. Mount the work between centers. Do not draw the tail center too tightly, as there is danger of springing the work.
3. Adjust the center rest so as to support the work most advantageously. Usually this will be near the point where work is to be performed or near the center. Tighten the clamping bolt.
4. Adjust the jaws so that each one comes lightly into contact with the work, Fig. 9-92. The work should rotate quite freely.
5. Fasten the jaws securely, withdraw the tailstock if necessary, and then proceed to machine the work in the usual manner.
6. When the work is completed, remove the steady rest, clean the lathe, and return equipment to the place where kept when not in use.

Procedure for the Follower Rest

1. Attach the follower rest to the saddle of the lathe.
2. Mount the work between centers, and turn a small portion of the work to size.
3. Adjust the jaws of the follower rest so that they bear directly against the rear of the turned part of the work, just back of the cutting tool, and on top of the work, Fig. 9-93.
4. Clamp the jaws in position; then proceed to machine the work in the usual manner.
5. When the work is completed, remove the follower rest, clean the lathe, and return equipment to the place where kept when not in use.

How To File and Polish Work Revolving in a Lathe

Filing work while it is revolving in a lathe often is resorted to when only a very small amount of stock is to be removed.

Procedure for Filing

1. Grasp the handle of the file in the right hand and the opposite end between the thumb and fingers of the left.
2. Place the file flat on the work near the left end of the part to be filed, with the tip of the file pointed toward the right, as in Fig. 9-94.
3. Press lightly on the file, and, at the same time, move it forward and to the right. At the end of the stroke, release the pressure, raise the file from the work slightly, and draw it back for the next stroke. Take long strokes, and continue in this manner until the piece is filed smooth.

Procedure for Polishing

1. Secure a strip of abrasive cloth, usually aluminum oxide. A strip about $1\frac{1}{4}''$ wide by $10''$ long will suffice.
2. Grasp the ends of the abrasive between the fingers; then place the cloth across the work, and draw it across the rotating surface as when filing.

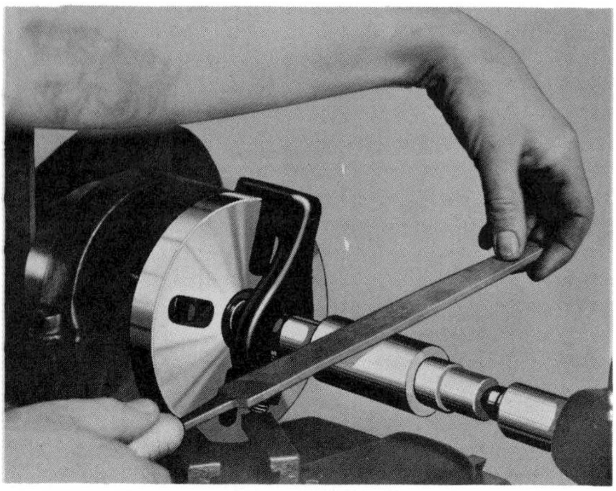

Fig. 9-94. **Filing Work Revolving in Lathe**
(South Bend Lathe)

3. Greater force may be applied if the abrasive is held under a file and used as in Fig. 9-95.
4. To produce a finer finish and polish, use a finer grade of abrasive and, for ferrous metals (iron or steel), apply a few drops of machine oil on the abrasive.

Fig. 9-95. **Polishing Work Revolving in Lathe**
(South Bend Lathe)

63 How To Knurl a Piece of Mild Steel

Certain machine parts, such as knobs, cylindrical handles, round nuts, and collars, are knurled to improve their appearance and to provide a surface which can be gripped more

Fig. 9-96. **Knurling Tool with Removable Rollers**
(South Bend Lathe)

effectively. Knurling tools are made with removable rollers, Fig. 9-96. To produce a fine, medium, or coarse knurl, merely select and insert the appropriate roller. See Fig. 9-97.

On the knurling tool shown in Fig. 9-98, the revolving head has three pairs of removable knurling rolls — coarse, medium, and fine. Knurling rolls are available which produce a knurled surface with either a diamond pattern or a straight-line pattern, as shown in Fig. 9-99. With each pattern, the surface may be coarse, medium, or fine. Removable knurling rolls are shown in Fig. 9-100.

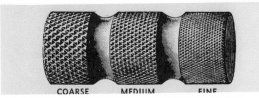

Fig. 9-97. Knurl (South Bend Lathe)

Fig. 9-98. Knurling Tool with Revolving Head
(Armstrong)

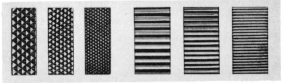

Fig. 9-99. Knurled Surfaces (Armstrong)
(Left) Diamond pattern; (Right) Straight-line pattern.

Fig. 9-100. Removable Knurling Rolls (Armstrong)
(Left) Diamond pattern; (Right) Straight-line pattern.

Fig. 9-101. Using the Knurling Tool (South Bend Lathe)

Procedure

1. Finish-turn the work to the dimension desired.
2. Select a knurling tool of the degree of coarseness desired.
3. Insert the knurling tool in the tool post, with the front of the rollers flat against the side of the work and both rollers in contact with it.
4. Fasten the tool *firmly* in the tool post.
5. Set the lathe for a longitudinal feed of 0.020″ to 0.030″ and for back-gear drive. Start the lathe on a slow speed.
6. With the apron handwheel, move the carriage over until the right side of the roller passes the right end of the piece about ⅛″.
7. With the hand cross feed, force the rollers about ¹⁄₆₄″ into the work. At the same time, engage the longitudinal feed of the carriage, and allow the knurling tool to travel across the face of the work, Fig. 9-101. Apply oil liberally throughout the operation.
8. When the left end of the knurling roller reaches the left end of the stock, stop the lathe.
9. Start the lathe *in reverse*, and, at the same time, advance the knurling tool about ¹⁄₆₄″. Immediately engage the longitudinal feed, and allow the tool to feed toward the right until the right side of the tool is even with the right end of the work.
10. Repeat the operation until the knurling is the depth desired.

Lathe Chucks and Faceplates

Lathe chucks and faceplates are devices for mounting and holding work while being machined on a lathe. When work is mounted on a faceplate, it usually is clamped with bolts and metal straps. The plate is equipped with slotted holes to allow for work of varying size and shape. Figs. 9-105 and 9-106 show work mounted ready for machining.

Chucks

Chucks hold work by means of jaws which may be adjusted to accommodate work of varying size or shape. Shown at the right in Fig. 9-107 is a four-jaw independent chuck. As the name implies, the jaws of this chuck move independently. This greatly increases the versatility of the chuck, as it may hold work which

Fig. 9-105. Work Mounted on Faceplate with Metal Straps (South Bend Lathe)

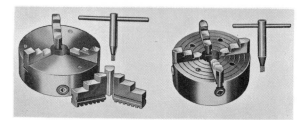

Fig. 9-107. Three-Jaw Universal and Four-Jaw Independent Chucks (South Bend Lathe)

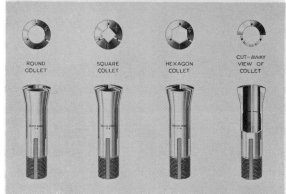

Fig. 9-106. Work Bolted on Faceplate
(South Bend Lathe)

Fig. 9-108. Collet Chuck and Collets
(South Bend Lathe)

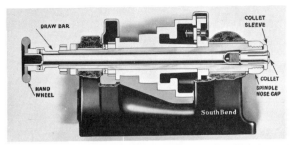

Fig. 9-109. Assembly of Draw-In Collet Chuck
(South Bend Lathe)

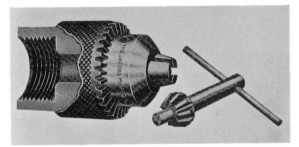

Fig. 9-110. Spindle Chuck (South Bend Lathe)

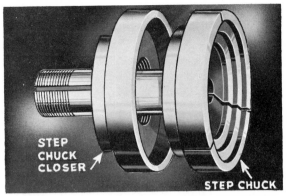

Fig. 9-111. Step Chuck and Closer (South Bend Lathe)

is round, square, rectangular, or irregular in shape. The jaws may be removed and reversed.

A three-jaw universal chuck is shown at the left in Fig. 9-107. All three jaws operate as a unit, opening or closing together. This makes it possible to center workpieces easily and rapidly. The jaws are also reversible.

Two sets of jaws normally are included with the universal chuck. The *outside jaws* are used for holding work externally, and the *inside jaws*, for holding workpieces from the inside. Universal chucks also are available with six jaws which operate simultaneously.

Universal three-jaw and six-jaw chucks are intended primarily for holding round workpieces. They hold work accurately to within 0.002″ or 0.003″ and retain this accuracy until either the jaws or the internal threads become worn or damaged.

The four-jaw independent chuck is more accurate than the universal chuck, since the workpiece may be centered exactly with the use of a dial indicator. However, even with considerable experience, it takes more time to center work in the four-jaw chuck.

Collet Chuck

The collet chuck is used chiefly in production and precision work, primarily for holding

small work. It is available in a number of sizes, designed for holding round, square, or hexagon stock, Fig. 9-108. A collet chuck centers the stock quickly and accurately.

A spring collet chuck should be used only for the size of stock it is designed to hold, for example, $\frac{5}{16}$″. Furthermore, to avoid danger of springing the chuck, it should not be used for holding stock which is more than 0.003″ oversize or undersize.

Fig. 9-109 shows an assembly of one form of draw-in collet chuck. The chuck is drawn tightly into the collet sleeve, inserted in the spindle by the turning of the handwheel at the rear end of the spindle toward the right, and loosened by turning the wheel toward the left.

Centering stock in a collet chuck is merely a matter of placing the stock in the opening in the collet and drawing the collet into the collet sleeve, so that the work is held securely.

Spindle Chuck

The spindle chuck, Fig. 9-110, resembles an ordinary drill chuck, except that it is designed to screw onto the nose of the lathe spindle. The movable jaws are tightened with a pinion key. A spindle chuck is used primarily for chucking small round work, which it does quickly and accurately within .002″ or .003″.

Step Chuck and Closer

The step chuck and closer, Fig. 9-111, is designed for centering and holding small round discs. It operates on much the same principle as the draw-in collet chuck.

How To Mount and Remove Lathe Chucks

Lathe chucks and faceplates are mounted to the spindle nose of the lathe. The chucks are equipped with adapter plates which fit three types of lathe spindles — (1) the *threaded* spindle nose (Fig. 9-112); (2) the spindle nose with the long taper *key drive* (Fig. 9-113); and (3) the spindle with the *cam-lock drive* (Fig. 9-114).

With the threaded spindle, the chuck (or the faceplate) is threaded directly to the spindle.

With the key-drive spindle, the chuck is mounted with the internal key slot properly aligned with the key on the spindle nose. The threaded collar is then threaded to the shoulder of the chuck and tightened with a spanner wrench.

With the cam-lock spindle, the notched holding pins on the chuck are inserted into the holes in the spindle flange. The chuck then is locked in position by turning the cam-locking screws in the flange with a T-handle chuck key.

Fig. 9-114. Cam-Lock Spindle (South Bend Lathe)

Fig. 9-112. Threaded Spindle Nose (South Bend Lathe)

Fig. 9-113. Spindle Nose with Long Taper Key Drive
(South Bend Lathe)

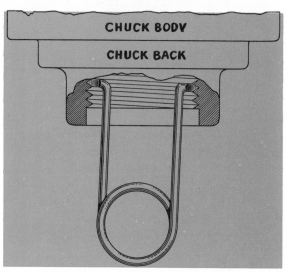

CHUCK BODY

CHUCK BACK

Fig. 9-115. Cleaning Threads in Chuck

When mounting or removing lathe chucks or faceplates, take care to avoid damage to the threads in the chuck or on the nose of the lathe spindle. With either the tapered key drive or the cam-lock spindles, care also should be taken to avoid nicking or damaging the internal surfaces of the chuck or the external surfaces on the spindle nose.

Regardless of the type of spindle nose, the internal threads or surfaces of the chuck must be clean and free from nicks. The external threads or surfaces of the spindle nose also must be clean and free from nicks. A small chip, nick, or burr will prevent the chuck from running true.

Procedure for Mounting Chuck to Threaded Spindle

1. Remove the live center by inserting a steel rod of appropriate size in the hollow spindle of the headstock. Grasp the projecting end of the center in the right hand and the rod in the left; then jar the center loose by gently striking the encased end with the rod.

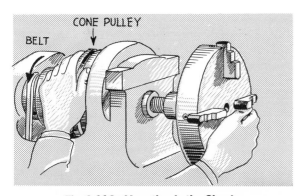

Fig. 9-116. Mounting Lathe Chuck

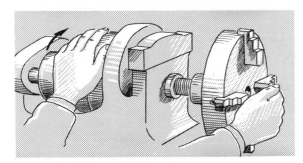

Fig. 9-117. Steadying Small Chuck with Right Hand

2. Insert a small wad of clean waste in the hole in the spindle. This will prevent entry of dirt or metal chips.
3. With the tool shown in Fig. 9-115, clean the threads in the chuck. This tool may be made from a $\frac{3}{16}$" diameter, round steel rod. It also is available commercially.
4. Wipe the threads with a piece of cloth or waste, remove any remaining lint or dust, and then apply a few drops of oil to the threads.
5. In a similar manner, clean the threads and shoulder of the spindle. Apply a few drops of oil.
6. Hold the chuck squarely against the nose of the spindle with the right hand and arm, as in Fig. 9-116. Then, with the left hand, rotate the spindle forward. Con-

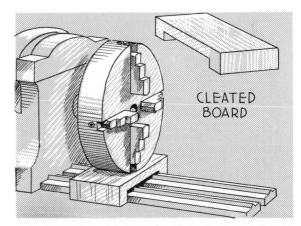

Fig. 9-118. Ways of Lathe Protected with Cleated Board

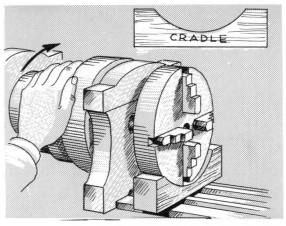

Fig. 9-119. Lathe Chuck Supported with Wooden Cradle

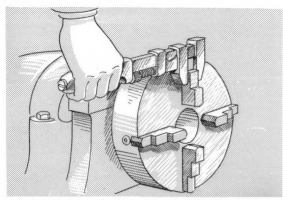

Fig. 9-120. Loosening Chuck with Monkey Wrench

Fig. 9-121. Loosening Chuck with Block of Wood
(South Bend Lathe)

tinue in this manner until the hub of the faceplate rests firmly against the shoulder of the spindle.

Procedure for Removing Chuck from Threaded Spindle

A lathe chuck is a heavy piece of apparatus. Consequently, when removing or mounting it, there is danger of injury to the operator, or of damage to the chuck or the ways of the lathe, unless care is exercised. The ways of the lathe may be protected by supporting the chuck with the right hand, as shown in Fig. 9-117. However, this is practicable only when the chuck is small.

Another means is a cleated board such as shown in Fig. 9-118. This device is hooked over the lathe bed under the chuck. Still another device is the wooden cradle shown in Fig. 9-119.

1. To remove the chuck, engage one jaw with a monkey wrench, as in Fig. 9-120, or place a strong bar between the jaws; then give the bar a sharp jerk.

2. Grasp the cone pulley or drive belt with the left hand. This will prevent the spindle from revolving. Then give the handle of the wrench a sharp jerk, which should loosen the chuck.

3. If the chuck cannot be thus loosened, place a block of wood under one jaw, with one end resting on the rear of the lathe bed, as in Fig. 9-121. Then throw in the back gears, and give the spindle a quick backward turn by hand.

4. After loosening the chuck, be sure to place the cleated board under it to protect the ways should the chuck fall. Grasp the chuck with the right hand and arm, Fig. 9-117; then rotate the spindle backward with the left hand. As the chuck approaches the end of the thread on the spindle, press it against the nose of the spindle and hold it firmly to prevent falling.

5. If the chuck is too heavy to hold with one hand and arm, use a wooden cradle (such as shown in Fig. 9-119) while dismounting it.

6. Carefully lift the chuck from the board or cradle on the ways of the lathe, and place it in the rack where it is kept when not in use (some place where it cannot fall or roll about).

How To Mount and True Up Work in a Four-Jaw Independent Chuck

A chuck with independent jaws often is a convenience, for example, when chucking an irregularly shaped piece or a cylindrical piece in such a position that a hole or a recess may be bored *off center*. Another feature of this chuck is that the jaws may be taken out and reversed for certain types of work. (This feature is not peculiar to independent-jaw chucks, as the same may be done, although it seldom is, with three-jaw universal chucks.) With a four-jaw independent chuck, work may be centered with any degree of accuracy desired. It is possible to center as accurately as 0.0001″ by using a dial test indicator, Fig. 9-125.

Procedure for Mounting Stock

1. Adjust the jaws of the chuck to approximately the size of the work by withdrawing or advancing the adjusting screw of each jaw with a chuck wrench, Fig. 9-126. Use the concentric circles on the face of the chuck for approximate centering of the jaws.

2. Place the work in the jaws of the chuck, and fasten it by lightly tightening the adjusting screw of two opposite jaws, for example, jaws 1 and 3. Tighten these just enough to hold the work securely.

3. In a similar manner, tighten jaws 2 and 4. *Remove the chuck wrench.* Make a practice of doing this; otherwise you may forget it and an accident may result.

4. Mount a suitable tool in the toolholder, and set it at the correct height for the work to be machined. In this case, the tool bit will be used as an aid in centering the work in the chuck. Therefore, if desired, a soft piece of steel may be inserted in the toolholder instead of a tool bit. This will prevent possible scratches or damage to the workpiece. The soft piece will work best if ground to a cone-shaped point, about ⅛″ in diameter at the end.

5. Revolve the spindle slowly by hand; then advance the tool slowly until the point just touches the high side of the work, A, Fig. 9-127. Center the work between only two opposite jaws, such as jaws 1 and 3, before attempting to center it between the two remaining jaws. The jaws with which you are working must be in a horizontal position.

Fig. 9-125. Centering Work with Dial Test Indicator
(South Bend Lathe)

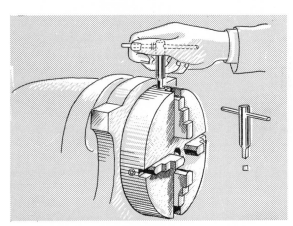

Fig. 9-126. Adjusting One Jaw of a Four-Jaw Independent Chuck

6. Give the work a half turn; then measure the distance from the point of the tool to the edge of the work, *B*, Fig. 9-127.

7. Loosen the jaw on the *low* side of the work an amount equal to one-half the distance from the point of the tool to the edge of the work.

8. Tighten the opposite jaw on the high side of the work. The work then should be approximately centered between the two jaws on which you are working, for instance, jaws 1 and 3.

9. Test the accuracy of the location of the work between the two jaws by backing the tool off slightly and inserting a slip of paper between the point of the tool and the work. Apply just enough pressure to the tool with the cross-feed screw to cause the paper to drag, but not tear, when it is pulled between the tool and the work. Run the carriage and tool to the right, clear of the work. Then rotate the spindle a half turn. Bring the carriage and tool back, and insert the piece of paper between the tool and the work on the opposite side. If the paper drags, but does not tear, the work is centered between the two opposite jaws to within several thou-

sandths of an inch. If the paper tears or does not drag, an adjustment should be made between the two jaws, using the procedure described in steps 5 through 9.

10. Give the chuck a quarter turn, and center the work between the remaining two jaws. Use the procedure described in steps 5 through 9 above.

11. Check to see that all jaws are tight against the work and that the work is centered accurately to within the thickness of the paper. The paper should drag between the tool and the work at each of the four jaw locations without cutting or tearing.

12. To locate work 0.001″ or closer, use a dial indicator. Note in Figs. 9-125 and 3-85 that a dial indicator with hole attachment is used to align the hole in a piece of work in a four-jaw chuck. For alignment of the outside diameter of round stock, place the contact point on the dial indicator directly against the workpiece. Considerable time will be saved in aligning work with a dial indicator if you work with one pair of opposite jaws until the work is aligned exactly between them first. Then the remaining two jaws may be brought into alignment rapidly.

13. If necessary, test the face of the workpiece for wobble by using a dial indicator, as shown in Fig. 9-128.

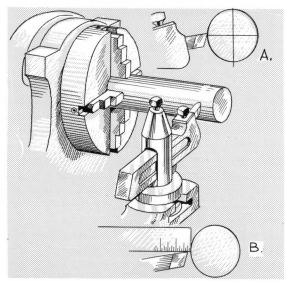

Fig. 9-127. Truing Work in a Four-Jaw Independent Chuck

Fig. 9-128. Testing Face of Work with Dial Indicator
(South Bend Lathe)

Fig. 9-129. Using Chalk to True Up Work

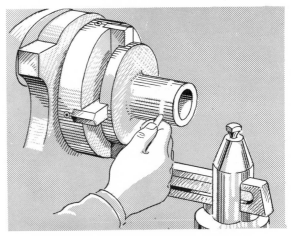

Fig. 9-130. Chalk Mark Indicates High Side

Procedure for Centering Stock, Chalk Methods

1. Mount stock as in preceding steps 1, 2, and 3.
2. Move the toolholder close to the work.
3. Revolve the work slowly by power or hand. Then, using the toolholder as a support for the arm, bring a piece of chalk lightly into contact with the revolving work, Figs. 9-129 and 9-130. The chalk will leave a mark on the high side only.
4. Stop the rotation, and locate the high spot (where the chalk has left a mark). Give the work a half turn; then slightly loosen the adjusting screw on the side opposite the high spot. Give the work another half turn, and tighten the adjusting screw, pushing the work toward the low side.

If the chalk mark extends as much as one-third the distance around the piece, it will be necessary to loosen two of the adjusting screws opposite the high spot, and then tighten the other two screws. Adjust one pair of jaws at a time.

5. Revolve the spindle as before, and again hold the chalk against the work. Make adjustments if necessary. Continue in this manner until the piece runs true, that is, until the chalk makes a line of uniform weight completely around the work.
6. When the work is running true, firmly tighten the adjusting screw of each jaw; then proceed with the other machining operations.

How To Face and Turn Work Mounted in a Lathe Chuck

Work may be mounted in a chuck and faced to a true plane or turned to a given diameter. Frequently the first step is to face or turn one side of the work to a true plane.

Procedure for Facing

1. Mount the stock in a suitable chuck. See Unit 66.
2. Select a sharp right-hand facing tool.

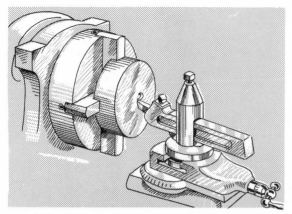

Fig. 9-131. Facing Stock Mounted in a Chuck

3. Mount the tool in the holder, and adjust the point or cutting edge of the bit so that it is the same height as the center about which the work rotates.

4. Incline the toolholder slightly toward the right of a line perpendicular to the face of the work. Then fasten both it and the bit securely.

5. Start the lathe, and with the cross-feed crank, move the point of the bit toward the center of the work, Fig. 9-131.

6. With the apron handwheel, advance the tool so as to make a cut sufficiently deep to get below the scale.

7. With the cross-feed crank, feed the tool steadily toward the left, until the cut is completed.

   The cut may be made with the power cross feed in the following manner if desired:

   a. Place the feed-change lever in position for power cross feed, Fig. 9-4. The cross feed should travel outward, toward the operator. A cross feed of 0.005″ is satisfactory.

   b. Advance the tool for the desired depth of cut, using the apron handwheel.

   c. Engage the clutch knob, Fig. 9-4.

   d. When the cut is completed, disengage the clutch knob.

8. Make other necessary cuts in a similar manner.

9. Finish with a light cut.

Procedure for Turning

1. Mount the stock in a suitable chuck. See Unit 66.

2. Select and mount a sharp, R.H. turning tool in the toolholder.

3. Adjust the point of the tool to the height desired.

4. Incline the toolholder very slightly toward the right; then fasten both the holder and bit securely.

5. Start the lathe, and with the cross-feed crank, advance the tool so as to take a cut of the depth desired, Fig. 9-132.

6. With the apron handwheel, advance the tool about $\frac{1}{8}$″. Then with a caliper or rule, test the work for size.

7. If necessary, make adjustments; then proceed to make the cut. Continue advancing the tool until the point of the tool is about $\frac{1}{2}$″ away from the jaw of the chuck.

8. Stop the lathe, and remove the work from the chuck by slightly releasing two of the jaws.

9. Turn the work around, and rechuck it, with the jaws of the chuck gripping the turned surface. Before starting to turn the unfinished part, be sure the turned part of the work is centered accurately.

10. Turn the unturned part of the circumference as in steps 5, 6, and 7.

11. Set the tool to make a light finishing cut.

12. When the cut has advanced about $\frac{1}{8}$″, stop the machine and carefully test the work for size.

13. If necessary, make adjustments; then complete the cut in the usual manner.

14. Stop the cut when the point of the tool is about $\frac{1}{2}$″ away from the jaws of the chuck.

15. With the apron wheel, run the carriage back so that the tool clears the work. Do not change the position of the tool unless necessary to compensate for a slight variation in the diameter of the work (caused by rapid cooling) following a long cut.

16. Slightly loosen two of the adjusting screws, and remove the work from the chuck.

17. Turn the work around, and rechuck it on the finished surface. Be sure the finished surface is running true.

If there is danger of the jaws of the chuck damaging the finished surface, insert a strip of copper or brass between the work and the nose of each jaw.

18. Start the cut on the unfinished part of the surface.

19. When the cut has advanced about $\frac{1}{16}''$, test the work for size and make adjustment if necessary. This may necessitate adjusting the screws in the chuck, in order to correct slight inaccuracy in rechucking.

20. Complete the cut in the usual manner.

21. When finished, remove the work from the chuck; then remove the chuck, and return it to the place where it is kept when not in use.

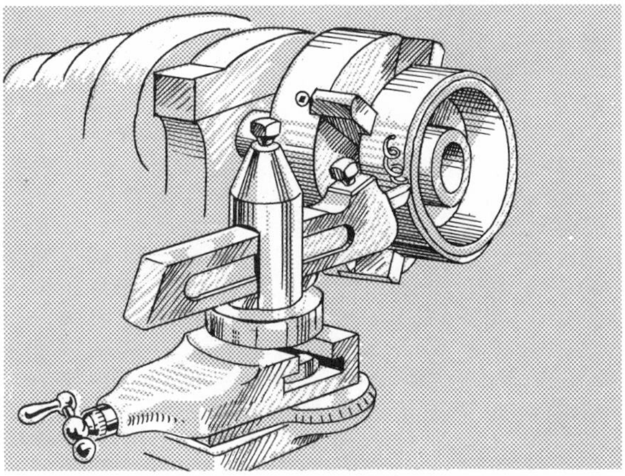

Fig. 9-132. Turning Circumference of Stock Mounted in a Chuck

How To Drill and Ream in a Lathe

Drilling, countersinking, reaming, and counterboring can be done readily in a lathe. In performing these operations, the workpiece is mounted in an appropriate lathe chuck, and the drill or other cutting tool is mounted in the tailstock.

For center drilling with a combination drill and countersink, Fig. 9-133, the tool is mounted in a drill chuck, which in turn is mounted in the tailstock. The tailstock is clamped to the lathe bed so that it remains stationary. The tool is fed to the desired depth with the tailstock handwheel.

Small drills (Fig. 9-134) and small reamers (Fig. 9-135) also are mounted in a drill chuck, which is mounted in the tailstock. Larger drills with taper shanks (Fig. 9-136) are mounted directly into the tailstock for drilling.

Taper-shank reamers, counterbores, and other taper-shank cutting tools also may be mounted in the tailstock for hole-machining operations. Small parts may be drilled with the drill mounted in the headstock chuck and the workpiece mounted against a crotch center, as shown in Fig. 9-137.

Fig. 9-133. Center Drilling in a Lathe
(South Bend Lathe)

267

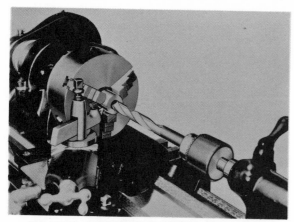

Fig. 9-134. **Small Drill Mounted in Drill Chuck in Tailstock** (South Bend Lathe)

Fig. 9-136. **Drilling with Taper-Shank Drill Mounted in Tailstock** (South Bend Lathe)

Fig. 9-135. **Reaming in a Lathe** (South Bend Lathe)

Fig. 9-137. **Drilling with Crotch Center in Tailstock** (South Bend Lathe)

Procedure

1. Check that the lathe centers are properly aligned, Fig. 9-72. If they are not, the hole will not be machined straight.
2. Mount the lathe chuck on the spindle; see Unit 65.
3. Mount the workpiece in the lathe chuck; be sure that it is centered properly. See Unit 66.
4. Select the proper cutting tool (center drill, drill, reamer, etc.).
5. Install a drill chuck in the tailstock if required, Fig. 9-133. Be sure that the hole in the tailstock spindle is clean.
6. Install the drill or reamer in the drill chuck, and tighten the chuck. (Taper-shank tools are installed directly in the tailstock spindle, Fig. 9-136.) Tap the end of the tool *lightly* with a lead hammer, to insure a snug fit in the tailstock.

7. Select the proper cutting speed (Table 8) and rpm (Table 41, appendix). Then start the lathe.
8. Feed the drill or reamer with the tailstock handwheel, Fig. 9-136. Feed at a steady rate for the desired chip formation. Small drills are fed at a lighter feed rate than larger drills. Apply cutting fluid as recommended in Table 43, appendix. When drilling or reaming deep holes, withdraw the tool periodically for chip removal. This practice will prevent tool breakage in deep holes.
9. Complete the drilling or reaming to the desired depth.
10. Remove the cutting tool, and return it to the proper location.
11. Remove the lathe chuck, and return it to the proper location, as required by your instructor.

How To Bore Work Mounted in a Lathe

Holes or recesses may be bored in work which is mounted in a lathe. For boring, the workpiece may be mounted on the faceplate (Fig. 9-140) or in a chuck (Fig. 9-141). Drilled or cored holes and recesses are bored with boring tools. The manner in which boring tools often are set in relation to the inside of the work is illustrated in Figs. 9-140 and 9-142. The cutting edge of the tool is set at the height of the horizontal center line of the work.

Different styles of boring bars and tool-holders commonly are used in a lathe. The boring tool in Fig. 9-143 includes the tool-holder, boring bar, and insert tool bits which are ground in much the same manner in which standard lathe tool bits are ground. The boring bar is equipped with end caps which hold the tool bit at 90°, 45°, and 30° angles. This type boring bar is available in a variety of sizes for boring holes ⅝″ in diameter or larger.

The boring tools in Figs. 9-144 and 9-145 have reversible bar clamps which make it possible for them to accommodate boring bars from ¼″ to ½″ diameter. The boring tool in Fig. 9-144 is equipped with a boring bar with

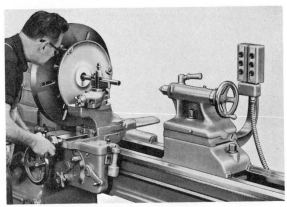

Fig. 9-140. Boring Work Mounted on Faceplate
(South Bend Lathe)

Fig. 9-141. Boring Work Mounted in a Chuck
(South Bend Lathe)

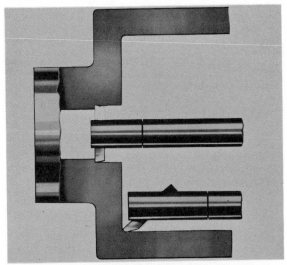

Fig. 9-142. Boring Tools in Relation to Workpiece
(Armstrong)

**Fig. 9-143. Boring Tool with 90°, 45°, and 30°
End Caps** (Armstrong)

insert tool bits. The boring tool in Fig. 9-145 has a forged boring bar. This type boring tool is available in small sizes for boring small-diameter holes.

The boring tool in Fig. 9-146 is equipped with three boring bars of different sizes for boring holes of various size.

All of the above types of boring tools may be used for internal-threading operations when the cutting tool is ground properly, Fig. 9-43.

Procedure for the Side Wall

1. Mount the work on a faceplate or in a chuck, Figs. 9-140 and 9-141.
2. Select a suitable tool.

Fig. 9-144. Boring Tool with Insert Tool Bits
(Armstrong)

Fig. 9-145. Boring Tool with Forged Boring Bar
(Armstrong)

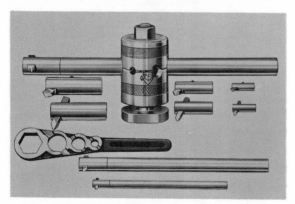

Fig. 9-146. Three-Bar Boring Tool (Armstrong)

3. Set the tool so that the point is level with the center line of the work, Figs. 9-142 and 9-147.
4. Make sure that both the tool and holder are fastened securely.
5. With the cross-feed screw, advance the tool so as to make a cut of the depth desired, Fig. 9-147.
6. With the apron handwheel, advance the tool into the work about $\frac{1}{8}$ ".
7. Stop the machine, and measure the diameter of the machined part of the recess with a rule or inside caliper, Fig. 9-141.
8. Make adjustment if necessary; then complete the cut.

    When machining a shoulder or a recess with a closed bottom, be sure to stop the cut just as the point of the tool reaches the shoulder or the bottom, Fig. 9-142.
9. If other cuts are necessary to enlarge the opening, proceed as in steps 6, 7, and 8.
10. Set the tool to make a light finishing cut.
11. Advance the tool into the work about $\frac{1}{16}$ "; then measure for size.
12. If necessary, adjust the depth of cut; then complete the cut.
13. When the work is finished, clean the lathe and return equipment to the place where it is kept when not in use.

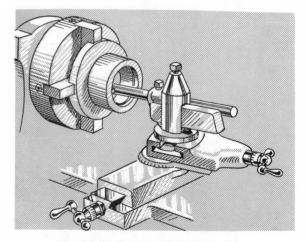

Fig. 9-147. Boring with a Boring Bar

270

Procedure for the Bottom

1. Select a boring tool which will enable you to machine to the center and to the outside edge of the bottom surface. A tool mounted in a 45° end cap, as shown in Fig. 9-142, is satisfactory for large-diameter holes. For smaller-diameter holes, use a forged boring bar, as in Fig. 9-145.

2. Starting at about ½″ to the left of the center of the work, feed the tool into the metal with the apron wheel.

3. When the tool has entered the metal the depth desired, feed it toward the right with the cross-feed screw until the center is reached.

4. Reverse the direction of travel, and feed toward the left inside wall.

5. When the cut almost reaches the side wall, stop the machine, and set the toolholder at an angle sufficient to permit machining into the corner.

The roundnose tool will leave a small fillet in the corner; this may or may not be permissible. In the event a square corner is required, remove the roundnose tool and insert a right-hand corner or side tool.

6. Advance the corner tool with the apron wheel until the blunt angle just strikes the bottom. Then with the cross-feed screw, feed the tool slowly toward the left wall of the recess.

7. Stop the feed when the left side of the tool just touches the left wall of the recess.

8. Finish both bottom and sides with light cuts if necessary.

9. Clean the lathe and return equipment to the place where it is kept when not in use.

How To Machine Work in a Lathe When Mounted on a Mandrel   70

Sometimes it is necessary to machine the exterior of cylindrical work accurately in relation to a hole that previously has been bored in the center of the piece. In such cases, the work often is mounted on a mandrel (Fig. 9-148) and turned between centers, Fig. 9-149. A mandrel usually is a cylindrical piece of hardened steel turned with a slight taper. For an emergency, a mandrel may be turned from a piece of soft steel. Since a mandrel of given diameter has only limited application, an expanding bushing (Fig. 9-150) often is used. The illustration shows a mandrel equipped with a slotted bushing. The bushing is bored with a taper corresponding to the taper of the mandrel. A series of such bushings greatly extends the adaptability of a mandrel of a given size.

Fig. 9-148. Mandrel (South Bend Lathe)

Fig. 9-149. **Work Mounted on a Mandrel**
(South Bend Lathe)

Fig. 9-150. **Mandrel with Slotted Expanding Bushing**
(South Bend Lathe)

Procedure

1. Secure or turn a mandrel of suitable size.
2. Apply a little oil to the surface of the mandrel and to the side walls of the hole. Distribute the oil evenly with the fingers.

    Unless a lubricant is applied, there is danger of the mandrel freezing in the work, in which case it cannot be removed without damaging the work or the mandrel or both.
3. Insert the small end of the mandrel in the hole in the object, and force it in tightly with a press or a *lead* hammer. The mandrel must be tight enough to prevent slipping while the work is being machined.

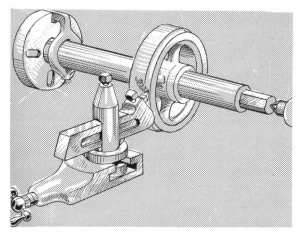

Fig. 9-151. **Turning Work Mounted on a Mandrel**

4. Mount the work between centers, apply center lubricant on the dead center, and turn in the usual manner. See Unit 59 and Fig. 9-151.
5. To remove the mandrel, apply pressure to the small end with a press or strike it with a lead hammer.
6. Clean the lathe, and return other equipment to the place where kept when not in use.

UNIT

71 Calculating Amount of Tailstock Setover for Turning Tapers

The setover of the tailstock for turning tapers may be calculated in three ways, depending on the length and location of the tapered surface. In each case, the total length of the workpiece (the distance between centers) is indicated in inches. A formula is listed for calculating the setover in each case. The following symbols are used in the formulas where they apply:

T = Total length of the workpiece
t = Length of the portion to be tapered
D = Large diameter of the taper
d = Small diameter of the taper
tpf = Taper per foot

Procedure When the Work Is Tapered Its Entire Length

Subtract the diameter of the small end of the taper from that of the large end. Divide the difference by 2; the quotient is the amount of setover required.

Formula:

$$\text{Setover} = \frac{D - d}{2}$$

Example: Calculate the amount of tailstock setover for turning a taper on a piece such as that shown in Fig. 9-153.

Solution: $\dfrac{1\frac{1}{2} - \frac{7}{8}}{2} =$

$\dfrac{1\frac{2}{8} - \frac{7}{8}}{2} = \dfrac{\frac{5}{8}}{2} =$

$\frac{5}{8} \div 2 = \frac{5}{16}''$ amount of setover required.

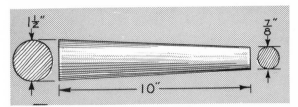

Fig. 9-153. Piece Tapered Its Entire Length

Procedure When the Taper Per Foot Is Given

Divide the *total length* of the stock (the distance between centers) in *inches* by 12. Multiply the quotient by one-half of the amount of taper per foot given. The result is the amount of setover required.

Formula:
Setover $= T/12 \times 1/2$ tpf

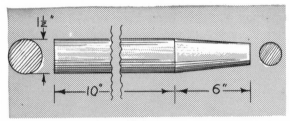

Fig. 9-154. Piece Tapered a Part of Its Length

Example: Calculate the tailstock setover for turning a taper of $\frac{5}{8}''$ per foot for a distance of $6''$ on a piece of shafting $16''$ long, Fig. 9-154.

Solution:
Setover $= \frac{16}{12} \times (\frac{1}{2} \times \frac{5}{8})$
$= \frac{16}{12} \times \frac{5}{16}$
$= \frac{4}{3} \times \frac{5}{16}$
$= \frac{20}{48} = \frac{5}{12}$ or $0.417''$

Procedure When Section Is Dimensioned But Not in Taper per Foot

Divide the *total length* of the piece by the length of the portion to be tapered. Multiply the quotient by one-half the difference between the large end of the taper and the small end.

Formula:
Setover $= T/t \times 1/2$ (D − d)

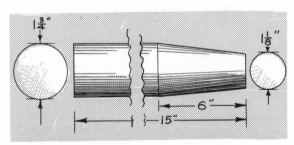

Fig. 9-155. Piece Tapered a Part of Its Length

Example: Calculate the tailstock setover for turning a taper for a distance of $6''$ on a piece of work $15''$ long. The large diameter of the taper is $1\frac{3}{4}''$ and the small end $1\frac{1}{8}''$, Fig. 9-155.

Solution:
Setover $= \frac{15}{6} \times \frac{1}{2} (1\frac{3}{4} - 1\frac{1}{8})$
$= \frac{5}{2} \times \frac{1}{2} (\frac{5}{8})$
$= \frac{5}{2} \times \frac{5}{16}$
$= \frac{25}{32}''$

How To Turn a Taper with a Metalworking Lathe

There are several ways of turning tapers in a lathe. The most common ones are: by setting the tailstock over the amount desired; by using a taper attachment; or by setting the compound rest at the angle desired. The latter method always is used when very sharp, short tapers are cut and when tapered holes are bored.

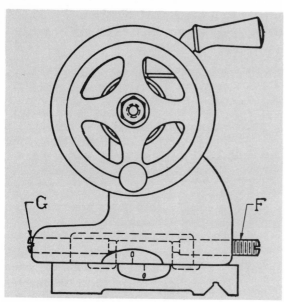

Fig. 9-157. Tailstock Setover Screws
(South Bend Lathe)

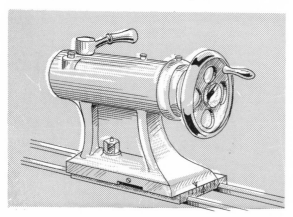

Fig. 9-158. Tailstock Set Over ¼"

Procedure For Setover Method

1. Find the center of the stock, and prepare it for the mounting between centers.
2. Turn stock to cylinder of size desired; then remove work from between centers.
3. Calculate the amount the tailstock should be set over.
4. Loosen both the clamping nut and the tailstock setover screw at the near side of the tailstock (for example, G, Fig. 9-157). This screw should be drawn out the distance required, such as ¼". Next, screw in the tailstock setover screw on the opposite side of the tailstock until the tailstock is set off center the distance desired by the witness mark on the base of the tailstock (for example, ¼", Fig. 9-158). Not all lathes have witness marks on the base of the tailstock.

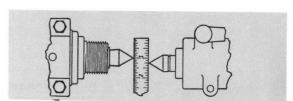

Fig. 9-159. Checking Amount of Tailstock Setover
(South Bend Lathe)

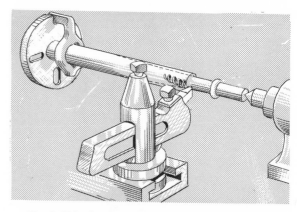

Fig. 9-160. Cutting a Taper with Work Mounted Between Centers

CAUTION: *The setover screws always should be drawn up snug, but not tight, to prevent a shift in position if the tailstock is moved.*

5. Fasten the tailstock in position by tightening the clamping nut.

   The amount the tailstock has been set over may be tested by moving the tailstock close to the headstock, and, with a rule, measuring the difference in alignment of the points of the two centers, Fig. 9-159.

6. Mount the stock between centers. *Be sure to apply center lubricant on the dead center.*

7. Select a tool of suitable size and shape, usually a right-hand turning tool. Mount the tool in the toolholder, with the point of the tool *just even* with a *line through* the center of the work.

8. With the apron handwheel, draw the tool forward until it is in position to make a cut. Then with the cross-feed crank, advance the tool so that it will take a fairly heavy cut.

9. Start the lathe, and feed the tool toward the left in the usual manner, Fig. 9-160.

10. Continue advancing the tool with the handwheel until the cut runs out. Withdraw the tool, and move the carriage back to the starting point. Take a second cut in a similar manner.

11. Measure a unit of length on the taper, for example, 1″ or 2″. At this point, measure the large end of the taper; then measure the small end.

12. Calculate the amount of taper in the unit of length. Compare this with the amount of taper required.

13. Make adjustment in taper if necessary.

14. With repeated cuts, reduce the stock to approximately the size desired.

15. Set the caliper to the exact dimension; then with a light finishing cut, reduce the piece to the size desired.

16. When the job has been completed, set the tailstock back in normal position.

   Objections to this method of turning tapers are: (1) The center holes wear unevenly. (2) Calculation is necessary for each length of stock. (3) The procedure cannot be employed to bore tapered holes, except in some special cases.

Procedure For Compound Rest Method

1. Mount the stock in the lathe, either between centers or in a chuck. Turn the piece to a cylinder of the size desired.

2. With a sharp scriber, lightly mark the terminus of the taper on the circumference of the work.

3. Mount a suitable tool in the toolholder; then set the point of the tool even with the center of the work.

4. Set the graduated compound rest at the angle desired, for example 60°, Fig. 9-161.

5. Advance the tool with the cross-feed crank and apron handwheel until it is in a position to make a fairly heavy cut.

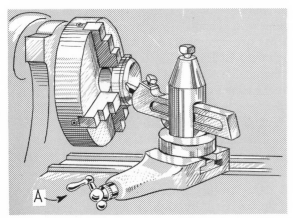

Fig. 9-161. Cutting a Taper by Setting Compound Rest

Fig. 9-162. Boring an Internal Taper with Compound Rest Set at Desired Angle (South Bend Lathe)

275

Fig. 9-163. Cutting a Taper with a Taper Attachment
(South Bend Lathe)

Fig. 9-165. Telescopic Taper Attachment
(South Bend Lathe)

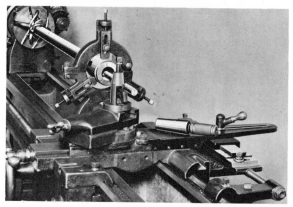

Fig. 9-166. Cutting an Internal Taper
(South Bend Lathe)

An internal taper may be bored with the compound rest set at the desired angle, as shown in Fig. 9-162.

Procedure For Taper Attachment Method

Fig. 9-163 shows a standard No. 5 Morse taper being cut on a lathe with a taper attachment. This device is standard equipment in commercial shops, but is not found so frequently in schools. Two forms of taper attachments are commonly available. The taper attachment in Fig. 9-164 is called a plain taper attachment; that in Fig. 9-165 is a telescopic taper attachment. When the latter is used, it is not necessary to disconnect the cross-feed screw, as described in step 1.

1. Disengage the cross-feed screw, removing the screw that holds the cross-feed control nut on the saddle, Fig. 9-164.

2. Attach the connecting slide arm to the cross feed by tightening handle *B*, Fig. 9-164.

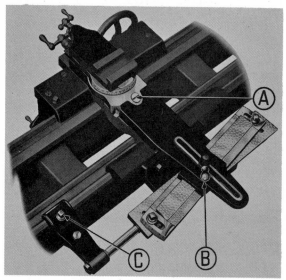

Fig. 9-164. Plain Taper Attachment (South Bend Lathe)

6. With the compound feed handle (*A*, Fig. 9-161), move the tool across the cut. At the end of the cut, draw the tool back and adjust it with the apron handwheel and cross feed to make a second cut.

7. Make repeated cuts until the taper is the size desired, finishing with a light cut.

The advantages of this method of turning a taper are: (1) The centers are always in line. (2) Once the machine is set up, a taper of the same degree can be turned, regardless of the length of the stock. (3) Given the degree of taper, no further calculation is necessary.

3. Engage the taper attachment on the ways, and fasten it with the setscrew, *C*, Fig. 9-164.

4. Set the taper slide bar at the angle desired, and clamp it in position with the setscrews.

5. Make the cut as in ordinary turning.

The advantages of this method of turning tapers are: (1) The centers are always in line. (2) A taper of a given amount may be cut independent of length. (3) This method can be used when tapering either external or internal surfaces, Figs. 9-163 and 9-166, respectively.

How To Cut Threads in a Lathe

Cutting threads in a lathe is a common practice. The operation is performed by causing the lead screw to revolve at a desired ratio with the spindle of the lathe through a series of gears. The lead screw provides a positive and constant feed.

The system of gears on modern lathes is such that threads with a great variety of pitches may be cut. The procedure to be followed in setting up the lathe to cut threads of the desired pitch depends upon whether or not the lathe is of the standard-change gear type or the quick-change type.

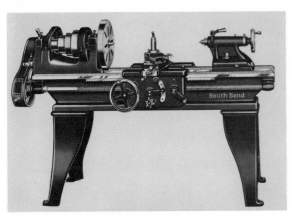

Fig. 9-170. Standard-Change Gear Lathe
(South Bend Lathe)

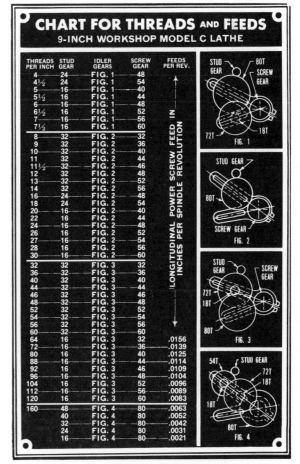

Fig. 9-171. Chart for Threads and Feeds
(South Bend Lathe)

277

Standard-Change Gear Lathe

In setting up a lathe with standard-change gears so as to cut threads of the desired pitch, the problem is one of determining the gears to be used on the stud and lead screw. This may be done by referring to the change gear chart found on the front of the gear cover at the headstock end of the lathe, Fig. 9-170. In the first column of the chart is found a list of common pitches of threads, Fig. 9-171; in the second, a list of the stud gears available; and in the fourth, a list of available screw gears. Assume you want to set up the lathe for cutting 20 threads per inch: follow down the first column until the number 20 is found; then read the number directly opposite in the second column, which here is 16; finally, read the number in the fourth column, which is 40. When these two gears are mounted on the stud and lead screws respectively, and are meshed with the upper idler gear as shown in the small Fig. 2 of Fig. 9-171, the lathe is set up for cutting 20 threads per inch.

CAUTION: *The numbers found in the second and fourth columns of the gear chart are not the same on all makes of lathes. They vary with the pitch of the lead screw.*

Fig. 9-172. End View of Standard-Change Gear Lathe
(South Bend Lathe)
(A) Stud Gear, (B) Lower Idler Gear, (C) Screw Gear

If no change gear chart is found on the lathe, the gears required for cutting 24 threads per inch may be determined in the following manner. Count the number of threads per inch on the lead screw. Assuming this is found to be 8, then the ratio of the stud gear to the lead screw gear will be as 8 is to 24. This is because the ratio of the number of teeth in the change gears used will be the same as the ratio between the threads to be cut and the threads on the lead screw. No gear with 8 teeth is likely to be found in the available change gears; however, since any multiple of the above gears will serve the purpose, the problem may be solved by multiplying both numbers by the same number, for example, 2. When 8 and 24 respectively are multiplied by 2, the products found are 16 and 48. Gears with 16 and 48 teeth respectively are commonly found among change gears.

Quick-Change Gear Lathe

In setting up this type of lathe for cutting threads of the desired pitch, the procedure is relatively simple. The lathe is equipped with a quick-change gear box which enables the operator to produce various pitches of screw threads through the use of control levers.

On some lathes of this type, the pitch of the thread to be cut is controlled through the use of the two tumbler levers on the quick-change gear box. See Figs. 9-12 and 9-13.

Fig. 9-173. Quick-Change Gear Mechanism
(South Bend Lathe)

On other lathes, the quick-change gear mechanism is somewhat different. The pitch of the thread is controlled by the position of the sliding gear, the top lever, and the tumbler lever, as shown in Fig. 9-173. In setting this machine to cut a thread (say 20 threads per inch), push in the sliding gear (*A*), turn the top lever (*B*) to the extreme right, and insert the tumbler lever (*C*) in the hole under the column in which the number 20 is found on the index chart, Fig. 9-174.

When threads are being cut in steel, a rough thread will result unless lard oil (or other good cutting oil) is applied freely throughout the operation. Apply the oil with a small paint or shellac brush *preceding* each cut.

Calculations for Screw Threads

Before cutting threads on a lathe, you should be thoroughly familiar with the type, form, classes of fit, and calculations necessary for cutting the threads. Information concerning American (National) form threads is included in Unit 16. The form of the thread profile and the formulas necessary for calculating any required dimensions are included in Fig. 4-4.

Information concerning Unified form threads is included in Unit 17. The form of the Unified thread profile and the formulas necessary for any required dimensions are included in Fig. 4-7. The thread profiles and the formulas necessary for making calculations for other types of threads are included in Unit 18.

Procedure Using a Threading Dial

1. Determine the number of threads to be cut per inch.
2. Adjust the change gears to obtain the ratio desired.

3. Mount the work on the lathe. Be sure the dog is fastened securely, or if it is mounted in a chuck, be sure the jaws are drawn down tight.

   If the threads end at some intermediate point on the surface of a straight cylinder, pencil a line at the point desired. If desired and permissible, cut a neck or groove at the end of the thread, to aid in extracting the tool at the proper point. The neck may be cut with a cutoff tool, to the depth of the desired thread, and equal in width or slightly wider than the cutoff tool.

4. Set the compound rest at 29°.

   Setting the compound rest at less than 30° makes accurate adjustment of the threading tool easier, should it be necessary to remove the tool before cutting of the thread has been completed. In addition, it makes possible the removal of most of the stock from one side of the thread only, when this is necessary because of a rough or inaccurate surface. Furthermore, for better finish, the tool should drag slightly on the right-hand side of the thread.

5. Select a sharp, correctly ground threading tool, Figs. 9-175, 9-41, and 9-42. The inclusive angle of the point of the tool should be 60°, with each cutting edge having the same degree of angularity. An end relief of 8° to 10° and a side relief of 8° to 10° should be provided on both sides. No side rake is required.

16-INCH SOUTH BEND QUICK CHANGE GEAR LATHE									
SLIDING GEAR	TOP LEVER	THREADS PER INCH—FEEDS IN THOUSANDTHS							AUTOMATIC CROSS FEED EQUALS 375 TIMES LONGITUDINAL FEED
IN	LEFT	4 .0841	4½ .0748	5 .0673	5½ .0612	5¾ .0585	6 .0561	6½ .0518	7 .0481
	CENTER	8 .0421	9 .0374	10 .0337	11 .0306	11½ .0293	12 .0280	13 .0259	14 .0240
	RIGHT	16 .0210	18 .0187	20 .0168	22 .0153	23 .0146	24 .0140	26 .0129	28 .0120
OUT	LEFT	32 .0105	36 .0093	40 .0084	44 .0076	46 .0073	48 .0070	52 .0065	56 .0060
	CENTER	64 .0053	72 .0047	80 .0042	88 .0038	92 .0037	96 .0035	104 .0032	112 .0030
	RIGHT	128 .0026	144 .0023	160 .0021	176 .0019	184 .0018	192 .0017	208 .0016	224 .0015

Fig. 9-174. Index Chart for Quick-Change Gear Lathe (South Bend Lathe)

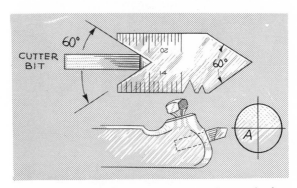

Fig. 9-175. Testing a Threading Tool for Correct Angles

279

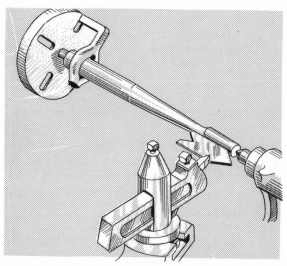

Fig. 9-176. Setting Threading Tool Square with Work

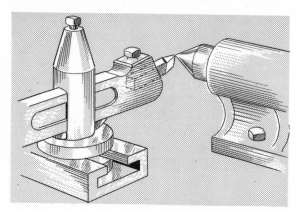

Fig. 9-177. Testing Height of Threading Tool

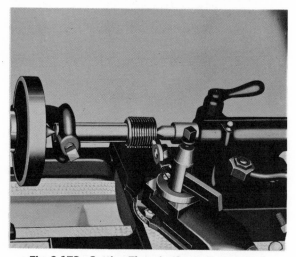

Fig. 9-178. Cutting Threads (South Bend Lathe)

6. Insert the tool in a holder with only the ground portions of the bit projecting beyond the nose of the holder.

7. Set the point of the threading tool even with the center of the work. See *A*, Fig. 9-175.

8. Hold a center gage against the side of the work. Then advance the threading tool, and set it square with the work, as in Fig. 9-176. Tighten the setscrew which holds the tool in the post, and again test it for squareness with the work.

9. Test the height at which the point of the tool is set, Fig. 9-177.

10. Advance the threading tool until the point just touches the work; then adjust the micrometer collar on the cross-feed screw (Fig. 9-178) to zero.

11. Draw the tool back past the right end of the work. Then advance the point of the tool about .002″ by turning the compound-rest screw toward the right.

Adjustments of depth of cut usually are made by advancing the compound rest, thereby causing the tool to cut on one side of the thread groove. If desired, however, the depth of cut may be set with the cross feed, thus causing the tool to cut on both sides of the thread groove. Experienced workmen often take cuts heavier than .002″.

12. Start the lathe; then engage the halfnut, (Fig. 9-179) when line No. 1 on the dial indicator (Fig. 9-180) is just even with the line on the rim of the indicator.

The halfnut may be engaged on any line when cutting an even number of threads per inch. When cutting an odd number of threads, the halfnut should be closed on a *numbered line only*.

CAUTION: *When cutting threads in steel, keep the point of the tool well lubricated throughout the operation. Apply oil with a small brush, Fig. 9-181.*

13. When the threading tool reaches the terminus of the thread, quickly draw the tool away from the work by giving the cross-feed screw one complete revolution toward the left, and, at the same time, *immediately disengage the halfnut.*

14. Draw the carriage back to the starting point with the apron handwheel; then advance the tool slightly by turning the compound-rest screw toward the right, so as to advance the tool about .002″.

15. Turn the cross-feed screw one complete revolution toward the right; then engage the halfnut when the indicator registers No. 1. Withdraw the tool at the terminus of the thread by giving the cross-feed screw one complete revolution toward the left. At the same time, immediately disengage the halfnut. A stop on the cross feed saves time, Fig. 9-182.

16. Repeat these operations until the thread is cut to the depth desired.

17. Finish the open end of the threaded section by neatly chamfering the end with a right-hand turning or facing tool. This operation may be performed with the threading tool, provided care is exercised.

Resetting Tool After Its Removal

When it is necessary to remove the threading tool for sharpening or for other reasons before the thread has been cut to the depth desired, great care must be taken in resetting the tool, to insure that it is following the original groove.

To again catch the thread, the tool must be set square with the work, Fig. 9-176. Back the tool up so that it will be clear of the work. Then start the lathe, and engage the halfnut lever. With the tool clear of the work, carry it longitudinally along the work a few turns to take up the backlash. Stop the lathe. Then feed the tool into the original thread groove by using the cross-feed knob and the compound-rest feed knob as necessary.

With the lathe stopped, the halfnut lever engaged, and the tool fitted to the original thread groove, set the micrometer collar on the cross-feed knob to *zero*. Also note the setting on the micrometer collar on the compound-rest knob; this collar may be set to a figure which indicates the depth to which the thread was cut, thus serving as an aid in determining when the thread has been cut to the desired depth. Then proceed with cutting the thread in the usual manner.

Fig. 9-179. **Parts of Lathe Carriage and Apron Assembly**
(South Bend Lathe)

Fig. 9-180. **Threading Dial Indicator**
(South Bend Lathe)

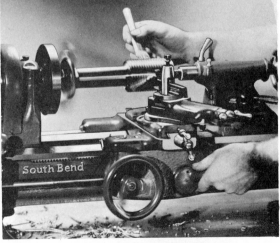

Fig. 9-181. **Apply Oil with Small Brush**
(South Bend Lathe)

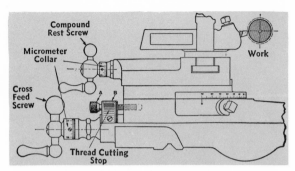

Fig. 9-182. **Thread Cutting Stop Attached to Dovetail of Saddle** (South Bend Lathe)

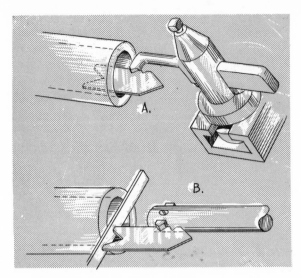

Fig. 9-183. **Setting the Boring Bar for Cutting Internal Threads**

Cutting Left-Hand Threads

A left-hand thread is cut in the same manner as for a right-hand thread, except that the direction in which the feed screw rotates is reversed, thus causing the direction of travel of the tool to change. On most lathes, this is accomplished by means of a lever at the left-hand end of the headstock. On some, however, it is accomplished by means of a lever on the apron.

In cutting left-hand threads, the compound rest is swiveled 29° to the left, instead of to the right. The thread is cut with the carriage feeding from left to right (toward the tailstock).

Procedure for Internal Threads

For cutting threads on the inside of a hole, a special threading tool (*A*, Fig. 9-183) or a boring bar fitted with a threading bit (*B*, Fig. 183 or 9-43) is required. The top of the point of the tool should be set at the same level as the axis (center) of the work.

1. Lay out and drill or bore a hole of the size required. Provide clearance at the bottom of the hole.

2. Select a correctly sharpened tool for cutting internal threads.

3. With a thread gage, set the tool so that a line through the center of the cutting part of the tool is *perpendicular* to the *wall* of the *hole* (*A* or *B*, Fig. 9-183).

4. Clamp the bit in the holder securely, and clamp the holder in the tool post.

5. With the apron handwheel, advance the tool to within about ¼″ of the work. Then with the cross-feed screw, adjust the tool until the point is even with the near wall of the hole.

6. With the compound-rest feed screw, advance the tool about .002″.

7. Start the lathe; then engage the halfnut when line No. 1 on the dial indicator is just even with the line on the rim of the indicator.

   When cutting threads in steel, be sure to keep the point of the tool well lubricated throughout the operation.

8. When the threading tool reaches the terminus of the thread, quickly draw the tool away from the work by giving the cross-feed screw one complete revolution toward the *right*. At the same time, *immediately disengage* the *halfnut*.

9. Draw the carriage back to the starting point, using the apron handwheel. Then, with the compound-rest screw, advance the tool about .002″.

10. Turn the cross-feed screw one complete revolution to the left. When the indicator registers No. 1, engage the halfnut.

11. Again withdraw the tool at the terminus of the thread, as in step 8.

12. Repeat these operations until the thread is cut to the depth desired.

Milling on a Lathe

Many schools and small machine shops are not equipped with a milling machine and, in many cases, do not have a volume of work which would justify the purchase of an expensive mill. To meet the needs of small shops, some manufacturers of lathes have designed and built milling attachments for their products. These attachments, when correctly mounted on the carriage of the lathe, enable the operator to perform many simple milling operations, for example, cutting keyways, gears, slots, and splines, as well as facing and squaring stock.

Milling Attachments

The attachment shown in Fig. 9-186 is simply a device for holding the work in the position desired. It may be swiveled on its base horizontally and the slide swiveled in a vertical plane, Fig. 9-187. The cutter may be mounted on a taper shank which fits the tapered hole in the lathe spindle, Fig. 9-188, or, if a cutter with a straight shank is used, it may be mounted in a collet or in a spindle chuck, Fig. 9-189. Cut-

ters also may be mounted on an arbor held between centers, as in Figs. 9-190 and 9-191. The work is brought into contact with the cutter by means of the handwheel on the carriage, the cross feed, and the vertical adjusting screw at the top of the attachment. The cut is con-

Fig. 9-187. Milling Attachment Swiveled Vertically
(South Bend Lathe)

Fig. 9-186. Milling Attachment in Place on a Lathe
(South Bend Lathe)

Fig. 9-188. Milling Cutter Mounted on a Taper Shank
(South Bend Lathe)

Fig. 9-189. Milling Cutter Mounted in a Spindle Chuck
(South Bend Lathe)

Fig. 9-190. Milling Cutter Mounted on an Arbor Between Centers (South Bend Lathe)

Fig. 9-191. Milling Cutter Mounted on an Arbor Between Centers (South Bend Lathe)

trolled by appropriate manipulation of these same adjusting devices.

The attachments illustrated in Figs. 9-190 and 9-191 are designed for cutting teeth on spur and bevel gears, spirals, and other forms of milling necessitating the use of a dividing head.

Accurate and efficient mill work requires sharp and correctly ground cutters. Figs. 9-192 and 9-193 illustrate a lathe attachment designed for grinding milling cutters, reamers, etc.

The procedures in setting up a lathe to perform a milling operation after the attachment has been mounted on the carriage are very similar to those described in setting up a standard milling machine; likewise, the manner of mounting the work in the vise or on an arbor is similar. See Section 11. The rotation of the cutter always should be opposite the direction of feed. When the direction of feed is toward the rear, the cutter will rotate clockwise.

Fig. 9-192. Grinding a Milling Cutter on a Lathe
(South Bend Lathe)

Fig. 9-193. Grinding a Reamer on a Lathe
(South Bend Lathe)

Test Your Knowledge
of Section 9

Unit 51: The Metalworking Lathe

1. List seven common external machining operations which may be performed on a metalworking lathe.
2. List six common hole-machining operations which may be performed on a lathe.
3. List several specialized production machines which are adapted from a lathe and which perform similar operations.
4. When, and by whom, was the first screw-cutting engine lathe built?
5. To what degree of accuracy can work be produced on a metalworking lathe?
6. How are the size and capacity of a lathe designated?
7. Describe how changes in spindle speed can be accomplished on lathes.
8. What is the function of the back-gear mechanism on a lathe?
9. Define the meaning of the amount of longitudinal feed on a lathe.
10. Define the meaning of the amount of cross feed on a lathe.
11. List the three basic components of the feeding and threading mechanism on a lathe.
12. What basic purpose do the controls on the carriage and apron assembly serve?
13. What purpose does the feed-change lever serve?
14. What control is used to engage the automatic feed on a lathe?
15. What control is used to reverse the lead screw on a lathe?
16. What do the large numbers on the index plate on the quick-change gear box indicate?
17. What do the small decimal numbers on the index plate on the quick-change gear box indicate?
18. How does one determine the amount of cross feed in comparison to longitudinal feed on a lathe, at a given setting?
19. Define the difference between a live center and a dead center.
20. Why must the center hole, in which the dead center is located, be lubricated?
21. How are hardened lathe centers resharpened when scored or nicked?
22. What is the included angle of the point of a lathe center?
23. For what purpose are lathe dogs used?
24. List several safety precautions which should be observed in setting up and operating a metalworking lathe.

Unit 52: Cutting Speeds for Lathe Work

1. Define cutting speed as it applies to lathe work.
2. List seven conditions which affect cutting speed on a lathe.
3. List the recommended cutting speeds for roughing cuts on a lathe with high-speed tool bits for the following materials: soft cast iron, machine steel, annealed tool steel, brass, bronze, aluminum.
4. List the formula used for calculating the cutting speed for lathe work.
5. List the formula used for calculating the rpm for lathe work.
6. Calculate the cutting speed in sfpm for a steel workpiece $1\frac{1}{2}''$ diameter, revolving at 200 rpm in a lathe.
7. Calculate the cutting speed in sfpm for a steel workpiece $\frac{1}{2}''$ diameter, revolving at 200 rpm in a lathe.
8. Calculate the rpm required for turning a piece of aluminum, $1''$ in diameter, at 200 sfpm.
9. Calculate the rpm required for turning a piece of aluminum, $\frac{1}{2}''$ in diameter, at 200 sfpm.

Unit 53: Lathe Cutting Tools and Toolholders

1. List three kinds of machine tools on which single-point cutting tools are used.
2. List five types or shapes of single-point cutting tools commonly used on a lathe.
3. How does the size of the nose radius compare on rough- and finish-turning tool bits?
4. Explain how to determine whether a toolholder is a right-hand or a left-hand holder.
5. For what purpose is the left-hand toolholder used?
6. For what basic kinds of tools are $16\frac{1}{2}°$ toolholders intended?

7. For what basic kinds of tools are zero-degree toolholders intended?

8. Describe a carbide-insert toolholder.

9. Describe three purposes for which cutoff tools are used.

10. Describe two kinds of toolholders used for holding threading tools.

11. List four kinds of materials from which metal-cutting tools are made.

12. List four properties which generally are required of cutting-tool materials.

13. Describe the properties of high-speed steel as a cutting-tool material.

14. List several kinds of cutting tools which are made of high-speed steel.

15. List the properties of cast-alloy cutting tools, in comparison with high-speed steel tools.

16. Why is cemented carbide so named?

17. What are the properties of cemented-carbide cutting tools, in comparison with high-speed steel and cast-alloy tools?

18. Define the meaning of the following terms as they apply to single-point cutting tools: (a) cutting edge, (b) face, (c) flank, (d) nose, (e) nose radius, (f) shank, (g) point, (h) base.

19. Define a right-hand, single-point cutting tool.

20. What is meant by toolholder angle?

21. Define the side-relief angle on a tool bit.

22. Define the normal end-relief angle on a tool bit.

23. Explain the difference between the normal end-relief angle and the working end-relief angle.

24. Explain how a tool-angle gage is used to measure the working end-relief of a tool bit which will be used in a $16\frac{1}{2}°$ toolholder.

25. Explain how a tool-angle gage is used to measure the normal end-relief angle of a tool bit.

26. List five factors which must be considered in determining the amount of end- and side-relief angle on a single-point tool bit.

27. What end- and side-working-relief angles may be used for general-purpose turning applications with the following kinds of

turning tools: (a) high-speed steel tools, (b) cast-alloy tools, (c) tungsten-carbide tools?

28. In what source may one find detailed information concerning tool angles for many various machining applications?

29. Define the meaning of back-rake angle. Upon what does it largely depend?

30. How does an increase in back-rake angle affect the strength of the tool at the cutting edge?

31. What is meant by side-rake angle?

32. How does a decrease in the side-rake angle affect the type of chip produced by a tool bit?

33. Define the nose angle of a tool bit.

34. Explain how a chip breaker functions on a tool bit.

35. On what types of grinders are chip breakers often ground on high-speed steel tool bits?

Unit 54: Grinding Lathe Cutter Bits

1. How do excessive end- and side-relief angles affect the strength of the cutting edge of a tool bit?

2. List the following approximate angles for a general-purpose turning tool: (a) working side-relief, (b) working end-relief, (c) side-rake, (d) back-rake.

3. List the recommended nose radius for a general-purpose turning tool for the following applications: (a) rough cuts, (b) general turning with moderate or light cuts, (c) light cuts requiring a smooth finish.

4. List the following approximate angles for a general-purpose facing tool: (a) side-relief, (b) working end-relief, (c) side-rake, (d) back-rake, (e) nose.

5. What end-relief angle generally is recommended for cutoff tools?

6. Why should one avoid cutoff operations on work mounted between centers?

7. List several precautions to be observed in making setups for cutoff operations.

8. List two general kinds of tools and toolholders used for cutting external Unified and American (National) form threads on a lathe.

9. What type of tool and toolholder is used for cutting internal threads on a lathe?
10. Why should a tool bit be whetted on an abrasive stone after grinding to the desired shape?

Unit 64: Lathe Chucks and Faceplates

1. Describe how workpieces generally are mounted on the faceplate of a lathe.
2. Describe how a four-jaw independent chuck operates.
3. List several different shapes of workpieces which may be held with a four-jaw chuck.
4. Explain how a three-jaw universal chuck operates.
5. For what types of workpieces are three-jaw or six-jaw universal chucks generally intended?
6. Which type of chuck (the three-jaw universal or the four-jaw independent) generally is considered to be most accurate?
7. What is the principal disadvantage of the four-jaw independent chuck?
8. For what basic types of work are collet chucks used?
9. What shapes of stock will collet chucks hold?
10. What type of chuck centers work more accurately and quickly than any other type?
11. Describe a spindle chuck.
12. For what purpose are step chucks used?

Unit 71: Calculating the Amount of Tailstock Setover for Turning Tapers

1. List the formula which may be used for calculating the tailstock setover for taper turning when the part is tapered for its entire length, with the diameters at the end of the work given.
2. Calculate the tailstock setover for turning cylindrical work with the following specifications: total length 12", to be tapered the entire length, $1\frac{1}{4}$" diameter at the large end, $\frac{3}{4}$" diameter at the small end.
3. List the formula which may be used for calculating the setover for taper turning when the taper per foot is given.
4. Calculate the tailstock setover for turning a lathe center having total length of stock 7", length of center $5\frac{1}{8}$", length to be tapered $3\frac{7}{8}$", with a No. 3 Morse taper of 0.602" per foot.
5. List the formula which may be used when the taper per foot is not given, but the drawing shows the dimensions of the tapered section.
6. Calculate the setover of the tailstock for turning the taper on a hammer handle having the following specifications: total length of stock $13\frac{1}{2}$", length of handle 12", length of tapered portion 6", diameter of large end of taper $\frac{3}{4}$", diameter of small end of taper $\frac{3}{8}$".
7. Calculate the setover of the tailstock for turning the taper on a center punch having the following specifications: total length of stock 6", length of punch 5", length of tapered portion $2\frac{1}{4}$", large end of taper $\frac{3}{8}$", small end of taper $\frac{3}{16}$".

Unit 74: Milling on a Lathe

1. List several types of milling operations which can be performed on a lathe.
2. Describe how a workpiece may be mounted in a lathe for milling a groove.
3. How may a milling cutter with a straight shank be mounted in the lathe spindle?
4. Describe how the teeth may be milled in a spur gear, using a lathe.

Regular Rhythm — Pulsebeat of the Shaper
(Cincinnati Shaper)

The Shaper and Its Operation

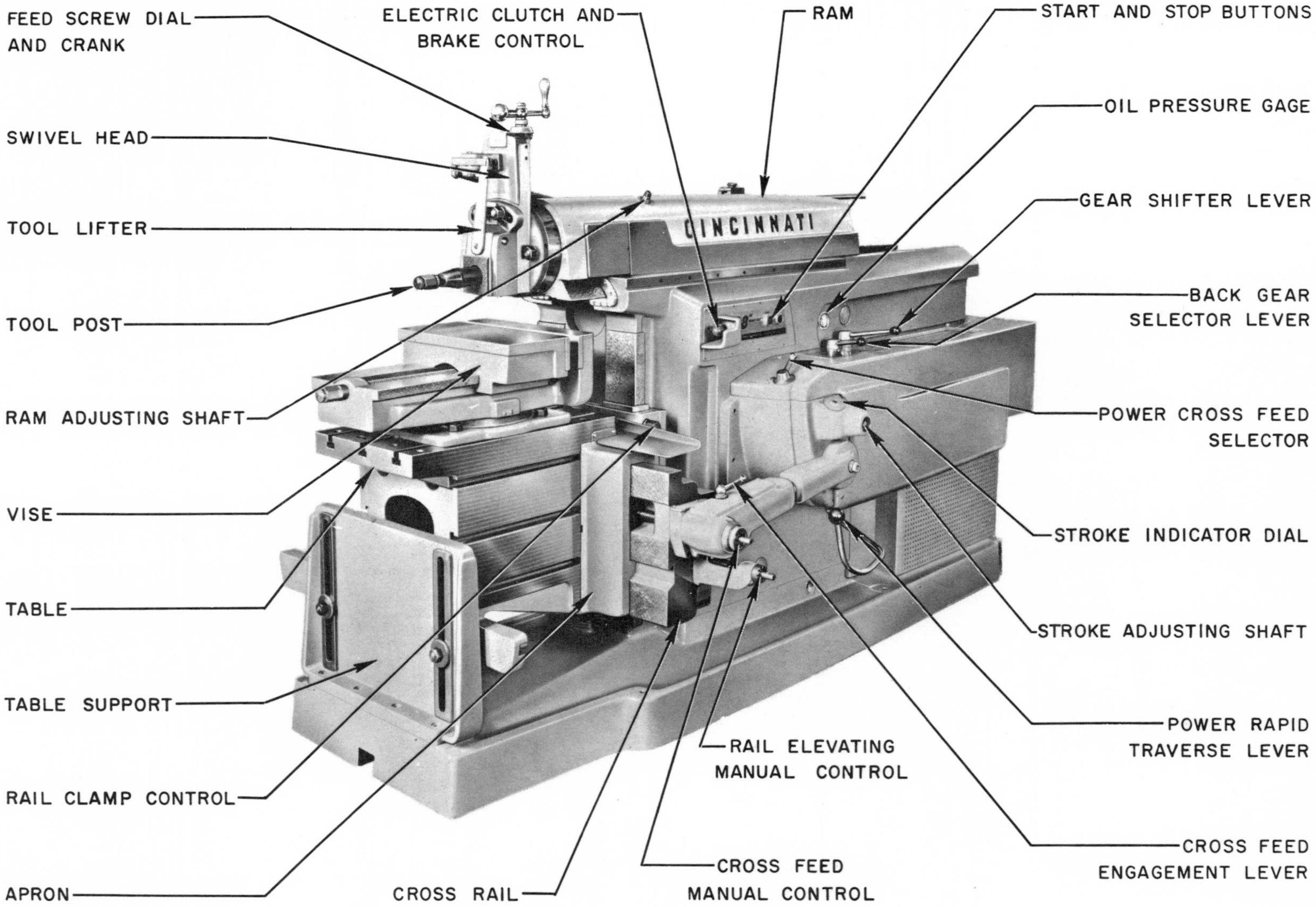

FEED SCREW DIAL AND CRANK

SWIVEL HEAD

TOOL LIFTER

TOOL POST

RAM ADJUSTING SHAFT

VISE

TABLE

TABLE SUPPORT

RAIL CLAMP CONTROL

APRON

ELECTRIC CLUTCH AND BRAKE CONTROL

RAM

START AND STOP BUTTONS

OIL PRESSURE GAGE

GEAR SHIFTER LEVER

BACK GEAR SELECTOR LEVER

POWER CROSS FEED SELECTOR

STROKE INDICATOR DIAL

STROKE ADJUSTING SHAFT

POWER RAPID TRAVERSE LEVER

CROSS FEED ENGAGEMENT LEVER

RAIL ELEVATING MANUAL CONTROL

CROSS FEED MANUAL CONTROL

CROSS RAIL

Fig. 10-1. Plain Heavy-Duty Shaper (Cincinnati Shaper)

290

The Shaper

The shaper is one of the most common and useful machines found in the machine shop, Fig. 10-1. A shaper is used primarily for machining flat surfaces with a single-point cutting tool, Fig. 10-20. The cutting tool is very similar to a lathe tool bit. The flat surfaces machined with a shaper may be in most any position, including horizontal, vertical, and angular positions. See Fig. 10-14. Keyways, grooves, and slots also may be machined with a shaper, Fig. 10-44. A skillful workman can manipulate a shaper so as to machine curved or irregular surfaces, Fig. 10-53.

The operation of the shaper is not particularly complicated. The work is held stationary on an adjustable table while the tool moves forward on the cutting stroke and returns quickly to the starting point without cutting. During this return stroke, the feed mechanism advances the table the amount desired for the next cut, usually not more than $\frac{1}{16}''$.

Size

The size of a shaper generally is designated by the maximum length of the stroke it will take, for example $7''$, $12''$, $14''$, $16''$, $24''$, $36''$, etc. In each case, the length of stroke may be varied within the range from 0 to the maximum length for the machine. However, the length of stroke is not the only factor used in designating the physical size and the work capacity of shapers.

Shapers are designed for light-duty, medium- or standard-duty, or heavy-duty work. A heavy-duty shaper is heavier and far more rigid than a light- or medium-duty type. For example, shapers with a $16''$ stroke are available which weigh from 2000 to 6000 pounds.

The heavy-duty shaper in Fig. 10-1 is available in several sizes, with maximum stroke lengths from $16''$ to $36''$. The shaper in Fig. 10-2, although classified as a $12''$ shaper, has a maximum stroke length of $13\frac{1}{2}''$. The shaper in Fig. 10-3 is a bench model which has a $7''$ maximum stroke length. This machine is de-

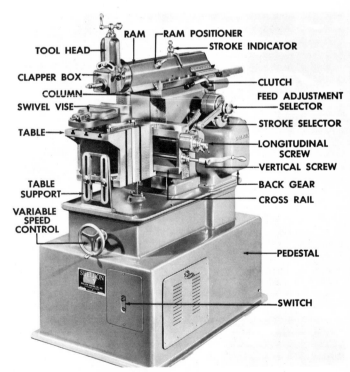

Fig. 10-2. 12″ Plain Shaper, Showing Principal Parts
(Sheldon)

signed for light work. Fig. 10-4 illustrates a heavy-duty shaper with a universal table.

Most modern shapers are operated by individual motors which activate the driving mechanism through belts, chains, gears, or hydraulic systems.

Parts

To the average person, the shaper looks like a rather simple piece of machinery. However, study of the sectional views, Fig. 10-5, and an examination of the labeled parts in Figs. 10-1 and 10-2, show it to be a rather complex machine.

The Driving Mechanism: The ram which moves the head holding the tool is driven by a slotted rocker or vibrating arm which is connected to the main gear or driving wheel by a crankpin and a sliding block, Fig. 10-5. As the driving wheel revolves, the crankpin and the sliding block are carried through a circular path. This causes the vibrating arm to

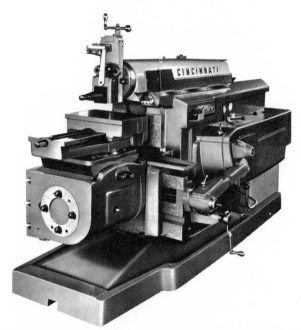

Fig. 10-4. Heavy-Duty Shaper with Universal Table
(Cincinnati Shaper)

Fig. 10-3. Bench Shaper with 7″ Stroke
(South Bend Lathe)

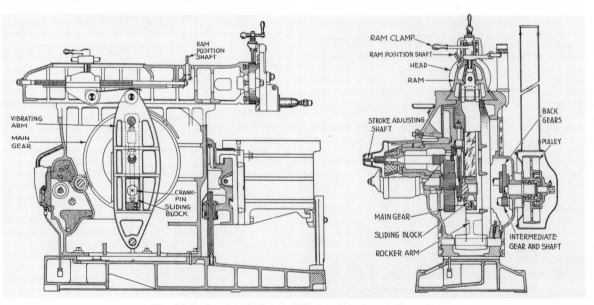

Fig. 10-5. Sectional Views of Shaper (Cincinnati Shaper)
(At Left) Side View; (At Right) End View.

move forward as the block travels one portion of the path, and in the opposite direction as it passes along the remaining portion. The crankpin which holds the sliding block is fastened to a second block which operates in a radial slide on the driving wheel. The position of this block is adjustable by means of a shaft and bevel gears. As the crankpin is drawn toward the center of the wheel, the distance the vibrating arm travels is shorter. Consequently, the distance (stroke) traveled by the ram also is shorter. Acceleration on the return stroke is a result of the action of the crankpin, which motivates the vibrating arm. The crankpin travels a much shorter distance to bring the vibrating arm back to the point where the stroke starts than it travels in making the stroke — a ratio of approximately 2:3, Fig. 10-6.

Speed: When set for any particular speed, a shaper will make a constant number of strokes, regardless of the length of the stroke. To maintain a constant cutting speed (rate at which metal is removed), the shaper must make twice as many strokes when making a cut 3″ long as when making one 6″ long. On many machines, increase or decrease of speed is accomplished through a system of speed-change gears mounted in a box on the side of the machine or on the inside of the column, Fig. 10-7. The gears are manipulated by levers conveniently placed near the position of the operator. An indicator or an index plate tells which gears to engage in order to produce a given speed.

Shapers generally have six to eight speeds, which vary from about 11 to 220 strokes per minute. Some smaller shapers, as in Fig. 10-2, are equipped with a variable-speed drive which is infinitely variable from 12 to 180 strokes per minute.

Feed: On shapers, the tool may be brought into contact with the work through the use of one or a combination of several methods. The table may be moved along the cross rail by means of a cross-feed screw operated by a hand crank. The tool head on the end of the ram may be lowered by means of a ball crank screw.

In addition to hand feed, shapers are provided with a horizontal automatic feed. This is accomplished on some types of machines by means of a notched wheel and pawl, operated from the driving wheel by a connecting rod and an adjustable link or similar device, Fig. 10-2. On many modern shapers, change of feed is accomplished by a series of cams; for exam-

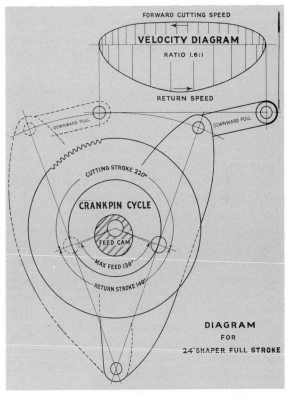

Fig. 10-6. Stroke Cycle of 24″ Shaper
(Cincinnati Shaper)

Fig. 10-7. Shaper Speed-Change Gears
(Cincinnati Shaper)

ple, see Fig. 10-8. The amount of feed is determined by the number of teeth (notches) the wheel advances on each *return stroke* of the shaper. The number of teeth advanced is determined by the position of the feed-adjusting knob or handwheel in relation to the link connecting the rod and the feed rocking arm. The farther this knob is from the center, the greater the amount of feed. On a cam-actuated machine, change of feed is accomplished by adjusting the direct-reading feed dial to the position desired, for example, a position which will give a feed of .06″. With this type, change of feed may be made while the machine is in operation.

Table: The table of a shaper consists of two parts: the table itself constitutes the front section, and the apron or saddle constitutes the rear section, to which the table is bolted. The apron has a gib or hook-like projection which engages the cross rail located on the front of the column. In addition to being a support for the table, the cross rail serves as a track along which the apron slides in a horizontal plane when activated by a feed screw. The cross rail carrying the apron and table may be raised or lowered by means of a vertical screw and bevel gears. Whenever *vertical adjustment* of the *cross rail* is made, the clamping bolts holding it to the column should be loosened slightly and tightened again as soon as the adjustment has been made.

Caution: *There are several clamping bolts on each column, but not all of these should be loosened. Only one bolt, a locking bolt provided for this purpose, should be loosened on each column.*

The top of the worktable is provided with T-slots. These are for convenience in clamping the work to the table or for attaching devices such as vises and jigs. The sides of the table have similar T-slots, but these are much less frequently used. The vise, a common feature of all shapers, is mounted on a swivel base. It permits clamping the work with the jaws of the vise either parallel with, perpendicular to, or angular with the face of the column.

A *universal table*, Fig. 10-9, is available on some shapers. This table may be swiveled on the apron and may be tilted toward or away from the column. These adjustments are useful when making angular or bevel cuts. The universal shaper shown in Fig. 10-4 is equipped with this form of table.

On some shapers, as in Figs. 10-1 and 10-4, the table is moved vertically or horizontally by power, either up or down, right or left. This feature is called *power rapid traverse*. With this device, the work can be brought into contact with the tool quickly. Also, when the job is completed, the table can be moved quickly to one side, so that the work clears the tool post and can be removed without hindrance.

Fig. 10-8. Table Feed Actuating Cams
(Cincinnati Shaper)

Fig. 10-9. Setup with Both Universal Table and Vise Swiveled (Cincinnati Shaper)

Head: The tool head, Fig. 10-10, consisting of a head piece, a swivel base, and an apron, is designed for holding and adjusting the tool for depth of cut. The down-feed screw has a collar graduated in thousandths of an inch. Thus fine adjustment of cut can be made very simply. The swivel arrangement between the ram and the head allows either vertical or angular cuts. The tool is held in a tool post which is attached to the hinged tool block or clapper block. During the cut, the clapper block is forced back against the base of the clapper box and thus is solidly supported. On the return stroke, the tool or clapper block swings free. This allows the tool to be drawn back across the work with only a slight rubbing effect and with consequent preservation of the cutting edge. By loosening the clamping bolt on the front of the apron, it can be swung to the right or left, thus providing clearance at the point of the tool for nearly all types of cuts, except grooves or keyways. By loosening the bolts which hold the graduated head swivel, the head may be turned for making angular cuts as in Fig. 10-11. Some modern shapers are provided with both hand and power down feeds.

Shaper Tools

Shaper and planer tools are single-point cutting tools which are very similar to lathe cutting tools. In fact, the terminology applied to the design and the grinding of shaper and planer tools is essentially the same as that used for lathe cutting tools.

Shaper and planer tools are of two basic kinds — forged tools and tool bits. The former are heavy tools of which *A*, *B*, and *C*, Fig. 10-12, are examples. Tool bits used on shapers and planers are similar to lathe tool bits and are held in a toolholder, Fig. 10-13.

Tool bits are made of high-speed steel, cast alloy, or cemented carbide. Since high-speed steel has greater impact toughness than cast alloy or cemented carbide, tool bits made of high-speed steel are used most often. Tool bits are more widely used than forged tools because of their economy, cutting life, and the ease with which they are sharpened.

Shaper and planer tools are ground for making right- or left-hand cuts. The left-hand tool is more commonly used because of the usual direction of feed — from the left side of the work toward the right, as viewed from the face of the column. This is the position from which the operator ordinarily observes the work when operating the machine.

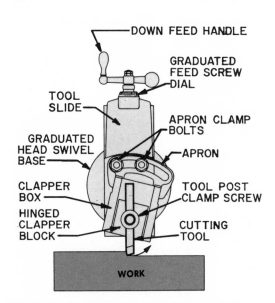

Fig. 10-10. **Tool Head Assembly** (Cincinnati Shaper)

Fig. 10-11. **Making an Angular Cut with a Shaper** (Cincinnati Shaper)

Toolholders: The type of toolholder shown in Fig. 10-13 commonly is used for holding shaper or planer tools. This type holds the base of the tool parallel to the base of the toolholder. Thus, the shank of the tool bit is perpendicular to the work being machined. Unless a back-rake angle is ground intentionally on the tool bit, no back rake is provided for the bit. Ordinarily little or no back rake is desired on shaper tool bits for most applications.

With the toolholder in Fig. 10-13, the tool bit may be *rotated* at different angles for various types of cuts, as shown in Fig. 10-14. By rotating both the toolholder and the angle of the tool bit, the tool can be manipulated in various corners, as shown in Fig. 10-15.

The position of the tool in a planer and shaper toolholder in relation to the direction of tool travel is important. For light cuts, the tool generally is clamped at the front of the tool-holder, as shown in Fig. 10-13. *For moderate to heavy cuts, the toolholder and the tool gen-*

erally are reversed, as shown in Fig. 10-16. With this procedure, the cutting edge is brought back of the shank of the toolholder,

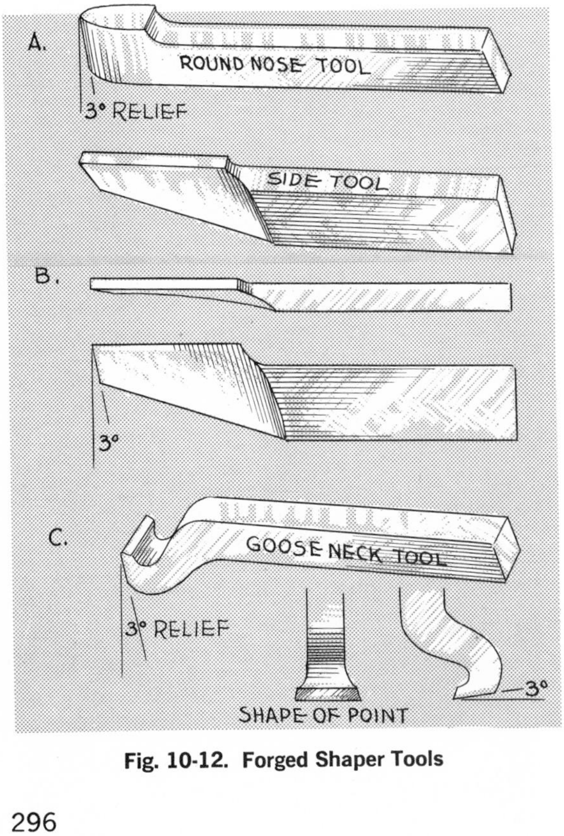

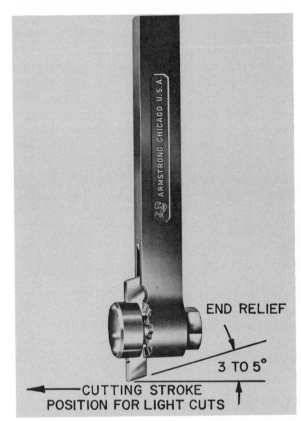

Fig. 10-13. Planer and Shaper Toolholder (Armstrong)

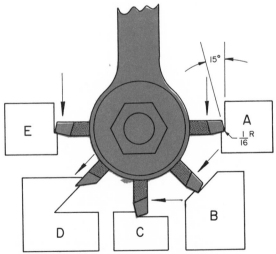

Fig. 10-14. Possible Tool Positions in Swivel Head of Planer and Shaper Toolholder
(A) Vertical cut; (B) Angular cut; (C) Horizontal cut; (D) Angular dovetail cut; (E) Vertical cut.

Fig. 10-12. Forged Shaper Tools

causing an effect similar to a gooseneck tool. This reduces the tendency of the tool to *chatter* or *dig in*, Fig. 10-17.

Lathe toolholders which hold the tool parallel to the base of the toolholder, as in Fig. 9-49, may be used on shapers. However, those which hold the tool at a 16° to 20° angle generally do

not work well on shapers. The 16° angle provides for a steep back-rake angle at the cutting edge of the tool, thus causing a tendency for the tool to chatter and dig in, Fig. 10-17.

An *extension shaper tool* is shown in Fig. 10-18. This type of tool has a bar, similar to a boring bar, mounted in the holder. A tool bit is mounted in the bar. Extension tools are used for machining the inside of holes or for internal machining operations (such as machining internal keyways, Fig. 10-19). Refer to Fig. 10-18.

Fig. 10-15. Use of Planer and Shaper Toolholder in Close Corners (Armstrong)

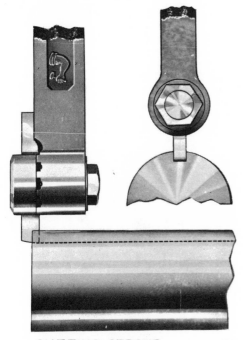

CUTTING STROKE →
POSITION FOR HEAVY CUTS

Fig. 10-16. Tool and Toolholder Reversed for Cutting Keyways and Making Heavy Cuts (Armstrong)
Note: When the tool bit is reversed and the toolholder is turned around, the cutting point is behind the center of the toolholder, thus reducing the tendency for chatter or for digging in.

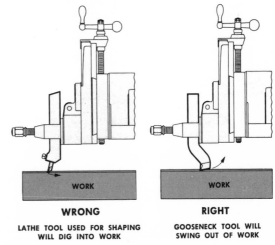

WRONG
LATHE TOOL USED FOR SHAPING WILL DIG INTO WORK

RIGHT
GOOSENECK TOOL WILL SWING OUT OF WORK

Fig. 10-17. Position of Tool and Angle at Which Tool Is Held Affects Cutting Action (Cincinnati Shaper)

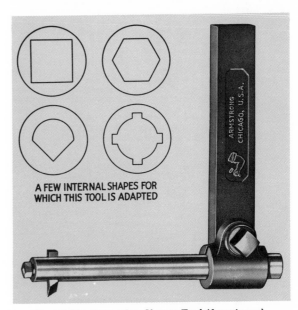

A FEW INTERNAL SHAPES FOR WHICH THIS TOOL IS ADAPTED

Fig. 10-18. Extension Shaper Tool (Armstrong)

297

Large solid shaper tools may be mounted directly in the tool post without a toolholder. Fig. 10-20 shows the kind of work which may be done on a heavy-duty shaper with a large, sturdy cutting tool.

Tool Terminology: The terminology which applies to shaper and planer tools is essentially the same as that for lathe tool bits or other single-point cutting tools. Information concerning single-point cutting-tool terms, cutting-tool angles, and cutting-tool materials is included in Unit 53. The terms used and the cutting-tool angles should be thoroughly understood before attempting to grind a shaper tool bit.

Relief Angles: Shaper tool bits are ground with very little end or side relief (relief formerly was called clearance). A side-relief angle of about 3° to 5° ordinarily is sufficient for most applications. An end-relief angle from 3° to 5° also is sufficient. A shaper tool must be ground with the correct relief, as there is no provision in the tool post whereby the tool may be set to provide relief or back rake, as in a lathe.

Rake Angles: A shaper tool ordinarily is ground with a side rake of from 8° to 10°. Little or no back rake is necessary or desirable for most applications, except for certain finishing tools which are given a slight back rake to increase keenness of the cutting edge.

Grinding Tool Bits: Shaper tool bits are ground in a manner similar to grinding lathe tool bits. The essential difference is in the grinding angles required. The procedure is included in Unit 55.

Similarity of Shaper and Planer

Shaper and planer operations involve machining surfaces with a single-point cutting tool. The surfaces may be flat, vertical, angular, or irregular. Planer operations are performed on a large machine called a *planer*, Fig. 1-15. Because of its large size and relatively high cost, it is not often included in schools. However, many of the principles involved in setting up, tooling, and operating a shaper also apply to a planer.

Shaper and planer operations are important because, in many instances, long surfaces may be machined with greater accuracy than by milling, especially where extreme flatness is re-

Fig. 10-19. Shaping an Internal Keyway
(Cincinnati Shaper)

Fig. 10-20. Making a Heavy Cut with a Large, Solid Cutting Tool on a Heavy-Duty Shaper
(Cincinnati Shaper)

Fig. 10-21. Shaper Vises (Cincinnati Shaper)

quired. The similarities and differences between shaper operations and planer operations should be understood. These are explained in Unit 3 and may be reviewed at this time.

Shaper Vises

Shaper vises generally consist of a fixed and a movable jaw which is operated by one or by two screws. See Fig. 10-21. Ordinarily, these vises are mounted on a graduated swivel base. This permits the vise to be swung so that the face of the jaws may be parallel with, perpendicular to, or at an angle with the line of travel of the tool. The jaws of the shaper vise may be made of either soft or hardened steel, and care must be taken to avoid scarring or otherwise damaging them.

Setup Tools

Before attempting to set up a workpiece in a shaper, one should be thoroughly familiar with setup tools and devices. The basic ones are essentially the same as those used for setting up work on the drill press, milling machine, or any other machine tool. The commonly used equipment for shaper setups include vises, parallels, hold-downs, angle plates, and a variety of other work-holding devices. These devices are explained in Unit 12 and should be reviewed before making setups in a shaper.

Safety Precautions for the Shaper

1. Wear approved goggles or face shield.
2. Be sure that the vise or setup fixture is securely fastened to the table.
3. Make certain that the workpiece is mounted securely.
4. Select the proper tool for the job.
5. Be sure that the tool, tool head, table, and table support are secure before starting the machine.
6. Do not run the ram back into the column with the tool slide set at an angle. To do so will make the slide strike the column and cause serious damage. See Fig. 10-43. On machines equipped with a handwheel, run the ram back by hand to insure that the tool slide clears the column and that the tool clears the work, *before starting the machine.*
7. Remove all wrenches before starting the machine.
8. Select the proper speed, feed, and depth of cut according to the kind of material, type of tool, and the method of holding the work.
9. Make certain that no one else is inside the safety zone for the machine.
10. Make sure that chips are prevented from striking anyone in the area.
11. See that the back of the ram will not strike anyone or anything on the return stroke. Stand parallel to the direction of the stroke of the machine when it is operating, and never reach across the table between strokes.
12. Avoid touching the tool, clapper box, or workpiece while the machine is running.
13. Remove chips only while the machine is stopped. Use a brush to remove these.
14. Make measurements on the work only when the machine is stopped.
15. Make adjustments on the work setup only when the machine is stopped.
16. Turn off the machine before leaving it.
17. Remove sharp edges from parts with a file to avoid being cut.
18. Clean the machine and the area with a brush.

80 Calculating the Cutting Speed of a Shaper

The rate or cutting speed at which metal may be removed with a shaper depends principally on: (1) the kind of material being cut; (2) the amount of material being removed at each cut; (3) the kind of material in the tool, as, for example, high-speed or carbon steel; and (4) the rigidity of the machine. Table 9 gives the ordinary speeds employed when high-speed steel and carbon steel cutters are used.

The speed at which a metalworking shaper removes metal cannot be calculated simply by multiplying the length of the stroke by the number of strokes per minute. Neither can it be found by dividing by two the time consumed in making the complete cycle of forward and return strokes, because, on most shapers, the cutting stroke takes approximately one and one-half times as long as the return stroke. The ratio of time spent on the respective return and forward strokes is $1:1\frac{1}{2}$, or when each is multiplied by two, this ratio may be represented by the products 2 and 3 respectively. Thus three-fifths of each full minute of running time is spent in making cutting strokes and two-fifths in return strokes.

Cutting speed always is given in feet per minute. Hence, when the stroke is given in inches, the product found by multiplying the length of the stroke by the number of strokes per minute also must be converted to feet per minute. Dividing this product by twelve gives the travel of the cutting tool in feet. Since only three-fifths of the time is spent in making forward strokes, the cutting actually has been done in three-fifths of a minute. Therefore, the distance traveled in feet per minute must be divided by $\frac{3}{5}$, to determine the rate at which the cutting tool moves across the work.

When $\quad$ CS = Cutting speed
$\quad\quad\quad\quad$ N = Number of strokes
$\quad\quad\quad\quad$ L = Length of stroke in inches
$\quad\quad\quad\quad \frac{3}{5}$ = Portion of time spent actually cutting
$\quad\quad\quad$ 12 = Inches per foot

Then $\quad$ $CS = \dfrac{N \times L}{\frac{3}{5} \text{ of } 12}$

or $\quad\quad$ $CS = \dfrac{N \times L}{7\frac{1}{5} \text{ (or roughly, 7)}}$

When using the shaper, the cutting speed desired and the length of the stroke will be known. Since it will be necessary to determine the number of strokes required to operate at the given cutting speed, the above formula for determining the cutting speed may be converted into the following form:

$$CS = \frac{N \times L}{7} \quad \text{or} \quad N = \frac{CS \times 7}{L}$$

Example

A piece of machine steel $8''$ in length is to be machined with a high-speed tool.

The known factors are:
$$CS = 90 \text{ ft. per min.}$$
$$L = 8''$$

Substituting the known values in the formula:
$$N = \frac{90 \times 7}{8} = \frac{630}{8} = 78.75$$

Setting the shaper to produce 80 strokes per minute will give a cutting speed within the allowable limits of operation.

Table 9
Cutting Speeds (fpm) for Shaping

Tool — High-Speed Steel	
Mild machine steel	80-100
Tool steel	50- 60
Cast iron, soft	60- 70
Brass	200
Tool — Carbon Steel	
Mild machine steel	40
Tool steel	25
Cast iron, soft	30
Brass	100

How To Adjust the Shaper for Stroke and Position

The length of the stroke of the shaper is determined by the position of the crankpin and block in the slide in relation to the axis of the driving wheel. The farther the crankpin is away from the axis, the longer the stroke. The procedure for setting the stroke varies slightly for different makes of shapers. (See Figs. 10-1, 10-2.)

Procedure for Setting Stroke Length

1. Loosen the knob or device that locks the stroke-setting shaft in position.

   Some shapers do not have a locking device; on such machines, the length of stroke once set is maintained automatically and can be changed only by revolving the shaft.

2. With the crank, turn the stroke-setting shaft in the direction desired until the pointer on the ram registers on the index plate the length of stroke desired, for example, 4″, plus the amount required for overlap at the start and finish of the cut. The amount of overlap required will depend upon the number of strokes per minute, the time needed for the tool to drop into position, the depth of cut, the kind of material, the rigidity of the machine, the tool, and the work. In all cases, for efficient operation, overlap of stroke should be kept at a minimum.

   CAUTION: *The stroke should be at least ¾″ longer than the cut. It should extend from at least ½″ before the work to at least ¼″ beyond the work.*

   On machines equipped with an indicator dial adjacent to the stroke-adjusting shaft, the shaft is revolved until the indicator registers the length of stroke desired.

3. When the machine has been adjusted for length of stroke, tighten the locking device, if any.

Procedure for Setting Stroke Position

1. Loosen the device that clamps the ram in position by turning the handle on the top of the rear part of the ram, Figs. 10-2 and 10-23.

2. With the clutch lever, engage the clutch lightly, and advance the vibrating arm to its extreme forward position. The instant this position is reached, disengage the clutch.

   Some machines are equipped with a handwheel on the driving shaft. This wheel is used to advance the arm to its extreme forward position.

3. With the crank, engage the projecting ram positioning shaft, at the rear of the head of the ram, Figs. 10-1 and 10-2. Then turn the shaft until the tool is in a position about ¼″ ahead of the work at the point where the cut ends.

Fig. 10-23. Rocker Arm Is Graduated for Accurate Stroke Adjustment (South Bend Lathe)

How To Make Horizontal Cuts with a Shaper

The principal use made of a shaper is to plane flat, true surfaces. When machining work of this kind, the work is held in the shaper vise, clamped to an angle plate, or, if very large, clamped to the shaper table. The vise is mounted on a graduated swivel base, which permits revolving the work at various angles for convenience in machining. The table on some shapers is mounted on a swivel base and can be turned at various angles. When occasion requires, the table may be tilted at right angles to the axis through a limited number of degrees.

Before placing work in a shaper vise or on the table, burrs on the work should be removed by carefully chipping or filing; likewise, burrs on the jaws of the vise or on the parallel bars used to align and support the work should be removed. All metal chips and dirt should be removed from the bottom of the vise and the surfaces of the work. The existence of any of these conditions can throw the work out of alignment and, frequently, can cause spoiled work.

CAUTION: *Before starting the shaper, be sure the head of the ram will clear at all points.*

Flat surfaces may be machined on shafts which are mounted between centers on an indexing attachment, Fig. 10-24. Any number of surfaces may be equally spaced, radially, on the circumference of the work with this device.

It is recommended that beginners read Unit 79 before operating the shaper.

Procedure for Roughing Cut

1. Examine the work to make sure there are no burrs or bumps on the surface. If any are found, remove them by carefully chipping or filing.
2. Examine the jaws and bottom of the vise, and remove any burrs, chips or other foreign matter found.
3. Select parallel bars of suitable width, thickness and length, Fig. 10-25. The use of two parallel bars is recommended whenever they can be employed. Otherwise, one may be enough.

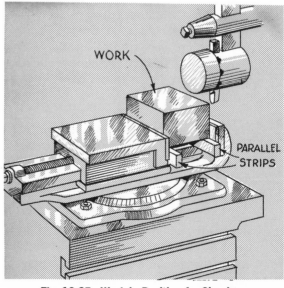

Fig. 10-24. Flat Surfaces Being Machined on Shaft with Indexing Head (South Bend Lathe)

Fig. 10-25. Work in Position for Shaping

4. Open the vise to accommodate the work; then place the parallel bars on the bottom plate of the vise.

5. Place the work flat on the parallel bars in the center of the vise, Fig. 10-25. Locate the work centrally whenever possible, to avoid unnecessary strain on the vise. To save cutting time, turn the work so that the longest stroke possible may be taken.

6. With the hand crank, draw the vise just sufficiently tight to grip the work. To make certain that the work is resting evenly on the parallels, tap it lightly with a lead hammer, and then tighten the vise

screw until the work is held securely. Strips of thin paper under the corners of the stock will aid in determining when the stock is resting on the parallels. If any of the strips is loose, the stock is not resting on the parallels at that point.

Rough castings may be mounted in the vise as shown in Fig. 10-26. Tapered workpieces can be mounted in a double-screw vise as shown in Fig. 10-27.

CAUTION: *To avoid springing the work, do not draw the vise too tightly when clamping thin or very wide stock.*

7. Select a suitable, correctly ground, sharp roughing tool, usually a roundnose (*A*, Fig. 10-28). *B* and *C*, Fig. 10-28, represent left- and right-hand roundnose tools.

8. Insert the tool in the holder or the tool post, placing it as close to the bottom of the tool block or clapper as the nature of the job will permit, Fig. 10-29. Incline the

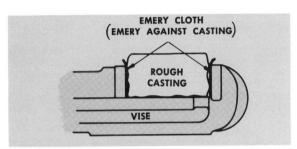

Fig. 10-26. Mounting Rough Castings in the Vise
(Cincinnati Shaper)

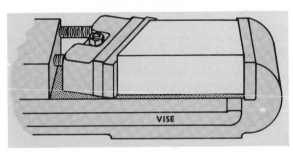

Fig. 10-27. Holding Tapered Work with Double-Screw Vise (Cincinnati Shaper)

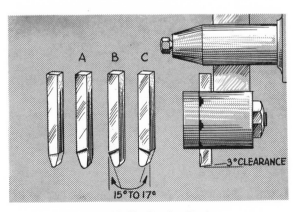

Fig. 10-28. Cutting Tools

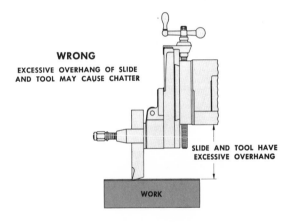

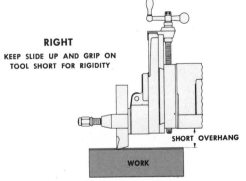

Fig. 10-29. Use a Short Overhang on Both Tool and Tool Slide (Cincinnati Shaper)

303

clapper box slightly away from the work, Fig. 10-30, so that its top slants somewhat away from the cutting edge of the tool. (This permits the tool to swing away from the work on the back stroke, thus protecting the cutting edge from unnecessary wear.) Then clamp the clapper box securely in position. The tool should be in a vertical position as shown in Fig. 10-30. For maximum rigidity, set the tool slide for as short an overhang as possible, Fig. 10-29.

CAUTION: *Be sure that the tool block works freely and that it seats itself properly against the bottom of the clapper box.*

9. Adjust the table until the part of the work to be machined is level with the point of the tool.

10. Determine the cutting speed desired (Unit 80), and adjust the machine accordingly.

11. Adjust the shaper for the length of stroke desired, Unit 81. The stroke should be about $\frac{3}{4}''$ longer than the work.

12. Next adjust the position of the ram, by loosening the clamping lever at the rear of the ram and then moving the vibrating arm forward as far as possible. Place the hand crank on the ram positioning screw,

near the head of the ram. Move the ram forward until the cutting tool is about $\frac{1}{4}''$ ahead of the front edge of the work. Then tighten the clamping lever at the rear.

13. Move the ram back to the end of the return stroke.

14. With the hand cross-feed screw, Fig. 10-1, move the table until the work is within $\frac{1}{16}''$ of the side of the cutting tool.

15. With the down-feed crank on the head of the ram, lower the cutting tool until it is in a position to make a cut of the depth desired. When cast iron is to be machined, set the tool to make a cut about $\frac{1}{8}''$ in depth. This will put the point of the tool well below the scale on the metal.

16. Check that the tool is tight in the holder and the work secure in the vise. The automatic feed should not be engaged.

17. Engage the clutch lever, Figs. 10-1 and 10-2.

18. At the end of the first return stroke, feed the work toward the cutter by giving the feed crank one-fourth of a turn to the right. Start turning the crank as soon as the ram starts on the return stroke.

19. After two or three strokes have been completed, stop the machine and examine the work. Make adjustments if necessary.

20. Engage the automatic feed knob (or lever), Fig. 10-1, and start the machine. The automatic feed should operate at the end of the return stroke. If it is set to operate at the end of the forward stroke, the tool will drag on the return stroke, thus damaging the cutting edge.

21. When the surface has been planed, stop the machine and remove the cutting tool.

Procedure for Finishing Cut

1. Select a suitable finishing tool, usually one with a rather broad, slightly curved cutting edge. Be sure the tool is sharp.

2. Mount the tool in the tool post or holder.

3. With the down-feed crank, adjust the machine to take a light cut, about 0.005".

4. Proceed as above in steps 16 through 21 inclusive.

5. When the work has been completed, clean the machine, and return the equipment to the place where it is kept when not in use.

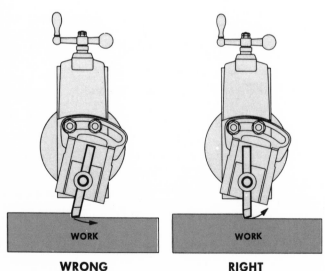

WRONG   **RIGHT**

Fig. 10-30. Position of Tool and Clapper Box for Cut
(Cincinnati Shaper)

How To Square Rectangular Stock with a Shaper

Frequently it is necessary to machine stock on all surfaces. In many instances, this may be done with horizontal cuts only. In other cases, a combination of horizontal and vertical cuts is most advantageous.

Procedure

1. Grip the stock in the shaper vise securely, and plane one *surface* true. See Unit 82.
2. Place the planed surface of the stock against the solid jaw of the vise. Then insert a round rod between the work and the movable jaw, Fig. 10-35. This is used to avoid change in the position of the stock caused by movement of the movable jaw or unevenness of pressure on the work.
3. Tighten the vise screw. Then, with a try-square, test to see if the work is standing in a vertical plane, Fig. 10-36.
4. Machine the *edge* as in step 1.
5. Release the vise, and turn the work around, with the machined edge down and the planed surface against the solid jaw of the vise.
6. Proceed for the *second edge* as when machining the first.
7. Next place the work on parallel bars, with the first machined face down, as in Fig. 10-37. Then proceed for the *second face* as in step 1.
8. To machine the *end*, stand the stock vertically in the vise. Test with a square. Then proceed as when planing the edge, steps 2, 3, and 4.
9. Plane the *second end* in a similar manner.

When the stock is quite wide or long, it may not be practicable to machine it when it is standing vertically in the vise. In such cases, adjust the vise and move the stock until one end projects a short distance beyond the jaws of the vise, Fig. 10-37. Then machine the end as when making vertical cuts. See Unit 84.

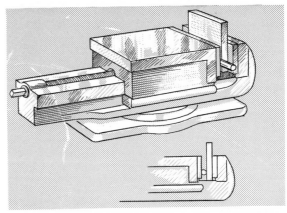

Fig. 10-35. Round Rod Between Work and Movable Jaw of Vise

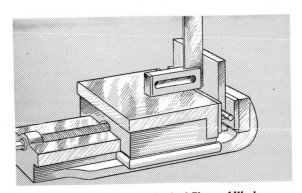

Fig. 10-36. Testing Vertical Plane of Work

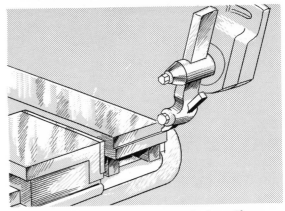

Fig. 10-37. Machining the End of a Long Piece

How To Make Vertical and Angular Cuts with a Shaper

A vertical cut usually is made when cutting a groove, a tongue, a shoulder or a keyway, and, occasionally, when planing the end of wide stock. An angular cut is made when cutting dovetails or bevels on the edges or ends of work. When such cuts are being made, the down feed is used.

Angular cuts may be made by one of several methods: (1) by setting the *head* of the shaper at an angle corresponding to the angle to be produced on the work, Fig. 10-11; (2) by setting the work at an angle and then machining it in the usual manner, Fig. 10-38; or (3) by mounting the work in the vise and swiveling the universal table to the desired angle. For machining compound angles, both the vise and the universal table may be swiveled, as shown in Fig. 10-39.

Commonly used devices for holding the work at a given angle are the vise, angle plates which have various degrees of angularity, and degree parallels. The latter are similar to ordinary parallels, except that one face is machined at an angle.

Ordinarily, such operations as planing a true surface on at least one side and squaring the ends and edges of stock are performed before vertical or angular cuts are attempted.

Procedure for Vertical Cuts

1. Lay out and mark the point (or points) where the cut is to be made in the stock.
2. Place the stock flat on parallels in the vise or on the shaper table, and clamp it securely. Before taking the final turn on the vise clamping screw, it is good practice to strike the work a light blow with a lead hammer.
3. With the down-feed crank, draw the tool slide up as far as the nature of the work

Fig. 10-39. Machining Compound Angle with Both Universal Table and Vise Swiveled (Cincinnati Shaper)

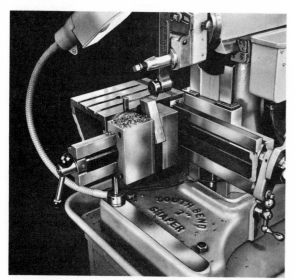

Fig. 10-38. Shaping Part at an Angle While Mounted in the Vise (South Bend Lathe)

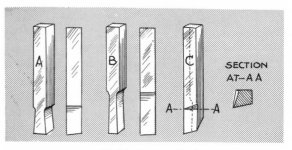

Fig. 10-40. Shaper Tools

will permit. In this way, the tool will have the optimum support from the ram throughout the operation, and vibration will be reduced to a minimum.

4. Select a suitable, sharp tool. Grind it if necessary.

Usually a *squaring tool* (A, Fig. 10-40) or a *cutoff tool* (B, Fig. 10-40) is used for cutting narrow grooves, shoulders, or keyways, Fig. 10-41. When cutting a narrow groove (for example, ¼″), it is good practice to select a tool which will make a cut of the width desired at one stroke. A *side tool* (C, Fig. 10-40) sometimes is used for cutting shoulders.

5. Insert the cutting tool in the holder, and tighten the clamping screw.

When cutting narrow grooves, do not swivel the clapper box. On the other hand, when cutting wide grooves or shoulders, swivel the clapper box through 15° to 20°, Fig. 10-41. This will give the tool clearance on the return stroke, as the tool block will then swing out and up.

When swiveling the clapper box, *always swing the top of the box away from the surface on which the cut is to be made.*

6. Adjust the table until the part of the work to be machined is level with the tool.

7. Determine the length of stroke required.

8. Adjust the stroke control so as to produce the required length. See Unit 81.

9. Loosen the clamping lever at the rear of the ram. Then with the hand crank engaged with the ram-positioning screw, ad-

vance the ram until the cutting tool is about ¼″ beyond the cut.

10. Lock the ram in this position by tightening the rear clamping lever.

11. Move the ram back to the starting point of the cutting stroke.

12. With the down-feed crank, lower the tool slide until the point of the tool is about .002″ below the work surface.

CAUTION: *When machining cast iron, be sure that the cut is sufficiently deep to penetrate about ⅛″ below the scale.*

13. With the feed crank, move the worktable until the point on the work at which the cut is to be made is correctly aligned with the cutting tool.

14. Re-check the position of the work with respect to alignment with the tool; then make certain that the tool is fastened securely in the holder and the clamping lever on the ram is tight.

15. Determine the correct cutting speed, and then adjust the machine to produce the speed desired. See Unit 80.

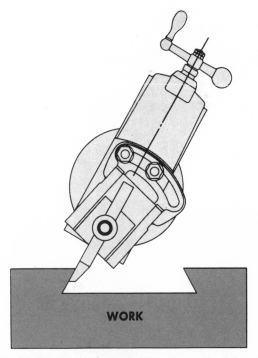

Fig. 10-42. Cutting an Angle with Shaper Head Set at an Angle (Cincinnati Shaper)

Fig. 10-41. Cutting Splines in a Shaft, Using Index Centers (Cincinnati Shaper)

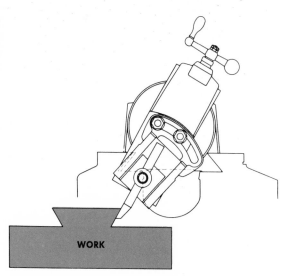

Fig. 10-43. Caution: Do Not Run the Ram Back into the Column with the Slide Set at an Angle: Slide will Strike Column (Cincinnati Shaper)

16. Start the machine by engaging the driving mechanism.
17. At the end of the first return stroke, stop the machine, and examine the cut for location. If the cut is not correctly located, make the necessary adjustments.
18. With the down-feed crank, lower the head about .004″, and again start the machine.
19. Repeat step 17 until two or three additional cuts have been made; then again stop the machine and check the position of the cut. Make adjustments if necessary.
20. Continue with the repeated cuts until the work has been machined to the depth desired.

Once the machine has been set correctly, somewhat heavier cuts may be taken.

When cutting a groove where more than two series of cuts are necessary to produce the width desired, make the two outside cuts before attempting to remove the stock in the center.

21. When the cut is completed, clean the machine, and return equipment to the place where it is kept when not in use.

Procedure for Angular Cuts

1. Proceed as in steps 1 and 2 under "Procedure for Vertical Cuts."
2. With the down-feed crank, draw the head up as far as the nature of the work will permit.
3. Loosen bolts holding the graduated swivel plate. Then revolve the head through the number of degrees necessary to produce a machined surface having the degrees of angularity required (for example, 30°). See Fig. 10-42. The tool slide must be set at the same angle as the angle to be cut.

   CAUTION: *Do not run the ram back into the column with the tool slide set at an angle, or the slide will strike the column, Fig. 10-43.*
4. When the head has been set at the angle desired, tighten the bolts holding the swivel plate.
5. *Swivel the top of the apron away* from the surface on which the cut is to be made, through 15° to 20°, Fig. 10-42.
6. Select a suitable, sharp tool. This may be an angle-cutting tool or a side tool.
7. Insert the tool in the holder, and tighten the clamping screw.
8. Proceed as in steps 6 to 21 inclusive, under "Procedure for Vertical Cuts."

How To Cut Keyways and Other Stop Cuts on a Shaper

When cutting keyways, slots, and recesses, it often is necessary to stop the cut somewhere in the metal. Under this condition, the chips are not completely severed at the end of the stroke. With repeated cuts, these pile up at the closed end of the groove and eventually put such a strain on the tool that it breaks. This condition can be prevented by drilling a hole at the closed end, or when both ends are closed, by drilling a hole at each end of the groove. The hole at the end where the cut starts makes possible the entry of the cutting tool and a full cut throughout each stroke.

Procedure with One Closed End

1. Locate and mark the length of the keyway on the stock, Fig. 10-44.
2. At the closed end of the keyway, drill a hole having the same diameter as the width of the keyway. The bottom of the hole should not be deeper than the depth of the keyway, which is *one-half the thickness of the key at the edge of the keyway.*

3. Place the work on a parallel bar in the shaper vise, with the marks up, Fig. 10-44. Then tighten the vise screw. Be sure the axis of the hole is aligned with the center of the cutter.

4. Proceed as in steps 3 through 21 inclusive, under "Procedure for Vertical Cuts," Unit 84.

Procedure with Both Ends Closed

1. Locate and mark both ends of the keyway (A, Fig. 10-45).

2. With a drill having the same diameter as the width of the keyway, drill one or more holes at each end of the keyway (B, Fig. 10-45). Be sure to drill in the waste stock and make each hole the same depth as the depth of the keyway.

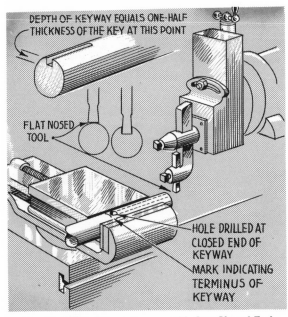

Fig. 10-44. Cutting a Keyway with One Closed End

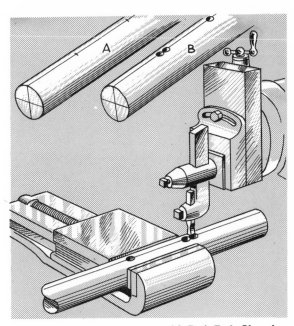

Fig. 10-45. Cutting a Keyway with Both Ends Closed

3. Proceed as under "Procedure with One Closed End," except that the stroke must be set so as to begin and end at about the center of the drilled holes, Fig. 10-45.

Procedure in the Hub of a Wheel

1. Locate and mark the position of the keyway on the face of the hub.
2. Grip the wheel in the shaper vise. Be sure the wheel is held vertically; test with a square.
3. Secure a suitable sharp tool. A tool similar to a boring bar often is used for this purpose, Figs. 10-18 and 10-46.
4. Insert the tool in the holder, and fasten it securely.

   If the cut is made on the upper side, as illustrated in Fig. 10-46, vibration will be decreased. Regardless of whether the cut is made from above or below, a very light cut should be taken, not more than .002".

5. Adjust the table until the center of the position at which the keyway is to be cut is exactly aligned with the center of the cutting edge of the tool.
6. Proceed as when making vertical cuts, steps 6 through 21 inclusive, Unit 84.

Procedure for Machining a Partially Enclosed Recess

1. Lay out the shape of the recess on the face of the stock (A, Fig. 10-47).
2. Drill a hole about ¼" in diameter in the enclosed corner (B, Fig. 10-47). The hole should be no deeper than the depth of the recess.
3. Select a pair of parallel bars which are wide enough to hold the bottom of the recess above the jaws of the shaper vise.
4. Place the stock on the parallel bars in the vise in such a manner that a cut can be taken across the closed end of the recess toward the drilled hole, Fig. 10-48.

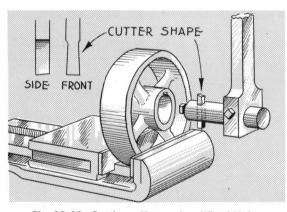

Fig. 10-46. Cutting a Keyway in a Wheel Hub

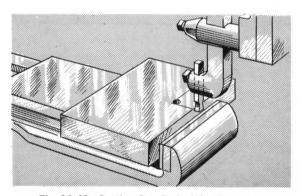

Fig. 10-48. Cutting One End of the Recess

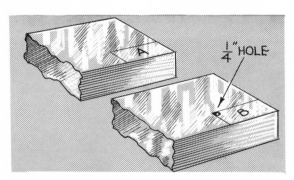

Fig. 10-47. Layout of a Partially Enclosed Recess

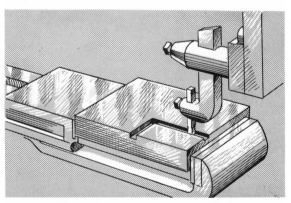

Fig. 10-49. Cutting the Side of the Recess

5. Tighten the screw on the vise so as to hold the stock securely.
6. Select a sharp ¼″ cutoff tool.
7. Proceed as under "Procedure for Vertical Cuts," steps 5 through 20 inclusive, Unit 84.
8. Turn the piece around in the vise, Fig. 10-49, and proceed as in step 7.

If much stock is to be removed, the roughing and finishing cut may be made as in steps 7 to 20, Unit 82.

9. Make the finishing cut as in steps 4 through 21 inclusive as under "Procedure for Vertical Cuts," Unit 84.

How To Plane Irregular Surfaces with a Shaper

Ordinarily, machining irregular surfaces with a shaper is merely a matter of using, in combination, the procedures for making horizontal and vertical cuts. An example of an irregular surface being machined on a shaper is illustrated in Fig. 10-50.

Procedure

1. Lay out the shape on the end of the work, which when held in the vise will first come into contact with the cutter. (See Fig. 10-51.) For greater accuracy, use a fine layout line with prick punch marks, as shown in Fig. 10-54 on page 312.

2. Place the work on parallels (if practicable) in the vise, and tighten the screw.

3. Secure a suitable sharp tool, usually a roundnose tool; insert it in the toolholder securely.

   Sometimes a special forming tool (Fig. 10-52) is used for machining irregular surfaces. When one is used, it usually is necessary to take a lighter cut than that taken with a standard tool.

4. Adjust the tool to start the cut at the highest point on the surface to be machined.

Fig. 10-50. Shaping an Irregular Shape

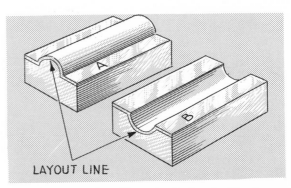

Fig. 10-51. Layout of Irregular Surface for Shaping

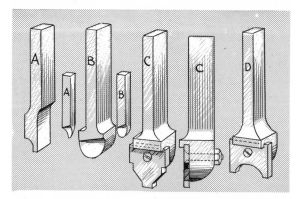

Fig. 10-52. **Special Forming Tools**

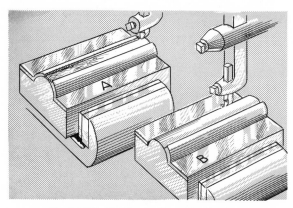

Fig. 10-53. **Cutting an Irregular Surface**

5. Adjust the stroke and speed of the shaper in the usual manner.
6. Engage the table feed for a light cut.
7. Start the machine, and on each return stroke, advance the tool, with the down hand feed, sufficiently to take a cut of the depth desired. See *A*, Fig. 10-53. Each roughing cut should follow the layout line closely.

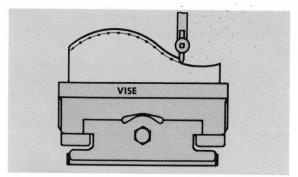

Fig. 10-54. **Shaping Contours** (Cincinnati Shaper)

8. When the entire surface has been rough cut, secure a finishing tool, if necessary, and mount it in the holder.
9. Disengage the table feed, if necessary. This frequently will be the case because more than one cut must be taken with the tool in the same vertical position.
10. Starting at the high point on the surface, take a light finishing cut, *A*, Fig. 10-53. If on the first stroke the tool does not cut quite to the layout, advance the down feed slightly and repeat the stroke.
11. With a combination of slight table and down-feed adjustments, continue machining the surface until it is completely machined to shape, *B*, Fig. 10-53. For an irregularly shaped object, such as that illustrated in Fig. 10-54, the part may be machined from a solid rectangular piece. First, the part is rough machined by using horizontal cuts to the rough outline. A final finishing cut then is made by hand feeding with a combination of both the table cross feed and the vertical tool slide, as required to machine to the fine layout line.

Test Your Knowledge
of Section 10

Unit 79: The Shaper

1. List several machining operations which a shaper can perform.
2. How is the size and the work capacity of a shaper usually designated?
3. Explain how speed changes (the number of strokes) are accomplished on a shaper.
4. What is the approximate speed range (strokes per minute) which is available on various shapers?

5. How are changes in automatic feed accomplished on the shaper?

6. Explain the general procedure for raising or lowering the cross rail and table on a shaper.

7. What purposes do the T-slots on the shaper table serve?

8. How does a universal shaper differ from a plain shaper?

9. How does a universal table differ from a plain table on a shaper?

10. What is the purpose of the power rapid traverse on shapers which are provided with this feature?

11. List the principal parts of the tool-head assembly on a shaper.

12. Why is the apron on the tool head swiveled for certain types of cuts?

13. For what type of shaping operation would it be necessary to swivel the head on the shaper?

14. How does the terminology used with shaper tools compare with that used for lathe cutting tools?

15. List two basic kinds of shaper and planer tools.

16. Why are high-speed steel tool bits widely used on shapers?

17. Why are tools with a left-hand cut used most widely on shapers?

18. At what angle is the tool bit generally held in a planer and shaper toolholder?

19. How much back rake generally is recommended for most shaper tool bits?

20. Why should the toolholder and the tool generally be used in the reverse position, Fig. 10-16, for heavy cuts?

21. What type of lathe toolholders may be used in a shaper?

22. For what purposes are extension toolholders used on a shaper?

23. What are the recommended end-relief and side-relief angles for shaper tools for most applications?

24. What are the recommended side-rake and back-rake angles for shaper tools for most applications?

25. In which unit is the procedure for grinding shaper tools included?

26. In what ways are shaper and planer operations similar?

27. In what principal way is a planer different than a shaper?

28. Why is a shaper vise mounted on a graduated swivel base?

29. In what unit of the book are tools and devices for shaper setups described?

30. List ten tools or devices which may be used in making setups on shapers.

31. List several safety precautions which should be observed in setting up and operating a shaper.

Unit 80: Calculating the Cutting Speed of a Shaper

1. List four factors upon which the cutting speed of a shaper depends.

2. List the recommended cutting speeds for shaping the following materials with high-speed steel tool bits: (a) cast iron, (b) machine steel, (c) tool steel, (d) brass.

3. List the formula which may be used for calculating the number of strokes required in order to shape at a given cutting speed.

4. Calculate the number of strokes per minute, at which the machine should be set, for shaping a piece of steel 10″ in length at 80 feet per minute.

5. Calculate the number of strokes per minute for shaping a piece of brass 10″ in length at 200 feet per minute.

6. Calculate the number of strokes per minute for shaping a piece of annealed tool steel, 16″ in length, at 50 feet per minute.

Versatile Workhorse — The Modern Vertical Mill
(Atlas Press)

The Milling Machine and Its Operation

The Milling Machine

A milling machine is a type of machine tool in which the work is fed against a rotating cutter, which is mounted in a revolving spindle of the machine, Figs. 11-1 and 11-2. The cutter is usually a multiple-tooth cutting tool, called a milling cutter. The spindle speed may be varied to accommodate cutters of various sizes, kinds, and shapes, and for cutting various kinds of metal. When desired, a number of cutters may be mounted on the spindle arbor to machine several surfaces at the same time.

Most milling machines, except certain small hand millers, have both hand and automatic longitudinal and transverse (cross) feeds. The table of most modern milling machines can be adjusted for height, and some are equipped with an automatic vertical feed. Most standard machines are equipped with adjustable trip

dogs which, when set at a particular position, automatically stop the feed at the end of the cut.

Milling Operations

The variety of milling operations which may be performed on a given milling machine depends on the type of machine, the type of cutter used, and the accessories or attachments available for use with the machine. Milling ma-

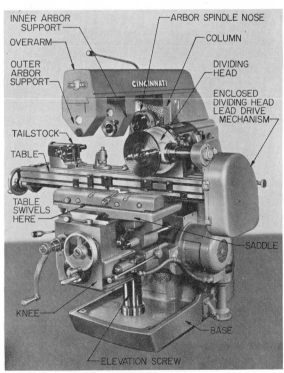

Fig. 11-2. **Universal Milling Machine, Showing Principal Parts** (Cincinnati Milling Machine)

Fig. 11-1. **Milling a Casting with Several Cutters Mounted on the Arbor** (Cincinnati Milling Machine)

chines are used for machining flat surfaces, including horizontal, vertical, and angular surfaces. They are used for machining many kinds of shoulders and grooves, including keyways, T-slots, and dovetails. They are used to machine formed or irregular surfaces with the use of many types of formed-tooth cutters.

Milling machines equipped with a dividing head, Fig. 11-2, may be used for machining equally spaced flat surfaces, straight grooves, or spiral grooves on parts with a cylindrical shape. This type of machining is involved in making gears, taps, reamers, drills, milling cutters, and splines on shafts.

Milling machines, particularly those of the vertical type (Fig. 11-4, p. 319), may be used for all of the common hole-machining operations which normally are performed on a drill press. With the milling machine, holes may be more accurately located, through the use of the table feed screws. The longitudinal- and cross-feed screws are equipped with micrometer collars accurately graduated in thousandths of an inch (or smaller). Hole depth also may be accurately controlled through the use of graduated collars on the vertical-feed control.

Because of the wide variety of operations which may be performed on a milling machine and because of its general efficiency and speed of metal removal, it is one of the most important of the basic machine tools. It ranks in versatility and importance with the metalworking lathe.

Types of Milling Machines

There are many makes of milling machines on the market, including machines of standard design and machines of special design for special purposes. Milling machines may be classified in a general way according to two types: the *knee-and-column* type and the *bed* type. Machines of the *knee-and-column* type, Fig. 11-2, are the most versatile. This type is most widely used in schools, maintenance machine shops, tool and die shops, job shops, and also in many phases of production work. The *bed* type generally is a larger machine used for more specialized production milling operations, Figs. 11-15 and 11-16.

Knee-and-Column Milling Machines

Milling machines of this general type have a table which is adjustable vertically, while the spindle height generally is stationary, Fig. 11-2. The table, which travels longitudinally, is mounted on the *saddle*. The saddle, which travels transversely (crosswise), is mounted on the knee, and the knee is mounted on the column in a manner which permits it, with the table, to be lowered or raised to the desired height. Thus the three directions in which the table may be moved on the knee-and-column machine are *longitudinal*, *transverse*, and *vertical*. On most of the larger standard machines,

Fig. 11-3. Plain Milling Machine, Showing Operating Controls (Cincinnati Milling Machine)

BACKLASH ELIMINATOR ENGAGING KNOB
SPINDLE STARTING LEVER
OVERARM CLAMPS
OVERARM POSITIONING SHAFT
POWER TABLE FEED LEVER
POWER CROSS FEED LEVER
RAPID TRAVERSE LEVER
TABLE TRAVERSE HANDWHEEL
REAR POWER TABLE FEED LEVER
SPINDLE SPEED SELECTOR DIAL
POWER VERTICAL FEED LEVER
CROSS TRAVERSE HANDWHEEL
VERTICAL TRAVERSE HANDCRANK
FEED CHANGE CRANK AND DIAL

the table may be moved in either of these three directions by hand or with power.

Knee-and-column milling machines may be further classified as follows: *Plain*, Fig. 11-3, *Universal*, Fig. 11-2, and *Vertical*, Fig. 11-4. Each of these types is available in a wide variety of sizes and with various capacities. Each also is available with various kinds of attachments or accessories.

Plain Type: Milling machines of the plain type (with a non-swiveling table as shown in Fig. 11-3) are used widely in schools and in small commercial shops. They are used for all of the common milling operations, except those requiring specialized operations which can be more efficiently performed

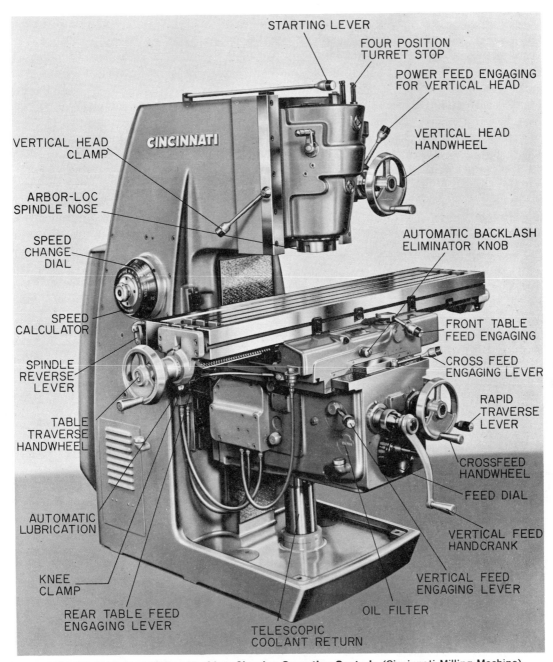

Fig. 11-4. Vertical Milling Machine, Showing Operating Controls (Cincinnati Milling Machine)

on universal or vertical types. Attachments which are available and adaptable, greatly extend the range of work which can be done on a plain milling machine.

Since the table cannot be swiveled on a plain machine, helical milling operations ordinarily cannot be produced. However, with the use of the universal spiral milling attachment and a dividing head (Fig. 11-30), such operations can be performed.

With the use of a vertical milling attachment of the type shown in Fig. 11-5, vertical milling operations can be performed on a plain milling machine. These devices enable the experienced operator to perform on a plain milling machine many of the operations for which the universal and the vertical milling machines are designed.

The principal parts and the operational controls on the plain machine, Fig. 11-3, are essentially the same as those on the universal machine in Fig. 11-2. The distinguishing difference is that the table does not swivel on the plain type.

Numerous small plain milling machines are available. These, of course, are much less expensive and have less capacity than the larger machines. The small machines are available with one of three feeds: with hand feed only, with power longitudinal feed only, or with both power longitudinal and power cross feed.

The small machines in Figs. 11-6 and 11-7 are equipped with power longitudinal table feed. Hand feed is used for transverse table travel or for changes in table elevation. Machines of this type produce good results on operations which do not require the heavy cuts normally produced on larger machines. Machines of this size and capacity often are used in schools, maintenance shops, and for light-duty work in many commercial shops.

Universal Type: Milling machines of the universal type, Fig. 11-2, have a table which swivels horizontally about its vertical axis. The table is mounted to a swivel block on the saddle. This distinguishing feature increases the versatility of the machine and makes certain operations possible which could not be performed on a plain machine without special attachments. With the use of a dividing head and the swivel table, it is possible to mill helical grooves for drills, milling cutters, and helical gears.

Fig. 11-5. Milling a Dovetail with a Vertical Milling Attachment on a Universal Milling Machine (Cincinnati Milling Machine)

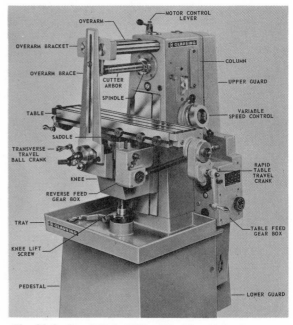

Fig. 11-6. Small Plain Milling Machine (Atlas Press)

A vertical milling attachment also may be used on a universal milling machine for vertical milling operations, Fig. 11-5. The universal milling machine is used widely by toolmakers and maintenance machinists. It also is used widely in school, since it is the most versatile of all types of standard milling machines.

Vertical Type: The distinguishing feature about the vertical milling machine is that the spindle normally is in a vertical position, Fig. 11-4. Otherwise, it is very similar to the standard plain or universal types shown in Figs. 11-2 and 11-3.

The operational controls on the knee-and-column assemblies of all three standard knee-and-column machines represented in these figures are similar. Many of the basic attachments and accessories also are interchangeable on these machines.

Various small vertical machines are available for light-duty milling operations. The one shown in Fig. 11-8 is available with either hand or power table feed and with spindle speeds ranging from 180 to 6500 rpm. The head may be swiveled for angular or bevel milling operations. This type machine is used widely in schools, maintenance shops, and for light-duty milling operations in many commercial shops.

Vertical milling operations may be performed with vertical milling machines, with vertical milling attachments on plain or universal machines, or with heavy-duty turret-head drilling machines, Fig. 8-19. Vertical milling machines use end-milling cutters of various types and sizes, Fig. 11-58, depending upon the kinds of operations to be performed, such as milling: horizontal surfaces, vertical surfaces, angular surfaces, shoulders, grooves, keyways, T-slots, and dovetails. Hence, many of the operations performed on a vertical milling machine are the same or similar to those performed on plain and universal types.

Vertical milling machines often are used for hole-machining operations which require extreme accuracy in hole location, such as for jig-boring operations. The center distances of holes generally may be located more accurately on a vertical milling machine than on a drill press, since the collars on the longitudinal and transverse feed screws are graduated in thousandths of an inch.

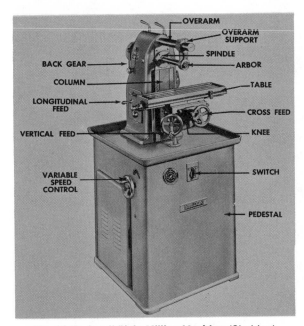

Fig. 11-7. Small Plain Milling Machine (Sheldon)

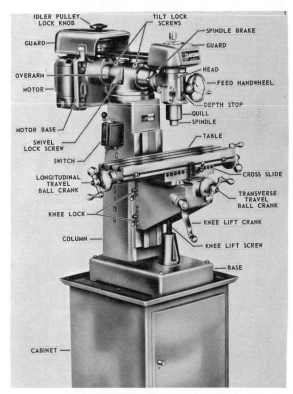

Fig. 11-8. Small Vertical Milling Machine (Atlas Press)

Numerical Control: Vertical milling machines are readily adaptable for automatic operation by numerical control, such as is being done in Fig. 11-9.

Fig. 11-9. Vertical Milling Automatically by Numerical Control (Cincinnati Milling Machine)

Numerically controlled vertical turret drilling and milling machines often are used for various combinations of drilling, boring, tapping, and end-milling operations. When used in this manner, the machine may be equipped with a turret head, Figs. 11-10 and 8-19.

The turret head may have 6, 8, or 10 tool stations. This makes it possible when machining a complex part to program the use of any or all of the tools for automatic operation, in any sequence desired. For a brief explanation of how vertical numerically controlled drilling and milling machines function, see Unit 39.

Size

Four basic size factors are used in identifying milling machines: horsepower, capacity, model, and type.

The *horsepower* (hp) rating of the machine is based on the horsepower of the spindle drive motor. On machines of standard size, this rating may vary from 3 to 50 hp. On smaller machines, it may be as low as ½ hp.

Fig. 11-10. Numerically Controlled Turret-Head Drilling and Milling Machine (Burgmaster)

The *capacity or size* of the machine is based on the amount of longitudinal table travel. Although the overall capacity of the machine is also related to the amount of cross and vertical table travel, only the longitudinal travel is used in identifying the machine. The six standard sizes which apply to knee-and-column milling machines follow:

Amount of Table Travel

No. 1	22″
No. 2	28″
No. 3	34″
No. 4	42″
No. 5	50″
No. 6	60″

The knee-and-column machines shown in Figs. 11-2, 11-3, and 11-4 are all No. 2 size. The smaller machines in Figs. 11-6, 11-7, and 11-8 are designed with less longitudinal table travel than for machines of standard size.

The *model* designation is determined by the manufacturer, and features vary with different brands. The *type* of milling machine is designated as plain or universal, horizontal or vertical, and knee-and-column or bed types. In addition, machines may have other special type designations.

Parts

As can be seen from Figs. 11-2 and 11-3, the milling machine has many parts. The names and functions of these can be learned by studying the illustrations and reading the accompanying descriptions.

Speed

Most modern standard milling machines have constant speed drive. Change in cutting speed is accomplished through sets of gears mounted in what is commonly called a gear box. By operating the speed-change dial (or lever) at the front or side of the machine, Fig. 11-2, the position of the quick-change gears may be altered. (One set is thrown out of gear and another is brought into *operation*.) This results in a change in the speed at which the spindle rotates, and a consequent change in cutting speed. Ordinarily, on modern standard machines, sixteen different speeds may be obtained by appropriately manipulating the speed-change dial or lever. Machines designed

to operate at high speeds have an even wider range of speeds. On the newer types, speed and feed changes can be made from either the front or side of the machine. On the older types, two series of four changes are provided through sliding gears and the back gears mounted in the gear case; also two series of four are provided through sliding gears and the clutch.

Feed

Change in the rate of feed is accomplished through a series of change gears which are mounted in the feed-change gear box and are operated by a dial or lever at the front or side of the machine, Fig. 11-2. Change in the direction of feed is accomplished by means of a reversing lever at the front of the machine.

Longitudinal, cross, and vertical feeds are operated by levers at the front of the machine. These engage or disengage respective clutches with the driving mechanism.

Some milling machines are equipped with an automatic *rapid power traverse*. The table moves forward rapidly until the cutter engages the work; then the feed motion slows down to the feed desired for a particular cutting speed. At the end of the cut, the table moves back rapidly to the starting point, where the direction of travel is reversed and the table again moves rapidly forward. Machines so equipped ordinarily can be adjusted

Fig. 11-11. Milling Work Held in a Special Jig
(Cincinnati Milling Machine)

to move rapidly toward or away from the work, either to the right or left, up or down, or toward or away from the column.

Methods of Holding Work

There are many ways in which work may be held while it is being machined on the milling

Fig. 11-12. Change Gears (Cincinnati Milling Machine)

machine. The most common of these are: (1) using a special jig to accurately locate the work in position for machining and at the same time hold it securely by means of clamping bolts, studs, and screws, Fig. 11-11; (2) fastening the work securely to an angle plate with clamps or bolts; (3) using a plain vise which is bolted to the table of the machine; (4) using a universal vise, which may be revolved through the horizontal plane to any angle desired, or which, by means of a hinged knee, may be tilted and held at any angle from the horizontal to the vertical; (5) supporting the work between the centers of the dividing head; and (6) using a chuck which screws onto the spindle of the dividing head. Fig. 11-26 shows such a chuck.

Spiral Milling

For milling spirals, a mechanism must be employed which will cause the stock on which the spiral is to be milled to rotate at a constant rate as the cut advances. Such a mechanism is an integral part of a universal milling machine. This mechanism includes a dividing head, tailstock, and a lead driving mechanism for the dividing head, as shown in Fig. 11-2.

With the necessary attachments, spiral milling operations also may be performed on a plain milling machine. These attachments, as

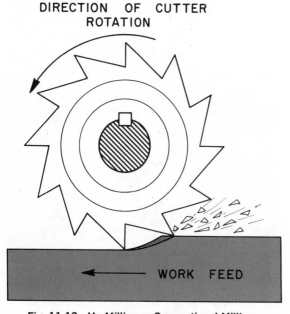

Fig. 11-13. Up Milling or Conventional Milling

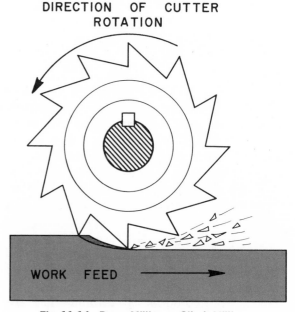

Fig. 11-14. Down Milling or Climb Milling

shown in Fig. 11-30, include a universal spiral milling attachment, dividing head, tailstock, and a dividing-head lead driving mechanism.

Differences in speed of rotation of the workpiece during spiral milling operations is accomplished through interchanging gears in the lead driving mechanism at the rear of the dividing head, Fig. 11-12.

A standard universal milling machine is equipped with a dividing-head driving mechanism with a lead adjustable from $2\frac{1}{2}''$ to $100''$. *Lead* is the longitudinal distance the cutter travels along the face of the work during one complete revolution of the work about its axis. Leads from $\frac{1}{4}''$ to $100''$ can be achieved by the introduction of special change gears or, as in some cases, an auxiliary reducing-gear bracket. With the use of a special long- and short-lead driving attachment, leads from $0.010''$ to $1000''$ may be achieved.

Direction of Feed

The direction of feed in relation to the direction of cutter rotation is one of the most important factors in milling operations. The direction of feed may be set for either of two methods of milling — down milling and up milling. When the direction of feed is against the direction of cutter rotation, as in Fig. 11-13, the method is called *up milling* (formerly called conventional milling). When the direction of feed is in the same direction as the cutter rotation, Fig. 11-14, the method is called *down milling* (formerly called climb milling).

Until recent years, up milling was the method recommended and used almost exclusively. Today, however, down milling is recommended and is being used on certain harder and tougher alloy steels and other metals.

CAUTION: *Down milling is recommended only on machines provided with "anti-back-lash devices."*

Most light-duty machines and older machines do not have these devices. Modern machines of the type shown in Fig. 11-3 are provided with this feature.

Up Milling: In up milling, the cutter tooth starts with a thin chip of zero thickness and ends with a thick chip. The cut starts in clean metal and ends by lifting off the rough surface scale, thus increasing cutting-tool life where a rough or dirty surface scale exists on the workpiece. The forces caused by the cutter on the work act in a direction which tends to pull the workpiece out of the vise or setup fixture. Hence the work must be fastened very securely for up milling. The feed forces the work against the cutter, thus compensating for backlash in the feed screw and feeding mechanism.

Up milling should be used generally for all milling operations on light-weight machines and on older machines which are not provided with anti-backlash devices. As a general rule, up milling is recommended for the softer and more ductile steels and other ductile metals. On materials of this type, a better finish usually is produced by this method.

Down Milling: With down milling, the cutter tooth starts with a thick chip of maximum thickness and ends with a thin chip of zero thickness; a scraping action results as the thinned edge of the chip is removed. Hence, down milling generally produces a good-quality surface finish on those applications where it is recommended.

The direction of cutter rotation in down milling tends to push the work down against the table, thus resulting in more rigid setups. This factor is an advantage for setting up thin workpieces or for setting up work on a magnetic chuck. As the cutter starts into the work, each tooth strikes the hard surface scale or the dirty surface of the work, thus reducing cutting-tool life.

The direction of cutter rotation tends to pull the work under the cutter. On machines not equipped with an anti-backlash device, vibration is developed. This can cause cutter breakage, damage to the machine, damage to the work, and possible injury to the operator. Hence, there always must be provision for anti-backlash devices on machines used for down milling.

Down milling is gaining wider use today and is recommended for a number of applications, including milling the harder steels, harder alloys, heat-treated materials, and materials which become work hardened. Improved surface finish results on these materials. It also is recommended for machining setups where two pieces are mounted on the machine table, one on each end. In this manner, one piece may be removed and another replaced while the opposite piece is being machined. Thus one piece is machined by up milling, and the piece at the opposite end of the table is machined by down milling. Small parts, thin parts, and parts which are otherwise difficult to hold often are recommended for down milling.

Metal sawing with thin cutters tends to cause the cutter to *walk* while up milling; this tendency is reduced and straighter cuts are made by using the down-milling technique. Down milling often is recommended where carbide cutters are used. Since the cut starts with a chip of maximum thickness, there is less rubbing action and, therefore, less wear on the cutting tool.

Bed Milling Machines

Bed-type milling machines are usually manufacturing or production machines used for producing duplicate parts rapidly. (See Fig. 11-15.) They are not as versatile as standard knee-and-column machines. The table on a bed machine rests on a stationary bed and, therefore, is very sturdy and rigid. The table travels longitudinally only.

Machines of this general classification may be equipped with one or more spindles. These are located in spindle heads which may be raised or lowered as desired. They also may be adjusted horizontally. Thus, adjustments for cutter height in relation to the workpiece are made by raising or lowering the spindle(s), instead of raising the table, as in the case of knee-and-column machines.

Bed milling machines are available in standard manufacturing types as well as specially designed types. These machines can perform a variety of milling operations, largely with face cutters or shell end-milling cutters. The milling machine in Fig. 11-15 is a special, bed-type milling machine. It is equipped with three milling heads which mill three surfaces simultaneously. In the illustration, three sides of a truck cylinder head are being milled at the same time. One head is mounted to each side of the fixture, which is mounted to the milling table.

A large milling machine of the bed type, called a *planer milling machine*, is shown in Fig. 11-16. It is equipped with three spindles which are adjustable horizontally and vertically. This type is used for machining very large castings and machine components which could not otherwise be handled.

The machine in Fig. 11-17 is another special manufacturing milling machine of the bed type. The illustration shows three identical parts being machined at the same time, with the three heads controlled numerically.

Fig. 11-15. Bed-Type Special Manufacturing Milling Machine (Cincinnati Milling Machine)

Fig. 11-16. Planer Milling Machine with Three Milling Heads (G.A. Gray)

Profiling Machine: The profiling machine is a special type of milling machine or, as illustrated in Fig. 11-18, a vertical milling machine with special attachments. Its unique feature is the use of a template and tracer finger, by means of which the cutter may be guided to follow a particular outline or profile. The table, on which the template or master block is fastened, may be moved by power or by hand. By keeping the tracer finger constantly against the template or master (shown at the right, Fig. 11-18), work corresponding to the profile of the template or master is produced.

The student is not apt to gain experience on special bed milling machines in the school. Experience on machines of this type generally is acquired "on the job" in manufacturing plants. The principles involved in milling on large machines of this type, however, are similar to those involved in basic milling operations learned in the school shop.

Safety Precautions for Milling Machines

1. Wear approved safety goggles.
2. See that the table is clean and dry before mounting holding devices for the work.
3. Be sure that the vise, index head, footstock, or fixture is fastened tightly to the table.
4. Check to see that the workpiece is mounted securely.
5. Select and mount the proper cutter, and see that it revolves in the proper direction.
6. Be sure that the arbor, cutter, and collars are clean before mounting them on the machine. Use a rag to handle sharp cutters.
7. Keep the fingers clear of the arbor hole when replacing the overarm. Fasten the overarm securely.
8. Use only correctly fitting wrenches on the machine.
9. Tighten the arbor nut by hand with a wrench.
10. Select the proper spindle speed, feed, and depth of cut. Make these adjustments only while the machine is stopped.
11. Use a lead or soft-head hammer to seat workpieces in the vise for setups.
12. Make certain that the table, holding device, and workpiece will clear the arbor and arbor support during the cut.

Fig. 11-17. Special Manufacturing Milling Machine
(Cincinnati Milling Machine)
Operation is automatic by numerical control, machining three parts at the same time.

Fig. 11-18. Vertical Milling Machine with Profiling Attachment (Cincinnati Milling Machine)

13. Disengage the handles when automatic feed is to be used.
14. Loosen the table, knee, and saddle clamps when making setup adjustments. After completion of the setup, tighten the clamps on the slides which should not be moved by automatic operation.
15. Make sure that unauthorized persons are not in the safety zone of the machine when the machine is started.
16. Keep clear of the revolving cutter. Do not reach over the cutter.
17. Stop the cutter to remove chips, and use a brush for chip removal.
18. Release all automatic feed controls when the job is completed.
19. Keep the floor around the machine free from oil.
20. Clean the machine and the area with a brush. Wipe up oil with a rag.

Milling Machine Attachments

In addition to the standard attachments which are furnished with a milling machine, many special devices or accessories are available. The use of these attachments greatly extends the range of work that can be done conveniently and effectively on a plain, a universal, or a vertical milling machine.

Attachments such as a universal vise, quick-change adapters, and a universal dividing head make setting up of work a simple process. Quick-change adapters enable the operator to change from one type of operation to another in a few seconds. The collar on the spindle nose, Fig. 11-24, permits arbors and adapters to be changed easily and rapidly.

Vises

Three types of vises are available: plain (Fig. 11-20), swivel (Fig. 11-21), and universal (Fig. 11-22). Plain vises may be bolted to the table of the milling machine in one of several positions: (1) as shown in the illustration; (2) turned, so that the faces of the jaws are parallel with the face of the column; and (3) with the jaws at some desired angle to the face of the column. Swivel vises generally resemble the plain type, but they can be swung, on a graduated base, to any angle desired in a horizontal plane. Universal vises are adapted particularly for holding work that is to be machined at a double angle. They are mounted

Fig. 11-20. Plain Vise (Cincinnati Milling Machine)

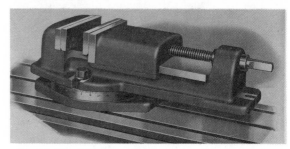

Fig. 11-21. Swivel Vise (Cincinnati Milling Machine)

on swivel bases that can be moved through 360° in a horizontal plane. Vertically, they can be swiveled through 90°. They are useful especially for holding small work on which machining is to be done at various points and at different angles.

Arbors, Collets, and Adapters

If carefully selected, such devices as arbors, collets, and adapters (Fig. 11-23) enable the operator to use a wide range of sizes and shapes of standard or special cutters. Furthermore, they make it possible to change quickly from one type of operation to another without having to reset the work, Fig. 11-24.

Dividing Head

The dividing head, Fig. 11-25, frequently is called an indexing head. It is a very versatile attachment which is mounted on the milling machine table. It is designed principally for

Fig. 11-24. Changing Adapter and Tool
(Cincinnati Milling Machine)

Fig. 11-25. Universal Dividing Head
(Cincinnati Milling Machine)

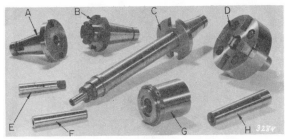

Fig. 11-22. Universal Vise (Cincinnati Milling Machine)

Fig. 11-23. Arbors, Collets, and Adapters
(Cincinnati Milling Machine)
(A) Collet adapter; **(B)** Shell end-mill arbor; **(C)** Arbor, style A; **(D)** Arbor adapter; **(E)** Reducing collet; **(F)** Solid collet; **(G)** Bushing; **(H)** Split collet.

Fig. 11-26. Chuck (Cincinnati Milling Machine)

holding work between centers for the purpose of machining surfaces, grooves, gear teeth, and similar operations at specified angular distances apart, Fig. 11-30. A chuck which screws on the nose of the dividing head, Fig. 11-26, further extends its usefulness and versatility. The chuck is being used on the dividing head for an angular milling setup in Fig. 11-28.

Vertical Milling Attachment

The vertical milling attachment, Fig. 11-27, is mounted on the column and to the spindle of plain or universal milling machines. It enables the machinist to perform operations

Fig. 11-27. Vertical Milling Attachment (Cincinnati Milling Machine)

Fig. 11-28. Making an Angular Cut with Vertical Milling Attachment (Cincinnati Milling Machine)

which ordinarily require a vertical milling machine, Fig. 11-5. The speed of the vertical spindle generally is the same as the speed of the horizontal spindle. This attachment may be used for machining angular surfaces by swinging the head in a plane parallel to the face of the column and clamping it at the desired angle. The head may be swiveled at any angle between 0° and 45° to the right or left of the vertical position. (See Fig. 11-28.)

High-Speed Attachment

The high-speed universal milling attachment, Fig. 11-29, may be used on plain or universal milling machines. It is designed to adapt these machines to a wide range of end-milling operations in many different positions. Because of the compound swivel arrangement, the head may be swiveled either parallel or at right angles to the face of the column. The cutter spindle runs at a higher speed than the machine spindle.

Universal Spiral Attachment

The use of a universal spiral milling attachment makes it possible to mill spirals with a plain milling machine, Fig. 11-30. This attachment is mounted to the face of the column and is driven by the machine spindle. Its com-

Fig. 11-29. High-Speed Universal Milling Attachment (Cincinnati Milling Machine)

pound swivel arrangement enables the head to be swiveled in both the vertical and horizontal planes. It then may be clamped at the desired angle. The cutter spindle speed is the same as the machine spindle speed.

This attachment also may be used on universal milling machines. When used on these machines, helices with angles greater than 45°

may be machined on items such as screw threads, gears, and worms. This attachment also may be used to mill rack teeth, Fig. 11-31.

Slotting Attachment

Although special machines are designed for cutting slots (such as the slots in a gear hub), this type machine frequently is not available in school or small commercial shops; consequently, the machinist must devise other means. The slotting attachment in Fig. 11-32, when mounted on the column and spindle of a plain or universal milling machine, will perform such operations.

The attachment is so designed that the rotating motion of the spindle is changed to reciprocating motion of the tool slide on the slotter, similar to the ram on a shaper. A single-point cutting tool is used. Since the tool slide can be swiveled through 360°, slotting can be done at any angle.

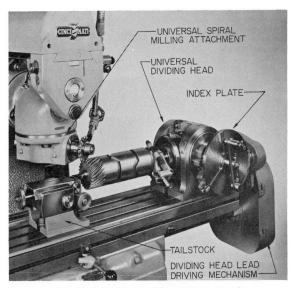

Fig. 11-30. Milling Helical Gear Teeth
(Cincinnati Milling Machine)
This plain milling machine is equipped with a universal spiral milling attachment and a universal dividing head.

Fig. 11-31. Using a Universal Spiral Attachment to Mill Rack Teeth (Cincinnati Milling Machine)

Fig. 11-32. Slotting Attachment
(Cincinnati Milling Machine)

331

Gear-Cutting Attachment

With the gear-cutting attachment, Fig. 11-33, teeth may be spaced and cut quickly and accurately on spur gears. In combination with a universal spiral attachment, Fig. 11-30, teeth may be cut on helical gears and worm gears. Since the spindle of the gear-cutting attachment cannot be swiveled at an angle, it is not as versatile as a universal dividing head.

Fig. 11-36. Circular Milling Attachment with Indexing Device (Cincinnati Milling Machine)

Fig. 11-33. Gear-Cutting Attachment (Cincinnati Milling Machine)

Fig. 11-34. Circular Milling Attachment, Hand Feed Only (Cincinnati Milling Machine)

Fig. 11-37. Using the Circular Milling Attachment (Cincinnati Milling Machine)

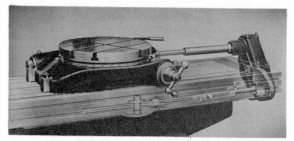

Fig. 11-35. Circular Milling Attachment, Power Feed (Cincinnati Milling Machine)

Fig. 11-38. Rack Milling Attachment (Cincinnati Milling Machine)

This attachment is indexed in the same way that the universal dividing head is indexed. Forty turns of the index crank turns the spindle of the index head one complete revolution. The work is placed between centers of the tailstock and index head. Indexing for the universal dividing head is described in Unit 97.

Circular Milling Attachment

With the circular milling attachment (Figs. 11-34 and 11-35), the operator can perform work on a plain milling machine which ordinarily requires a milling machine with a rotary table. One such attachment equipped with an indexing unit is shown in Fig. 11-36. The indexing crank may be used instead of the hand crank for accurate spacing of holes or slots.

Circular milling attachments may be used on plain, universal, or vertical milling machines. A setup with the use of the attachment is shown in Fig. 11-37.

Rack Milling Attachment

The rack milling attachment, Fig. 11-38, may be used on either plain or universal milling machines. For cutting long racks, a long *rack vise*, also shown in Fig. 11-38, is mounted on the table and used to hold the workpiece. A special *rack indexing* attachment often is used in conjunction with the rack milling attachment on universal milling machines.

Milling Cutters and Holders

The cutting tool used in a milling machine is called a *milling cutter*. Standard milling cutters are made in many shapes and sizes for milling both regular and irregular shapes, Fig. 11-44.

Various cutters designed for specific purposes also are available, as for example, a cutter for milling a particular kind of curve on some intermediate part of the workpiece. However, a capable and resourceful operator, using a standard cutter, can perform economically and effectively many of the operations for which special cutters are designed.

Milling cutters generally take their names from the operation which they perform. Those commonly recognized are: (1) *plain milling cutters* of various widths and diameters, used principally for milling plain flat surfaces, which are parallel to the axis of the cutter; (2) *angular milling cutters*, designed for milling V-grooves and the grooves in reamers, taps, and milling cutters; (3) *face milling cutters*, used for milling flat surfaces at right angles to the axis of the cutter; and (4) *forming cutters*, used for the production of surfaces with some form of irregular outline.

Cutter Materials

Milling cutters, or the teeth on these cutters, generally are made of one of the following three cutting-tool materials: high-speed steel, cemented carbide, or cast alloy. The cutters may be either the solid type or the inserted-tooth type. The *solid type*, Fig. 11-45, may be made of a solid cutting-tool material such as high-speed steel, or they may be made of either carbon steel, alloy steel, or high-speed steel with cemented-carbide cutting teeth brazed to the body of the cutter (Fig. 11-49, page 336).

Cutters of the *inserted-tooth type* have cutting teeth made of either high-speed steel, cast alloy, or cemented carbide. The body of the cutter generally is made of a tough grade of alloy steel, thus reducing the cost of the cutter.

Fig. 11-44. Milling Cutters and Cutting Tools (Cincinnati Milling Machine)
Most standard types and several kinds of milling cutters are represented.

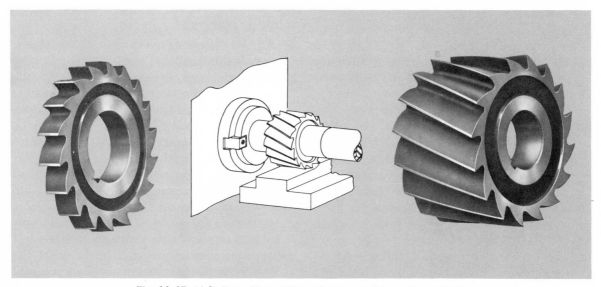

Fig. 11-45. Light-Duty Plain Milling Cutters (National Twist Drill)

The inserted teeth may be replaced when worn after long use and repeated sharpening. Cutters of this type are used widely for heavy production milling applications, Fig. 11-15.

The majority of the cutters used for general machining applications in schools are the solid type, made of high-speed steel. They rank high in impact resistance and general toughness. Hence they are able to withstand the abuse as well as the vibration which sometimes develops on the lightweight milling machines often used in schools. Rigidity of the machine and the setup is important when machining with carbide cutters. Vibration or chatter will cause them to fracture more readily than high-speed steel cutters.

Small-diameter end mills made of solid cemented carbide are available for special milling applications. They are recommended for milling materials such as zinc, aluminum, and certain plastics, where maximum wear resistance to abrasion is important.

The properties and characteristics of high-speed steel, cast alloy, and cemented-carbide cutting-tool materials are explained in Unit 140. The relative cutting speeds recommended for milling with cutters made of these materials are included in Unit 90.

Types of Milling Cutters

Milling cutters fall into two major classifications — standard and special. *Standard* types are made according to dimensional standards established by the American Standards Association. The dimensions apply to diameter, width, hole size, size of keyway, etc. *Special* types are designed for special applications. These may or may not be made to standard dimensions. Sometimes they are designed to combine several different milling operations, in either a regular or irregular type of cut. Some of the most common standard types of milling cutters and their uses are explained below.

Plain Milling Cutters: Plain milling cutters are cylindrical, with teeth on the periphery (circumference) only, Fig. 11-45. They have an accurately ground hole and are mounted on the arbor of the milling machine. They are used primarily for milling plain flat surfaces. However, they may be combined with cutters of other types to produce surfaces with various forms. Cutters within this broad classification are available in a wide variety of widths and diameters. The terminology applied to various elements or parts of milling cutters is shown in Fig. 11-46. Plain milling cutters may be further subdivided into the following three groups:

1. *Light-duty plain milling cutters* have rel- which are narrower than ¾" generally have straight teeth parallel to the axis of the cutter (left, Fig. 11-45). Those over ¾" generally have helical teeth at an angle of about 25° (right, Fig. 11-45). The helical teeth enable the cutter to use a shearing action, with less power required when starting the cut, and with less vibration or chatter; in addi-

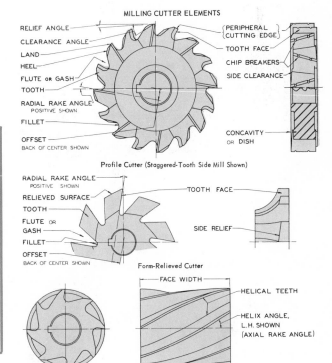

MILLING CUTTER ELEMENTS

Profile Cutter (Staggered-Tooth Side Mill Shown)

Form-Relieved Cutter

Helical Plain Milling Cutter

Fig. 11-46. Milling Cutter Elements (ASME)*

*Extracted from American Standard Milling Cutters, (ASA B5.3 — 1960), with the permission of the publisher, The American Society of Mechanical Engineers, 29 West 39th Street, New York 18, N.Y.

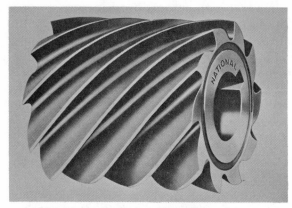

Fig. 11-47. Heavy-Duty Plain Milling Cutter
(National Twist Drill)

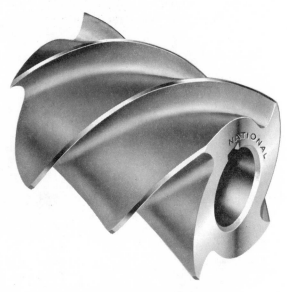

Fig. 11-48. Helical Plain Milling Cutter
(National Twist Drill)

Fig. 11-49. Plain Side Milling Cutters
(National Twist Drill)
(Left) Solid high-speed steel; (Right) Carbide tipped.

tion, they produce a better surface finish. Since the teeth on these cutters are relatively small and of fine pitch, they are designed for light cuts with fine feeds.

2. *Heavy-duty plain milling cutters* are called *coarse-tooth milling cutters*, Fig. 11-47. They are made in the larger width only, and have larger and fewer teeth than the light-duty type. A 3″ diameter coarse-tooth cutter usually has 8 teeth, and a 4″ cutter, 10 teeth. The teeth generally have a helix angle between 25° and 45°.

These cutters are designed for heavy, plain milling cuts. The strongly supported cutting edges and the wide flutes provide strength and adequate space for heavy chip removal. Wide cutters often are called *slab mills*.

3. *Helical plain milling cutters*, Fig. 11-48, have fewer and coarser teeth than the heavy-duty type. A 3″ diameter cutter usually has about 4 teeth. The helix angle of the teeth generally is between 45° and 60°, and it may be even greater. The high helix angle tends to absorb the load in end thrust. This type cutter is efficient for taking wide, shallow, profiling cuts on brass or soft steel. It is not as efficient as the heavy-duty type for heavy feeds and deep cuts on slab milling operations.

Plain milling cutters of all types are resharpened by grinding the land (Fig. 11-46) on the periphery of the cutter. They are resharpened on a cutter and tool grinder, Fig. 11-73.

Side Milling Cutters: Side milling cutters, Fig. 11-49, are similar to plain milling cutters in that they have cutting teeth on the periphery of the cutter. However, they also have teeth on one or both sides, depending on the type. The teeth on the periphery do most of the actual cutting, while those on the sides finish the side of the cut to size. The teeth may be either straight or helical. The terminology shown in Fig. 11-46 also applies to side milling cutters. These cutters are used for side milling, slotting (Fig. 11-49), and straddle milling. (In *straddle milling*, Figs. 11-50 and 11-51, two side milling cutters are mounted on a milling arbor, with the desired distance between the cutters established with spacers. Thus, both sides of the part are machined parallel to each other simultaneously. When two cutters are so mounted, they are called *straddle mills*.) Several types of side milling cutters are in common use:

1. *Plain side milling cutters*, Fig. 11-49, have straight teeth on the periphery and on both sides. Those on the side are provided with *concavity* or taper toward the center of the cutter, thus giving side relief or clearance, Fig. 11-46. These cutters are used for moderate-duty side milling, slotting, and straddle milling.

2. *Half side milling cutters*, Fig. 11-51, have helical teeth on the periphery and on one face only. Cutters of this type are recommended for heavy-duty face milling and straddle-milling operations where teeth are required on only one side of the cutter. The teeth are deeper, longer on the side, and thus provide more chip clearance.

3. *Staggered-tooth side milling cutters*, Figs. 11-52 and 11-46, are narrow cylindrical cutters with teeth alternating on opposite sides. This tooth arrangement reduces dragging and scoring, thus providing a free cutting action. It also provides more space for chip removal. This cutter is recommended for heavy-duty keyway and slotting operations.

Side milling cutters are resharpened on a cutter and tool grinder. Ordinarily, the side teeth do not require sharpening as frequently as the teeth on the periphery.

Metal-Slitting Saws: Metal-slitting cutters are called *slitting saws*. These cutters are designed for ordinary cutoff operations and for cutting narrow slots. For deep cuts, saws with side chip clearance should be used. Several common types of slitting saws are available.

Plain metal-slitting saws, Fig. 11-53, are essentially thin plain milling cutters. However, the sides are slightly tapered toward the hole, thus providing side relief which prevents binding on the sides of the cutter. The teeth are much finer and there are more teeth per inch of diameter than on plain milling cutters. Hence, the feed rate must be much less, usually from one-eighth to one-quarter of that used with plain milling cutters. Plain slitting saws normally are available in widths from $\frac{1}{32}''$ to $\frac{3}{16}''$, and in diameters from $2\frac{1}{2}''$ to $8''$.

Metal-slitting saws with side teeth (Fig. 11-54, left) are similar to side milling cutters. The side teeth provide clearance for chips and prevent the cutter from binding on the sides. These cutters are available in widths from $\frac{1}{16}''$

Fig. 11-50. Straddle Milling (Cincinnati Milling Machine)

Fig. 11-51. Half Side Milling Cutters
(National Twist Drill)
(Left) LH cutter; (Center) straddle milling setup;
(Right) RH cutter.

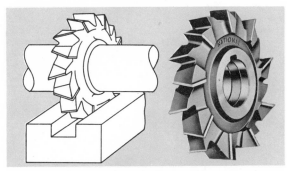

Fig. 11-52. Staggered-Tooth Side Milling Cutter
(National Twist Drill)

to ³⁄₁₆″, and in diameters from 2½″ to 8″. Cutters of this type are designed for deeper slotting and cutoff operations than those normally recommended for plain slitting saws.

Staggered-tooth metal-slitting saws (Fig. 11-54, right) are similar to staggered-tooth side milling cutters. They are recommended for cuts of ³⁄₁₆″ and wider. They may be used for

deeper cuts and with standard feeds. Normally they are available in widths from ³⁄₁₆″ to ¼″ and in diameters from 3″ to 8″.

Screw-slotting cutters, Fig. 11-55, are special-purpose plain metal-slitting saws which are designed for cutting slots in screw heads. They also may be used for light-duty slotting operations, such as the slotting of copper tubing, piston rings, and similar work. Screw-slotting cutters have fine-pitch teeth, and, therefore, are designed for fine feeds. The sides of the cutter are ground straight and parallel. Hence no side relief is provided. They normally are available in widths from 0.020″ to 0.182″, and with a maximum diameter of 2¾″.

Angular Milling Cutters: Angular milling cutters, Figs. 11-56 and 11-57, are used for angular milling operations such as cutting V-notches, V-grooves, dovetails, serrations, and reamer teeth. Two basic types of angular cutters normally are available.

Single-angle cutters, Fig. 11-56, have one angular surface, and they have teeth on the angular surface as well as the adjacent side.

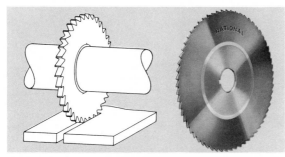

Fig. 11-53. Plain Metal-Slitting Saw
(National Twist Drill)

Fig. 11-54. Metal-Slitting Saws (National Twist Drill)
(Left) Staggered tooth; (Right) With side teeth.

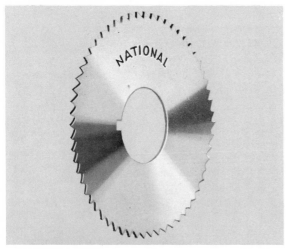

Fig. 11-55. Screw-Slotting Cutter (National Twist Drill)

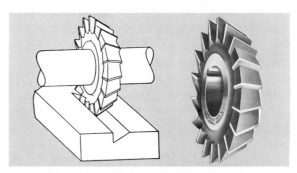

Fig. 11-56. Single-Angle Milling Cutter
(National Twist Drill)

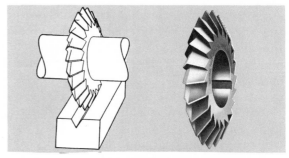

Fig. 11-57. Double-Angle Milling Cutter
(National Twist Drill)

This type cutter is used for milling dovetails, notches on ratchet wheels, and similar operations. These cutters normally are available with 45° or 60° angles.

Double-angle cutters, Fig. 11-57, are used for machining V-notches or grooves. They have V-shaped teeth. Those cutters with equal conical angles on both faces normally are available with an included angle of 45°, 60°, or 90°. However, the angles need not necessarily be the same. When they are not, each angle must be specified as the angle between the conical face and the intersection of a plane between the two conical faces.

End Milling Cutters: End milling cutters may be the *solid type,* with the teeth and the shank as an integral part, Fig. 11-58. They also may be the *shell type,*

Fig. 11-59, in which the cutter body and the shank or arbor are separate. End milling cutters have teeth on the circumference and on the end. Those on the circumference may be straight or helical.

Except for the shell type, all end mills have either a *straight shank* or a *taper shank,* which is mounted into the spindle of the machine

Fig. 11-59. Shell End Mill (National Twist Drill)

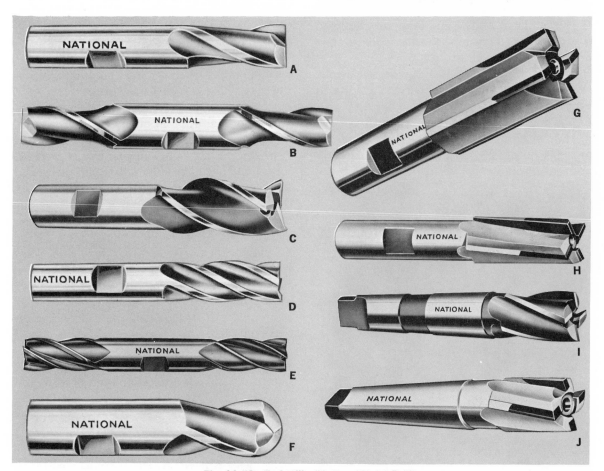

Fig. 11-58. End Mills (National Twist Drill)

(A) Two-flute single-end; (B) Two-flute double-end; (C) Three-flute single-end; (D) Multiple-flute single-end; (E) Four-flute double-end; (F) Two-flute ball-end; (G) Carbide-tipped, straight flutes; (H) Carbide-tipped, RH helical flutes; (I) Multiple-flute with taper shank; (J) Carbide-tipped with taper shank and helical flutes.

for driving the cutter. Various kinds of adapters are available for securing end mills to the machine spindle, Figs. 11-23 and 11-72.

End milling involves the machining of surfaces, either horizontal, vertical, angular, or irregular, with the use of end milling cutters. Common operations include the milling of slots, keyways, pockets, shoulders, and flat surfaces, and the profiling of narrow surfaces.

End milling cutters are used most often on vertical milling machines; however, they also are used frequently on machines with horizontal spindles. Many different kinds of end milling cutters are available. They may be made of high-speed steel, they may have cemented-carbide-tipped teeth, or they may be solid cemented carbide.

Two-flute end mills have only two teeth on the circumference. The end teeth are designed so that they can cut to the center. Hence, they may be used to feed into the work like a drill; they then may be fed lengthwise to form a slot. These mills may be either the single-end type with cutters on one end only, or they may be the double-end type, Fig. 11-58.

Multiple-flute end mills have three, four, six, or eight flutes, and normally are available in

diameters up to 2″. They may be either the single- or double-end type, Fig. 11-58.

Ball end mills, Fig. 11-58, are used for milling fillets or slots with a radius bottom, for rounding pockets and the bottoms of holes, and for all-round die-sinking and die-making work. Two-fluted end mills with end-cutting lips can be used to drill the initial hole, as well as to feed longitudinally. Four-fluted ball end mills with center cutting lips also are available These work well for tracer milling, fillet milling, and die sinking.

Shell end mills, Fig. 11-59, have a hole for mounting the cutter on a short (stub) arbor, Fig. 11-23. The center of the shell is recessed to provide space for the screw or nut which fastens the cutter to the arbor. The teeth usually are helical. These mills are made in larger sizes than solid end mills; normally they are available in diameters from 1¼″ to 6″. Cutters of this type are intended for slabbing or surfacing cuts, either face milling or end milling.

Face Milling Cutters: A face milling cutter, Fig. 11-60, is a special form of a large end mill. Facing cutters are made in sizes 6″ in diameter or over. Similar cutters under 6″ in diameter are called *shell end mills*. Facing cutters usually have inserted teeth which cut on the periphery and the face. Most of the cutting takes place on the periphery, but some finishing also is done by the face teeth. Facing cutters generally are mounted directly to the spindle nose of the machine. They are used for face milling of large flat surfaces.

Face milling means to produce a flat surface on a piece of work so that the surface is at right angles to the axis of the milling cutter. See Fig. 11-15.

T-Slot Milling Cutters: The T-slot cutter, Fig. 11-61, is a special type of end mill designed for cutting T-slots. Typical examples of T-slots are those on the

Fig. 11-60. Face Milling Cutter
(Cincinnati Milling Machine)

Fig. 11-61. T-Slot Cutter (Cincinnati Milling Machine)

tables of machine tools such as drill presses, shapers, and milling machines. In producing a T-slot, a groove for the narrow portion of the slot first is machined with an end mill or a side mill. To provide clearance, the cutter teeth are usually of the staggered-tooth design. Light feeds per tooth should be used with cutters of this type, since they actually cut on five surfaces.

Key Seat Cutters: These cutters are of special design for cutting key seats for Woodruff keys. An end mill Woodruff key seat cutter is shown at the left of Fig. 11-62. An arbor type also is shown in the same illustration at the right. These cutters are available in sizes for all standard Woodruff keys

(which have the shape of a half circle). The end mill type is available in diameters from $\frac{1}{4}$" to $1\frac{1}{2}$"; the arbor type, in diameters from $2\frac{1}{8}$" to $3\frac{1}{2}$".

Form-Relieved Cutters: Formed-tooth milling cutters, Fig. 11-46, are used for machining surfaces with an irregular outline. They are available in a variety of standard shapes and sizes for cutting teeth on gears, reamers, taps, and milling cutters and for shaping edges or surfaces. Concave milling cutters are used to mill convex half circles, Fig. 11-63. See also Fig. 11-64.

As the name implies, corner rounding cutters are used for rounding outside corners, Fig. 11-65, and are available in either the right-hand or left-hand style. Gear cutters (left, Fig. 11-66) are used for cutting gear teeth. Fluting cutters (right, Fig. 11-66) are used for cutting flutes in reamers and cutters. Formed-tooth cutters also are available in special shapes, such as those shown in Fig. 11-67.

Formed-tooth cutters are machined to shape, and the stock at the rear of the cutting edge is then backed off slightly to provide relief.

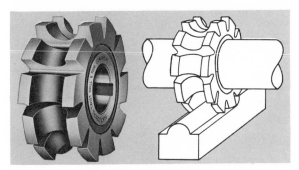

Fig. 11-62. Woodruff Key Seat Cutters
(Cincinnati Milling Machine)

Fig. 11-63. Concave Milling Cutter
(National Twist Drill)

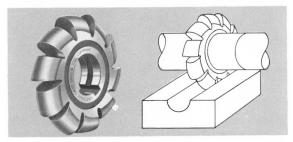

Fig. 11-64. Convex Milling Cutter (National Twist Drill)

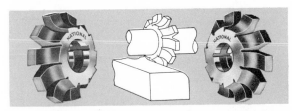

Fig. 11-65. Corner Rounding Milling Cutters
(National Twist Drill)

Fig. 11-66. (Left) Gear Milling Cutter; (Right) Fluting Cutter (National Twist Drill; Cincinnati Milling Machine)

341

The cutter is then hardened and tempered. (Terminology applied to these cutters is shown in Fig. 11-46.)

Formed-tooth cutters are sharpened by grinding the front, or face, of each tooth radially in relation to the center of the cutter. This method preserves the original profile form of the cutter tooth. A formed-tooth cutter cannot be used to make undercuts, that is, to mill an arc of more than 180°. Formed cutters are used frequently in combination with cutters designed for plain or angular milling.

Fly Cutters: A fly cutter consists of one or more single-point tool bits or cutters mounted in a bar (A, Fig. 11-68) or cylinder which is attached to the spindle of the milling machine. In principle and in operation, it is similar to a boring tool. Setscrews gener-ally are used to hold the tool bits securely. Fly cutters are used for experimental work and for special applications.

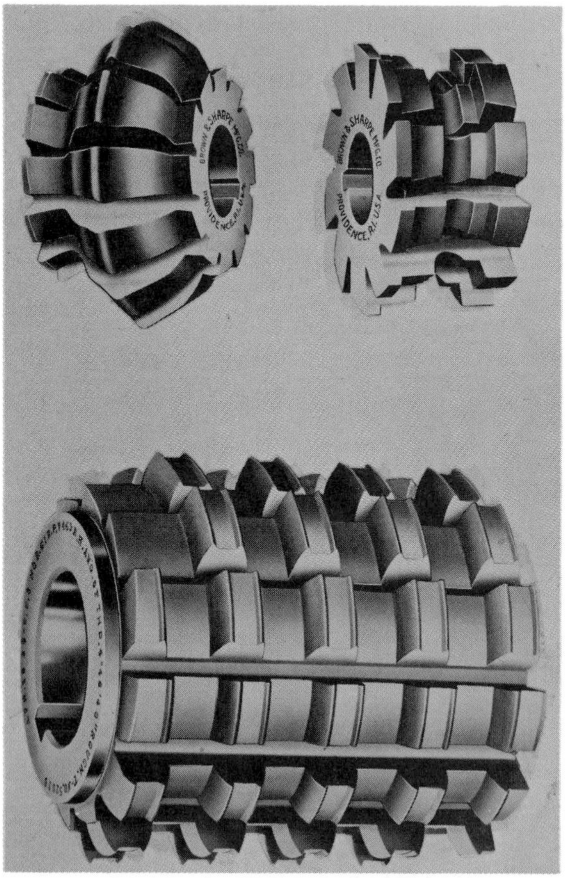

Burrs or Rotary Files: Burrs or rotary files look very much like end mills, but they are not actually milling cut-ters. They are available in various shapes and sizes, and are made of either high-speed steel or carbide. They have many fine gashes, simi-lar to file gashes, on the periphery. Rotary files generally are used on portable tools such as flexible shaft machines or portable drilling machines. They are used for smoothing welds, dies, and molds and for other applications not requiring large amounts of metal removal.

The "Hand" of a Milling Cutter

The term *hand* is used to describe the direc-tion of rotation of a milling cutter. It also is used to describe the helix of the teeth.

Hand of cut refers to the direction that a cutter must rotate in order to cut. It may be determined by viewing the front end of the cutter (looking toward the spindle nose or col-umn), while it is mounted in the spindle. A right-hand cutter requires counter-clockwise spindle rotation; a left-hand cutter, clockwise rotation.

Hand of helix refers to the direction of heli-cal teeth on a milling cutter. It is determined by viewing the end of the cutter and noting the direction in which the teeth twist. If the flutes twist toward the left, the helix is left-hand, Fig. 11-47. Those cutters with straight teeth have no helix.

Fig. 11-67. Special Formed Cutters
(Cincinnati Milling Machine)

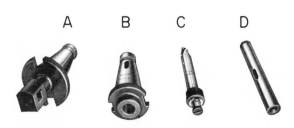

Fig. 11-68. Milling Arbors, Collets, and Adapters
(Cincinnati Milling Machine)
(A) Fly cutter arbor; (B) Adapter for regular taper-shank end mills; (C) Adapter for small shell end mills; (D) Collet for taper-shank end mills.

Care of Milling Cutters

Milling cutters should not be nicked by bumping against tools, machines, or accessories. When not in use, they should be stored in a manner which prevents nicks or damage. When cutters show evidence of becoming dull, they should be sharpened. If they are allowed to become very dull, extreme forces build up at the cutting edge of the teeth, thus causing possible chipping or fracture. Dull cutters also cause extreme forces on the milling arbor and other parts of the machine.

Milling cutters never should be forced onto the arbor. To do so may damage the cutter or the arbor; also, the cutter will be difficult to remove.

Means of Holding Cutters

One of four means of holding milling cutters generally is employed: (1) mounting them on the nose of the spindle, Fig. 11-69; (2) using a shank inserted in the spindle hole; (3) using collets and adapters, Fig. 11-68; (4) mounting them on a milling arbor, Fig. 11-70.

Three standard types of arbors are used for holding and driving cutters in standard milling machine spindles: (1) the *style A* arbor, top of Fig. 11-70; the *style B* arbor, bottom of Fig. 11-70; and the *style C* arbor, which also is called a shell end-mill arbor, Fig. 11-23. (These are described in more detail later.) A collet adapter is used for holding shank end mills, either directly or through the use of collets, Fig. 11-23.

Arbor Shanks: Manufacturers of milling machines have attempted to standardize the tapers on milling machine spindles and arbors. Most manufacturers have adopted the standard *national milling machine taper* which is available in four sizes, designated by the numbers 30, 40, 50, and 60. The No. 50 taper is most common. The No. 40 taper is used on some smaller machines.

Standard milling machine tapers are steep tapers of the *self-releasing type*. The amount of taper is $3\frac{1}{2}''$ per foot ($16°\ 36'$ included angle). Arbors or adapters with this type of taper must be retained in the spindle socket with a locking device such as a *collar* or a *draw-in bolt*. Positive drive is provided by two keys bolted to the face of the spindle. The keys engage the slots in the back of the arbors and adapters. They also engage the keyway in the back of face mills.

Style A arbors, above in Fig. 11-70, have a pilot at the outer end. The pilot fits in a bearing in the style A arbor support, which is suspended from the overarm. See Fig. 11-50. This type arbor is used chiefly in milling machines of smaller size, and primarily for light-duty milling applications. It provides the distinct advantage of allowing the work to be brought up close to the arbor. Hence, in many setups, small-diameter milling cutters may be used more readily than with the style B arbor. It also is possible to use an inner arbor support in conjunction with the arbor. With this setup, the bearing sleeve is keyed to the arbor and runs in the bearing of the inner arbor support.

Style B arbors, below in Fig. 11-70, do not have a pilot. Rather, they are provided with one or more bearing sleeves which are keyed to

Fig. 11-69. Cutter Mounted on Nose of Spindle
(Cincinnati Milling Machine)

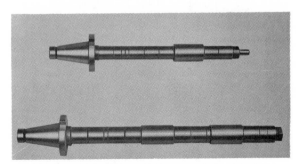

Fig. 11-70. Milling Arbors (Cincinnati Milling Machine)
(Top) Style A; (Bottom) Style B.

the arbor. The bearing sleeves run in the bearings of style B arbor supports, as illustrated in Fig. 11-71. Style B arbors are used for heavy-duty milling operations on both large and small machines, where maximum clearance is not required under the arbor supports. Care must be taken to see that the bushings in the support are adjusted to fit the bearing sleeves properly. If they are too loose, chatter will develop; if too tight, heat will develop. The bushing should be adjusted to provide a free-sliding fit. Additional arbor supports may be used for maximum rigidity.

Spacing collars are provided on the arbor for spacing the cutters and the bearing sleeves. They also keep the arbor straight and rigid. The collars are precision-ground and are lapped on the faces to hold the arbor straight. Care should be taken to avoid nicks or scratches on the face of the collar. A tiny nick is sufficient to bend the arbor when the arbor nut is turned up tightly. Before the collar and cutter are installed, they always should be wiped clean. The cutter also should be keyed to the arbor with a properly fitted key. If not, it may slip and score the faces of the collars, thus damaging them seriously.

Style C arbors, Fig. 11-23, are also called shell end mill arbors. They are used for hold-ing shell end mills and face mills which are too small to be bolted directly to the spindle nose of the machine.

Adapters: The term *adapters* designates devices which are used to mount cutters of various types and sizes on a milling machine spindle. The *arbor adapter* (*D*, Fig. 11-23) is used to mount face mills on the spindle.

The *collet adapter* (*A*, Fig. 11-23) is used for mounting end mills on the spindle. The tapered hole or socket in this adapter is a *self-holding* type, the most common being the *Morse* taper and the *Brown and Sharpe* taper. A number of standard taper sizes exist for each of these tapers.

End mills with tapered shanks may be fitted directly into the collet adapter if the tapered shank is the same size as the tapered hole. If the shank is smaller, it may be fitted to the hole with the use of a reducing collet or sleeve, Fig. 11-23.

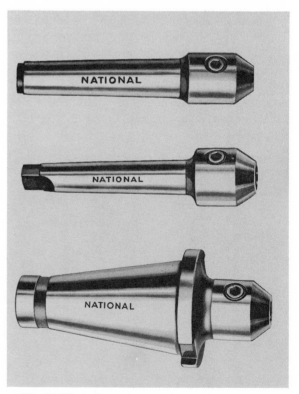

Fig. 11-72. Holders for Straight-Shank End Mills
(National Twist Drill)

Fig. 11-71. Milling a Crankshaft Mounted in a Special Fixture (Cincinnati Milling Machine)
In this heavy-duty milling operation, a Style B arbor is used with two arbor supports.

The *holders* in Fig. 11-72 are used for holding straight-shank end mills. They are available with holes to fit end mill shanks of various sizes. The setscrew locks the end mill securely in place. The two holders at the top of the figure have Brown and Sharpe tapers of the self-holding type. The holder at the top is threaded for a draw-in bolt, and that at the center is provided with a driving tang. The holder at the bottom fits spindles with a standard milling machine taper.

Removing Self-Holding Arbors

Some older milling machines and certain small, vertical milling machines are equipped with a spindle nose which has a self-holding taper, usually a Brown and Sharpe taper. Arbors and arbor adapters usually are installed and held in spindles of this type with a draw-in bolt. The bolt should not be pulled up too tightly when these devices are installed. Otherwise, they are very difficult to remove.

The arbors or adapters generally are removed by turning the draw-in bolt opposite to the direction used for installation. This may be to either the right or the left, depending on the type of machine or adapter. As the draw-in bolt is turned, a shoulder on the bolt is pushed against a retaining collar; this forces the arbor out of the spindle. If the arbor does not release when a normal force is applied to the arbor bolt with a wrench, request further instructions from your instructor.

Removing Standard Arbors

Milling machine arbors and adapters with standard national milling machine taper shanks are held in the spindle nose with a locking collar or a draw-in bolt. To remove an arbor or adapter which is held with a draw-in bolt:

1. Loosen the lock nut on the draw-in bolt about two turns.
2. Strike the end of the draw-in bolt with a hammer. This will release the arbor shank from the spindle hole.
3. Grasp the arbor with the left hand. Then unscrew the draw-in bolt.
4. Remove the arbor from the spindle.

Sharpening Milling Cutters

A cutter and tool grinder, Fig. 11-73, is recommended for sharpening milling cutters. In this unit, only a brief introduction to the methods used in grinding milling cutters is presented.

The teeth of milling cutters should be kept sharp for optimum production and wear. Cutters with plain or inserted teeth are sharpened by grinding away a little of the land on the periphery (circumference) of the tooth at the rear of the cutting edge. (See Figs. 11-74, 11-75, and 11-76.)

The maintenance of proper clearance is especially important. A clearance of 6° to 7° is recommended for cutters under 3″ in diam-

Fig. 11-73. Grinding a Plain Milling Cutter on a Cutter and Tool Grinder (Cincinnati Milling Machine)

Fig. 11-74. Setup for Grinding a Plain Milling Cutter with Helical Teeth (Cincinnati Milling Machine)

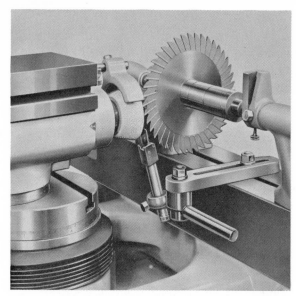

Fig. 11-75. Setup for Grinding Periphery of Straight Teeth on a Slitting Saw (Cincinnati Milling Machine) This type of setup also may be used on plain cutters and side milling cutters.

Fig. 11-76. Setup for Grinding an End Mill with Helical Teeth (Cincinnati Milling Machine)

eter. End and side teeth are ground with less clearance, approximately 2°. The teeth on form-relieved cutters are sharpened by grinding the front of each tooth radially, Fig. 11-77. If the tooth is ground other than radially (parallel with a line from the point of the tooth

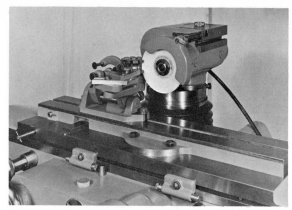

Fig. 11-77. Setup for Grinding Face of Teeth on Form-Relieved Cutters (Cincinnati Milling Machine)

through the axis of the cutter), the ground tooth will not be the proper shape.

Inexperienced persons should not attempt to grind cutters without competent instruction and supervision. Milling cutters are expensive and may be damaged very easily by inaccurate and improper grinding. The procedure for grinding a plain milling cutter on a universal grinding machine is included in Unit 127, and this general procedure can be adapted to other grinding machines and other types of cutters.

Use of Cutting Fluids

The use of an appropriate cutting fluid is recommended for all milling operations on steel, aluminum, and copper alloys. Gray cast iron may be machined dry, or it may be cooled with compressed air. For recommended cutting fluids for various metals, see Table 42, appendix.

Cutting fluids reduce wear and prolong cutter life between sharpenings. They perform the following functions: cooling the cutting tool and the work, lubricating the face of the tool and the chip, preventing the adhesion or welding of a built-up edge on the cutting tool, as well as aiding in flushing away chips. Detailed information concerning the nature and purpose of various cutting fluids is included in Unit 139.

Determining Cutting Speeds and Feeds for Milling

Both the cutting speed and feed at which metals may be machined by milling vary for different metals. The feed also varies according to the type of cutter, the size of the cutter teeth, and the rigidness of the machine and the work setup. As we have noted before, the terms *cutting speed* and *rpm* (revolutions per minute) are interrelated.

Cutting Speed

Cutting speed for milling is the circumferential speed of the milling cutter, and it is expressed as surface feet per minute (sfpm). It is the distance which the outer cutting edge of a milling cutter tooth travels in one minute. Cutting speed may be visualized as the distance the cutter would roll on the floor in one minute. If the cutting speed is too high when milling, the cutter will become overheated and dull; even without overheating, it will wear and become dull in machining a few pieces or in removing a small amount of metal. If the cutting speed is too low, the production rate will be low and inefficient.

Revolutions per minute (rpm) has a different meaning than cutting speed (sfpm). These terms should not be confused. The rpm refers to the number of revolutions of the milling cutter during one minute. A small milling cutter must rotate at a higher rpm to cut at a given cutting speed than a larger cutter. To cut at 50 sfpm, a 1″ diameter cutter must rotate at 191 rpm, while a 3″ diameter cutter must rotate at only 64 rpm. Consequently, the milling machine operator must know how to calculate or determine the rpm necessary for a given cutting speed. He must then set the spindle speed of the machine accordingly. The method for calculating rpm will be explained shortly.

Cutting Speed Selection: There is no one exact and correct cutting speed for milling any single type of material. It is common practice to select a cutting speed which is *average* or slightly below average for milling a certain type of material. The cutting speed selected may then be increased or decreased, according to the results produced and according to the factors affecting the particular job setup.

For example, there are many kinds of tool steels, and their machining properties vary considerably. A cutting speed which produces satisfactory results with one type may dull the cutter rapidly on another type. Consequently, it often is advisable to start with a cutting speed slightly lower than average. With satisfactory results, the speed may be increased.

Machinability: One of the most important factors affecting cutting speeds for milling (as well as for other types of machining operations) is the machinability of the metal. In general terms, *machinability* refers to the ease with which the metal may be machined. It is based on such factors as rate of metal removal, tool life, and surface finish.

Most of the common metals have a machinability rating as a comparison with that of B1112 steel, which is used as the base — or 100 percent. The machinability ratings for various metals are included in Table 30, appendix. In the table, C1015 steel (a low-carbon steel) is rated at 50 percent. A satisfactory cutting speed for milling this steel is about 80 sfpm. As the machinability rating increases, the cutting speed also may be increased. Since the rating for B1112 steel is double that for C1015 steel, the cutting speed may be doubled also, if a recommended cutting fluid is used; hence a cutting speed of 160 sfpm generally will produce satisfactory results with B1112 steel. Recently developed free-machining steels have ratings as high as 300 percent. Steel of this type, therefore, may be machined at about six times the cutting speed for C1015 steel.

The following factors affect cutting speeds (and also feeds) selected for milling operations:
1. Kind of material being machined (e.g., aluminum, mild steel, or tool steel).
2. Hardness of the material being machined (heat treatment).
3. Machinability rating of the material being machined.
4. Kind of cutting-tool material (carbon steel, high-speed steel, cast alloy, or cemented carbide).
5. Whether cutting fluid is used, and the kind of fluid.
6. Type of cutter, its size, and the coarseness of the teeth.
7. Amount of metal being removed (roughing cuts or finishing cuts).

Suggested Cutting Speeds: Average suggested cutting speeds for milling roughing cuts with high-speed steel cutters are shown in Table 10.

Table 10
Cutting Speeds for Milling Roughing Cuts with High-Speed Cutters

Material	Cutting Speed Range in sfpm
Low-carbon steel....................	60-80
Medium-carbon steel, annealed.......	60-80
High-carbon steel, annealed..........	50-70
Tool steel, annealed.................	50-70
Stainless steel......................	50-80
Gray cast iron, soft..................	50-80
Malleable iron......................	80-100
Aluminum and its alloys.............	400-1000
Brass.............................	200-300
Bronze............................	100-200

These suggested speeds may be vared as follows:
  For finishing cuts............Increase 25%- 50%
  For carbon-steel cutters.......Decrease about 50%
  For cutters with cast-alloy tips..Increase 50%- 75%
  For cutters with cemented-
    carbide tips...............Increase 200%-400%

Feeds should be as much as the cutter, the setup, and the equipment will safely stand. Recommended cutting fiuids should be used, see Table 43, appendix.

For finishing cuts, the cutting speeds suggested in Table 10 may be increased by 25 to 50 percent. With carbon steel cutters, the suggested speeds should be reduced by approximately 50 percent. On the other hand, with cast-alloy tipped cutters, these speeds may be increased by 50 to 75 percent. For cutters with cemented-carbide teeth, the speeds may be increased from two to four times those recommended for high-speed steel cutters.

When cutting fluids are not used, the lower range of the suggested cutting speeds should be selected; cast iron is an exception, since it generally is machined dry. Further specific cutting speed recommendations are included in standard handbooks for machinists.

Calculating Revolutions Per Minute

With the cutting speed selected, the problem is to determine the rpm of the cutter, so that the machine spindle speed can be set accordingly. On modern milling machines, the rpm generally is set to one of several speeds which is the nearest to the figure desired, using the speed-selector dial or speed-selector levers. The rpm for a given cutting speed may be calculated with the following formula:

$$rpm = \frac{CS' \times 12}{D'' \times \pi}$$

Where: CS = Cutting speed in sfpm
      D = Diameter of cutter in inches
      π = Pi = 3.1416
      rpm = Revolutions per minute

Example: Calculate the rpm for a 3″ diameter cutter which is to mill steel at 80 sfpm.

$$rpm = \frac{80 \times 12}{3 \times 3.1416}$$

$$rpm = \frac{960}{9.4248}$$

$$rpm = 102$$

Substitute the figure 3 for Pi when calculating the *approximate* rpm. This procedure is satisfactory in most applications.

Calculating Cutting Speed

Occasionally it is necessary for the machinist to determine the cutting speed when the machine is set at a given rpm, with a cutter of a given diameter. In this case, he would use the following formula:

$$CS = \frac{D'' \times \pi \times rpm}{12}$$

Example: Calculate the *approximate* speed for a ¾″ diameter end mill operating at 306 rpm. (Use the figure 3 instead of 3.1416 for Pi when calculating approximate cutting speeds.)

$$\text{Approx. CS} = \frac{0.750 \times 3.1416 \times 306}{12}$$

$$\text{Approx. CS} = \frac{688}{12}$$

Approx. CS = 57 sfpm

When the diameter of the cutter and the cutting speed are known, the rpm may be determined simply by referring to a *table of cutting speeds*, such as Table 41, appendix. However, a competent machinist or machine operator also should be able to calculate the rpm and cutting speeds when necessary.

Rate of Feed

Feed is the rate at which the work is advanced under the cutter. It is the most important factor in determining the rate of metal removal and overall machining efficiency. The feed rate, in conjunction with the width and depth of the cut, determines the number of cubic inches of metal removed during a given period of time.

The tendency with inexperienced milling machine operators is to use a cutting speed which is too high and a feed rate which is too low. The feed rate generally should be as coarse as the machine, the cutter, the workholding method, and the workpiece will safely stand, and, at the same time, it should produce a satisfactory finish. Of course, if the feed rate is too great, the cutter may fracture, or the machine or the workpiece may be damaged. If the workpiece is not held securely, too great a feed rate may cause it to be thrown out of the machine, thus causing possible injury. Suggested feed rates per tooth, per revolution, are included in Table 11. The feed rate on a milling machine is controlled in the three ways described below.

Manual Feed: This type of feed is used on some small milling machines which are not provided with a power-operated table-feeding mechanism. On machines of this type, the feed rate is controlled by manually feeding the work with the use of the longitudinal table handwheel or hand crank. The rate of feed is largely a matter of judgment on the part of the operator. With small cutters or with fine-tooth cutters, the rate of feed per cutter tooth is less than for larger and coarser-tooth cutters.

If the feed rate is too coarse or too rapid, a poor-quality finish will result, or the cutter

Table 11
Feeds (Inches per Tooth) for Milling Roughing Cuts with High-Speed Cutters

Material	Plain Mills (Heavy-Duty)	Plain Mills (Light-Duty)	Face Mills	Side Mills	End Mills	Form Relieved Mills	Slitting Saws
Low-carbon steel, free machining	.010	.006	.012	.006	.006	.004	.003
Low-carbon steel	.008	.005	.010	.005	.005	.003	.003
Medium-carbon steel	.008	.005	.009	.005	.004	.003	.002
High-carbon steel, annealed	.004	.003	.006	.003	.002	.002	.002
Stainless steel, free machining	.008	.005	.010	.005	.004	.003	.002
Stainless steel	.004	.003	.006	.004	.002	.002	.002
Cast iron, soft	.012	.008	.014	.008	.008	.004	.004
Cast iron, medium	.010	.006	.012	.006	.006	.004	.003
Malleable iron	.010	.006	.012	.006	.006	.004	.003
Brass and bronze, medium hardness	.010	.008	.013	.008	.006	.004	.003
Aluminum and its alloys	.016	.010	.020	.012	.010	.007	.004

These feeds are suggested for roughing cuts on heavy-duty machines, and they may be increased or decreased depending on machining conditions. For average conditions, it may be necessary to reduce these rates by 50%. For finishing cuts the rates generally should be reduced 50%.

may fracture. With a feed rate which is too slow, the cutter will become dull more rapidly, and the rate of metal removal will be inefficient. With hand-feed machines, it usually is advisable to start with a finer or lower feed rate. This may then be increased as the operator acquires the "feel" of the feed mechanism and the machine. A slower feed rate generally is better for heavy roughing cuts or for cuts requiring a smooth finish. A faster feed rate may be used for lighter cuts.

Inches per Revolution of the Spindle or Cutter: This type of feed mechanism is found on a few small milling machines and on some older machines. As the rpm of the spindle or cutter increases, the feed rate increases. Typical feeds may vary from 0.005″ to 0.200″ per revolution of the cutter.

If a feed of 0.022″ were selected for a 4-tooth end mill, the feed per tooth would be 0.0055″, regardless of the spindle rpm. If the same feed were used with a 10-tooth plain cutter, the feed per tooth would be 0.0022″.

Inches per Minute: The majority of large milling machines have a feeding mechanism which is set in terms of inches per minute. This type of feed is independent of spindle rpm. Thus, if a feed of 4″ per minute were selected, this feed rate would

remain constant regardless of the spindle rpm selected. A change in spindle speed would not affect the feed.

The following is the usual procedure in determining the feed rate setting in inches per minute:

1. Select the desired cutting speed, for example, 80 sfpm for low-carbon steel, Table 10.
2. Determine the rpm of the cutter.
3. Determine the number of teeth on the cutter.
4. Determine the amount of feed per tooth, Table 11.
5. Calculate the feed rate, using the following formula:

   $F = R \times T \times rpm$

   Where:

   F = Feed rate in inches per minute
   R = Feed per tooth, per revolution
   T = Number of teeth
   rpm = Revolutions per minute of cutter

   Example: Determine the feed rate for machining low-carbon steel at 80 sfpm, 122 rpm, using a heavy-duty plain milling cutter which is 2½″ in diameter, with 8 teeth, and with 0.005″ feed per tooth.

   $F = 0.005 \times 8 \times 122$
   $F = 4.88″$ per minute

   With the feed-selector dial or feed-selector levers, select the feed rate which is nearest to 4.88″ per minute for the machine.

Suggested Feed Rates: The feed rates for various milling operations vary considerably. Factors determining the rate of feed include: depth of cut, width of cut, diameter of cutter, number of teeth in cutter, speed at which cutter revolves, manner in which cutter is held, power of machine, and rigidity of machine and work. Accuracy cannot be achieved if a heavy cut is taken on a machine lacking in rigidity or on work whose nature makes it impracticable (or, in some instances, virtually impossible) to eliminate vibration.

Fig. 11-87. Finish Cut Before Stopping Feed

When all of the above factors have been considered, the feed rate may be determined. It is general practice first to select a feed rate per tooth, per revolution, from Table 11 and then to modify this rate according to the operating conditions. These rates are considered fairly good production feed rates on sturdy machines. For average conditions, it may be necessary to reduce these rates as much as 50 percent or more. For finishing cuts, they generally should be reduced 50 percent. Finally, the feed desired must be calculated and the machine set accordingly.

Generally, at least two cuts are required to finish work satisfactorily — a *roughing cut* followed by a *finishing cut*. The usual practice is to take a heavy roughing cut using as rapid a feed as the cutter will stand, without causing excessive vibration. The finishing cut usually is a light one, ordinarily from 0.010″ to 0.032″ depth, with the use of a finer feed and, generally, a higher cutting speed.

The feed never should be stopped before the cut is finished. If it is, a slight groove will be milled into the surface of the work, Fig. 11-87; this can be removed only by taking another cut.

Since it is practically impossible to grind or mount a cutter on a milling machine so that it will run perfectly true, some teeth cut slightly deeper than others; this is one cause for a groove being cut into the metal when the feed is stopped. Another cause is that under normal cutting conditions, the work tends to spring away from the cutter because of the pressure being exerted against it; when the feed is stopped, the pressure is released, so the teeth dig a little deeper into the metal leaving a groove at that point.

How To Plain Mill a Flat Surface

UNIT 91

There are two common methods of milling a flat surface — *plain milling* and *face milling*. This unit is concerned with the procedure for plain milling. The procedure for face milling is included in Unit 93.

Plain milling is also called *peripheral* milling. When wide, flat surfaces are milled, it often is called *slab milling*. The term *plain milling* applies to the machining of a flat surface with a plain milling cutter mounted on an arbor; the flat surface is parallel to the axis of the cutter.

After learning to mill a flat surface with a plain milling cutter, milling operations with other arbor milling cutters will be easy. The procedures used are similar.

Making a cut with a milling machine is a very simple matter after the machine has been properly set and the work accurately and securely fastened to the worktable by means of a vise, clamping bolts, or other suitable device. Skill in the operation of a milling machine is principally a matter of knowing: how to adjust the machine to the correct cutting speed in feet per minute for the particular metal to be machined; how to determine the correct rate of feed per minute and set the machine accordingly; how to set up the work accurately, firmly, and securely on the table of the machine; how to select a suitable cutter; how to mount the cutter on the machine; and how to sharpen the cutter when necessary.

Procedure for Roughing Cut

1. Secure the desired stock, Fig. 11-88. Then with a file or grinder, remove any burrs or other foreign projections.

2. Select a sharp cutter of suitable shape, diameter, and width — preferably one no larger in diameter than necessary, but it should extend the width of the surface to be milled, Fig. 11-47. If the cutter is dull, ask your instructor to show you how to grind it. Never use a dull cutter because of danger of spoiling the work or permanently damaging the cutter.

3. Place a plain vise on the worktable of the milling machine. Locate the vise near the rear of the table and as close to the column as the work and the necessary collars on the arbor will permit and still allow sufficient clearance. Then partially tighten the bolts holding the vise on the table.

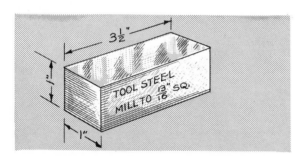

Fig. 11-88. Layout for Flat Surface Milling

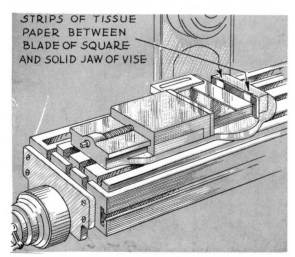

Fig. 11-89. Vise Aligned with Machined Column

If necessary, slightly loosen the clamping screws on both the knee and saddle, *but be sure to tighten them before starting the cut.*

4. With a try square, align the stationary jaw of the vise with the machined face of the column, as in Fig. 11-89. Then tighten the clamping bolts.

A higher degree of accuracy may be achieved by placing a couple of test strips of tissue paper between the jaw of the vise and the blade of the square, as shown in the illustration, and adjusting until both are held with equal firmness. When greater accuracy of setting is required, a dial indicator, Fig. 11-90, is used.

5. Select a pair of parallel bars of such width that the work (when placed upon them) will project above the jaws of the vise sufficiently to give at least $\frac{1}{8}''$ clearance when the cut is made.

6. With a whisk broom or duster, carefully remove all metal chips or dirt from the bottom and jaws of the vise and from the parallels.

7. Place the workpiece on the parallels, and then, with the crank, tighten the vise until

Fig. 11-90. Testing Squareness with Dial Indicator

it just grips the work. To seat the stock firmly on the parallels, strike it light blows near each end with a lead or copper hammer. Then draw the vise tightly enough to hold the stock securely. If the stock is rough, protect the jaws of the vise by placing pieces of sheet aluminum, copper, or brass between the work and the jaws.

Long stock or large pieces may be clamped directly to the table of the machine with clamping straps and bolts, Fig. 11-91.

8. Select a suitable arbor and collars. Choose an arbor as short as the work and the necessary accessories will permit. A short arbor reduces vibration.

9. Carefully and thoroughly wipe the shank of the arbor with a piece of *clean, dry* cloth. Then wrap a small wad of cloth around the end of a bent scriber. Insert the cloth in the shank hole of the spindle, and give the scriber a few turns, thus removing chips or dirt from the recess.

10. Insert the arbor in the spindle, place one or more collars on the arbor, and then position the cutter. Key the cutter to the arbor, and finally add sufficient collars to fill the arbor just beyond the threaded part.

When placing the cutter, be sure to turn it so that the cutting edges of the teeth are pointed in the same direction as the desired rotation of the spindle, Fig. 11-92.

Milling machine spindles may rotate either clockwise or counterclockwise. Cut-

ters should be placed on the arbor so that if the cutter slips on the arbor, the arbor nut will be tightened. This means that the direction of rotation is determined by whether the thread on the arbor is right- or left- hand. Most cutters and arbors are so made that the cutter can be keyed to the arbor. When this is the case, the cutter may be rotated in either direction without danger of slipping. When a keyway is provided, the cutter always should be keyed to the arbor.

11. Place the nut on the arbor, and draw it tightly against the collar with the wrench.

12. Adjust the overarm, and slide the arbor bearing over the end of the arbor. *Or*, insert the dead center into the arbor bearing, and advance it until it fits into the center hole in the arbor. Then fasten it in position.

13. Lock the overarm in position by tightening the clamping bolts or by using the clamping lever (if so equipped).

14. With the crank or wheel for making longitudinal adjustments, run the table back until the work is under the center of the cutter, Fig. 11-92.

15. Using the vertical-adjustment crank, raise the table until the work is about .01″ away from the cutter.

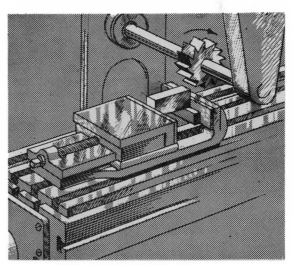

Fig. 11-92. Cutting Edges Should Point in Direction of Rotation

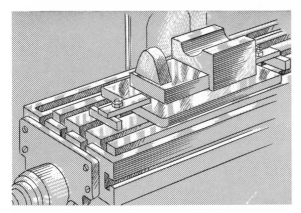

Fig. 11-91. Stock Fastened with Clamping Straps and Bolts

Fig. 11-93. Making Roughing Cut

16. With the longitudinal-adjustment crank, draw the table back until it just clears the front of the cutter. Then with the vertical adjustment, raise the table an amount equal to the desired depth of the cut plus .01″. Finally, tighten the column clamping screws. Also see that the saddle clamping screws are tight.

When there is much stock to be removed, it usually is necessary to take a rough and a finishing cut. The finishing cut should be much lighter, usually from $\frac{1}{64}″$ to $\frac{1}{32}″$.

17. Determine the correct cutting speed for the metal to be machined, as for example, tool steel; see Table 10 in Unit 90.

18. By the speed index plate, set the speed control levers so as to produce the cutting speed desired.

19. Determine the correct feed for the work to be done. See Table 11, Unit 90.

20. Refer to the feed index plate; then set the feed control to produce the desired feed.

21. Start the machine; turn on the cutting fluid; and then, with the hand feed, advance the work until the cutter is just cutting its full depth, Fig. 11-93. If necessary, stop the machine, move the table until the work clears the cutter, and test the depth of the cut.

NOTE: Use a cutting fluid freely with all milling operations.

22. Make adjustments if necessary; then again start the machine and *immediately* engage the longitudinal automatic feed.

CAUTION: *Do not stop the feed while the cutter is revolving. To do so will cause an undercut or groove in the face of the work, Fig. 11-87.*

23. When the cut is completed, shut off the power and remove the work, unless a finishing cut is to be taken.

CAUTION: *Always lower the table slightly or stop the machine before moving the work back under the cutter.*

24. When finished using the machine, remove the cutter and arbor, and clean them. Return parts to the place where kept when not in use. Then with a brush, remove all chips from the table and the machine.

Procedure for Finishing Cut

1. Set the machine in the usual manner for the depth of cut desired.

2. Proceed as in steps 21 through 24 inclusive.

How To Square Stock with a Milling Machine

Sometimes it is necessary to machine a piece of rectangular stock to a specific thickness, width, and length. The sequence of operations generally followed in performing this operation is given below. This may be varied, and often is, to meet particular conditions or occasions.

Procedure for One Broad Surface

1. Prepare the stock and mount a *swivel vise*, if available, on the table of the machine, steps 1 through 7 inclusive, Unit 91.
2. Proceed as in steps 8 through 23, Unit 91.

Procedure for First Edge

1. Swing the vise through 90°, so that the jaws of the vise are parallel with the machined face of the column of the machine, Fig. 11-95. If necessary, test for alignment with parallel bars or other suitable means.
2. Lay a suitable parallel at the bottom of the vise, if needed; then place the machined surface against the stationary jaw, protecting it, if necessary, with pieces of heavy paper or sheets of aluminum, copper, or brass.
3. Hold a piece of rod between the movable jaw of the vise and the stock (A, Fig.

11-95). With the hand crank, draw the movable jaw tightly against the rod. Be sure to place the rod about half way between the top of the parallel and the top of the jaw.
4. Proceed as in step 2, under "Procedure for One Broad Surface."

Procedure for Second Edge

1. Loosen the vise, and turn the stock end-for-end, being sure that the machined edge lies flat on the bottom of the vise or the parallel.
2. Proceed as when machining the first edge.

Procedure for Second Broad Surface

1. Revolve the swivel vise back through 90°. Make sure the jaw is perpendicular to the machined part of the column.
2. Proceed as under "Procedure for One Broad Surface," steps 1 and 2, inclusive.

Procedure for First End

1. Again swing the vise through 90°. Be sure the jaws are parallel with the face of the column.

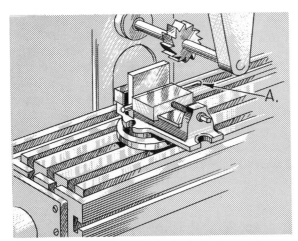

Fig. 11-95. Stock in Position for Machining Edge

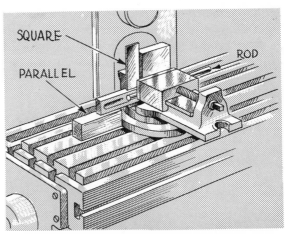

Fig. 11-96. Checking for Squareness Before Machining End

2. Place one end of the stock on the bottom of the vise or on the parallel. Then with a try square held against one edge, test for perpendicularity, Fig. 11-96.

If the piece does not stand quite perpendicular, place shims of paper or metal under the low corner of the stock; then test again. Continue making adjustments until the machined edge is perpendicular to the bottom of the vise. This is important; otherwise, the ends will not be at right angles to the sides.

3. Proceed as under "Procedure for First Edge," steps 3 and 4 inclusive.

Procedure for Second End

1. Turn the stock end-for-end, and clamp it securely in the vise.
2. Proceed as when machining the first end.

UNIT

93 How To Face Mill a Surface

Face milling refers to the process of machining a surface which is parallel to the face of a cutter and at right angles to the axis of the cutter. Face milling usually is performed with face milling cutters in production shops, Fig. 11-15. Shell end-milling cutters (Fig. 11-97) often are used for face milling smaller surface areas. These commonly are used in tool and die shops and in schools. An end mill may be used for face milling very small surface areas.

Face milling may be performed on milling machines having either a horizontal spindle or a vertical spindle. The operating principles are similar with both. The procedure in this unit is for face milling on a knee-and-column machine with a horizontal spindle.

As can be seen in Fig. 11-97, shell mills, like face mills and end mills, have cutting edges on the periphery and on the side. However, the teeth on the periphery do most of the cutting. The function of those on the side is to take a light finishing cut, leaving a smooth surface. The teeth should be kept sharp.

Procedure

1. Select a suitable facing cutter, and mount it in the spindle of the milling machine. If a cutter with a taper shank is used, first select one of suitable shape and size. Next clean both the tapered hole in the spindle and the shank of the cutter; then insert the shank in the hole. If the machine is equipped with a draw-in bolt, insert the bolt, and draw the cutter into the recess.
2. Fasten an angle plate on the table of the machine. Be sure the face of the plate is parallel with the machined face of the column. Test as in Fig. 11-98.

Frequently, it is necessary to use a jig specially designed for holding the work in the position desired. In this case, the jig

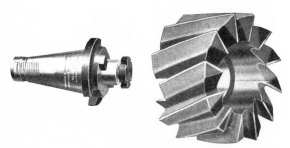

Fig. 11-97. Shell End Mill and Shell End Mill Arbor
(Brown & Sharpe)

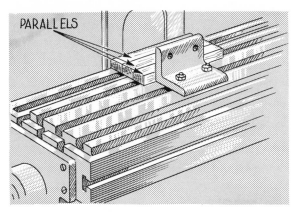

Fig. 11-98. Checking Alignment of Angle Plate

is clamped to the table of the machine and the work to the jig.

3. With the longitudinal and hand cross feed, advance the work until the cutter is in position to make the cut.

4. Using the vertical adjustment crank, raise the table until the cutter is in position for making a cut of the width desired.

5. Determine the correct cutting speed for the metal to be machined. See Table 10, Unit 90.

6. By the speed index plate, set the speed control levers for the cutting speed desired.

7. Determine the correct feed. See Table 11, Unit 90. Then by the feed index plate, set the feed control levers for the rate of feed desired.

8. With the spindle reverse mechanism, set the machine so that the direction of rotation will tend to press the work toward the face of the table, Fig. 11-99.

   See that the column lock screw and the saddle lock screws are tight.

9. Start the machine, and with the longitudinal hand feed, advance the work until

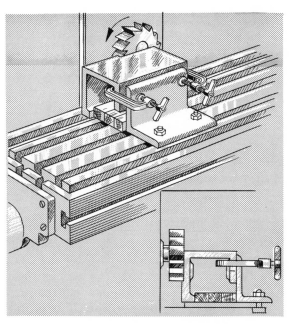

Fig. 11-99. Making the Facing Cut

the cutter is cutting the depth desired, Fig. 11-99. Then, if necessary, stop the machine, and test the width of the cut.

10. Make adjustments, if necessary; then again start the machine and immediately engage the automatic longitudinal feed.

11. When the cut is completed, shut off the power and remove the work.

   If a second cut is necessary, be sure to lower the table or stop the machine before running the work back.

12. When through using the machine, remove the cutter and clean it thoroughly. Then return the cutter and other fixtures to the place where kept when not in use. With a brush, remove all chips from the table and other parts of the machine.

94 How To Mill a Chamfer or Bevel on Rectangular Stock

Milling a chamfer or a bevel is merely a variation of straight milling, such as is discussed in Unit 91. A *bevel* is an angular cut extending from surface to surface and completely removing the perpendicular edge, while a *chamfer* is an angular cut removing only part of the edge. Ordinarily, work that is to be chamfered or beveled will have been machined to size either by milling or planing. There are several ways to hold the work at the angle desired while it is being machined. Two common procedures are: (1) clamping the stock in a universal vise, Fig. 11-100; (2) holding the work in position with a setting strip (a form of jig).

Chamfers or bevels may be machined with milling machines which have either a horizontal or a vertical spindle.

Procedure for a Universal Vise

1. Fasten the vise on the table with the stationary jaw parallel with the face of the column.
2. Loosen the clamping bolt, and raise the outside of the upper part of the vise until it registers the angle desired (as, for example, 45°). Then tighten the clamping bolt.
3. Place the work in the vise, Fig. 11-100, being sure that one edge is resting flat on the bottom of the vise or on a parallel; protect the machined surface, if necessary.
4. Tighten the vise; then check to see that the edge to be machined is parallel with the face of the column.
5. Select a suitable cutter, and mount it on the machine in the usual manner.
6. Make the cut, following the usual procedure.
7. Machine other edges in a similar manner.

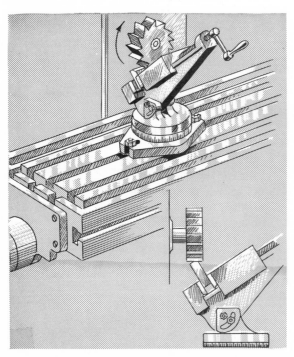

Fig. 11-100. Milling a Chamfer with Work Held in Universal Vise

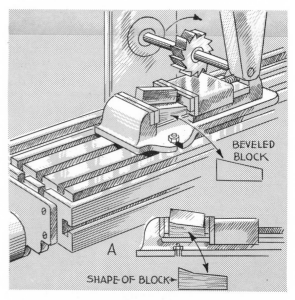

Fig. 11-101. Milling a Bevel with Work Held in Plain Vise

8. When the operation is completed, remove the work, clean the machine, and return all appliances to the place where kept when not in use.

Procedure for a Setting Strip

1. Prepare a suitable setting strip or strips, Fig. 11-101. If only one or a small number of pieces is to be machined, the setting strips may be made of hard wood, although metal is recommended because it can be machined more accurately.
2. Clamp a plain vise on the table of the milling machine with the jaws either perpendicular or parallel to the face of the column.
3. Place the setting strips in the vise, and lay the work upon them, being sure there are no chips between the strips and the work.
4. Align the edge to be machined parallel with the face of the column; then tighten the vise.
5. Make sure the work is seated solidly on the setting strips by tapping it lightly with a lead or copper hammer.
6. Proceed as in steps 5 through 8 inclusive, under "Procedure for a Universal Vise."

If both sides of the piece are beveled, prepare a second setting strip (for example, *A*, Fig. 11-101); then proceed as in steps 3 through 6 inclusive.

How To Mill a Square, Hexagon, or Similar Shapes

Milling a square or other polygons with a flat surface may be accomplished with the stock held between the centers of the dividing head or held vertically in the dividing head chuck. The latter is recommended when practicable. Work also may be held at any desired angle in the dividing head, Fig. 11-28. More information about dividing heads can be found in Unit 97.

Procedure for a Square
— Using an End Mill

1. Place the dividing head on the table of the milling machine, and fasten it in position as near the column as practicable.
2. Withdraw the stop pin in the index plate, if necessary. Then disengage the worm by turning the knob or handle through a part of a revolution.
3. Remove the dividing head center, and revolve the head spindle to a vertical position, Fig. 11-103.
4. Remove the nose guard, and mount the chuck on the spindle. See Fig. 11-28.
5. Insert the cap that closes the end of the hole in the dividing head spindle. If a cap

Fig. 11-103. Miling a Square with an End Mill

is not available, put a little waste in the hole.

Closing the hole prevents chips from falling through it, thus becoming lodged between the swivel block and the base plate.

6. Secure a suitable, sharp end mill (A, Fig. 11-103). Clean the shank of the mill and the spindle hole thoroughly; then insert the shank firmly in the spindle hole. If equipped with a draw-in bolt, insert the bolt and tighten with a wrench.

7. Secure a piece of waste stock of approximately the same diameter or size as the work to be milled, and insert it between the jaws of the chuck. Draw the jaws tight with the key wrench.

Assume that the stock has been turned to $1\frac{1}{2}$" diameter and that a 1" square section is to be milled on the end. Subtracting 1" from $1\frac{1}{2}$" leaves $\frac{1}{2}$" of stock to be removed, or $\frac{1}{4}$" from each side.

8. With the longitudinal feed, advance the table until the cutter almost touches the work. Then, with the vertical adjustment, raise the work so as to take a cut about $\frac{1}{8}$" in depth.

9. With the cross feed, move the table until the stock is in such position that $\frac{1}{4}$" of stock will be removed from one side of the work. See that the column clamp screw and the saddle clamp screws are tight before making each cut.

10. Start the machine, and with the longitudinal feed, advance the cutter and make the cut. Use a cutting compound freely.

Fig. 11-104. Milling a Square with a Plain Cutter

11. Stop the machine; then advance the table until the cutter clears the work.

12. Revolve the direct index plate, on the front of the spindle, through one-half turn, 180°, or half the number of equally spaced holes in any evenly spaced circle of holes (for example, 20 or 24). Lock the plate in position with the plunger pin located in the head.

13. Start the machine, and advance the cutter.

14. When the cut is completed, stop the machine. Then accurately measure the distance across the flats. If the work measures more than 1" across the flats, feed the table *toward* the column (with the cross feed) half the amount the stock is oversize, for example, $\frac{1}{32}$" if $\frac{1}{16}$" too large; and if undersize, feed the table half the amount *away* from the column.

15. When the machine has been set correctly, remove the piece of waste stock, and mount the stock to be machined in the chuck. Then raise the table so as to make a cut of the depth desired, provided the cutter is large enough to remove the stock at one cut.

If the cutter is not large enough for this, then set it for the first cut. After the first cut has been made, set the machine for the second cut and, if necessary, in turn for other cuts.

16. When the first flat has been completely machined, withdraw the plunger, and revolve the index plate through one-quarter turn. Lock it in position with the plunger pin.

17. Machine the second flat in a manner similar to the first.

18. Continue as in steps 15 through 17 until all four sides have been machined.

19. When the operation is completed, remove the dividing head and cutter. Clean them, and return all to the place where kept when not in use. With a brush, remove all chips from the table of the machine.

Procedure for a Hexagon — Using an End Mill

1. Begin as in previous steps 1 through 7 inclusive.

2. Assume the stock has been turned to 1⅜″ diameter and that one end is to be milled in the form of a hexagon which measures 1″ across the flats. Subtracting 1″ from 1⅜″ leaves ⅜″ of stock to be removed, or 3/16″ from each side.

3. With the cross feed, advance the table until the work is in such a position that 3/16″ of stock will be removed from one side.

4. Proceed as in steps 10 through 15 inclusive.

5. When the first flat has been completely machined, withdraw the plunger located in the dividing head. Revolve the direct index plate through one-sixth turn, and lock it in position with the plunger pin.

6. Machine the second and subsequent flats in a manner similar to the first.

7. Clean up as in step 19.

Procedure for an Octagon
— Using an End Mill

1. Begin as in "Procedure for a Square, Using an End Mill, " steps 1 through 7 inclusive.

   Assume the stock has been turned to 1½″ diameter and that a 1¼″ octagon is to be milled on one end. Subtracting 1¼″ from 1½″ leaves ¼″ to be removed, or ⅛″ from each side.

2. With the cross feed, move the table until the stock is in such a position that ⅛″ of stock will be removed from one side of the work.

3. Continue as in "Procedure for a Square, Using an End Mill," steps 10 through 13 inclusive.

4. Stop the machine, and accurately measure the distance across the flats. If the work measures more than 1¼″ across the flats, feed the table *toward* the column (with the cross feed) half the amount the stock is oversize. If undersize, feed the table half the amount *away* from the column.

5. When the machine has been set correctly, remove the waste stock, and mount the stock to be machined in the chuck.

6. Start the machine, and raise the table so as to make a cut of the depth desired. Then make the cut.

7. When the first flat has been completely machined, withdraw the plunger, and revolve the direct index plate through one-eighth turn. Lock it in position.

8. Machine the second flat in a manner similar to the first.

9. Continue as in steps 7 and 8 until all eight sides have been machined.

10. When the operation is completed, remove all special attachments, and clean both these and the table of the machine.

Procedure for a Square
— Using a Side Cutter or Plain Cutter

NOTE: A side cutter is preferred.

1. Begin as in "Procedure for a Square, Using an End Mill," steps 1 through 5 inclusive.

2. Secure a sharp side milling cutter of suitable size; also secure a cutter arbor and the necessary collars.

3. Wipe the arbor, collars, sides of the cutter, and the hole in the spindle with a piece of clean waste.

4. Insert the arbor, and mount the cutter as close to the column as the work will permit, Fig. 11-104. Then insert such collars as necessary, and draw them tight with the nut.

5. Slide the overarm bearing over the end of the arbor, and clamp it in position, Fig. 11-104.

6. Proceed as in "Procedure for a Square, Using an End Mill," steps 7 through 19 inclusive.

Procedure for a Square
— Using a Straddle Mill

1. Begin as in "Procedure for a Square, Using an End Mill," steps 1 through 5 inclusive.

2. Secure two sharp side milling cutters of suitable size, as well as an arbor and the necessary collars.

3. Insert the arbor, and mount the first cutter as close to the column as the work will permit. Next select collars that will give the *desired width* between cutters, for

Fig. 11-105. Cap-Type Arbor Support Used in Straddle Milling (Cincinnati Milling Machine)

Fig. 11-106. Milling a Square with a Straddle Mill

example, 1″. Place these collars in position on the arbor; then place the second cutter and other necessary collars and, finally, the clamping nut. Draw the nut tight, and adjust the overarm.

Figs. 11-50 and 11-105 illustrate a milling machine set for straddle milling. The cap-type arbor support (Fig. 11-105) permits removal of the arbor without disturbing the position of the cutters. An arbor support practically eliminates vibration.

4. Center the cutter over the work, and make a trial cut in the usual manner, Fig. 11-106. Then measure for size.

If necessary, adjust the size by inserting a wider or narrower collar between the cutters. Sometimes very thin discs of metal or even paper are used to change the space between the cutters.

5. When the machine has been set correctly, mount the stock to be machined in the chuck; then raise the table so that a cut of the depth desired will be made.

6. Start the machine, and make the cut, using a cutting compound freely.

7. Revolve the direct index plate one-half turn, and make the second cut.

8. When the operation is completed, remove and clean the cutter, arbor, and index head, and return them to the place where

kept when not in use. Then, with a brush, remove all chips from the table of the milling machine.

Procedure for a Hexagon — Using a Straddle Mill

1. Begin as in "Procedure for a Square, Using a Straddle Mill," steps 1 through 6 inclusive.

2. Revolve the direct index plate one-sixth turn, and make the second cut.

3. Revolve the index plate another one-sixth turn, and make the third cut.

4. Clean up as in "Procedure for a Square, Using a Straddle Mill," step 8.

Procedure for a Square — Using Centers of the Dividing Head

1. Place the dividing head and tailstock on the table of the milling machine, locating them as close to the column as practicable.

2. Adjust the tailstock, and mount the work between the centers of the dividing head, Fig. 11-107.

3. Select a suitable plain milling cutter or an end mill, as preferred.

4. Mount the cutter in the milling machine.

5. With the cross feed, adjust the table so that the axis of the work is under the center of the cutter, if the cut is to be made along the top of the work.

If an end mill is used, the cut may be made along the top or along the side. When the latter, bring the axis of the work and the cutter into the same horizontal plane; then, with the cross feed, adjust for depth of cut.

6. Measure the stock, and carefully calculate the amount of stock to be removed from each side.

7. With the vertical adjustment, raise the table until the bottom of the cutter is just even with the work.

8. Start the machine, and, with the vertical adjustment, raise the table until the cutter just touches the work. Then move the table until the revolving cutter just clears the end of the work.

9. Set the vertical adjustment micrometer dial at zero. Raise the table an amount equal to the amount of stock to be removed, for example, $\frac{3}{16}''$.

10. Feed the work toward the cutter, and make the cut. Be sure to use a cutting compound freely.

11. At the end of the cut, stop the machine, and move the work back until it clears the cutter.

12. Withdraw the plunger pin in the dividing head, and revolve the direct index plate through one-half turn.

13. Again, feed the work toward the cutter; at the end of the cut, stop the machine, and move the work back.

14. With a pair of calipers or a micrometer, measure the distance across the flats.

    If the work is too large, raise the table half the amount the stock is oversize, and take a second cut on both flat surfaces.

15. When the machine has been set correctly, turn the index plate one-fourth turn, and machine the third side.

16. Index one-half turn, and machine the fourth side.

17. When the operation is completed, remove and clean the dividing head, cutter, and arbor, and return them to the place where they usually are kept. With a brush, remove all chips from the table of the machine.

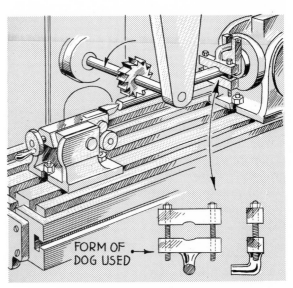

FORM OF
DOG USED

Fig. 11-107. Cutting a Square with Stock Held Between Centers

Procedure for a Hexagon
— Using Centers of the Dividing Head

1. Begin as in "Procedure for a Square, Using Centers of the Dividing Head," steps 1 through 14 inclusive.
2. When the machine has been set correctly, turn the direct index plate one-sixth turn; then make the cut in the usual manner.
3. Continue indexing by one-sixth turns and making the cuts until all six sides have been machined.
4. Remove all special attachments; clean them and the table of the machine.

Procedure for an Octagon
— Using Centers of the Dividing Head

1. Begin as in "Procedure for a Square, Using Centers of the Dividing Head," steps 1 through 14 inclusive.
2. When the machine has been set correctly, turn the direct index plate one-eighth turn. Make the cut in the usual manner. Use a cutting compound freely.
3. Continue indexing by one-eighth turns and making the cuts, until all eight sides have been machined.
4. Remove all special attachments; clean them and the table of the machine.

How To Mill a Keyway or Similar Groove

A keyway or a similar groove may be cut with either a plain milling cutter, an end mill, a side mill, or a special key cutter. The most common ways of holding the stock while the groove is being cut are: (1) in a V-block; (2) in a vise; (3) between centers in the indexing head; and (4) in a chuck on the indexing head.

Procedure for Centering the Cutter with Straight Stock

1. With the center head and square, scribe a line on the end of the stock, Fig. 11-108.
2. Accurately lay off the length of the groove on the stock. Then mark the terminus with a scriber or, very lightly, with a prick punch (*A*, Fig. 11-108). This step is

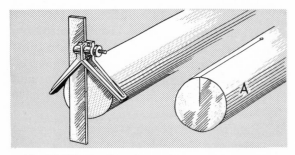

Fig. 11-108. Scribing Center Line on End of Stock

omitted when the groove extends the entire length of the work.

3. Mount the stock with the scribed line perpendicular. Clamp the stock in position. Be sure the axis of the work is parallel with the face of the column of the machine.
4. Select and mount a suitable cutter.
5. With the cross feed, move the table until the scribed line on the end of the stock is exactly in the center of the cutter, Fig. 11-109. Test by measuring carefully with a rule.

Procedure for Centering the Cutter with Shouldered Stock

1. Accurately lay off the length of the groove on the stock; then mark the terminus with a scriber, or, very lightly, with a prick punch. This step is omitted when the groove extends the entire length of the work.
2. Place the stock in a V-block or between centers in the dividing head. If mounted in a V-block, clamp the stock in position. Be sure the axis of the work is parallel with the face of the column.

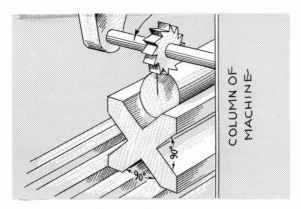

Fig. 11-109. Stock in Position for Cut

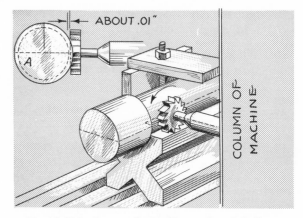

Fig. 11-110. Keyway Cutter Mounted on Spindle

3. Select and mount a suitable cutter on the spindle of the machine, for example a keyway cutter, Fig. 11-110.

4. With the vertical adjustment crank, raise the table until the axis of the work is even with the axis of the cutter (*A*, Fig. 11-110), but with the cutter not quite in contact with the work.

5. Start the machine, and carefully advance the work with the cross feed until it just barely touches the cutter. Test with a piece of tissue paper placed between the work and the side of the cutter. Stop advancing the work when the cutter starts to tear the paper.

> CAUTION: *Moisten one edge of the paper so that it will adhere to the surface of the work. Do not hold the tissue with the fingers.*

6. Stop the machine; then lower the table until the top of the work is just even with the underside of the cutter.

7. With the cross feed, advance the work one-half the diameter of the work plus one-half the width of the cutter.

> For example, assume the diameter of the stock is $1\frac{1}{8}''$ and the width of the cutter is $\frac{1}{4}''$ — then $\frac{9}{16}''$ plus $\frac{1}{8}'' = {}^{11}\!/_{16}''$, the distance to move the work toward the column.

8. Hold a square against the work, as in Fig. 11-111, and measure the distance from the edge of the square to the side of the cutter. In the example given above,

the distance should be $\frac{7}{16}''$, because $\frac{9}{16}'' - \frac{1}{8}'' = \frac{7}{16}''$. Make the test from both sides of the stock.

9. If the center of the cutter is not located exactly over the center of the stock, make the necessary adjustment, and again test as in step 8.

Procedure for Cutting a Groove — Stock in a V-Block

1. Position and clamp the stock in place by either method described.

2. Move the table back so that the work just clears the cutter, Fig. 11-112.

3. Set the micrometer vertical adjustment at zero. Then raise the table an amount equal to the desired depth of groove, for example, $\frac{5}{32}''$. Since this measurement is taken at the edge of the groove, the table

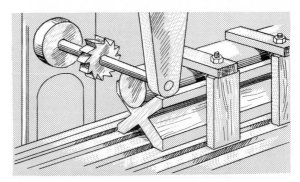

Fig. 11-112. Milling Groove with Stock Mounted in V-Block

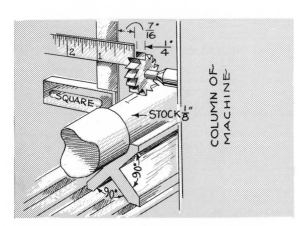

Fig. 11-111. Centering Work Under Cutter

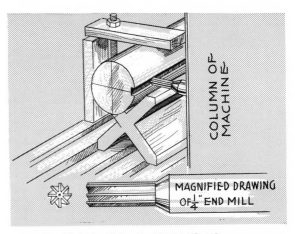

Fig. 11-113. Using End Mill to Cut Groove

must be raised $\frac{5}{32}$" plus the difference between the top edge of the groove and the top of the stock (in the example given, about .01").

4. Make sure the setting is correct and the work is correctly aligned and securely clamped. Then start the machine, and feed the work toward the revolving cutter with the longitudinal feed.

5. When the cutter reaches the end of the groove, shut off the power and immediately lower the table.

If it becomes necessary to stop the feed before the end of the groove is reached (to change clamps or for any other reason), shut off the power at the same time the feed is stopped.

Fig. 11-114. Milling Groove with Stock Held Between Centers

Fig. 11-115. Cutting Keyway for Woodruff Key

If preferred and convenient, this operation may be performed with an end mill mounted in the spindle of the milling machine, Fig. 11-113. The work must be fastened to the table securely or held in a vise.

A groove milled in the manner described above and terminated at some intermediate point in the stock may be finished with a twist drill and a chisel. Still another possibility is to mount an end mill in a drill press and mill out the remaining stock.

Procedure for Cutting a Groove — Stock on Dividing Head Centers

1. Find the center of the stock. See Unit 56. In most cases, this operation will have been performed in connection with other machine work performed on the stock.

2. Fasten the dividing head and the tailstock on the column side of the table.

3. Place the stock between the centers of the head and draw the tailstock tight.

4. Select a suitable cutter, and mount it on a milling machine arbor.

5. Center the axis of the cutter over the axis of the work, Fig. 11-114, using one of the methods described under centering the cutter.

6. Continue as in "Procedure for Cutting a Groove, Stock in a V-Block," steps 2 through 5 inclusive.

If an end mill is used, bring the axis of the work and the axis of the mill into alignment. Then, with the cross feed, advance the work an amount equal to the depth of the groove.

7. When through cutting the groove, return all equipment to the place where kept when not in use, and clean the machine.

Procedure for Cutting Keyway for Woodruff Key

1. Mount the stock in a suitable manner on the table of the milling machine.

2. Lay off the longitudinal center of the key or keys (*A*, Fig. 11-115).

3. Select a key cutter of suitable diameter and width.

4. Mount the cutter in the machine.

5. Center the cutter over the axis of the work and midway of the longitudinal center of the key, Fig. 11-115. Then raise the table until the cutter barely touches the surface of the stock. See above procedures on centering the cutter.

6. Set the micrometer vertical adjustment at zero. Then start the machine, and (with the vertical adjustment) continue raising the table until the cutter is cutting at the depth desired, for example, $\frac{7}{32}''$.

7. When the groove is cut to the depth desired, lower the table; then shut off the power.

8. Cut other grooves in a similar manner.

9. When the job is completed, return equipment to the place where kept when not in use, and clean the machine.

The Dividing or Indexing Head and Its Operation

The dividing head may be thought of as an essential in the operation of a milling machine. In fact, without this apparatus, the utility of the milling machine is much restricted. The complete dividing head has two parts — the head and the tailstock, Fig. 11-117. The *head* is rather complex, consisting of a base plate, swivel block, spindle, worm and worm wheel, a direct and a standard indexing plate, side index plate, and sector. In contrast, the tailstock is a rather simple piece used for supporting the outer end of the stock being milled. The tailstock center can be moved longitudinally by means of a handwheel and by adjusting the block which holds it; the center may be moved vertically in either a horizontal or an inclined plane.

Typical milling operations preformed with the use of the dividing head are shown in Figs. 11-28, 11-30, 11-143, 11-146, and 11-152.

Simple Indexing

Simple indexing is achieved by means of a worm wheel attached to the spindle of the head and activated through a worm, keyed to the worm shaft to which a hand crank is attached. One complete turn of the crank causes any one tooth on the worm to make a complete revolution. Since there are 40 teeth on the worm wheel, 40 turns of the crank are required to cause the worm wheel to make a complete revolution. Likewise, the dividing head spindle requires 40 turns, because the worm wheel is attached to the spindle.

An example should clarify the operation of indexing. Assume that a reamer is to be cut with 10 equally spaced teeth. If 40 turns of the index crank are required to make one complete revolution of the work, then $\frac{1}{10}$ of 40 turns or 4 turns of the index crank after each cut are required to space the teeth correctly on a 10-tooth reamer. It is good practice always to turn the index crank to the right.

Fig. 11-117. Dividing Head (Cincinnati Milling Machine)

367

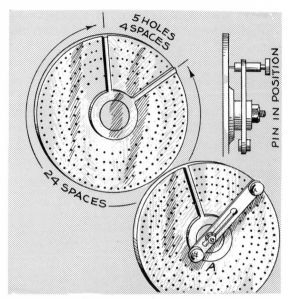

Fig. 11-118. Sector Used to Enclose 6/7 of Index Plate Within Obtuse Angle

Fig. 11-119. Set of High-Number Indexing Plates
(Cincinnati Milling Machine)

Fig. 11-120. Wide-Range Divider
(Cincinnati Milling Machine)

In the illustration given, a number was chosen by which 40 was divisible without leaving a remainder. If, instead of 10 teeth, we assume the problem is to cut a reamer with 14 teeth, then $\frac{1}{14}$ of 40 turns, or $2\frac{12}{14}$ ($2\frac{6}{7}$) turns of the crank are required after each cut.

From the above examples, it can be seen that the rule for calculating the number of turns of the index crank required to move the work through one division of any number of equally spaced divisions in a circle is as follows:

$$T = \frac{N}{D}$$

Where:

N = the number of teeth on the worm wheel
D = the number of divisions
T = the number of turns

Example 1

$$T = \frac{40}{14} = 2\frac{12}{14} \text{ or } 2\frac{6}{7}$$

$$T = 2\frac{6}{7} \text{ turns.}$$

So long as whole turns are involved, indexing is simply a matter of counting the turns. To divide a turn into sevenths and move the index handle through six of these would be difficult were it not for the fact that the index plate is provided with a series of circles of holes which are evenly spaced. See Fig. 11-118. Each circle contains a different number of holes, for example, 24, 25, 28, 30, 34, and so forth. These holes engage a plunger in the handle of the index crank whenever the plunger comes exactly over a hole. To allow the plunger to enter any particular row of holes, an adjustment is provided. Simply loosen the clamping nut at the center, and move the crank toward or away from the center of the plate.

Our problem is to index for $\frac{6}{7}$ of a turn. Taking the example of the number of holes given above, it is observed that one of these rows — 28 — may be divided evenly by 7, giving a quotient of 4. Thus, in each seventh of a turn, the index crank must be moved four holes. To index for $2\frac{6}{7}$ turns, the index crank must be moved 2 complete turns and through $\frac{6}{7}$ or 24 of the 28 spaces in the circle having 28 holes.

To avoid the problem of counting holes each time the crank is turned, not to mention the probability for error, the dividing head is provided with a sector, Fig. 11-118. This device is fastened in front of the index plate. It has two radial arms which can be adjusted to any angle desired by loosening a clamping screw.

To divide the index plate so that $^6/_7$ of its area is included within the obtuse angle made by the arms of the sector (A, Fig. 11-118), one arm of the sector must be moved against the plunger in the handle and the other arm swung around until 24 of the 28 spaces are included in the obtuse angle. After moving the arms of the sector, always check for accuracy, and then tighten the clamping screw.

When dividing space with a sector, it should be remembered that *it is the spaces that count and not the holes.* A good way to be sure you are doing this is to call the hole in which the pin is engaged zero or to count the spaces only. When revolving the index handle for a part of a revolution, release the pull on the plunger between the last two holes and let it slide across the space until it drops into the hole. After indexing, it is good practice immediately to move the sector for the next indexing.

Example 2: As another example, assume the problem is to cut 54 teeth on a spur gear.

Solution: $T = \dfrac{N}{D} = \dfrac{40}{54} = \dfrac{20}{27}$ turns.

This fraction tells us we must take 20 holes on the 27 circle, or 40 holes on the 54 circle.

Setting Degrees: The ordinary index plate also can be used for indexing by degrees. It is known that there are 360° in a circle and 40 teeth on the worm wheel, which must make one complete revolution as the work is revolved through 360°. It follows that, for each turn of the crank, a point on the circumference of the work will rotate through 9° or $^1/_{40}$ of a circle ($360° \div 40 = 9°$).

If by moving the crank through one complete turn, the work is revolved 9°, then, by moving the crank through 2 spaces of an 18-space circle, or 6 spaces of a 54-space circle, the work will be rotated 1°; and if through 1 or 3 spaces respectively, $^1/_2$°.

Direct Indexing

Direct indexing is accomplished by disengaging the worm from the worm wheel. This permits a plate, which is attached to the spindle in the head, to revolve when a retaining plunger in the head is drawn back. This plate has a circle of equally spaced holes, usually 24 or some other number divisible by 4. For direct indexing, disengage the worm, draw the plunger back, and rotate the plate through the number of spaces desired, for example, 6 spaces for $^1/_4$ turn, since $^6/_{24}$ equals $^1/_4$.

Fine Spacing: For indexing when it is necessary to achieve very fine spacing or to divide a circle into a number of spaces not achievable with the standard index plate, a high-number indexing attachment is available. This consists of a set of plates with very fine spacing, Fig. 11-119. These plates are interchangeable with the standard index plate.

Fig. 11-120 illustrates a wide-range dividing head. This allows a rapid selection of divisions, from 2 to 400,000, at any angle and at intervals of 6 seconds, without the use of change gears or additional index plates.

98 How To Mill Flutes or Grooves

An object may be fluted for ornamentation, to increase holding quality (for example, the handle of a screwdriver), or to provide a cutting edge and give clearance to such tools as reamers, taps, and milling cutters. Fluting may be done on a flat, a cylindrical, or a conical surface.

Procedure for a Flat Surface

1. Select suitable parallels, and grip the stock in a vise, as in Fig. 11-121.
2. Select a sharp fluting mill of suitable size and shape, and mount it on the arbor as close to the column of the machine as the nature of the work will permit.
3. Adjust the machine to make the cut; then proceed in the usual manner.

Fig. 11-121. Milling a Flute with Stock Held in Vise

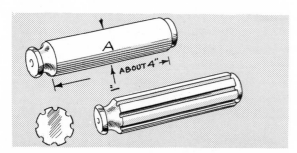

Fig. 11-122. Fluted Cylinder

Procedure for a Cylindrical Surface

1. Center and turn the stock to the size and shape desired (A, Fig. 11-122).
2. Fasten the dividing head and tailstock on the column side of the table.
3. Determine the number of flutes to be cut. If the number is small, direct indexing may be used, in which case the worm must be disengaged.

   To cut a groove with one face radial, it is necessary to offset the workpiece laterally. To facilitate this, draw a radial line on the tailstock end, as in A, Fig. 11-162, Unit 105. Then rotate the work until the radial line is aligned with the short face of the cutter, usually the 12° face.
4. Determine the number of holes in the front index plate; then divide this number by the number of flutes to be cut. Assuming that 8 flutes are to be cut and that there are 24 holes in the plate, then the index plate must be advanced 3 spaces for each flute.
5. Attach a suitable dog to the headstock end of the workpiece. See Fig. 11-124

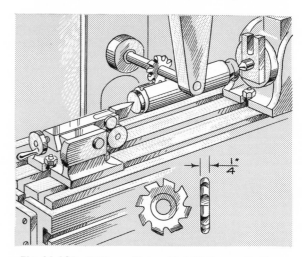

Fig. 11-123. Milling a Flute with ¼" Convex Cutter

(page 372). Then place the stock between the centers of the head in such a manner that the direction of the cut will be away from the tailstock. Draw the tailstock center against the stock.

6. Select a sharp cutter of suitable size, shape, or type. A ¼″ convex cutter (Fig. 11-123) can be used for fluting, and a double-angle cutter (Fig. 11-125, page 372) for milling reamers, taps, or helices.

7. Mount the cutter on a suitable arbor, as close to the column as the work will permit.

8. With the cross feed, move the table until the axis of the stock is exactly under the center of the cutter.

9. Raise the table until the bottom of the cutter just touches the top of the work. Test with a piece of tissue paper. *Do not hold the paper with the fingers.*

10. Move the table so that the end of the work just clears the cutter.

11. Set the micrometer vertical adjustment at zero; then raise the table an amount equal to the desired depth of cut, Fig. 11-123. If a smooth finish is desired, allow about ¹⁄₃₂″ for a finishing cut.

12. Check carefully to see that the setting is correct and the work is correctly aligned and securely fastened.

13. Start the machine, and feed the work against the cutter, Fig. 11-123.

14. When the cutter reaches the end of the flute, shut off the power, and immediately lower the table very slightly.

15. Move the table back to the starting position, and index for the next cut, for example, 3 spaces.

16. Raise the table the amount required, as in step 11.

17. Start the machine, and make the cut in the same manner.

18. Continue as in steps 13 through 16 inclusive, until all flutes have been milled.

19. Set the machine for the finishing cut; then proceed in the usual manner.

20. When the job is completed, clean the machine thoroughly, and return all special equipment to the place where kept when not in use.

Procedure for a Conical Surface

Ordinarily, a flute or groove milled on a conical surface is somewhat deeper and wider at the large end than at the small end. Also, the land between the grooves is narrower at the small end. This means that the small end must be raised an amount nearly equal to half the difference between the diameters of the large and small ends. The greater this difference, the larger the amount the small end must be raised above the horizontal plane of this end. Since the difference in the levels of the horizontal planes of the two ends varies for stock having different tapers, it is recommended that variation in plane levels be determined by making a series of shallow trial cuts. When only a portion of the cylinder is tapered, the amount of setover required (actually setup, in this case) may be calculated by using the formula given in Unit 71. However, the bottom of the groove must be used as a basis.

1. Make a full-size layout of both ends of the fluted cone, if practicable. See Figs. 11-124 and 11-125.

2. Proceed as under "Procedure for a Cylindrical Surface," steps 1 through 8 inclusive.

3. Release the clamp on the vertical slide, and raise the tailstock center an amount nearly equal to one-half the difference in diameter between the large and small ends of the stock, Fig. 11-124.

   If the amount the tailstock center is to be raised has been calculated mathematically, then raise the center that amount.

4. Tighten the vertical clamp. Then, with a surface gage, test the difference in horizontal levels of the large and small ends, Fig. 11-124. Compare the differences found with the differences in the layout (or the amount found by calculation); make adjustments if necessary.

5. When the correct level at each end of the cone has been achieved, raise the table until the cutter just touches the top of the work at the small end. Test with a piece of tissue paper; then move the table so that the cutter just clears the end of the work.

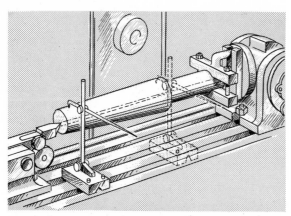

Fig. 11-124. Setting Up to Mill a Flute on a Conical Surface

Fig. 11-125. Milling a Flute on a Conical Surface

6. Set the micrometer vertical adjustment at zero; then raise the table sufficiently to make a cut of nearly the required depth. Make the cut as usual, Fig. 11-125.

7. Carefully compare the proportional difference in width of both ends of the machined groove with the widths of the respective layouts made in step 1.

8. If the difference seems to be relatively proportional, adjust the machine to make a cut which will remove about one-half the remaining stock; then test as before. If too much stock is being removed from either end of the groove, adjust the vertical slide in the tailstock so as to move the small end of the stock in a direction which will cause less stock to be removed from whichever end of the machined groove is too wide. Then make a second light cut.

9. When the machine has been adjusted to cut a groove of the desired depth and width at each end, proceed as under "Procedure for a Cylindrical Surface," steps 12 through 20 inclusive.

99 Spur Gears and Gearing

A gear is a wheel cr roll upon which teeth have been cut. See Fig. 11-127. A gear mounted on one shaft transmits force or rotary motion to a gear mounted on a second shaft. This transmission is at a uniform rate of speed. Gears may be used to change direction of motion, to increase speed, or to decrease speed.

Gear action can be understood more readily by comparing them with *friction wheels*, as shown in Fig. 11-128. Although such friction wheels or pulleys will transmit motion and power, they are inefficient, since slippage occurs under heavy loads. Also, since the spacing and contact of friction pulleys must be

Fig. 11-127. Spur Gears (Ill. Gear and Machine)
(Lower) Rack and pinion; (Upper) Large spur gear.

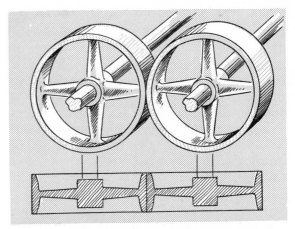

Fig. 11-128. Friction Wheels Transmit Motion
Inefficiently

exact, any wear causes the efficiency to be reduced.

Instead of friction contact, *belts* could be used on the pulleys. While this is more efficient than friction wheels, some loss of efficiency results due to slippage or stretching during sudden increases in speed. The addition of gear teeth to the pulleys or wheels makes it possible to transmit motion or force at a completely uniform rate.

Gears are used on nearly all types of machines ranging from wristwatches and egg beaters to machine tools, automobiles, tractors, mining machinery, and heavy manufacturing machinery. The significance of gears in machines can be readily realized by answering this question: How could these machines be designed to operate efficiently if all of the gears were removed and other means of power and motion transmission devices were employed?

Gears may be used to transmit motion between shafts which are parallel, intersecting, or neither parallel nor intersecting. A given amount of motion on one shaft will produce a definite amount of motion on the shaft which

it drives. The gear connected to the source of power is called the *driver*, and the one to which motion is transmitted is called the *driven*. These terms have no relation to the size of the gears. The speed ratios of the shafts may be increased or decreased as desired. If it is desired that the shaft to which the driven gear is attached revolve at three times the speed of the drive shaft, then the driver must have three times as many teeth as on the driven gear. If the driven shaft is to revolve at only one-third the rate of the driver, then the driver must have only one-third as many teeth as the driven gear.

Gears normally are mass-produced on special machines designed for this alone. These machines are of several types, including *form-cutting* machines and *gear-generating* machines (Fig. 11-130). The latter usually are further classified according to two types — *gear-shaping* machines and *gear-hobbing* machines. When large numbers of a given type of gear are required, manufacturers either produce them with one of these special machines or purchase them from a manufacturer of gears.

Machinists in maintenance departments, job machine shops, and experimental machine shops frequently are required to produce gears of various types on a milling machine. The machinist, therefore, should be familiar with some of the basic kinds of gears and the terminology which applies to them.

When two gears of unequal size are mated, the smaller one is called a *pinion*. A *rack* (Fig. 11-127) is a type of gear which has teeth spaced along a straight line for the purpose of interchanging rotary motion and reciprocating motion. A *basic rack* is one which is adopted as the basis for a system of interchangeable gears. The proportions of gear teeth for standard gear systems often are illustrated on the outline drawing of the basic rack. (Fig. 11-136 is an example.)

Types of Gears

Various types of gears are used in the design of machines. Those which are most common include *spur*, *bevel* and *miter*, *internal*, *helical*, and *worm* gears.

Spur Gears: Spur gears are cylindrical and have teeth which are parallel with the axis of the gear, Fig. 11-127. They are designed for use on shafts whose axes are parallel with each other. A *spur rack* has teeth at right angles with the axis of motion. Spur gears are the most commonly used type of gear on industrial machines. Normally they are used under conditions of moderate speed and moderate tooth load. Spur gears of the removable type are readily adaptable to pairs of shafts requiring variations in speed ratios.

Bevel Gears: Bevel gears are conical and are used on shafts with intersecting axes, Fig. 11-129. They are used for transmitting power around corners. The shafts generally are at right angles, but they may be at various angles. Bevel gears on shafts at angles other than 90 degrees are called *angular gears*.

Two bevel gears of equal size, with equal numbers of teeth, and designed for use on shafts at right angles are called *miter gears*. Bevel gears with straight-tooth elements, which

Fig. 11-129. Bevel Gear and Pinion (Ill. Gear and Machine)

Fig. 11-130. Bevel Gear-Generating Machine Produces Large Spiral Bevel Gears (Ill. Gear and Machine)

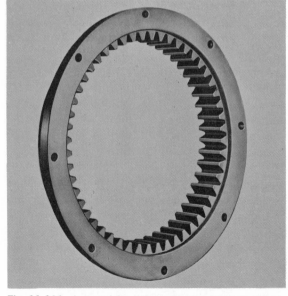

Fig. 11-131. Internal Spur Gear (Ill. Gear and Machine)

pass through the intersection of their axes when extended, are called *straight bevel gears*, Fig. 11-129. Those which have teeth which are curved or oblique are called *spiral bevel gears*; see left foreground of Fig. 11-130.

Internal Gears: Internal gears have teeth on the inner surface of a cone or cylinder, Fig. 11-131. This type may have spur, bevel, or helical teeth. They are meshed with external gears. An advantage in combining internal and external gears is their compactness. Since the centers of the gears are closer together, less space is required. They also possess increased operational efficiency: more teeth are in mesh, the tooth lines curve in the same direction, and friction is reduced.

Helical Gears: Helical gears are similar to spur gears, except that the teeth form a helix twisting around the body of the gear, Fig. 11-132. The helical teeth provide greater strength and smoother operation at high speeds. The teeth do not hit each other as in the case of spur gears. Instead, they slide across each other, thus reducing noise and vibration. Since several teeth are in contact at the same time, their strength is greater than for spur teeth of the same size.

A disadvantage of helical gear teeth is that increased friction and heat are caused by the sliding action of the teeth. This disadvantage may be overcome with good lubrication. Hence helical gears which operate at high speeds generally are run in an oil bath.

Helical gears may be used for connecting shafts that are parallel (Fig. 11-132) or at an angle with each other, provided their axial lines do not intersect. When used on parallel shafts, they are called *parallel helical gears* and are of opposite hand. This means a right-hand gear is meshed with a left-hand gear. Those gears which operate on shafts with crossed axes are called *crossed helical gears*. They may have gears with teeth of the same hand or of the opposite hand.

Herringbone Gears: Herringbone gears have the appearance of a pair of right- and left-hand helical gears located side by side, Fig. 11-133. Since they have both right- and left-hand teeth, they frequently are called *double-helical gears*. They are designed for operation on parallel shafts. This tooth design eliminates the side thrust that normally results from the sliding action which single-helical gears exert against each other. With the latter type, in many instances, thrust bearings must be employed to compensate for the side thrust. However, with the double-helical gear design, the side thrust is neutralized, and thrust bearings are not required.

Herringbone gears have greater bearing surface contact than other gears of similar size, and, therefore, have greater load-carrying capacity. They generally withstand continuous, heavy-duty, high-speed operation better than other types of gears.

Fig. 11-132. Helical Gear Train with Shafts Parallel
(Ill. Gear and Machine)

Fig. 11-133. Herringbone Gears
(Ill. Gear and Machine)

Worm Gears: Worm gears are meshed with a *worm;* the gear and the worm constitute what is called a *worm gear mechanism,* Fig. 11-134. The teeth on the worm gear are helical and conform with the helix angle of the tooth on the worm. The helical tooth on the worm is a form of thread, similar to an acme thread, and it often is called a *thread.*

Worms may have single, double, or triple threads. With the single thread, one revolution of the worm revolves the worm gear a distance equal to that which exists between a point on one tooth and a corresponding point on the next tooth, or one circular pitch. One revolution of a double-thread worm revolves the gear an amount equal to two teeth on the gear, and so on.

Worm gearing is used largely for speed reduction. The worm gear cannot turn the worm when a single-thread worm is used. This type of gear mechanism is *self-locking.* Engineers take advantage of this feature when they employ worm gears in steering mechanisms and in hoisting equipment or devices.

Knowing About Gears

Spur gears are the most common type of gears. Normally they are mass-produced on special gear-making machines. However, when a replacement spur gear is needed, or when one or a small number of gears is needed, the machinist often is called upon to produce them with a milling machine.

To cut gears on a milling machine, it is not always necessary that the operator know how to lay out the teeth of a gear or that he even know the conventional shape of the teeth or the names of the different parts. However, the operator who does know these things is likely to derive greater satisfaction in his work and to be a more intelligent and satisfactory employee.

Modern gears generally have involute teeth. This means that the shape of the tooth is generated or drawn with an involute curve; such a curve may be drawn with a pencil inserted in the loop of a string wound about a cylinder and held taut as the string is unwound, Fig. 11-135. This form of tooth has been found to give the most satisfactory results in terms of quietness and smoothness of operation.

The size of a gear is given in terms of its *diameter at the pitch line,* which is called the *pitch diameter.* (This term should not be confused with the term *diametral pitch,* which

Fig. 11-134. Worm Gear Mechanism (Ill. Gear and Machine)

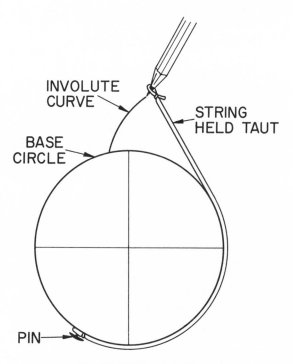

Fig. 11-135. Involute Curve

refers to the ratio of the number of teeth per inch of pitch diameter.)

The term *pitch*, as used in gearing, often means the same as diametral pitch; however, in order to avoid confusion, the full terms should be used, such as *diametral pitch, circular pitch, linear pitch*, etc.

To say that a gear is a 10-diametral-pitch (10-pitch) gear means that it has 10 teeth for each inch of pitch diameter, as measured across the pitch circle, Fig. 11-136. Thus, a 10-pitch gear of 2″ pitch diameter has 20 teeth. A 10-pitch gear of 2½″ pitch diameter has 25 teeth. A 4-pitch gear of 30″ pitch diameter has 120 teeth, and so on.

The term *circular pitch* refers to the distance along the pitch circle on a gear or along the pitch line on a rack, from a point on one tooth to a corresponding point on the next tooth, Fig. 11-137. The circular pitch on a gear is also equal to the *linear pitch* on a mating rack, Fig. 11-136.

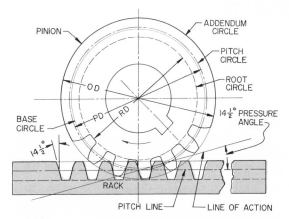

Fig. 11-136. Pinion and Rack with 14½° Composite Spur Gear Teeth

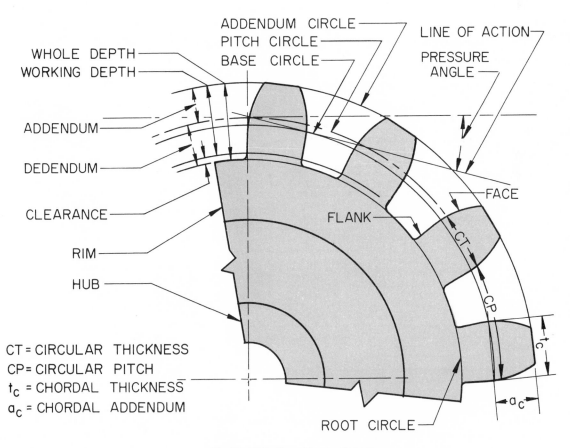

CT = CIRCULAR THICKNESS
CP = CIRCULAR PITCH
t_c = CHORDAL THICKNESS
a_c = CHORDAL ADDENDUM

Fig. 11-137. Gear Nomenclature

Gear Terms and Definitions: Gear nomenclature, including spur gear tooth forms, terms, definitions, and letter symbols, has become fairly well standardized. This standardization was initiated by the American Gear Manufacturer's Association (AGMA) and later was completed by the joint efforts of AGMA, the American Standards Association (ASA), and the American Society of Mechanical Engineers (ASME).*

The following definitions are extracted from American Standard Gear Nomenclature (ASA B6.10-1954), with the permission of the publisher:

Involute Teeth of spur gears, helical gears, and worms are those in which the profile in a transverse plane (exclusive of the fillet curve) is the involute of a circle. (See Fig. 11-135.)

The *Base Circle* is the circle from which involute tooth profiles are derived. (See Fig. 11-136.)

A *Pitch Circle* is the curve of intersection of a pitch surface of revolution and a plane of rotation. According to theory, it is the imaginary circle that rolls without slipping with a pitch circle of a mating gear. (See Figs. 11-136 and 11-137.)

A *Pitch Line* corresponds in the cross section of a rack to the pitch circle in the cross section of a gear. (See Fig. 11-136.)

The *Addendum Circle* coincides with the tops of the teeth in a cross section. (See Fig. 11-136.)

The *Root Circle* is tangent to the bottoms of the tooth spaces in a cross section. (See Fig. 11-136.)

The *Line of Action* is the path of contact in involute gears. It is the straight line passing through the pitch point and tangent to the base circles. (See Fig. 11-136.)

Pressure Angle is the angle between a tooth profile and the line normal to a pitch surface, usually at the pitch point of profile. This definition is applicable to every type of gear. The term *pressure angle* originally meant an angle between the line of pressure and the pitch circle. In involute teeth, *pressure*

angle is often described as the angle between the *line of action* and the line tangent to the *pitch circles*. (See Fig. 11-136.)

Center Distance (C) is the distance between parallel axes of spur gears and parallel helical gears or between the crossed axes of crossed helical gears and worm gears. Also, it is the distance between the centers of pitch circles.

Addendum (a) is the height by which a tooth projects beyond the pitch circle or pitch line; also, it is the radial distance between the pitch circle and the addendum circle. (See Fig. 11-137.)

Dedendum (b) is the depth of a tooth space below the pitch circle or pitch line; also, it is the radial distance between the pitch circle and the root circle. (See Fig. 11-137.)

Clearance (c) is the amount by which the dedendum in a given gear exceeds the addendum of its mating gear. (See Fig. 11-137.)

Working Depth (h_k) is the depth of engagement of two gears, that is, the sum of their addendums. (See Fig. 11-137.)

Whole Depth (h_t) is the total depth of a tooth space, equal to addendum plus dedendum, also equal to working depth plus clearance. (See Fig. 11-137.)

Pitch Diameter (D, d) is the diameter of the pitch circle. (See Fig. 11-136.)

Outside Diameter (D_o, d_o) is the diameter of the addendum (outside) circle. In a bevel gear, it is the diameter of the crown circle. In a throated worm gear, it is the maximum diameter of the blank. The term applies to external gears. (See Fig. 11-136.)

Root Diameter (D_R d_R) is the diameter of the root circle. (See Fig. 11-136.)

Circular Thickness (t_G, t_P) is the length of arc between the two sides of a gear tooth, on the pitch circles unless otherwise specified. (See Fig. 11-137.)

Chordal Thickness (t_c) is the length of the chord subtending a circular-thickness arc. (See Fig. 11-137.)

Chordal Addendum (a_c) is the height from the top of the tooth to the chord subtending the circular-thickness arc. (See Fig. 11-137.)

Number of Teeth or Threads (N) is the number of teeth contained in the whole circumference of the pitch circle.

Gear Ratio (m_G) is the ratio of the larger to the smaller number of teeth in a pair of gears.

Full-Depth Teeth are those in which the working depth equals 2.000 divided by normal diametral pitch.

Stub Teeth are those in which the working depth is less than 2.000 divided by normal diametral pitch.

*The following are several of a group of standards concerning gearing which are published by The American Society of Mechanical Engineers, New York, N. Y.:

ASA B6.1-1932, Spur Gear Tooth Form
ASA B6.5-1954, Letter Symbols for Gear Engineering
AGMA 112.03, ASA B6.10-1954, Gear Nomenclature

Measuring Tooth Thickness: The chordal thickness (t_c) and the chordal addendum (a_c) of spur gear teeth, Fig. 11-137, may be accurately checked for size with a gear-tooth vernier caliper (shown in Unit 102). The values for these parts may be secured in standard handbooks for machinists. The vertical scale on the vernier caliper is set at the value thus found for the chordal addendum (sometimes called corrected addendum). The chordal thickness is then checked against the proper value by using the sliding vernier scale.

Symbols: The following symbols and abbreviations are used in conjunction with spur gear formulas:

Symbol*	Term	Abbreviation
P	Diametral pitch	DP
p	Circular pitch	CP
D	Pitch diameter	PD
D_o	Outside diameter	OD
N	Number of teeth	N
t	Circular thickness	CT
a	Addendum	A
b	Dedendum	D
h_k	Working depth	WkD
h_t	Whole depth	WD
c	Clearance	C
C	Center distance	
L	Length of rack	

*Symbols from ASA B6.5-1954

Gear-Tooth Forms

In order for mating gears of the same diametral pitch to mesh with a smooth, quiet, rolling action, they must have the proper gear-tooth form. Two basic forms (or curves) for gear teeth are used — one with an *involute curve* (Fig. 11-135) and a second which is a *composite* of the *involute curve* and *cycloidal curves* (Fig. 11-136).

Mating gears with either of these forms will roll together smoothly and quietly without interference when operated at the prescribed pressure angle. Several systems of gear-tooth form have been standardized, and each system is designed to operate at a specified pressure angle, usually at $14\frac{1}{2}°$ or $20°$.

Gears with the involute curve tooth design are the most widely used in American industry. They are mass-produced on production types of gear-generating machines, including gear-shapers and gear-hobbing machines.

The teeth of gears with the composite tooth form are very similar to those of the involute form, except for the design of the basic rack teeth. This rack has an involute curve in the area of the pitch line, but it is modified slightly with cycloidal curves in areas above and below the pitch line. The modification prevents interference of mating gears which have a small number of teeth.

Gears with the composite tooth form normally are produced on milling machines, with form-type rotary milling cutters, Fig. 11-138. The use of this form system largely is limited to the production of gears with milling machines in small job shops, maintenance shops, and shops where small numbers of gears are produced. This form of gear also may be produced by hobbing or with other gear-generating machines.

Fig. 11-138. Ten-Pitch Gear Cutter (No. 3)
(Cincinnati Milling Machine)

Four standard gear tooth forms were approved by the American Standards Association in 1932 (ASA B6.1-1932), and all are being used to some extent for various purposes:

14½° Composite System
14½° Full-depth Involute System
20°   Full-depth Involute System
20°   Stub Involute System

14½° Composite: Gears within the 14½° composite system have full-depth teeth with a pressure angle of 14½°. The tooth form on the basic rack is a composite of involute and cycloidal curves, as described above. The sides of the basic rack tooth are curved slightly at the top and bottom. This form of gear tooth is utilized for gears which are milled on milling machines with form-type rotary cutters.

14½° Full-Depth Involute: Gears in the 14½° full-depth involute system have full-depth teeth with a 14½° pressure angle. This type is satisfactory when the numbers of teeth are large enough to avoid excess undercutting of the tooth form. Undercutting occurs when the pinion has less than 32 teeth, and it may become excessive when there are less than 22 teeth. For this system, the teeth on the basic rack have straight sides.

20° Full-Depth Involute: Gears in the 20° full-depth involute system have full-depth teeth with a 20° pressure angle. The tooth form is similar and has the same parts as the 14½° involute type, except that the tooth is thicker at the base and, therefore, is stronger. Pinions may have fewer teeth without the occurrence of undercutting. With less than 18 teeth, undercutting starts to occur, and it may be excessive with less than 14 teeth. This form of gear is widely used for general power transmission purposes.

20° Stub Involute: Gears in the 20° stub involute system have a 20° pressure angle and differ from the 20° full-depth system in that the teeth are shorter. The whole depth of the tooth is equal to 1.8 divided by the diametral pitch. The shorter tooth, together with the 20° pressure angle, provides for strengthened teeth on pinions with only 12 or 13 teeth, without significant undercutting. Gear teeth of this form are often used in automotive transmissions, where smaller gears are required and where maximum power transmission must be provided.

Spur Gear Formulas

The rules or formulas in Table 12 are used in making calculations for the following American Standard Spur Gear Tooth Forms (ASA B6.1-1932): 14½° composite full-depth teeth, 14½° involute full-depth teeth, and 20° involute full-depth teeth.

The rules and formulas for spur gears with 20° involute stub teeth or with 20° involute fine-pitch teeth, are available in standard handbooks for machinists.

Table 12
Spur Gear Formulas

To Find	Rule with Diametral Pitch (P) Known	Formula
Diametral Pitch P	Divide circular pitch by 3.1416.	$P = \dfrac{p}{3.1416}$
Circular Pitch p	Divide 3.1416 by diametral pitch.	$p = \dfrac{3.1416}{P}$
Pitch Diameter D	Divide number of teeth by diametral pitch.	$D = \dfrac{N}{P}$
Outside Diameter D_o	Add 2 to number of teeth, and divide this sum by the diametral pitch.	$D_o = \dfrac{N+2}{P}$
Circular Thickness (on pitch line) t	Divide 1.5708 by diametral pitch.	$t = \dfrac{1.5708}{P}$
Addendum a	Divide 1.0 by diametral pitch.	$a = \dfrac{1.0}{P}$
Dedenum (min.) b	Divide 1.157 by diametral pitch.	$b = \dfrac{1.157}{P}$
Working Depth h_k	Divide 2.0 by diametral pitch.	$h_k = \dfrac{2.0}{P}$
Whole Depth (min.) h_t	Divide 2.157 by diametral pitch.	$h_t = \dfrac{2.157}{P}$
Clearance (min.) c	Divide 0.157 by diametral pitch.	$c = \dfrac{0.157}{P}$
Length of Rack	Multiply number of teeth in the rack by circular pitch.	$L = N \times p$

Spur Gear Problem: Given a gear with 36 teeth and 10 diametral pitch, calculate the following:

1. D_o (Outside diameter)
2. t (Circular thickness)
3. a (Addendum)
4. b (Dedendum)
5. h_t (Whole depth)
6. c (Clearance)

Solution:

1. $D_o = \dfrac{N+2}{P} = \dfrac{36+2}{10} = \dfrac{38}{10} = 3.8''$

2. $t = \dfrac{1.5708}{P} = \dfrac{1.5708}{10} = .157''$

3. $a = \dfrac{1.0}{P} = \dfrac{1.0}{10} = 0.100''$

4. $b = \dfrac{1.157}{P} = \dfrac{1.157}{10} = 0.1157''$

5. $h_t = \dfrac{2.157}{P} = \dfrac{2.157}{10} = 0.2157''$

6. $c = \dfrac{0.157}{P} = \dfrac{0.157}{10} = 0.0157''$

Gear Cutters

Form-tooth gear cutters for milling machines, Fig. 11-138, are made in standard sets of eight cutters for each diametral pitch. Some common pitches include 6, 8, 10, 12, and so on. The profile of the tooth on a 13-tooth gear of a given pitch is different than that on a 40-tooth gear. Therefore, a cutter with a different profile form must be used to cut gears with different numbers of teeth. With a standard set of eight cutters, a satisfactory tooth profile can be produced on a gear with any number of teeth, ranging from 12 teeth or more, up to and including a rack.

The individual cutters in a standard set are numbered as follows:

Cutter Number	Cutting Capacity
1	135 teeth to a rack
2	55 to 134 teeth to a rack
3	35 to 54 teeth to a rack
4	26 to 34 teeth to a rack
5	21 to 35 teeth to a rack
6	17 to 20 teeth to a rack
7	14 to 16 teeth to a rack
8	12 to 13 teeth to a rack

For example, a No. 6 cutter is used for cutting a gear with 18 teeth. In each instance, the cutter is designed for the lower number of teeth. In the case of the No. 6 cutter, a 17-tooth gear would have a profile which would operate more efficiently than a 19-tooth gear.

Cutters are available for producing more accurate tooth profiles on gears requiring more efficient operation, such as those used in automotive transmissions. Cutters of this type are available with half numbers such as $1\frac{1}{2}$, $2\frac{1}{2}$, through $7\frac{1}{2}$. Thus a No. $5\frac{1}{2}$ cutter is designed to cut 19 to 20 teeth. A 19-tooth gear cut with this cutter would operate more smoothly than if it were cut with the No. 6 cutter.

Bevel Gears

Bevel gears are conical in shape and are used on shafts with intersecting axes, Fig. 11-129. They are used primarily for transmitting motion or force around corners. Bevel gears usually are produced on special gear-generating machines. However, a machinist occasionally is called upon to produce a bevel gear with a milling machine. He will more readily understand the procedures involved in making a gear on a milling machine if he understands the terms used and the method employed in making a layout for a bevel gear.

If instead of two flat rolls or pulleys in contact with each other, two conical or tapered rolls are brought into contact, as in Fig. 11-139, the driver will transmit motion to the driven. But when a load is applied, there again will be slippage and consequent loss of effectiveness. Positive motion to the driven roll is accomplished by cutting teeth on each roll. A gear with a conical shape, such as shown in Fig. 11-140, is called a *bevel gear*. When it is desired to give positive motion to a shaft running at an angle to a second shaft, a set of bevel gears is used, Fig. 11-140. Usually one gear, the pinion, is much smaller than the other. When both gears are the same size, they generally have a face angle of 45° and are called *miter gears*. A miter gear is merely a special form of bevel gear. Fig. 11-141 shows other forms of bevel gears. In *A*, the two shafts are in planes less than 90° apart, while in *B*, they are in planes more than 90° apart.

Laying Out a Bevel Gear

The shape and size of the teeth on a bevel gear at the large end are the same as those in a spur gear, and the method of laying them off at the large end is practically the same. The first step in laying out a bevel gear is to determine the center angle, for example, 30°, *A*, Fig. 11-142. Then the pitch diameter must be determined, followed by the number of teeth, the diametral pitch and the width of the face.

Assume the gear is to have a 5″ pitch diameter and 30 teeth; then the diametral pitch will be $\frac{N}{D}$ or $\frac{30}{5} = 6$ or a 6 P gear. Also assume that the width of the face is to be three-tenths of the hypotenuse of the center angle *AOP*, Fig. 11-142. Having made the necessary calculations, draw the angle AOB, Fig. 11-143. Then draw line AB at a point where it will be equal to the pitch diameter of 5″. Through points A

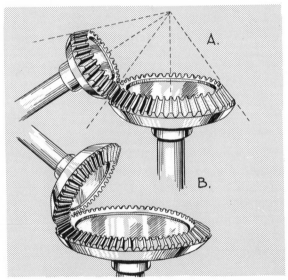

Fig. 11-141. Other Forms of Bevel Gears

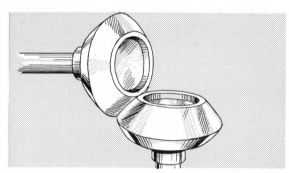

Fig. 11-139. Flat Rolls Transmit Motion Inefficiently

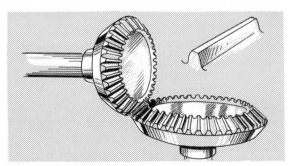

Fig. 11-140. Bevel Gears

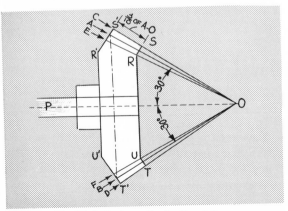

Fig. 11-142. Layout of a Bevel Gear

and B respectively, draw lines R'S' and T'U' perpendicular respectively to AO and BO. Next, on lines AO and BO, at a distance equal to three-tenths of AO, draw lines RS and TU parallel to R'S' and T'U'. Calculate the outside diameter of the large end of the teeth, and draw lines CO and DO, Fig. 11-142. (The necessary formulas are available in standard handbooks for machinists.) Calculate the dedendum of the tooth and the clearance required (the total height of the tooth below line AO); then draw lines EO and FO, Fig. 11-142. Next calculate the thickness of the tooth.

To construct the tooth, extend line AB around the periphery of the wheel; then, using the thickness of the tooth, set the dividers, and, on the extension of line AB on the periphery, space off one or two teeth. Through the spacing marks on the peripheral line AB, draw involute curves, thus forming the sides of the teeth at the large end.

As can be seen from Fig. 11-142, all lines converge toward the apex of the cone. This

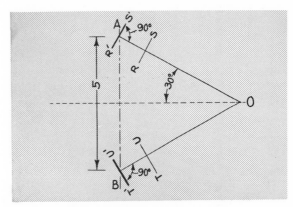

Fig. 11-143. Preliminary Layout of a Bevel Gear

means that each tooth is thinner and shorter at the apex end than at the base end. A bevel gear cannot be cut very accurately on an ordinary milling machine using a standard gear cutter. In factories where much bevel gear cutting is done, a special gear-cutting machine is used.

How To Mill Teeth on a Spur Gear

Gear cutting constitutes one of the many interesting kinds of work that can be accomplished on a milling machine and one that appeals very much to young workers. Before the invention of the dividing head, it was the custom to cast the teeth on gears, or, when they were cut, to space and lay out each tooth accurately. The cutting process involved the laborious hand setting of the machine for each tooth. The dividing head, cutters, and other features of modern milling machines have made spur gear cutting a very simple operation, once the machine has been properly set and adjusted, as shown in Fig. 11-144.

Fig. 11-144. Cutting Teeth on a Spur Gear
(Cincinnati Milling Machine)

Fig. 11-145. Cutter in Position Over Axis of Dividing Center

Procedure

1. Select a fairly short tapered mandrel of a diameter that will fill the hole in the hub of the gear blank.
2. Wipe the mandrel clean with a handful of waste; then lightly oil the surface.
3. Force the mandrel into the hub with an arbor press or by means of a lead hammer.
4. With the cross feed, run the table as close as practicable to the column.
5. Secure the dividing head and tailstock, and place them on the table of the milling machine as close to the column as the nature of the work and the dividing head will permit. Be sure the index handle is toward the front of the table.
6. Adjust the position of the head and tailstock so that the edge of the gear blank nearest the dividing head (when mounted between the centers) will be slightly ahead of the cutter.
7. Fasten the dividing head securely in position. Then slide the tailstock forward until the centers just touch.
8. Examine the position of the points of the centers. Both must be in the same horizontal plane. If not, adjust the tailstock center vertically until it is in the same plane as the point of the center in the head.
9. Move the tailstock back to the position desired, and fasten it securely.

10. Secure a gear cutter of suitable size, for example, a 10-pitch gear cutter (No. 5). Also secure a cutting arbor, collars, and a dog.
11. Wipe the shank of the cutting arbor clean and dry, and insert it in the spindle of the milling machine. Then place the cutter on the arbor so that the center of the cutter is as nearly as possible over the axis (point) of the dividing center, Fig. 11-145.
12. Place the nut on the arbor, and draw it tight against the collar, using the wrench. Then adjust the overarm, and slide the arbor bearing over the end of the arbor.
13. With the longitudinal feed, move the table back until the cutter is slightly to the left of the point of the center in the dividing head. Then with the vertical adjustment, raise the table until the point of the center is slightly above the level of the bottom edge of the cutter.
14. With the cross and longitudinal feeds, adjust the table until the center of the cutter is exactly over the point or axis of the center in the dividing head.

    A more accurate setting may be achieved by mounting a trial blank between the centers of the dividing head. Make a trial cut; then turn the piece end-for-end, and cut from the opposite direction. If the cutter is removing stock from the top of one side of the first cut and from the bottom of the second, the cutter is not centrally located. In this case, the work should be moved *laterally away* from *the side* of the cut on which stock was being removed at the *top* of the first cut.
15. When the cutter has been accurately centered, lower the table, and mount the work between the centers of the dividing head, Fig. 11-144. The large end of the arbor should be toward the headstock.
16. Insert the tail of the dog in the carrier slot, and clamp lightly.
17. Assume that the gear to be cut has 100 teeth. Also assume that one turn of the index handle advances the worm which turns the dividing head spindle 1/40th of a turn. Then, the number of turns of the crank divided by the number of teeth to be cut will give the number of turns of

the index handle required to advance the work for the next cut, $40 \div 100 = .4$ of a turn.

18. Adjust the index pin to any circle of holes which is divisible by 10. Then loosen the binding screw, and set the sector arms to include four-tenths of the number of spaces, for example, four-tenths of 30, which equals 12. Remember, it is the number of *spaces* that counts and that within the total space encompassed by the sector arms, there will be one more hole than spaces. When adjusting the sector, be sure the index handle and the sector move freely. See Unit 97.

19. Move the index handle toward the *right*, until the pin enters the last hole in the index plate, encompassed between the sector arms. Then immediately advance the sector until the left arm touches the pin. Make it a practice always to advance the sector immediately after indexing and to move the index handle toward the right.

20. Start the machine; then run the work under the cutter, and raise the table until the cutter just touches the work. Test with a piece of tissue paper placed between the work and the cutter.

21. Move the table back until the near edge is just to the rear of the front of the cutter.

22. Set the micrometer dial for vertical adjustment at zero. Raise the table to within about $\frac{1}{32}''$ of the depth of the finished cut, in this case about .190 on the dial. The total depth of tooth space of a 10-pitch gear is .216. See Unit 99, Solution 7.

23. Engage the automatic longitudinal feed, and make the cut. *Be sure to use a cutting fluid freely.*

24. At the end of the cut, disengage the feed, and draw the table back to the starting position for the next cut.

25. Index four-tenths of a turn for the next cut, and proceed as in steps 23 and 24.

26. When all teeth have been rough cut, set the machine to make the finishing cut. Proceed as in steps 22 through 25 inclusive.

    CAUTION: *Before starting the finishing cut, be sure the cutter is sharp. Do not stop the cut at some intermediate point or run the table back without first stopping the machine.*

27. When the job is finished, remove the work, cutter, and dividing head, and return them to the place where kept when not in use. Then, with a brush, clean the machine.

How To Mill Teeth on a Bevel Gear

UNIT 102

Teeth cannot be cut with good accuracy on a bevel gear with an ordinary bevel gear cutter on a standard milling machine. In large establishments where many gears are cut, a special gear-cutting machine is used for this purpose. However, small concerns do not have sufficient volume of business to warrant purchasing a special machine; consequently, workers are at times confronted with the problem of cutting teeth on a bevel gear. Bevel gears can be cut with sufficient accuracy for many applications by using a standard milling machine. The machining setup is made by mounting the bevel gear blank in the dividing head chuck or spindle, Fig. 11-146.

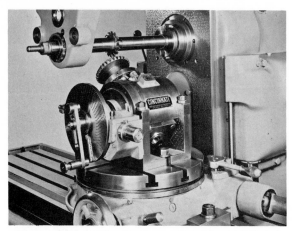

Fig. 11-146. Cutting Teeth on a Bevel Gear Mounted on a Dividing Head (Cincinnati Milling Machine)

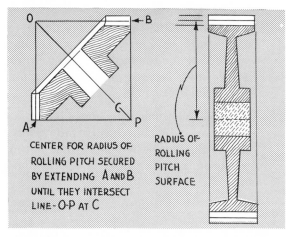

CENTER FOR RADIUS OF
ROLLING PITCH SECURED
BY EXTENDING A AND B
UNTIL THEY INTERSECT
LINE-O-P AT C

RADIUS OF
ROLLING
PITCH
SURFACE

Fig. 11-147. Determining Rolling Pitch of a Bevel Gear

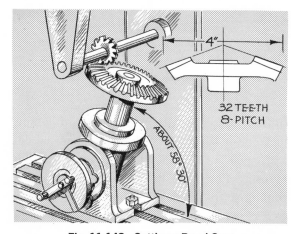

4″

32 TEETH
8-PITCH

ABOUT 58° 30′

Fig. 11-148. Cutting a Bevel Gear

When choosing a bevel gear cutter, remember it is made thin enough to pass between the teeth at the small end and is shaped to cut the teeth of a spur gear having a *rolling pitch* of the same magnitude as the bevel gear in question, Fig. 11-147. A spur gear with a 10″ rolling pitch surface may have many more teeth than a bevel gear of the same rolling pitch surface. However, it is the rolling pitch (and not the number of teeth) that determines the size of cutter to be used. The same cutter should not be used for cutting both the gear and pinion, except when cutting miter gears. Each member of a pair of miter gears has the same number of teeth; this is not the case with a bevel gear and pinion.

A table giving the size of cutter to use for cutting gears and pinions with varying numbers of teeth can be found in a standard handbook for machinists.

Cutters used for cutting bevel gears on a milling machine are similar to those used for cutting spur gears. However, they are thinner, in order to pass between the teeth at the small end of the gear. Bevel gear cutters are made in sets, and are stamped with the word *bevel*. Instructions for the selection of bevel gear cutters generally are included in cutter manufacturer's catalogs or in standard handbooks for machinists.

Procedure

1. Select a suitable gear blank, and machine it accurately according to the dimensions given.
2. Secure a dividing head and a dividing chuck. Fasten the head on the table of the milling machine, and mount the chuck on the dividing-head spindle.
3. Set the dividing head at the cutting angle as given on the drawing; see Fig. 11-148.
4. Select a bevel-gear cutter of a size suitable for cutting teeth of the size specified, for example, 10 P.
5. Secure a spindle arbor and collars of suitable size. Be sure all chips are removed from the arbor and collars.
6. Mount the cutter on the arbor as near the nose of the spindle as practicable and in such manner that the cut will be made

away from the dividing head. Position the overarm and arbor bearing, and fasten securely.

7. Mount the gear blank in the chuck, being sure it is seated accurately, Fig. 11-148.

8. Adjust the table until the center of the point of the cutter is in line with the axis of the gear blank, Fig. 11-148.

9. Start the machine; then raise and advance the table until the cutter just touches the surface of the gear blank.

10. Set the micrometer dial for vertical adjustment at zero. Then raise the table the depth of cut, for example, .216″.

11. Make the cut in the usual manner, using a cutting fluid freely.

12. Index for the next tooth, and make the cut.

13. Accurately caliper the thickness of the tooth at the large end. Use a gear-tooth vernier caliper, Fig. 11-149. Assuming the large end is found to measure .194″, then from this measurement subtract the finished thickness of the tooth, for example, .157″, and divide the remainder by 2.

$$\frac{.194'' - .157''}{2} = \frac{.037''}{2} = .0185''$$

This figure represents the amount of stock to be trimmed from each side of the large end, A, Fig 11-150.

14. In a similar manner, calculate the amount to be trimmed from the small end. Ordinarily, only a very small amount, if any, will need to be trimmed.

15. Paint the cut surfaces of the tooth with layout dye.

The correct setting of the machine cannot be achieved by merely moving the index pin a hole or two to the right, as this would move the small end of the gear proportionately with the large end and result in too much stock being removed from the small end. The amount of setover and the amount of roll for trimming teeth of various sizes will be found in the handbook of the particular machine being used or in a standard handbook for machinists.

16. Loosen the clamping screws, and offset the table of the milling machine about one-eighth of the thickness of the tooth at the large end, for example, about .02″. Then

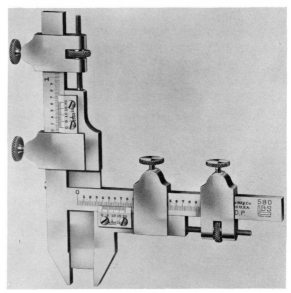

Fig. 11-149. Gear-Tooth Vernier Caliper
(Brown & Sharpe)

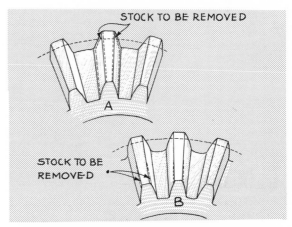

Fig. 11-150. Layout of Stock to be Removed on Finishing Cut

clamp the table securely. Be sure to adjust for backlash.

17. Withdraw the index pin, and, with the side index plate, rotate the blank until the edge of the cutter is in position to take a cut of the amount desired, for example, .0185″.

If the pin does not fit in a hole when the blank has been revolved to the position desired, loosen the index plate lock and move the plate until one of the holes comes under the pin.

18. Start the machine, and carefully trim the side of the tooth. This should remove all of the dye except at the extreme of the small end.

19. Again measure the ends of the tooth. If the tooth is still too thick at either end, offset the blank (as in step 16) in the direction desired and take another light cut.

    CAUTION: *For this second adjustment, the amount of offset will be the difference between the required thickness of the tooth plus one-half the difference found when the tooth was first measured, for example, .157" + .0185" = .1755", and the magnitude of the last measurement, for example, .1805". Then .1805" − .1755" = .005", the amount to be removed.*

20. Set the sector for the number of spaces through which the index handle is to be moved; then index for the next tooth.

21. Start the machine, and proceed in the usual manner, observing the normal precautions. Continue thus until all the teeth have been cut on one side.

22. Offset the table in the opposite direction an amount corresponding with the offset for the first cut. Be sure to adjust for backlash.

23. Rotate the index handle the same number of holes as before, but in the opposite direction.

24. Start the machine, and trim the second side of the first tooth.

25. Carefully measure the finished tooth at both ends. Make adjustments, if necessary, and again trim the tooth.

26. When the first tooth has been cut to the size required, proceed to trim the second side of the remaining teeth.

    Because the cutter does not have the proper curvature for cutting the top part of the small end of the tooth, it will be necessary to remove a little stock with a file.

27. File the top of the teeth until the desired curvature is achieved, *B*, Fig. 11-150.

Milling Helices

Helices, or spirals, usually are milled on a universal miller, which, as standard equipment, is provided with a dividing head and a dividing-head driving mechanism, as illustrated in Figs. 11-2 and 11-25. Steep helices, such as the helix for a worm thread, may be produced on either a plain or universal milling machine equipped with a universal spiral milling attachment, a divider, and a short lead attachment, Figs. 11-152 and 11-30. The universal spiral milling attachment is useful on universal milling machines when the angle of the helix exceeds the swivel angle of the machine table.

A *helix* is a line or, more generally, a groove, which advances longitudinally on a cylindrical or conical object at a constant rate as the object is rotated about its axis. A helix may be either right- or left-handed. To determine which, hold the object in a horizontal plane before the eyes. If the helix leads or travels upward toward the left, it is a right-hand helix and if downward, toward the left, it is a left-hand helix. The distance the helix travels longitudinally in inches while the object makes one complete revolution about its axis is called the *lead*.

The cylinder in Fig. 11-153 is 12″ in length, and the helix has traveled twice around it in traversing its complete length. Thus, the helix has a lead of 6″. If the same cylinder were only 3″ long, as indicated at A, the helix would still have a 6″ lead, because (as the illustration shows) the helix has traveled only half way around the cylinder in its one complete revolution. On the other hand, if in two revolutions of a cylinder 3″ long, the helix had traveled twice around the cylinder (as in B), then the helix would have a lead of 1½″.

From the above example, it can be seen that the lead equals the distance in inches traveled by the helix, divided by the number of revolutions made while the helix is traveling the length of the cylinder. For instance, assume a cylinder 15″ long makes 2½ revolutions while the helix is traversing its length. Then 15″ divided by 2½ turns equals 6″, and the helix has a lead of 6″.

Change Gears

Variations in the rate at which the helix advances are achieved by variations in the size of gears used in the driving mechanism. These are called change gears. Ordinarily, there are twelve gears in a set of change gears. In a compound train of four gears, two are driving gears and two are driven. To achieve a given lead, one must select gears having a ratio that will cause the work to rotate at a given speed while advancing toward the cutter a given distance.

Change in the direction of rotation of the stock is accomplished by introducing an idler gear into the train of gears. Since the sole function of the idler is to change the direction of rotation, it in no way affects the gear ratio. After the helical mechanism has been adjusted, indexing for subsequent helices is done.

Included with universal milling machines and with dividing-head driving mechanisms is a set of instructions entitled "Table of Change Gears, Angles and Leads." These tell what gears to use and the position in which they are to be placed in the driving mechanism in order to produce a given lead in inches for each revolution of the stock. In the event of the loss of the instructions or of the need of computing a gear ratio not given, a mathematical formula is given in Unit 104.

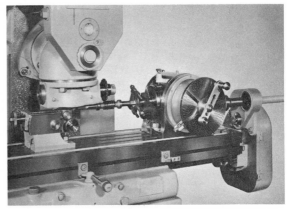

Fig. 11-152. Milling a Worm Thread
(Cincinnati Milling Machine)
A universal spiral milling attachment and a divider with a short lead attachment are used.

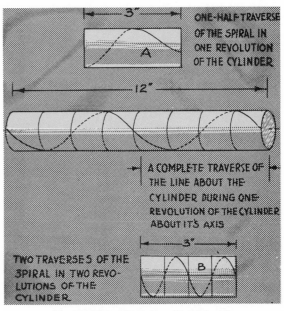

Fig. 11-153. RH Helix with 6″ Lead

Positioning the Work

When a helix is milled, the work must be set at an angle to the axis of the cutter by swiveling the table of the machine, except when using an end mill, C, Fig. 11-154. Even when the work is set at an angle, a helix with straight sides cannot be milled true and smooth with a circular cutter having parallel sides, for example, the cutter illustrated in A, Fig. 11-154. This is because a circular mill with straight sides cannot fit in a curved groove without

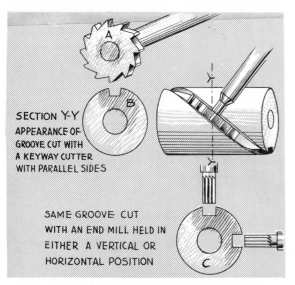

Fig. 11-154. Helices Cut with Keyway Cutter and End Mill

Fig. 11-156. Cutting a LH Helix

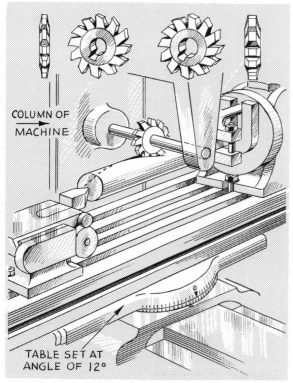

Fig. 11-155. Helix Being Cut with Cutter Having Formed Teeth

Fig. 11-157. Cutting a Rather Steep LH Helix
(Cincinnati Milling Machine)

striking and thus tearing the sides of the groove as it revolves, thereby making the groove wider at the top than the dimension given, *B*, Fig. 11-154. On the other hand, a formed circular cutter on which the sides of the teeth tend to converge toward the point can be used to mill a helix having sides which conform to the slope of the teeth, for example, Fig. 11-155. This is because the sides of the teeth are only in full contact with the sides of the groove at the moment a given tooth is removing the metal at the bottom of the groove. After passing this point, the sides of the tooth swing clear of the finished part of the groove.

The method of computing the angle at which the table should be swiveled for different helix leads is explained in Unit 104.

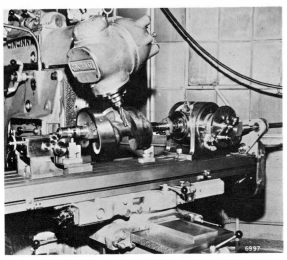

Fig. 11-158. Helical Milling with End Mill
(Cincinnati Milling Machine)

For a right-hand helix, the table should be swiveled toward the right from the zero line on the saddle through the desired number of degrees, Fig. 11-155. For a left-hand spiral, the table is swiveled toward the left from the zero line, as in Fig. 11-156. Fig. 11-157 illustrates the table swiveled to the left for cutting a rather steep helix.

Because of the impracticability or, in some cases, impossibility of swiveling the table for a steep helix, the use of a universal spiral milling attachment (Fig. 11-152) is recommended.

Helical milling also may be done with an end mill on a vertical milling machine equipped with a dividing head and a dividing-head lead driving mechanism, Fig. 11-158.

Change Gears, Angles, and Leads for Helical Milling

When a helix is milled, the work must rotate at a constant rate as the cutter advances. This is accomplished by gears (having a definite ratio) mounted in the dividing-head driving mechanism, Fig. 11-159. A set of about eighteen gears with various numbers of teeth normally is available with the driving mechanism, but other sets also are available. These gears may be interchanged in the four positions, A through D, in order to cut a helix of the desired length.

Charts usually are available with the machine or in machinist's handbooks, which indicate the gears that will produce various leads. If the exact lead desired is not on the chart, a lead within a few thousandths of an inch, which is listed, generally will be sufficiently accurate. Closer leads may be calculated by formula. The chart indicates the gear which

should be used in each of the positions, A, B, C, and D, in Fig. 11-159.

For most helical milling setups on universal milling machines, the table is swiveled to the angle of the helix being cut. When a universal spiral milling attachment is used, it usually is not necessary to swivel the table. With this attachment, *steep* helix angles (those which are not within the swivel range of the table) may be produced on either universal or plain milling machines, Figs. 11-30, 11-152, and 11-158.

When the dividing head is connected to the table lead screw through the train of change gears, the dividing-head spindle rotates simultaneously with the lead screw. When a workpiece is mounted between the dividing-head centers, a helix is generated on its surface by the cutting tool. The lead of this helix varies according to the ratios of the change gears.

391

Calculation of Change Gears

If a chart is not available which indicates the gears to be used in the dividing-head driving mechanism to produce a given lead, the machinist can determine this by using a simple formula. However, before he can do this, he must know the pitch of the longitudinal feed screw on the milling machine. Usually the threads on this screw have a ¼″ pitch. Thus, in 40 turns of the feed screw, the table will advance 10″. If a single pair of gears is used (one mounted on the feed screw and the other on the driving head worm) and if each has the same number of teeth (for example, 80), a one to one ratio will exist. The work will then make one complete revolution about its axis while the table has advanced 10″. Such a helix would have a 10″ lead. The same ratio would exist if four gears of the same size were used, two driving and two driven (for example, four gears each having 40 teeth).

The length of the lead is changed by changing the gear ratios between the table feed screw and the worm screw on the index head. This is done with change gears which include two *driving* and two *driven* gears. The gears on

Fig. 11-159. Dividing Head and Change Gears
(Cincinnati Milling Machine)

392

most dividing-head drive mechanisms, though not all of them, are labeled as indicated in Fig. 11-159:

A = Gear on worm shaft (driven)
B = First gear on idler stud (driving)
C = Second gear on idler stud (driven)
D = Gear on table screw (driving)

The following formula may be used for determining the change gears required to produce a desired lead:

$$\frac{\text{Lead of helix}}{\text{Lead of machine}} = \frac{\text{Driven gears}}{\text{Driving gears}} = \frac{A \times C}{B \times D}$$

Example: Determine the change gears required for a lead of 30″. The lead of most standard milling machines is 10″.

$$\frac{\text{Lead of helix}}{\text{Lead of machine}} = \frac{30}{10} = \frac{\text{Driven gears}}{\text{Driving gears}}$$

Therefore, the fraction 30/10 is the ratio of $\frac{\text{Driven gears}}{\text{Driving gears}}$ necessary to produce a helix with a 30″ lead. If a simple train of two gears could be used, the driven gear would have 30 teeth and the driver would have 10 teeth. However, such gears are not available. A train of four gears makes it possible to obtain a much greater range of ratios.

When four gears are used, the ratio of each gear is obtained by splitting into two fractions the fraction derived when the lead of the helix is the numerator and the lead of the machine is the denominator (in this case, 30 and 10 respectively). This is done by factoring.

$$\frac{30}{10} = \frac{5 \times 6}{2 \times 5} = \frac{A \times C}{B \times D}$$

These represent the four change gears needed. But gears with 5, 6, and 2 teeth are not available. In order to make the numbers in the numerator and denominator correspond to change gears which are available, both terms of the first factor must be multiplied by the same suitable number, and both terms of the second factor usually by some suitable number. (Multiplying both members of a fraction by the same number does not change the value of the fraction.)

$$\frac{(5 \times 11) \times (6 \times 6)}{(2 \times 11) \times (5 \times 6)} = \frac{55 \times 36}{22 \times 30} = \frac{A \times C}{B \times D}$$

Gear A has 55 teeth (driven)
Gear B has 22 teeth (driving)
Gear C has 36 teeth (driven)
Gear D has 30 teeth (driving)

The positions of gears A and C may be interchanged without changing their products. This is also true for gears B and D. Thus, several different combinations of driven and driving gears may be used to produce a helix with the same lead.

Example 2: For a helix with an 18″ lead, the ratio would be as follows:

$$\frac{\text{Lead of helix}}{\text{Lead of machine}} = \frac{18}{10} = \frac{\text{Driven gears}}{\text{Driving gears}}$$

$$\frac{18}{10} = \frac{3 \times 6}{2 \times 5} = \frac{A \times C}{B \times D}$$

$$\frac{(3 \times 10) \times (6 \times 6)}{(2 \times 10) \times (5 \times 6)} = \frac{30 \times 36}{20 \times 30}$$

Gear A has 30 teeth (driven)
Gear B has 20 teeth (driving)
Gear C has 36 teeth (driven)
Gear D has 30 teeth (driving)

Idler Gear

As previously mentioned, the setup for cutting a left-hand helix requires an idler gear in the train of gears. This in no way affects the gear ratio, but merely changes the direction of rotation of the stock. Usually, the idler gear is mounted on an adjustable idler bracket. On some machines, an idler is used when cutting a right-hand rather than a left-hand helix.

The Angle of the Helix

The angle of the helix determines the angle at which the table of a universal milling machine should be swiveled when milling a helix with a cutter having parallel sides, except an end mill.

Swiveling the table at an angle is not feasible when milling very long or steep helices, for example, those with a 6″ lead. In such cases, the use of a universal attachment or the use of an end mill is recommended.

Two methods of determining the angle of a helix are discussed here. These are the graphical and the mathematical methods.

Graphical Method: The angle of the helix may be determined graphically by laying out a right triangle using the *circumference* of the object or stock as a base and the lead of the helix as the altitude.

For example, assume the stock is a cylinder 1¾″ in diameter, and a lead of 24″ is planned. Hence, the base = 1¾″ × 3.1416 = 5.4978″ or approximately 5½″ and the altitude = 24″. Then the angle of helix equals Angle A, Fig. 11-160.

Determine the number of degrees in Angle A by measuring it with a protractor. This is found to be approximately 12°54′ or 12⁹⁄₁₀°. The line marked "hypotenuse" in Fig. 11-160 represents the line of the helix as it would traverse the cylinder if the triangle were cut out and wrapped around the cylinder.

Mathematical Method: The angle of a helix may be found by dividing the circumference of the stock by the lead.

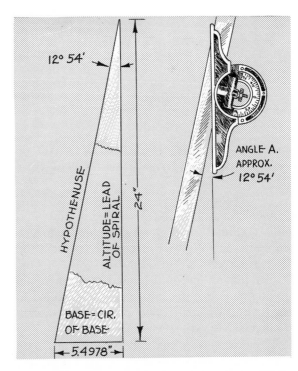

Fig. 11-160. Graphical Method of Finding Angle of Helix

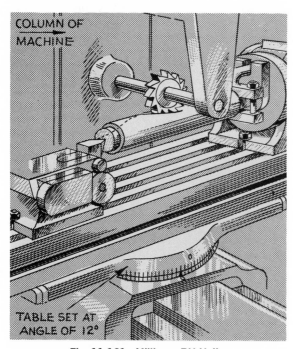

COLUMN OF MACHINE

TABLE SET AT ANGLE OF 12°

Fig. 11-161. Milling a RH Helix

Therefore,

$$\frac{\text{Circumference of stock}}{\text{Lead of helix}} = \text{Tangent of the helix angle.}$$

Assume the diameter of stock is $1\frac{3}{4}''$ and the lead is $24''$.

Then,

$$\frac{1\frac{3}{4}'' \times 3.1416}{24''} = \frac{5.4978''}{24''} = .2291'' \text{ tangent of angle.}$$

Examination of a table of trigonometric functions reveals that .2291 is approximately the tangent of an angle measuring 12° 54′.

When given the diameter of the workpiece and the angle of the helix, the lead may be determined by dividing the circumference of the workpiece by the tangent of the angle. For tangent of an angle, see a table of trigonometric functions (such as Table 45, appendix).

Example: Find the lead of the helix of a workpiece $2\frac{1}{4}''$ in diameter, having a helix angle of 15°. From a table of trigonometric functions, it is found that the tangent of an angle of 15° is .2679.

Solution.

$$\text{Lead} = \frac{\text{Circumference of work}}{\text{Tangent of angle}}$$

$$\text{Lead} = \frac{2.25'' \times 3.1416}{.2679} = \frac{7.0686''}{.2679}$$

$$\text{Lead} = 26.3852'' \text{ — roughly } 26\frac{1}{2}'', \text{ which is sufficiently close.}$$

NOTE: When calculating the helix angle of a helical gear, take the pitch diameter as the base.

UNIT

105   # How To Mill a Helix with a Universal Milling Machine

A helix or spiral may be milled with an end mill (*C*, Fig. 11-154), with a double-angle cutter (Fig. 11-57), with a convex cutter (Fig. 11-64), or with a fluting cutter (Fig. 11-66). If any but an end mill is used on a universal milling machine, the table must be swiveled to correspond with the angle of the helix, unless a universal spiral attachment is used.

The procedure which follows is for milling a right-hand helical (spiral) cutter on a milling machine on which the headstock of the divid-ing head is mounted on the right-hand end of the table. For a machine on which the head-stock is mounted on the left-hand end, the procedure is reversed. Compare *C* with *D*, Fig. 11-163 (page 395).

Procedure for a Double-Angle Cutter

PROBLEM: Machine a cutter $2\frac{1}{4}''$ in diame-ter, having 15 teeth with radial faces, $\frac{1}{32}''$ land, helix angle 12°. Use a double-angle cut-ter 48° — 12°.

1. Prepare and turn the stock to size.
2. Determine the number of grooves or teeth to be cut. The number of teeth and the width of the land will determine the amount of offset. See *A*, Fig. 11-164 (page 396).
3. Determine the lead.

$$\text{Lead} = \frac{\text{Circumference of workpiece}}{\text{Tangent of angle}}$$

(See Unit 104.)

Tangent of an angle of $12° = .2126$ or $.213$

Applying data gives:

$$\text{Lead} = \frac{2.25 \times 3.1416}{.213} = 33.15, \text{ or roughly}$$

$33''$, which is sufficiently close.

4. Mount the dividing head and tailstock on the table of the milling machine, Fig. 11-161.
5. Determine the change gears necessary to produce a helix with the lead desired. Mount the gears on the respective shafts and studs on the dividing head. (See Unit 104.)
6. Operate the longitudinal hand feed to determine that the dividing head mechanism operates freely.
7. Adjust the sector on the dividing head to include the desired number of spaces between the arms; then withdraw the stop-pin.

   To mill 15 teeth on a helical cutter, the workpiece must be rotated through $24°$ for each tooth ($360° ÷ 15 = 24°$). Since the revolution of the dividing head rotates the workpiece through $9°$, then $24° ÷ 9° = 2\frac{2}{3}$ turns of the index crank for each

tooth space; or, since $360° ÷ 9° = 40$, then $40 ÷ 15 = 2\frac{2}{3}$ turns of the index crank. This requires 2 full turns of the crank and $\frac{2}{3}$ of any circle of holes divisible by 3, for example, 16 spaces on a 24 circle, 32 spaces on a 48 circle, or 26 spaces on a 39 circle. See Unit 97.

8. Secure a suitable mandrel, arbor, cutter, dog, and surface gage.
9. After applying a little oil to the surface of the mandrel, press it firmly into the workpiece.
10. Place the dog on the large end of the mandrel; then place the piece between the centers of the dividing head.
11. Loosen the swivel clamping bolts, and then temporarily swivel the table to the angle desired, for example, $12°$. Feed the table crosswise until it clears the face of the column by $\frac{1}{2}''$ to $\frac{3}{4}''$.

   NOTE: For a right-hand helix, move the zero line on the swivel plate to the right of the zero line on the saddle, Fig. 11-161. For a left-hand helix, move the zero line on the swivel plate to the left of the zero line on the saddle, Fig. 11-156.

12. Apply layout dye to the tailstock end of the workpiece.
13. Set the point of the surface gage at the exact height of the axis of the dividing head center.
14. Scribe a radial line on the coated end of the workpiece, as illustrated in Fig. 11-162. Also see *A*, Fig. 11-163.

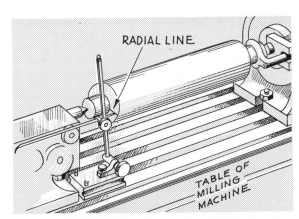

Fig. 11-162. Scribing a Radial Line on the Tailstock End of Workpiece

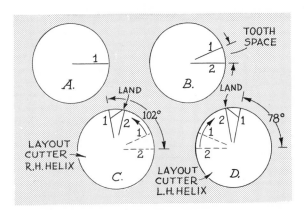

Fig. 11-163. Layout for RH and LH Helices

15. Index the work for one tooth space, and draw a second radial line, *B*, Fig. 11-163. Then index the work back one tooth space so that the first radial line will be in its original position, *A*, Fig. 11-163.

16. Wipe the arbor, and insert it in the spindle. Then draw it tight.

17. Mount the cutter on the arbor as nearly over the axis of the work as possible. Position the overarm and bearing, and then draw the clamping nut tight. In this position, the axis of the cutter and the pivot center of the table should be approximately in the same vertical plane.

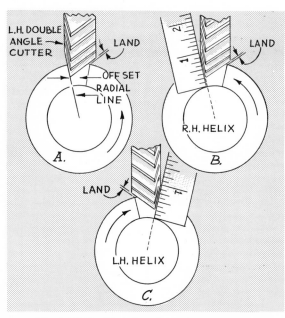

Fig. 11-164. Workpiece in Position for Cut

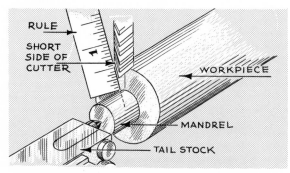

Fig. 11-165. Checking Position of Workpiece

18. Move the table longitudinally until the end of the workpiece at which the cut is to start is under the center of the cutting arbor.

19. Swivel the table back to its normal position (zero on the graduated base). Adjust the table laterally until the axis of the workpiece, at the work end, is exactly under the vertical axis of the cutter.

20. Index the workpiece counterclockwise through 102° from the horizontal, 9⅓ turns of the index crank. See *A* and *B*, Fig. 11-164.

21. Raise the table until the work just touches the cutter. Then adjust the table transversely until the 12° side of the cutter is aligned with the radial line (in the same plane) on the end of the workpiece. Test by holding a rule against the 12° side of the cutter, as in Fig. 11-165. This relationship will be changed when the table is raised to make the cut. To compensate for the change, the table must be adjusted in a manner that will again align the 12° side of the cutter with the radial line. When correctly positioned, the side of the cutter with the acute angle should split the radial line.

   C, Fig. 11-164, shows the work rotated through 78° clockwise and the short side of the cutter aligned with the radial line. Rotated clockwise, the work is in position for milling a left-hand helix.

22. Swivel the table to the angle desired, and tighten the clamping bolts.

23. Determine the depth of the groove.

24. Set the graduated collar on the vertical feed at zero.

25. Set the graduated collar on the cross feed at zero. This facilitates making slight lateral (crosswise) adjustments, if and when necessary. Be sure to adjust for backlash, if any.

26. Start the machine; then engage the reverse traverse. When the cutter has cleared the workpiece, disengage the power feed and raise the table an amount equal to the depth of the helix groove, less about 1/16″.

27. Engage the power feed. When the cutter enters the work and is cutting its full depth, stop the machine. Examine the cut

to make certain that the 12° side of the cutter is within .01″ of splitting the radial line on the end of the workpiece.

If it is not, lower the table, reverse the feed, and move the table back until the work just clears the cutter. Then make the necessary adjustment by moving the table laterally in the direction desired. Be sure to adjust for backlash.

28. If adjustment was found necessary and has been made, again start the machine and continue the cut until the cutter is cutting its full depth. Stop the table feed, and examine the cut. If further adjustment is necessary, lower the table, reverse the direction of travel, and make the needed adjustment.

29. When the cutter has been positioned correctly, advance the table until the cutter is cutting full depth; then reverse the table travel, and index for one tooth space.

30. Proceed until the cutter is cutting its full depth. Then stop the machine and examine the width of the land (the flat spot at the end of the tooth). See A, Fig. 11-164. If the land is too narrow, the table must be lowered an amount sufficient to increase the land the amount desired; if too wide, the table must be raised.

CAUTION: *In either event, the table must be adjusted laterally to re-align the radial line with the 12° side of the cutter.*

31. When the cutter has been properly aligned and set to depth, start the machine and make the cut, as in Fig. 11-161. Use a cutting fluid freely.

After the cutter has been set for depth of cut, it is good practice to set the graduated collar on the vertical feed at zero. This facilitates resetting for subsequent cuts.

32. At the end of the cut, lower the table. Then reverse the feed, and allow the cutter to travel back to the starting point.

33. Index for the next groove. Raise the table, and proceed as in steps 31 and 32.

34. Proceed as in steps 32 and 33 until all grooves have been rough cut.

35. When all first cuts have been made, adjust the vertical feed for the finishing cut, if one is necessary. Then proceed as in steps 31 through 34 inclusive.

How To Mill a Helix with an End Mill

A helix having straight sides may be milled with an end mill, using either a plain or a universal milling machine, as it is unnecessary to swivel the table. See Figs. 11-154 and 11-158.

Procedure

1. Turn the workpiece to size.
2. Determine the number of grooves to be milled.
3. Determine the change gears necessary to produce a helix having a lead of the specified size.
4. Mount the dividing head on the table of the milling machine. Mount the gears on the respective shafts and studs of the dividing-head mechanism. See Unit 104.
5. Mount the stock between the centers of the dividing head, parallel with the face of the column.

6. Secure a suitable end mill, insert it in the spindle, and fasten it securely.

7. Adjust the sector arms on the side index plate to include the desired number of spaces; then withdraw the stop-pin. If spacing can be accomplished by direct indexing, this step may be omitted.

8. Move the table longitudinally until the forward part of the cutter is aligned approximately with the end of the work where the helix starts.

9. With the vertical feed, raise the table until the axis of the work and the axis of the cutter are in the same horizontal plane (C, Fig. 11-154).

10. Set the graduated collar on the vertical feed at zero. This facilitates making adjustments, if and when necessary.

11. With the cross feed, move the table until the end of the cutter just touches the side of the work; then set the graduated collar at zero.

12. Check to make sure that the horizontal axis of the work and that of the cutter are in the same horizontal plane.

13. With the longitudinal feed, move the work forward until the cutter clears the end of the work. Then with the cross feed, move the work toward the column of the machine an amount equal to the depth of the groove.

14. After setting for depth of groove, it is good practice to reset the graduated collar at zero. This facilitates setting the depth of cut for cutting subsequent grooves and eliminates a possible source of error.

15. Start the machine, and engage the longitudinal feed. Use a cutting fluid freely.

16. At the end of the cut, draw the table away from the column enough that the work can clear the cutter. Then reverse the feed, and allow the cutter to travel back to the starting point.

17. Index for the next groove, if any.

18. Move the table toward the column until the graduated collar on the cross feed registers zero; then engage the table travel, and proceed as in steps 15 through 17 inclusive.

19. Continue as in steps 15 through 18 inclusive until all helices have been cut.

UNIT

107 How To Mill a Helix with a Universal Spiral Attachment

With a universal milling attachment, an operator can mill a helix on a plain milling machine, Fig. 11-30. This device is particularly well adapted for milling helices which have a steep lead angle.

Procedure

1. Turn the workpieces to size.
2. Determine the number of grooves to be cut.
3. Determine the helix angle; see Unit 104.
4. Determine the change gears necessary to produce a helix having a lead of the specified size.
5. Mount the dividing head on the table of the machine. Mount the gears on the respective shafts and studs. (See Unit 104.)
6. Mount a spiral attachment on the nose of the spindle of the miller. (See Fig. 11-30.)
7. Attach a suitable dog; then mount the work between the centers of the dividing head.

8. If necessary, draw a radial line on one end of the workpiece. (See *A*, Fig. 11-163.)

9. Secure a suitable cutter, and mount it in the spiral attachment. Be sure to fasten it securely.

10. Swivel the spiral attachment to the angle desired, and fasten it securely in position.

11. Adjust the sector on the dividing head to include the required number of spaces between the arms; then withdraw the stop-pin.

12. With the cross and longitudinal hand feeds, position the work for the first cut. Check the end of the work with a rule, as in Fig. 11-165.

13. With the vertical feed, raise the table until the cutter comes into contact with the work. Test with a piece of tissue paper placed between the work and the cutter. Then set the graduated collar at zero.

14. Start the machine in reverse, and allow it to travel back until the cutter clears the workpiece. Then raise the table sufficiently to make a cut of the depth required.

Some operators reset the graduated collar at zero after the table has been raised, to facilitate setting the machine for depth of cut for subsequent grooves.

15. Reverse the direction of table travel. When the cutter has advanced far enough to cut its full depth, stop the machine and examine the cut.

16. If it is necessary to change the position of the work with respect to the cutter, reverse the direction of table travel, adjust the table, start the machine, and complete the cut. Use a cutting fluid freely.

17. At the end of the cut, lower the table until the cutter clears the work. Then reverse the direction of travel, and allow the cutter to travel back to the starting point.

18. Index for the next helical cut.

19. Raise the table an amount equal to the amount it was lowered in step 17, engage the longitudinal feed, and proceed as in steps 17 and 18.

20. Continue as in steps 17 through 19 until all helices have been cut.

Test Your Knowledge of Section 11

Unit 87: The Milling Machine

1. Describe the action of a milling cutter in relation to the workpiece on a milling machine.

2. List the three directions in which a milling machine table may be fed or moved.

3. What types of machining operations can be performed on milling machines?

4. For what kinds of milling operations is a dividing head used?

5. What type of milling machine generally is used for hole-machining operations?

6. What is the advantage in performing hole-machining operations on a milling machine?

7. In what kinds of machine shops are knee-and-column milling machines most widely used?

8. For what basic purpose are bed milling machines used?

9. List three kinds of knee-and-column milling machines.

10. Describe how helical milling operations may be performed on a plain milling machine.

11. Describe how vertical milling operations may be performed on a plain milling machine.

12. Explain the distinguishing difference between plain and universal milling machines.

13. What types of feed are available on small, plain milling machines?

14. What types of operations are more readily performed on universal milling machines than on plain machines?

15. What type milling machine generally is more versatile than all other types?

16. What is the distinguishing feature about vertical milling machines?

17. List several common vertical milling operations.

18. List three types of machine tools on which vertical milling operations may be performed.

19. Describe a vertical turret drilling and milling machine, and list several types of operations for which it is used.

20. List four basic factors used in identifying standard knee-and-column milling machines.

21. Upon what factor is the size of a standard knee-and-column milling machine usually based?

22. What type of control device often is used to change the *speed* on milling machines?

23. What type of control device often is used to change the *feed* on milling machines?

24. Explain the nature of rapid power traverse on machines so equipped.

25. List six methods which may be used for holding workpieces on a milling machine.

26. What type of device or accessory is necessary for performing a spiral milling operation on a milling machine?

27. Explain how differences in speed of rotation of the work are provided for in spiral milling operations.

28. Explain the meaning of *lead*, as applied to spiral milling.

29. What range of leads normally is available on universal milling machines?

30. Explain the difference between up milling and down milling.

31. What feature must be provided on machines which are used for down milling?

32. For what types of machines are up-milling feeds generally required?

33. What are the advantages of down-milling feeds on machines where this method of feeding may be used?

34. What probable dangers are involved if down-milling feeds are used on machines not equipped with an anti-backlash device?

35. What is the distinguishing difference in the design of a bed milling machine as compared with the knee-and-column type?

36. What type of milling operations generally are performed on bed milling machines?

37. Describe a planer milling machine and its basic purpose.

38. Describe the type of milling machine which is used for profile milling.

39. List several safety precautions which should be observed in the operation of milling machines.

Unit 88: Milling Machine Attachments

1. For what purpose are quick-change adapters used on milling machines?

2. Explain the features of each of the following vises used on milling machines: (a) plain, (b) swivel, (c) universal.

3. For what purpose are milling arbors, collets, and adapters generally used?

4. For what purposes is a dividing head used on a milling machine?

5. On what types of milling machines can vertical milling attachments be used?

6. Describe a high-speed milling attachment and its uses.

7. Describe a universal spiral milling attachment and its use.

8. Describe a slotting attachment and the kind of operations it is designed to perform.

9. What is the distinguishing difference between a gear-cutting attachment and a dividing head?

10. Describe a circular milling attachment and its use.

11. Describe a rack milling attachment and its use.

Unit 89: Milling Cutters and Holders

1. List three materials which are used for making either milling cutters or the teeth for milling cutters.

2. Describe the general characteristics of high-speed steel milling cutters, in comparison with cemented-carbide cutters.

3. Describe three general types of plain milling cutters, and list a principal use for each.

4. Describe how plain milling cutters are re-sharpened.

5. Describe three kinds of side milling cutters, and indicate an application for each type.

6. Describe how straddle milling is done.

7. For what purposes are metal-slitting saws used?

8. Indicate three types of metal-slitting saws.

9. For what purposes are angular milling cutters used?

10. List several common types of end-milling operations.
11. On what types of milling machines may end-milling cutters be used?
12. List four types of end mills.
13. What type of end mill is often used for cutting slots with a rounded bottom, or for die sinking?
14. Describe face milling cutters, and indicate their principal use.
15. Explain how a T-slot is produced.
16. Describe two kinds of key seat cutters.
17. List several types of form-relieved cutters.
18. Explain how form-relieved cutters are resharpened.
19. What is a fly cutter?
20. Explain how to determine whether a milling cutter is a right- or left-hand cut.
21. Explain how to determine whether a helical cutter has right- or left-hand helical teeth.
22. List four means used for mounting or holding milling cutters in the machine.
23. List three styles of milling arbors, and indicate a principal use for each.
24. What type of taper often is used on milling arbor shanks?
25. How will nicks on the face of spacing collars affect the accuracy of a milling arbor?
26. What damage can result if a milling cutter is not keyed to the arbor during operation?
27. For what purposes are collet adapters used?
28. Describe how a milling arbor with a standard milling taper is removed from the machine spindle.
29. Describe the type of grinding machine which is used to sharpen milling cutters.
30. List several functions of cutting fluids as used for milling.

Unit 90: Determining Cutting Speeds and Feeds for Milling

1. Define the meaning of cutting speed as applied to milling.
2. Explain the relationship between cutting speed and rpm.
3. Explain how the cutting speed for a given milling application is determined or selected.
4. What is meant by the machinability rating for a metal?
5. What general relationship exists between the machinability rating of a given metal and the cutting speed which may be used?
6. List several factors which affect cutting speeds and feeds for milling.
7. List the average recommended cutting speeds for milling several common metals with high-speed steel milling cutters.
8. How do the recommended cutting speeds for carbide milling cutters compare with those for high-speed steel cutters?
9. Calculate the rpm for a $2\frac{3}{4}''$ diameter cutter which is to cut at 90 sfpm.
10. Calculate the rpm for a $\frac{3}{4}''$ diameter end mill which is to cut at 70 sfpm.
11. Calculate the approximate cutting speed for a $1\frac{3}{4}''$ diameter end mill which is operating at 165 rpm.
12. Calculate the approximate cutting speed for a $2\frac{1}{2}''$ diameter milling cutter which is operating at 160 rpm.
13. Define feed as applied to milling operations.
14. In very general terms, what should the feed rate be for milling operations?
15. How is the feed rate determined for manually feeding the work for milling?
16. Explain the operation of a feeding mechanism based on *inches per revolution of the spindle.*
17. Explain the type of relationship which exists between the feed mechanism and the rpm of the cutter when the feed is set in *inches per minute.*
18. Determine the feed rate in inches per minute for machining annealed, high-carbon steel at 60 sfpm, 90 rpm, using a heavy-duty plain milling cutter which is $2\frac{1}{2}''$ in diameter, with 8 teeth, and with 0.004" feed per tooth.
19. Explain the basic differences in depth of cut, rate of feed, and rpm for roughing cuts and finishing cuts for milling.
20. Why is it advisable not to stop the feed on a milling machine before the cut is finished?

Unit 97: The Dividing or Indexing Head and its Operation

1. List several important parts of the dividing-head mechanism.
2. List several kinds of milling operations for which a dividing head is used.
3. State the rule or formula which may be used to determine the number of turns of the index crank required to move the work through one division of any number of equally spaced divisions in a circle.
4. Why are the index plates on a dividing head provided with circles of equally spaced holes, each circle with a different number of holes?
5. Explain how the sector is used on a dividing head.
6. Explain how indexing may be done by degrees with a dividing head.
7. Explain how direct indexing is accomplished with a dividing head.
8. For what purpose is a wide-range dividing head used?

Unit 99: Spur Gears and Gearing

1. For what purpose are gears used?
2. What two types of special machine tools generally are used for mass producing gears?
3. Define the following: gear, pinion, and rack.
4. List five commonly used types of gears.
5. Describe spur gears and the kinds of applications for which they are used.
6. For what principal purpose are bevel gears used?
7. List several advantages of helical gears in comparison with spur gears.
8. List a disadvantage of helical gears in comparison with spur gears.
9. Explain the difference between parallel and crossed helical gears.
10. Describe several advantages of herringbone gears.
11. Describe worm gear mechanisms and their chief uses.
12. Explain the difference in the meaning of the terms pitch diameter and diametral pitch.

13. How many teeth are on a 12-diametral-pitch gear which has a pitch diameter of $6\frac{1}{2}$ inches?
14. Explain how the chordal thickness of a gear tooth is measured.
15. Explain the difference in the circular thickness and the chordal thickness of a gear tooth.
16. List two basic kinds of profiles or forms which are used in gear tooth design.
17. What type of gear tooth design generally is used for gears which are mass produced on gear generating machines?
18. What type of gear tooth design generally is used on gears which are cut on a milling machine with a form-type rotary milling cutter?
19. List four common standard gear-tooth forms.
20. List several advantages of gears which operate with a 20° pressure angle.
21. Calculate the outside diameter for a 12-diametral-pitch spur gear with 32 full-depth teeth.
22. Calculate the whole depth for the gear teeth in item 21 above.
23. Calculate the amount of clearance for the gear in item 21 above.
24. Determine the number of the gear cutter (on a milling machine) to be selected for cutting the gear in item 21 above.

Unit 103: Milling Helices

1. What is a helix?
2. How can one determine whether a helix is right-handed or left-handed?
3. How is the milling of helices accomplished on a plain milling machine?
4. Define the meaning of lead as applied to helices.
5. How are variations in the length of the lead accomplished for work mounted on the dividing head?
6. How is a change in the direction of rotation of the dividing-head spindle accomplished?
7. For what purpose is a *Table of Change Gears, Angles, and Leads* used?
8. Describe how helical milling may be performed on a vertical milling machine.

Unit 104: Change Gears, Angles, and Leads for Helical Milling

1. How are steep helix angles, those beyond the swiveling range of the table, accomplished?
2. How are changes in lead accomplished with the dividing-head mechanism?
3. What pitch generally is used on the lead screw of standard milling machines?
4. List the formula which may be used for determining the change gears required to produce a desired lead with a dividing-head mechanism.
5. Explain the graphic method for determining the angle of a helix.
6. List the formula which may be used for determining the angle of a helix mathematically.

Variety Unlimited — Fine, Coarse, Coated, Solid
(Norton)

Abrasives and Grinding Wheels

Fig. 12-1. Common Types of Tool Grinding Wheels (Norton)

Types of Abrasives and Their Use

An abrasive is a hard and tough substance which has many sharp edges. It is used to cut or wear away materials softer than itself. Abrasives are used as cutting tools or cutting materials in machine shops and in many other areas of the metalworking industry. They are used in several forms which include *grinding wheels* (as shown in Fig. 12-1), *sharpening stones or sticks*, and *coated abrasives*. The latter is cloth or paper with a coating of abrasive grains cemented to its surface. Coated abrasives used in the machine shop usually are in the form of abrasive-coated cloth. The abrasive cloth is used in belt or disc form for machine buffing and grinding, and it is used in sheet or strip form for hand buffing and polishing. *Abrasive grains* (or *powder*) also are used in bulk form for certain polishing and lapping operations.

Abrasives have been used throughout recorded history. Prehistoric man used sand and sandstone as an abrasive to sharpen edge tools. Emery and other types of stone later were used to sharpen metal edge tools. The first abrasive materials were used in their natural form, usually as grains of sand or as a piece of stone.

Properties of Abrasives

Penetration hardness, fracture resistance, and wear resistance are the necessary properties of abrasives. *Penetration hardness* refers to the ability of the abrasive to scratch or cut a softer material. The abrasive must be harder than the material it is to cut.

Fracture resistance refers to the ability of an abrasive material to resist breaking or cracking under load. This resistance should be neither too great nor too little. When an abrasive grain is fractured, sharp edges should appear without loss of the entire grain. Fracture of the grain should occur after the original point has started to dull, but before it becomes too dull. Excessive resistance to fracture also causes excessive pressure and heat while grinding.

Wear resistance refers to the ability of the abrasive grain to maintain sharpness and resist wearing rapidly. Wear resistance largely is related to penetration hardness, but not entirely so. It also is related to the chemical or solubility effect of the abrasive in relation to the work being ground. In several instances, a harder abrasive material may dull faster than a softer one when grinding the same piece of work. For example, silicon-carbide abrasive is harder than aluminum oxide, yet it dulls more rapidly on hardened steel. Therefore, it appears that the chemical nature of the abrasive in relation to the work being ground affects the wear resistance of the abrasive.

Mohs Hardness Scale: The *hardness* of abrasives often is rated according to the *Mohs hardness scale*. This is an older method for rating the hardness of various minerals. The scale ranges from a rating of No. 1 for talc to No. 10 for diamond, the hardest substance known. Except for diamond, the natural abrasives rank below 9, and most artificial abrasives above 9. The following are the approximate Mohs hardness ratings for natural abrasives: Crocus, 6.0; flint,

6.9; garnet, 7.5 to 8.5; emery, 8.5 to 9.0. In the measurement of abrasives, the range from 9 to 10 actually is as broad and significant as the whole range from 1 to 9.

Knoop Hardness Value: A more recent method, developed by the National Bureau of Standards, used for indicating the hardness of an abrasive material and certain other materials is the *Knoop hardness value*. The material is tested with a microhardness tester, which utilizes a principle similar to that employed with the Rockwell hardness tester for measuring the hardness of metals. Under a certain load, the tester presses a diamond point into the material being tested. The depth of the impression is indicated by a number value. As with the Mohs system, the higher the number, the harder the material. However, the Knoop number more clearly indicates the relative difference in the hardness of various abrasive materials. The hardness values (100-gram load) of several abrasives and other materials ground by abrasives are indicated in Table 13.

Natural Abrasives

Abrasives are grouped in two broad classifications — natural abrasives and artificial or manufactured abrasives. *Natural abrasives* are those which are used as derived from nature.

Table 13
Relative Hardness Values of Abrasives and Other Materials

	Mohs' Scale	Knoop Scale
Common Glass (depending on composition)		300-500
Hard Steel, Rockwell C. 60.5		740
Quartz	7	820
Synthetic Blue Spinel		1270
Topaz	8	1350
Garnet		1350
Cemented Carbides		1400-1800
Tungsten Carbide (not cemented)		1880
Aluminum Oxide (Alundum) and Corundum	9	2000
Silicon Carbide (Crystolon)		2500
Boron Carbide (Norbide)		2800
Diamond (mined or manufactured)	10	greater than 7000

(Courtesy Norton Co.)

In the past, they were used widely in both woodworking and metalworking, but they are being replaced rapidly by artificial abrasives. Those natural abrasives still used in industry include flint, garnet, emery, crocus, and diamond. Except for diamond, the natural abrasives are relatively soft in comparison with artificial abrasives. Flint and garnet are used in the form of coated abrasives in the woodworking industry. Although artificial abrasives largely have replaced the natural abrasives in the metalworking industry, emery, crocus, and diamond still are used somewhat. For this reason, their properties and uses should be understood.

Crocus: Crocus is a reddish-brown oxide of iron and may be natural or synthetic. It is used in very fine powder form as a rouge, or as a coating on cloth known as crocus cloth. Crocus cloth or rouge is used for polishing corroded metals or rare metals where a minimum of base metal is to be removed.

Emery: Emery is one of the oldest natural abrasives used in the metalworking industry. It is black and is composed largely of a combination of corundum and iron oxide. Some emery deposits have a larger percentage of corundum than others, thus resulting in a better abrasive material. Corundum is aluminum oxide, Al_2O_3. Prized gems such as ruby and emerald are the purest forms of corundum found in nature. Emery used for abrasives usually is composed of about 60% corundum and 40% iron oxide and other impurities. Emery is used in making the coated abrasive, emery cloth. Although emery cloth still is manufactured in four grades of fineness, artificial abrasives rapidly are replacing it for use in buffing and polishing metals. Emery abrasive grains are not as sharp nor as hard as artificial abrasive grains; hence they are slower cutting.

Diamond: Diamond, the hardest material known, is used in the form of grains bonded together to form an abrasive stick or grinding wheel. A diamond cluster abrasive stick or nib is used to cut or true other softer grinding wheels. Diamond grinding wheels are used to grind very hard materials such as cemented carbide cutting tools, ceramic cutting tools, glass, stone, and other types of ceramic materials. The diamonds used for making grinding wheels are industrial diamonds in the form of chips. They are relatively inexpensive when compared with the large, clear diamonds used for jewelry. Synthetic or man-made industrial diamonds are now being manufactured, and they serve about as well as natural diamonds.

Artificial Abrasives

Artificial abrasives are man-made. They also are known as manufactured or synthetic abrasives. The commonly used artificial abrasives include *silicon carbide, aluminum oxide,* and *boron carbide.* The manufactured abrasives are harder and have greater impact toughness than any of the natural abrasives except diamond.

Silicon Carbide: The first artificial abrasive developed in the United States was crystalline silicon carbide. It was discovered by Dr. Edward G. Acheson about 1891. He discovered the new abrasive material, which consisted of brilliant crystals of small size, while searching for a way to make artificial diamonds or other materials of great hardness. The new crystalline material was made by fusing silica sand and coke in a small electric furnace at extremely high temperatures. The crystals of silicon carbide were hard enough to cut glass and scratch diamonds.

During this period, electric furnaces were not highly developed, and available electricity was limited. Therefore, silicon carbide proved to be very expensive. Its early use was limited to fine abrasive grains used for polishing diamonds and other valuable gems. It was almost as costly as the materials on which it was used.

After 1900, improved methods of production made silicon carbide available for wide use, and at low cost. Large electric furnaces were developed for its production. The principal ingredients in silicon carbide are silica sand, which contains the silicon, and coke, which provides the carbon. A small amount of sawdust is added to make the mixture porous.

Properties: The properties of silicon carbide depend upon its purity in manufacture. Its

hardness and sharpness are ideal. Its Knoop hardness value is approximately 2500, in comparison with diamond rated at approximately 7000. However, silicon carbide generally is considered brittle, as compared with aluminum oxide, and its grain fracturing properties limit its use to grinding specific materials. It is hard enough to cut aluminum-oxide abrasive materials.

Uses: Silicon carbide abrasives are used for grinding wheels, abrasive stones or sticks, and coated abrasives. The grinding wheels are used for materials of low-tensile strength, including: cast iron, bronze, aluminum, copper, tungsten carbide, rubber, glass, marble, ceramics, pottery, plastics, magnesium, and fiber.

Aluminum Oxide: About 1897, several years after silicon carbide was developed, aluminum oxide was discovered. Charles P. Jacobs, an engineer in the laboratories of the Ampere Electro-Chemical Company at Ampere, New Jersey, produced aluminum oxide. He was conducting experiments in an effort to create a better grade of abrasive material. He heated bauxite ore (whose chief ingredient is aluminum oxide) to extremely high temperatures in an electric furnace. At these temperatures, he was able to extract the impurities from the ore.

After 1900, improved methods of production and greater availability of electric power also made aluminum oxide available at low cost as an artificial abrasive. The principal ingredient used in manufacturing aluminum oxide is bauxite ore, the same material from which metallic aluminum is derived. The bauxite ore is purified to crystalline form by heating to extremely high temperatures in large electric furnaces. Greater toughness is imparted to the aluminum oxide by adding titanium.

Properties: The properties of aluminum oxide are dependent on its purity in manufacture. Aluminum oxide of 99% purity commonly is available with modern manufacturing methods. Since the addition of titanium imparts varying degrees of toughness, several types of aluminum oxide are available with slightly varying characteristics.

Fig. 12-2. Using Norbide® (Boron Carbide) Dressing Stick to Dress Grinding Wheel (Norton)

Aluminum oxide is not as hard as silicon carbide. The Knoop hardness value of a typical aluminum oxide material is 2000, in comparison with silicon carbide at 2500 or diamond at approximately 7000. However, aluminum oxide generally is considered tougher and more shock resistant than silicon carbide.

Uses: Aluminum oxide abrasives are used for grinding wheels, abrasive sticks and sharpening stones, and coated abrasives. The grinding wheels, because of their toughness, shock resistance, and grain fracturing properties, are used for grinding materials of high-tensile strength, including: carbon steels, alloy steels, soft or hard steels, wrought iron, malleable iron, and tough bronze. Approximately 75 percent of all grinding wheels used today are manufactured from aluminum oxide.

Boron Carbide: A third kind of artificial abrasive material is boron carbide. It is known by the trade name "Norbide," produced by the Norton Company. A typical Knoop hardness value of boron carbide is 2800, which is harder than silicon carbide, but not as hard as diamond. It is produced from coke and boric acid at tremendously high temperatures in an electric furnace.

Norbide may be used in stick form to dress grinding wheels 10″ in diameter or smaller, Fig. 12-2. It also may be used in powder form in place of diamond dust for many lapping operations on very hard materials. It may be used for lapping hardened dies and cemented-tungsten-carbide materials. Norbide is very resistant to hard wear. It may be used in solid form for such items as linings for nozzles used in high-pressure sandblasting.

UNIT

111   Grinding Wheels and Their Selection

Grinding wheels are made of thousands of crushed abrasive grains held together by an appropriate substance called a *bond*. Between the abrasive and the bonding material are pores or air spaces. These spaces provide clearance for chips removed in the grinding process, and they minimize wheel loading.

Cutting Action of a Grinding Wheel

Actually, each abrasive grain in a grinding wheel is a cutting tool. Each has sharp cutting edges or corners which scratch or cut off tiny particles from the metal being ground. Under a magnifying glass, the small particles appear as metal chips similar to chips removed by a

410

shaper or lathe tool, Fig. 12-6. Thus a grinding wheel, with many thousands of exposed abrasive grains, each acting as a miniature cutting tool, is able to remove metal as it revolves rapidly. Because of the heat created by the speed of the revolving wheel, the metal chips appear as sparks which are readily visible.

On *finish-grinding* operations, grinding wheels remove metal relatively slowly in comparison with other cutting tools. Grinding operations such as surface grinding, cylindrical grinding, and tool grinding usually have been considered finish-machining operations. Finish grinding usually follows other rough-machining operations, and it generally involves machining to very close tolerances.

On *abrasive-machining* operations, metal is removed more rapidly than on finish-grinding operations. During recent years, this type of machining has come into wider use. The term *abrasive machining* is used for grinding applications which involve the removal of a relatively large amount of metal, usually $\frac{1}{16}''$ or more in depth. Both grinding wheels and coated abrasives are used. Abrasive machining involves machining castings, forgings, weldments, and bar stock to commercial tolerance and finish without previous machining operations. See Figs. 12-7 and 12-8. It frequently is used for grinding applications which may be

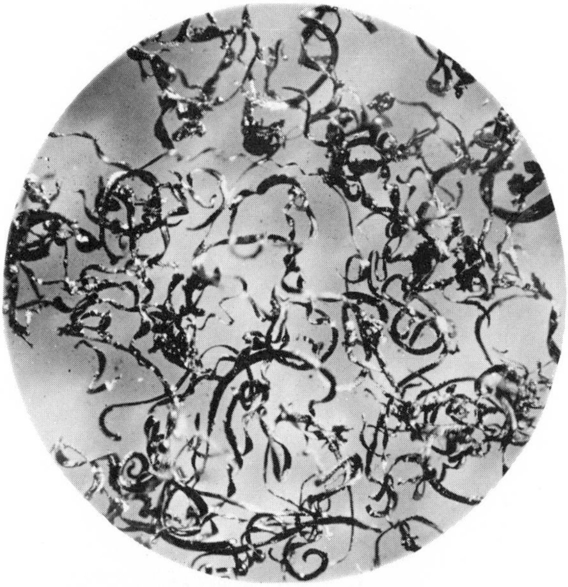

machined more profitably by grinding than by other machining methods.

The quality of the work achieved in grinding operations may be controlled to a large extent by selecting a proper grinding wheel. As a grinding wheel is used, the cutting edges of the abrasive grains become dulled. When this happens, the grinding pressure should cause these dull edges to break off, thus exposing new sharp edges without breaking off the entire grain. Once the grain has been broken down sufficiently, the grinding pressure should cause the bonding material to re-

Fig. 12-7. Abrasive Machining a Worm Screw from a Solid Piece (Norton)

Fig. 12-8. Abrasive Machining on a Rotary Surface Grinder (Norton)

Fig. 12-6. Magnified View of Metal Chips Produced by Abrasive Wheel (Norton)

411

lease the remaining portion of the grain, thereby exposing a new, sharp grain. This process should continue repeatedly when the right grinding wheel is selected for the job.

Classification of Grinding Wheels

Grinding wheels are classified according to their size and shape, type of abrasive used, grain size, type of bond, grade or hardness, and structure.

Size and Shape: The size of a grinding wheel is given in terms of its diameter in inches, the diameter of the spindle hole or opening at the center, and the width of the face. Grinding wheels are manufactured in many different shapes and sizes for special applications. However, the most frequently used types are manufactured in standard wheel shapes.

Manufacturers have adopted standard *type-number* designations for most of the basic shapes for grinding wheels. Wheels of each basic shape are manufactured in standard dimensional sizes. Cross-sectional views of several basic shapes most commonly used in tool-room and cylindrical grinding are shown in Fig. 12-9.

Grinding wheel faces may be shaped with various contours for grinding contoured surfaces on cutting tools such as milling cutters, taps, and special tools. Grinding wheels are manufactured with standard wheel faces which are designated by letters. Some typical, standard face shapes are illustrated in Fig. 12-10. When no specific face is specified for straight wheels, the straight *A* wheel face usually is furnished by the manufacturer.

Kinds of Abrasives

The most common types of abrasive used in grinding wheels are aluminum oxide and silicon carbide. Industrial diamond also is used in making grinding wheels.

Aluminum Oxide: Aluminum oxide grains or crystals, although not the hardest artificial abrasive, are tough and usually are preferred for grinding materials of high-tensile strength. They are used to grind carbon steels, alloy steels, soft or hard steels, cast-alloy cutting tools, wrought iron, and tough bronze. Aluminum oxide grinding wheels are sold by various manufacturers under such trade names as the following:

Abrasive Company . . . . Borolon
Carborundum Company . . . . Aloxite
Exolon Company . . . . Exolon
General Abrasive Company . . . . Lionite
Norton Company . . . . Alundum

Silicon Carbide: Silicon carbide abrasive grains are harder and generally are considered more brittle than aluminum oxide. The grain fracturing characteristics of silicon carbide are different than those for aluminum oxide. Silicon carbide grinding wheels are used to grind materials that are easily penetrated, such as copper, aluminum, rubber, plastics, magnesium, and fiber; they also are used to grind hard materials of low-tensile strength, such as cast iron, cast bronze, glass, marble, ceramics, and pottery. Cemented-tungsten-carbide cutting tools must be ground on either silicon carbide or diamond grinding wheels. Silicon carbide grinding wheels sold by manufacturers under various trade names are:

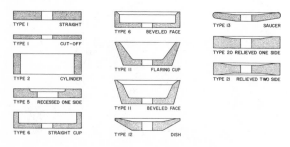

Fig. 12-9. Some Standard Grinding Wheel Shapes with Type-Number Designations

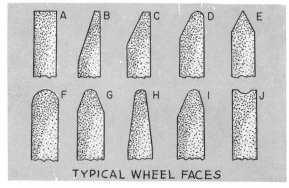

Fig. 12-10. Typical Standard Wheel Faces

Carborundum Company .....Carborundum
Exolon Company ....Carbolon
General Abrasive Company ......Carbonite
Norton Company ....Crystolon

Grain Sizes

Grain refers to the size of the particles of abrasive used in the manufacture of the grinding wheel. Abrasive materials, as they come from the electric furnace, are in large chunks. They then are crushed into fine particles called grains. These are graded according to size by allowing them to pass through a series of screens. The grain size is indicated by a number which refers to the screen size used. For example, a 36-grain wheel is one made of particles of abrasive which just pass through a 36-mesh screen, but which will be retained on a 46-mesh screen, the next finer screen .(A 36-mesh screen has 36 openings per lineal inch, or 1296 openings per square inch. See Fig. 12-11.) Grain numbers are sometimes called grit numbers.

Grains Available: Grain sizes vary from 10 to 600 and are classified in the following general relative ratings:

Coarse: 10, 12, 14, 16, 20, 24
Medium: 30, 36, 46, 54, 60
Fine: 70, 80, 90, 100, 120, 150, 180
Very fine: 220, 240, 280, 320, 400, 500, 600

Uses of Various Grits: *Fine-grain* wheels are used on small-diameter work, to produce small fillets or for fine finishes. Fine wheels also are preferred for grinding hard materials, since they have more cutting edges and, therefore, cut faster than coarse-grain wheels. See *A*, Fig. 12-12. Because a coarse-grain wheel has fewer grains, the grains cannot penetrate the hard material deeply without burning, and so the coarse wheel does not cut as rapidly on hard materials (*B*, Fig. 12-12).

Coarse-grain wheels are used for rapid metal removal on softer materials (*C*, Fig. 12-12). Coarse wheels also are used for grinding large workpieces.

The grain size selected should be determined by the type of material to be ground, the finish desired, and the amount of metal to be re-

Fig. 12-11. Silk Screen Used for Separating Abrasive Grain, a 20-Mesh, Enlarged Approximately Nine Times (Norton)

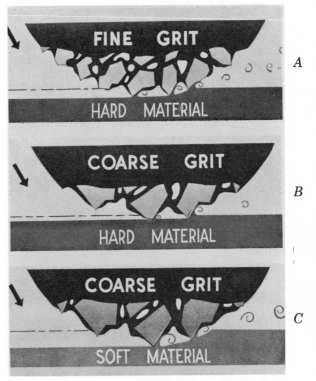

Fig. 12-12. Comparison of Grain Size and Rate of Metal Removal with Grinding Wheels (Norton)

413

moved. Each grain is a cutting tool. Collectively they form the grinding wheel which removes small metal chips in grinding operations.

Bonding Materials: The bond is the material which holds the abrasive grains together to form the grinding wheel. As the grains get dull, pressure on the wheel causes the bond to break down and release the dull grains, thus exposing new sharp grains. The bond holds the individual grain in much the same manner in which a toolholder holds a tool bit, Fig. 12-13. There are five basic types

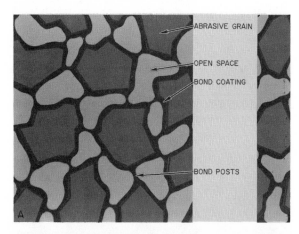

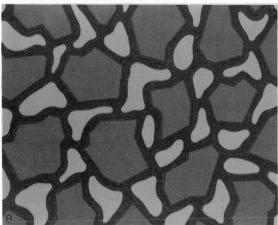

Fig. 12-13. Kind and Amount of Bonding Material Affects Hardness or Grade of Grinding Wheel (Norton)
(A) Abrasive grains with light bond coatings and weak bond posts, as in a relatively soft-grade wheel. (B) Similar grains, but with heavier bond coating and thicker, stronger bond posts, as in a harder-grade wheel.

of bonds used in grinding wheels: vitrified, silicate, rubber, shellac, and resinoid. Additional modifications of these five materials are also produced by some manufacturers.

Vitrified: The vitrified bond is the most commonly used bond for grinding wheels. Approximately 75% of all wheels are made with vitrified or a modified vitrified bond. This bond is preferred for the general run of grinding. Vitrified-bonded wheels are strong, porous, and not affected by rapid changes in temperature. Also, they are not affected by oils, acid, or water. These wheels are uniform in structure, free from hard spots, and hold their form well. The bond is formed when special clays are mixed with abrasive grains and heated to high temperatures; the mixture forms a molten glass which cements the grains together as it cools.

Silicate: Wheels bonded with silicate (silicate of soda) are known as silicate- or semi-vitrified-bonded wheels. This is a common type of wheel, but not recommended generally for cylindrical grinding. Silicate-bonded wheels release the grains more readily than vitrified bond. Hence, the wheel is softer and it breaks down more readily, thereby exposing new sharp grains. Silicate-bonded wheels are used for grinding edge tools, drills, reamers, milling cutters, and similar tools.

Fig. 12-14. Typical Abrasive Cutoff Wheels (Norton)
The first has a shellac bond; the others, a resinoid or rubber bond.

Rubber: Wheels which are rubber bonded are elastic in nature, very strong, resilient, and shock resistant. This bond may be used for very thin wheels, such as cutoff wheels for abrasive cutoff machines, Fig. 12-14. Cutoff wheels are used for cutting pipe, angle iron, or bar stock, Fig. 12-15. For safety, rubber bond is used for high-speed grinding. It also produces a very good finish.

Shellac: Wheels with a shellac bond are also elastic in nature, resilient, and cool cutting. They produce a very fine finish. Hence, they are used to grind such items as mill rolls, camshafts, and fine cutlery. See Fig. 12-16.

Resinoid: Wheels with a resinoid bond have high strength and mechanical shock resistance. Resinoid bond is used for large, heavy-duty, high-speed wheels. They may be operated at speeds higher than those recommended for vitrified wheels. They are used for rough grinding operations involving rapid stock removal, or for cutoff wheels. Resinoid wheels frequently are used in foundries and steel mills for snagging castings and for cleaning steel billets. (*Snagging* means to grind off the rough spots or surplus metal.)

Grades

Wheels from which the grit or abrasive is readily torn are termed *soft grade*. Conversely, wheels that steadfastly retain the abrasive over a considerable period of use are called *hard grade*.

Hard-grade wheels generally are used for grinding soft metals such as mild steel; soft-grade wheels generally are used for grinding hard metals such as high-carbon steel.

It should be remembered that the term *hard* as used with respect to grinding wheels has no relationship to the hardness of the abrasive, but rather to the ease or difficulty with which the worn particles of the abrasive are torn from the face of the wheel. With a given bond material, it is the amount of bond which determines the hardness or softness of the wheel — the more bond material, the harder the wheel. See Fig. 12-13.

The grade of grinding wheels is designated by letters of the alphabet, *A* being the softest and *Z* the hardest, Table 14.

Structures

The structure of a grinding wheel refers to the spacing between the grains, or the density of the wheel. Grains which are very closely spaced are more dense or *close*, while grains which are wider apart are less dense or *open*. See Fig. 12-13.

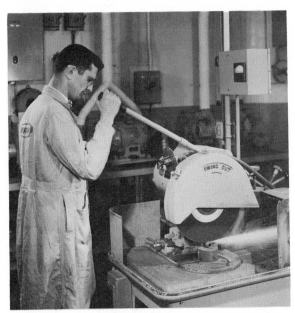

Fig. 12-15. Cutting Pipe with an Abrasive Cutoff Wheel
(Norton)

Fig. 12-16. Shellac-Bonded Wheel Used for Grinding a Mill Roll (Norton)

The structure of a wheel often is rated by manufacturers with numbers from 1 (dense) to 15 (open). The rate of metal removal usually is greater for open-grain wheels than for close-grain wheels. However, those with close grains usually produce a finer finish.

Grinding Wheel Markings

In 1944, the Grinding Wheel Manufacturers' Association approved a standard system for marking grinding wheels, Table 14. Then this system (with minor modifications) was approved by the American Standards Association in 1958 (ASA B5.17-1958). The system applies to bonded abrasives other than grinding wheels, including sticks, hones, and rubs. However, it does not apply to sharpening stones or diamond wheels. Most manufacturers use this system for identification markings on grinding wheels.

The standard system for marking wheels includes six parts in sequence, as listed across the top of Table 14. Note that the prefix to item one in the sequence is optional for each manufacturer. For example, where several types of a given abrasive are available, such as several variations of aluminum oxide, the pre-

fix number indicates the exact type of aluminum oxide. Also note that items four and six in the sequence are optional with the manufacturer; item six is the manufacturer's record concerning specific bonds.

The marking on the grinding wheel indicated in Table 14 is 32A46-H8VBE. This marking indicates that the abrasive is (Norton) type 32 Alundum; with a 46 medium grain size; with H grade (which is rated between soft and medium); structure 8 (middle density); bond type V (which is vitrified); and BE represents the manufacturer's mark for the specific type of vitrified bond. A grinding wheel of this type (or similar and equal) will do a good job in surface-grinding hardened carbon tool steel.

Several manufacturers may use the same number to identify a given type of grinding wheel, but this does not mean that all of the wheels so identified will produce equal results or equivalent grinding action. The physical properties of the materials used may vary with different manufacturers.

Grinding Wheel Speeds

Grinding wheels should be operated at cutting speeds as near as possible to those recommended by the manufacturer of the wheel.

Table 14
Standard Marking System for Grinding Wheels
(Example is a Typical Marking: 32A46—H8VBE)

(Prefix)	(1) Kind of Abrasive	(2) Grain Size		(3) Grade or Hardness		(4) Structure		(5) Bond Type	(6) Manufacturer's Record
32	A	46		— H		8		V	BE
Manufacturer's Symbol Indicating Exact Kind of Abrasive	A Aluminum Oxide C Silicon Carbide	(Coarse) 10 12 14 15 20 24 (Medium) 30 36 46 54 60	(Fine) 70 70 90 100 120 150 180 (Very Fine) 220 240 280 320 400 500 600	Soft to Hard A Soft B C D E F G H I J K L M	N O P Q R S T U V W X Y Z Hard	Dense to Open 1 Dense 2 3 4 5 6 7 8	9 10 11 12 13 14 15 Open	V Vitrified S Silicate R Rubber B Resinoid E Shellac O Oxychloride	Manufacturer's Private Marking To Identify Wheel. May be a Letter or Number or Both to Designate Modification of Bond or Wheel Characteristics.
(Use Is Optional)						(Use Is Optional)			(Use Is Optional)

When a wheel is recommended for a particular grinding operation, it is assumed that it will be used at approximately the recommended cutting speed. *Cutting speed* refers to the speed at which the circumference (the cutting face) of the wheel is traveling in *sfpm* (surface feet per minute). The cutting speed of a wheel is increased or decreased by increasing or decreasing the *rpm* of the grinding wheel spindle. For methods of calculating the cutting speed or rpm for grinding, see Unit 121.

The rpm of the wheel spindle may or may not be adjustable, depending on the type of grinding machine used. Bench grinders and floor-model grinders used for offhand grinding generally cannot be adjusted; on these grinders, the wheel usually is mounted on the motor spindle. On some cylindrical grinders, tool grinders, and surface grinders, the rpm of the wheel can be varied through the use of step pulleys or a variable-speed mechanism.

The maximum speed at which a wheel should be operated is indicated on the wheel. This speed should never be exceeded. For example, a wheel designed for a maximum speed of 1800 rpm should not be used on a grinding machine which has a spindle speed of 3600 rpm. When used at speeds above those recommended, a grinding wheel may fly apart, thus causing serious injury to the operator.

The following are general recommended cutting speeds in sfpm: general offhand grinding with vitrified-bonded wheels, 5000 to 6000; surface grinding, 4000 to 6500; tool and cutter grinding, 4500 to 6000; and cylindrical grinding, 5500 to 6500. Hence, an average speed of about 5000 sfpm is recommended.

Specific cutting speeds to be used with different types of grinding wheels on various grinding applications are available in standard handbooks for machinists.

Diamond Grinding Wheels

Diamond grinding wheels are in a class by themselves. They are used to grind cemented-tungsten-carbide cutting tools, ceramic-oxide cutting tools, wear-resistant die steel, ceramics, glass, granite, marble, and jewels. See Fig. 12-17.

Diamond grinding wheels are made of fine particles or grains of natural or manufactured diamond, which are held together with a bonding material. The diamond particles are graded in grain sizes ranging from 36 to 500. Wheels with 100-grain size often are used for rough grinding, 220 for finish grinding, and 150 for combination rough and finish grinding. For fine lapping operations, diamond abrasive in bulk form as fine as 2000-grain size is available.

Diamond wheels usually are made of a special composition material to which a layer of abrasive mixture is applied on the cutting surface. The mixture is made of diamond grains and bonding materials (either metal, resinoid, or vitrified). The abrasive layer is available in thicknesses from $\frac{1}{32}$" to $\frac{1}{4}$"; it also is available in several different concentrations or proportions of diamond to bonding material — low, medium, and high. In addition, numerous grades of hardness are manufactured and are indicated by letters of the alphabet.

The identification marking methods used for diamond grinding wheels are different from those used for aluminum-oxide and silicon-carbide wheels. At the present time, there is no standard system used by all manufacturers of diamond grinding wheels. However, one somewhat similar to the system used for aluminum-oxide and silicon-carbide wheels has been developed by the Norton Company, and it is being adopted by several other manufacturers of diamond wheels. See Fig. 12-18.

Fig. 12-17. Commonly Used Shapes of Diamond Wheels for Carbide Grinding (Norton)

Since diamond grinding wheels have a relatively high initial cost, care must be taken in selecting and using them. Cutting speeds from 4500 to 6000 sfpm usually should be used. A liberal supply of cutting fluid also may be used. The manufacturer's recommendations should be carefully followed. Several manufacturers of diamond wheels supply literature without cost concerning the selection, care, and use of their wheels. Recommendations concerning the selection of diamond grinding wheels for particular job applications are also available in standard handbooks for machinists.

Selecting and Using Wheels

The following factors must be taken into consideration in recommending and selecting a wheel for a particular job:

1. Type of grinding operation: offhand grinding, surface grinding, tool grinding, cylindrical grinding, internal grinding, etc.
2. Material to be ground.
3. Type of abrasive and bond to be used.
4. Amount of stock to be removed.
5. Finish required.
6. Area of wheel in contact with work: a wide wheel face may require a soft-grade wheel.
7. Wheel speed.

8. Work speed: for surface grinding and cylindrical grinding.
9. Whether grinding is wet or dry.
10. Machine condition: capacity and rigidity.
11. Abrasive grain size, grade, and structure.

Recommended grinding wheels for use on a number of basic grinding applications are indicated in Table 15. Recommendations for other grinding applications are available in standard handbooks for machinists and from manufacturers.

Ordering a Grinding Wheel: In ordering a grinding wheel, one may use the standard identification number to specify the type of abrasive, grain size, grade, structure, and specific bond type. In addition, the following specifications must be indicated: wheel type, wheel size (including diameter and width of face), type of face, diameter of hole or opening at the center, and the maximum rpm of the wheel.

Precautions in Using Wheels:

1. The grinding machine should be rigid, in order to prevent vibration or chatter.
2. Spindle bearings on the grinding machine should be adjusted properly, in order to prevent vibration and chatter.
3. Wheels always should be mounted with proper cardboard or blotting paper discs

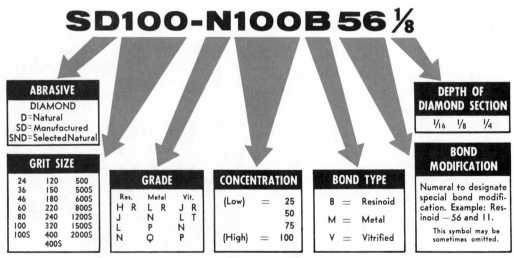

Fig. 12-18. Marking Chart for Diamond Wheels and Hones (©Norton)
Hand hones omit the grade designation.

Table 15
Grinding Wheel Selection and Application

Suitable For	Wheel Material	Grain	Grade
External Cylindrical Grinding			
	Aluminox	2946	L
Good all-around wheels;	Alundum	3836	L
best adapted to soft steel	Aloxite	401	N
Hardened steel	Aluminox or Alundum	46	K
Soft steel of small diam.	Aluminox or Alundum	36	M[1]
Reamers, drills and general tool work	Aluminox or Alundum	80	K
Hard steel, dry grinding	Aluminox or Alundum	100	I
Cast iron and bronze	Crystolon	45	L
Facing Shoulders			
Ordinary work	Aluminox or Alundum	60	H or I
Fine finish	Aluminox or Alundum	80	I[1]
Surface Grinding			
	Alundum or Aluminox	46	H
Hardened steel	Alundum or Aluminox	46	G[2]
	Alundum or Aluminox	60	F[2]
Hardened high-speed steel or very thin	Aloxite	367	U
pieces of hardened carbon steel	Alundum or Aluminox	46	G
Cast iron	Carborundum or	36	M
	Crystolon	36	J
Disk Grinding			
Thick pieces, wet grinding	Aluminox or Alundum	30	K
Thin pieces, wet grinding	Aluminox or Alundum	30	J
High-speed steel, dry grinding	Aluminox or Alundum	60 or 80	H or I
Washers and similar pieces	Aluminox or Alundum	60	I
Internal Cylindrical Grinding			
Good all-around wheel	Aluminox or Alundum	46	2[1] I[1]
Roughing hardened steel	Aluminox or Alundum	46	J or K
Finishing hardened steel	Aluminox or Alundum	120	J or K
Ordinary finish without roughing	Aluminox or Alundum	80 & 90	J or K
Roughing brass	Crystolon	36	H or I
Finishing brass	Crystolon	80	H
Automobile cylinders	Crystolon	46	K
Automobile cylinders	Carborundum	36	M to P
Automobile cylinders, roughing or fair finish	Carbolite	36	H or I
Automobile cylinders, fine finish	Carbolite	60	H
Sharpening Carbon-Steel Cutters, Dry Grinding			
Milling cutters	Aluminox or Alundum	46 or 60	I
Formed and gear cutters	Aluminox or Alundum		
Sharpening High-Speed Steel Cutters, Dry Grinding			
Milling cutters	Aluminox or Alundum	46 or 60	I
Formed and gear cutters	Aluminox or Alundum		
Sharpening High-Speed Steel Cutters, Wet Grinding			
Milling and gear cutters	Aluminox or Alundum	46	I
Sharpening Carbon-Steel Cutters, Wet Grinding			
Formed cutters	Alundum	46	J
Tungsten-Carbide Grinding			
Tool grinding			
Roughing	Green Crystolon	60	I
Finishing	Green Grit Carborundum	80 or 100	S
Roughing	Diamond Grit	100	
Finishing	Diamond Grit	150	

(Courtesy, Brown & Sharpe Manufacturing Co.)   [1]Elastic Wheel   [2]Silicate Wheel

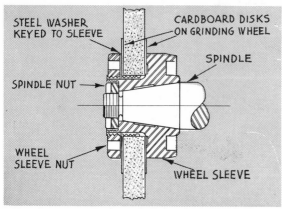

Fig. 12-19. Cross Section of Wheel Mounted on Arbor

between the wheel and properly relieved steel flanges or washers, Fig. 12-19.

4. Wheels should be mounted with the spindle nut fastened snuggly; if the nut is too tight, the wheel may crack.
5. Sound the wheel before installing it, in order to test for cracks. The wheel will ring when struck very lightly with a metallic object. A dull thud will be heard if the wheel is cracked.
6. The wheel should not be forced on the machine spindle. If the wheel is too tight, scrape the inside of the wheel bushing lightly and evenly all around until it will just slide on.
7. A new grinding wheel should be allowed to run at full speed, with the operator standing to one side, before it is used.
8. *Wheel glazing* is indicated by a smooth, glass-like appearance. It is caused when the abrasive grains wear too much before being released. This condition may be corrected by using a wheel of softer grade.
9. *Wheel loading* is caused by grinding the wrong material with the wheel or by using too heavy a grinding action. The wheel must be cleaned with a wheel dressing tool, as explained in Unit 28.
10. The wheel must be kept true and in balance as shown in Unit 115.

UNIT 112 — Coated Abrasives

Fig. 12-20. Variety of Commonly Used Coated Abrasives (Norton)

A coated abrasive is composed of a flexible backing material to which abrasive grains are glued or cemented. The backing materials include paper, cloth, fiber, or a combination of these materials. The abrasive materials include flint, garnet, emery, aluminum oxide, silicon carbide, and crocus.

The coated abrasives used in the metalworking industry include emery, aluminum oxide, silicon carbide, and crocus. For information concerning the properties of these materials, see Unit 110. Emery rapidly is being replaced by aluminum oxide and silicon carbide.

Coated abrasives used for metalworking and other industrial jobs are available in the form of belts, rolls, sheets, discs, spiral points, and cones. See Fig. 12-20. Sheets usually are used for hand buffing and polishing, while the other forms are used for machine grinding and buffing or polishing.

Selecting Coated Abrasives

Various coated abrasives differ in the following characteristics: the abrasive material, the backing material, the bonding material, the method of coating, and the size of the grains. Each of these factors must be considered in selecting and purchasing the type to be used.

Abrasive Materials: The type of abrasive selected is determined by the type of material to be buffed, the amount of material to be removed, and the quality of finish desired. *Silicon carbide* abrasive is used on metals of low-tensile strength, such as cast iron, aluminum, brass, and copper; it also is used on plastics, glass, and marble.

Aluminum oxide abrasive is used on metals of high-tensile strength, such as carbon steel, alloy steel, stainless steel, and tough bronze. When considerable material is to be removed and a fine finish is desired, the material is buffed with several grades of abrasive — from coarse to medium to fine. *Crocus cloth* is made with a very fine crocus powder. It is used for polishing corroded metals or rare metals where a minimum of base metal is to be removed.

Backing Materials: The backing materials used for coated abrasives include paper, cloth, fiber, or various combinations of these materials. *Paper backing* is used largely for hand applications on woodwork and for finishing. Cloth or fiber is used as backing on coated abrasives used in metalworking and for industrial machine buffing and polishing applications on many other materials.

The *cloth backing* used for coated abrasives is of two types, one lightweight and the other heavier. The lightweight cloth, called *jean*, is more flexible. On the other hand, the heavier-weight cloth, called *drill*, is more stretch resistant, and therefore usually is used for machine buffing or grinding with belt or disc machines. *Fiber backing* is strong and durable, and it is used for tough disc applications.

Bonding Materials: Several types of bonding or adhesive materials are used on coated abrasives to hold the grain particles to the backing. Some are for dry buffing only, while others may be used for either wet or dry buffing. *Hide glue* is used as a bond for dry, light, hand or mechanical buffing. *Synthetic resins* are used for waterproof cloth and for wet belt grinding and buffing. Various bonding materials which are modifications or combinations of glue, resin, and varnish also are used for coated abrasives. These materials add toughness, heat resistance, and moisture resistance to the abrasive cloth or belt.

Types of Coating: Coatings on coated abrasives are of two basic types — open coating and closed coating. With an *open coating*, part of the backing surface is not covered with abrasive grains, thus leaving open space which resists filling or clogging when used for buffing certain materials. With a *closed coating*, all of the backing surface is covered. Closed coating is used for severe cutting operations which involve a high rate of stock removal. Special heavy-duty coatings of adhesive and abrasive grain also are available for severe grinding operations.

Grain Sizes: The system used for designating abrasive grain sizes for coated abrasives is essentially the same as that used for grinding wheels. However, since coated abrasives have more of the grain exposed, the relative rating for coarseness is different. The following abrasive grain sizes, listed according to relative coarseness, are used for coated abrasives:

Extra coarse: 12, 16, 20, 24, 30, 36
Coarse: 40, 50
Medium: 60, 80, 100
Fine: 120, 150, 180
Extra fine: 220, 240, 280, 320, 360, 400, 500, 600

Forms Available: Coated abrasive cloth is available in the form of belts, rolls, sheets, discs, spiral points, and cones. Rolls for hand use usually are manufactured in widths from ½" to 3". Sheets generally are 9" x 11". Belts, rolls, discs, spiral points, and cones are available in sizes to fit standard machines.

Polishing with Abrasive Cloth

1. Tear a strip of abrasive from a sheet or roll.
2. For hand use, place the abrasive strip under a piece of wood. Apply a few drops of oil to the abrasive, and polish the workpiece.
3. When considerable stock is to be removed and a fine finish is to be produced, use several grades of abrasives: first use medium, follow with fine, and finish with an extra-fine grade.
4. When polishing work on a lathe, use a strip of abrasive cloth under a stick of wood. Apply several drops of oil to the abrasive, and polish with overlapping strokes. Another method of polishing is to hold one end of the abrasive strip with each hand while applying pressure against the revolving work. Be careful to avoid striking the lathe dog or the chuck with the fingers or hands. A high speed should be used.

Test Your Knowledge of Section 12

Unit 110: Types of Abrasives and Their Use
1. What is an abrasive material?
2. In what forms are abrasives used as cutting tools?
3. What is meant by coated abrasive?
4. What were the first abrasives used by man?
5. List three properties necessary for abrasives.
6. Explain what type of fracture characteristics an abrasive should have.
7. How is the hardness of an abrasive material rated?
8. Why is the range from 9 to 10 on the Mohs hardness scale of great significance?
9. What is meant by natural abrasives?
10. List five natural abrasive materials.
11. List three natural abrasive materials which are used in metalworking.
12. What are the properties of emery?
13. In what form is emery used?
14. In what form is diamond used as an abrasive material?
15. What are artificial abrasives?
16. List three artificial abrasives.
17. How is silicon-carbide abrasive material made?
18. What are the properties of silicon carbide?
19. What abrasive tools are made of silicon carbide?
20. How is aluminum oxide made?
21. Compare the properties of aluminum oxide with those of silicon carbide.
22. What abrasive tools are made of aluminum oxide?
23. What materials may be ground on aluminum oxide grinding wheels?
24. What are the properties of boron carbide?
25. What uses are made of boron carbide abrasives?

Unit 111: Grinding Wheels and Their Selection
1. What basic materials are used in making a grinding wheel?
2. Explain the cutting action of a grinding wheel.
3. Why is the proper selection of a grinding wheel important?
4. How are grinding wheels classified?
5. List several standard grinding wheel shapes.
6. What types of abrasive materials are used to make grinding wheels?
7. What materials usually are ground with silicon-carbide grinding wheels?
8. List several trade names used for aluminum-oxide grinding wheels.
9. Explain how abrasive grains are sized and graded.
10. What purpose does the bonding material serve in a grinding wheel?

11. List five common types of bonding materials used in the manufacture of grinding wheels.
12. What are the properties of a vitrified bond for grinding wheels?
13. What are the properties of a silicate bond for grinding wheels?
14. What are the properties and uses of resinoid-bonded grinding wheels?
15. Explain what is meant by the grade of a grinding wheel.
16. How is the grade of a grinding wheel designated?
17. Explain what is meant by *open-* and *close-*grain structure.
18. How is the structure of a grinding wheel designated?
19. What six factors may be included in the standardized marking system used to identify various grinding wheels?
20. Interpret the meaning of the following grinding wheel markings: 32A60-K5VBE, 39C60-I8VK.
21. What is meant by the cutting speed of a grinding wheel?
22. How is the cutting speed increased on a grinding machine?
23. What danger is involved if a grinding wheel is operated at a speed exceeding that recommended by the manufacturer?
24. What surface cutting speed is recommended for general offhand grinding with vitrified wheels?
25. In what sources can one find specific grinding wheel selection and cutting speed recommendations for various grinding applications?
26. What principal factors must be considered in recommending and selecting a grinding wheel for a specific grinding operation?
27. What factors must be specified in ordering a specific grinding wheel?
28. What precautions must be taken in mounting a grinding wheel properly?
29. What causes a grinding wheel to glaze?
30. What causes a grinding wheel to load?
31. On what materials are diamond grinding wheels used?
32. How are diamond grinding wheels constructed or produced?
33. In what source can one find specific recommendations concerning the selection of a diamond grinding wheel for a particular job application?

Unit 112: Coated Abrasives

1. What principal types of materials are required to make a coated abrasive?
2. What types of backing materials are used for coated abrasives?
3. What principal types of coated abrasives are used in the metalworking industry?
4. In what forms are coated abrasive materials available?
5. What factors must be considered in selecting a coated abrasive for a particular job?
6. On what materials are aluminum-oxide coated abrasives usually used?
7. For what applications is crocus cloth used?
8. What types of cloth backing are used for coated abrasives?
9. What types of bonding material are used on coated abrasives?
10. What is meant by *open* coating and *closed* coating on coated abrasives?
11. What system is used for grading grain sizes used on coated abrasives?
12. In what sizes are rolls of abrasive cloth usually made?
13. In what size are sheets of abrasive cloth usually made?
14. In what sizes are belts and discs of coated abrasives usually available?
15. Describe the procedure used in hand polishing with abrasive cloth.
16. Describe the procedure used in polishing work which is mounted in a lathe, using abrasive cloth.

Size or Dimensional Feedback — Basic to Precise Workmanship
(Federal Prod.)

Grinding Machines and Their Operation

Grinding and Grinding Machines

Grinding machines are precision machine tools designed to machine metal parts to very close tolerances and to produce high-quality surface finishes. Numerous precision grinding machines are available for producing a variety of precision-ground surfaces. Grinding machines are available for grinding plain flat surfaces, external cylindrical surfaces, internal cylindrical surfaces, tapered surfaces, and irregular surfaces.

It is common industrial practice to grind many mass-produced parts to tolerances of plus or minus 0.0001″. Special parts for precision instruments are ground to tolerances within plus or minus 0.000 020″ (20 microinches). In addition to the close dimensional tolerances possible, a second distinct advantage of grinding is that it often is the only method by which parts hardened by heat treatment may be machined.

Grinding machines make our modern mass-production methods possible. With these machines, parts readily are produced to the close tolerances which permit them to be used interchangeably on modern precision machines. A few examples of the many precision-ground parts in the modern automobile engine include: crankshafts, camshafts, piston pins, and roller and ball bearings. Precision-ground parts range in size from the small parts in a wristwatch to the large rolls used for rolling sheet steel in steel mills.

The cutting tool used on grinding machines is an abrasive wheel. This tool differs from the ordinary machine cutting tool in that each particle of abrasive on the surface of the wheel is a cutter. Thus, for each revolution of the wheel, thousands of tiny chips of metal are removed from the workpiece, Fig. 12-6. As the particles of the abrasive become worn and dull, they are torn loose from the wheel, thus exposing new and sharp cutting particles to the work.

Different types of grinding machines are available for various kinds of grinding operations. Some grinders are standard machines which perform a variety of grinding operations. Other grinders are special types designed for only one specific operation.

Kinds of Grinding Operations

There are several basic kinds of precision grinding operations.

Surface Grinding: This produces an accurate flat surface on a part, Fig. 13-1. Several types of surface grinders may be used.

Cylindrical Grinding: This produces a straight or tapered surface on a workpiece which has a cylindrical or conical shape. The workpiece is mounted between centers or in a chuck, and the face of the grinding wheel passes over the external surface of the revolving piece, Fig. 13-2. Cylindrical grinding usually is done on either plain or universal cylindrical grinding machines.

Internal Grinding: This produces a smooth and accurate surface in a cylindrical hole. The surface may be

427

straight, tapered, or irregular. Internal grinding is a form of cylindrical grinding, Fig. 13-70. This type of grinding may be done on universal grinding machines, internal grinding machines, and with tool post grinders mounted on a lathe.

Form Grinding: This produces a smooth and accurate surface of special shape. It is done with a grinding wheel which usually is ground to conform to the shape of the surface which it is designed to produce. An example of form grinding is the grinding of a thread from solid stock, as was shown in Fig. 12-7. The grinding of fillets, rounds, or irregular shapes is another example. Form grinding may be performed with various types of grinding machines, including surface grinders, cylindrical grinders, internal grinders, and special grinding machines.

Plunge Grinding: This is another form of cylindrical grinding which produces a straight, tapered, or formed surface on a workpiece as the grinding wheel moves into the work. In some cases, the grinding wheel also moves a very short distance horizontally across the work surface. Automotive crankshafts and similar objects with deep shoulders often are ground by this method. A cylindrical grinding machine equipped with a plunge-type grinding wheel head generally is used for operations of this type.

Centerless Grinding: This is also a form of cylindrical grinding which produces accurately ground parts without requiring them to be mounted between centers. Rather, parts are held in position on a work-rest blade, which is located between a grinding wheel and a regulating wheel, Fig. 13-3. The regulating wheel rotates the work which rests on the blade; at the same time, the grinding wheel, which is located opposite the regulating wheel, grinds the surface. Straight or tapered objects may be ground in this manner.

Lathe centers, piston pins, roller bearings, and similar objects without center holes are examples of objects ground by the centerless grinding method. A centerless grinding machine is required for this purpose.

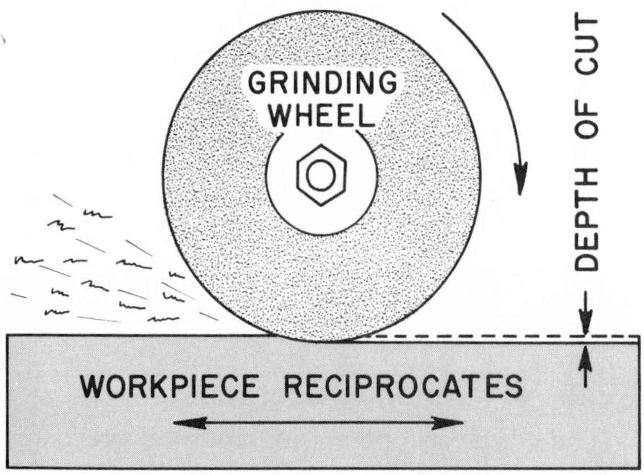

Fig. 13-1. Relationship of Grinding Wheel and Workpiece with Horizontal-Spindle Surface Grinder

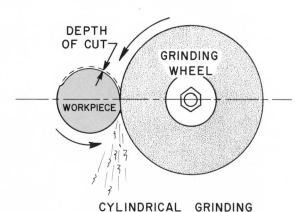

Fig. 13-2. Relationship of Grinding Wheel and Workpiece in Cylindrical Grinding

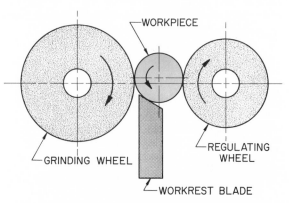

Fig. 13-3. Relationship of Grinding Wheel and Workpiece in Centerless Grinding

428

Cutter and Tool Grinding: This involves the grinding of milling cutters, counterbores, reamers, and many kinds of cutting tools. This type of grinding normally is done on a cutter and tool grinder, Fig. 11-73.

Offhand Grinding: This is the non-precision type of grinding done on a bench- or floor-model tool grinder, as shown in Fig. 5-1. Cold chisels, center punches, lathe tool bits, and shaper tool bits often are ground by offhand grinding. The tool or object being ground is held by hand, with or without a guiding device.

Kinds of Grinding Machines

Like other metalworking machines, grinding machines designed for many purposes are available. The more common of these machines are: the surface, the plain, the universal, and the internal types of grinders, as well as the cutter and tool grinder and the universal cutter and tool grinder. Some special types of grinders are drill grinders, thread grinders, and tool post grinders.

Usually grinding machines are classified as to size by an arbitrary number given by the manufacturer. Some, however, are classified in terms of their maximum capacity to accommodate work in terms of diameter and length. In this unit, the most common types of grinding machines, their applications, and their principal parts are described briefly. More detailed information concerning machine accessories, controls, and other operational factors is explained in succeeding units which include the procedures for specific types of grinding operations.

Surface Grinders: Surface grinding machines are designed primarily for grinding flat surfaces. However, with special setups, angular and formed surfaces also may be ground on a surface grinder. These machines may be of two general types — the *horizontal-spindle type* (Figs. 13-4 and 13-5) and the *vertical-spindle type* (Fig. 13-6).

Machines with horizontal spindles are most common in tool-and-die shops, toolrooms, maintenance shops, and schools. With this type machine, the work may be mounted on the table in a number of ways, often with a magnetic chuck. The table, with the work, recipro-

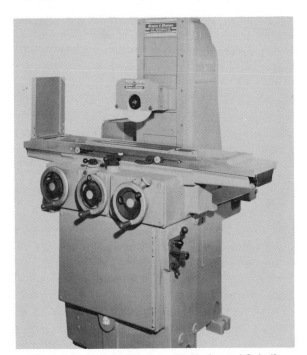

Fig. 13-4. Surface Grinder with Horizontal Spindle (Brown & Sharpe)

Fig. 13-5. Surface Grinder with Horizontal Spindle and Rotary Table (Norton)
Safety goggles are recommended.

429

cates back and forth under the grinding wheel. With each succeeding table stroke, the work is fed crosswise under the wheel. Machines of this type are available with either manual or power longitudinal and transverse (crosswise) feeds. They may be operated dry or wet.

For dry grinding, an exhaust attachment generally is used to catch the dust. For wet grinding, a special attachment pumps fluid or a mist in the vicinity of the grinding area.

Further details concerning horizontal-spindle surface grinders are included in Unit 114. The parts, accessories, work setup procedures, and operational procedures are included in the unit.

A second type of surface grinder with a horizontal spindle is the *rotary* type, Fig. 13-5. This machine has a rotary table mounted on a supporting table which travels longitudinally. The workpiece revolves under the grinding wheel, and, at the same time, the table is fed longitudinally under the wheel. Workpieces of larger diameter may be ground on machines of this type.

Surface grinders of the type shown in Fig. 13-6 have a vertical spindle. As the grinding wheel revolves, the work is fed back and forth under the wheel. This type of grinder generally cuts much faster than those with horizontal spindles; hence, they are used more widely for production purposes. Because of the amount of heat developed with this type of grinder, a cutting fluid always should be used.

Plain Grinders: Plain grinding machines (Fig. 13-7) are designed primarily for production grinding of external cylindrical surfaces. They are used for cylindrical grinding of straight surfaces, tapered surfaces, and shoulders. They also may be used for plunge grinding of formed surfaces which conform to the shape of the grinding wheel.

The principal parts or mechanisms on a plain grinding machine are: a heavy bed which gives the machine stability; a wheel head mounted on a slide base; a headstock mounted on a table which can be swiveled through 8°; a footstock or tailstock; a sliding table on which the swivel table is mounted; a longitudinal table feed mechanism; and a manual or automatic cross-feed mechanism. These and other parts are shown in Figs. 13-7 (and 13-73 in Unit 128).

The wheel head is set permanently at right angles with the table travel and cannot be swiveled. The headstock on many plain grind-

Fig. 13-6. Surface Grinder with a Vertical Spindle
(Brown & Sharpe)

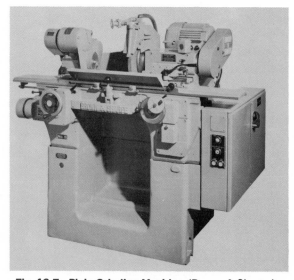

Fig. 13-7. Plain Grinding Machine (Brown & Sharpe)

ing machines cannot be swiveled. On some machines, such as the one in Fig. 13-7, the headstock may be swiveled up to 45° for grinding steep tapers. (See Fig. 13-80 in Unit 128.) The headstock spindle has four step pulleys which provide work speeds ranging from about 200 to 800 rpm. To change the headstock speed, the "O" rings are shifted to the desired step pulley.

Longitudinal table travel may be operated manually or automatically. Six rates of power travel are provided, ranging from about 6″ to 133″ per minute. The feeds are selected through the use of table speed-selector levers. Table reverse dogs may be set for automatic table reversal.

Plain grinding machines often are equipped with features such as wheel slide rapid travel, independent automatic cross feed, and a wheel spindle reciprocating mechanism. Other features and information concerning plain grinding machines are given in Unit 128. These features include the cross-feed mechanism, cross-feed control, wheel-slide rapid travel, and general precautions to be observed before starting the machine.

Universal Grinders: As the name implies, a universal grinding machine (Fig. 13-8) is designed to perform a wide variety of cylindrical grinding operations. It is far more versatile than the plain grinding machine, being designed to perform both external and internal cylindrical grinding operations, including the grinding of straight surfaces, tapered surfaces, shoulders, steep tapers, and face grinding. Also, straight fluted reamers and milling cutters can be ground on a universal grinder. See Unit 127.

Universal grinding machines are made in sizes ranging in swing capacity from 10″ to 14″ or more. Their capacity between centers ranges from 20″ to 60″ or more.

Principal Parts: The parts and controls for a typical universal grinding machine are illustrated in Fig. 13-52. The principal parts include: a heavy base which gives the machine stability, a table which can be swiveled 8° for grinding tapers, a wheel spindle head which may be swiveled for grinding angles, a headstock which may be swiveled for grinding steep angles or faces, a footstock for holding work between centers, and an internal grinding unit which is mounted directly above the external grinding spindle.

A variety of work-holding devices and accessories also is available to extend further the versatility of this machine. Work may be mounted in a chuck on the headstock spindle, Fig. 13-67, for either face or angular grinding.

Further details concerning universal machines and their parts, controls, and operational features are included in Unit 122. The procedures for performing basic grinding operations on this machine also are included in succeeding units.

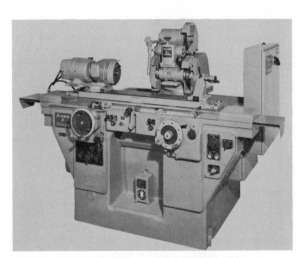

Fig. 13-8. Universal Grinding Machine
(Brown & Sharpe)

Fig. 13-9. Universal and Tool Grinding Machine
(Brown & Sharpe)

Internal Grinders: The internal grinding machine is used for finishing round or tapered holes. It is a highly specialized machine which rarely is found in schools or small commercial shops. In such shops, internal grinding usually is done with a universal grinding machine equipped with an internal grinding fixture, Fig. 13-71. Internal grinding also may be done with a tool post grinder mounted on a lathe.

Cutter and Tool Grinders: The cutter and tool grinding machine is designed for grinding milling cutters, reamers, taps, and certain special cutting tools used on milling and drilling machines, Fig. 11-73. When equipped with the appropriate accessories, cutter and tool grinding machines also may be used for accurately grinding single-point cutting tools. An introduction to the use of the cutter and tool grinding machine for sharpening milling cutters is included in Unit 89. Also, Unit 127 gives details for sharpening plain milling cutters on a universal grinder, and this procedure may be adaptable to some other types of grinders.

Fig. 13-10. Dial Indicating Grinding Gage Indicates Size Directly (Federal Prod.)

Universal and Tool Grinders: The universal and tool grinding machine, Fig. 13-9, is a general-purpose machine which may be used for an unusually large number of grinding applications. It is an extremely versatile machine which is particularly useful in toolrooms, small commercial shops, and schools. It will perform small and medium cylindrical grinding operations which normally are performed on a universal grinder, including both external and internal grinding operations.

As the name implies, the universal and tool grinding machine can be used for grinding all of the common cutting tools (such as milling cutters, reamers, and taps) and many special cutting tools. Numerous accessories and holding devices are available for the machine, including the universal scroll chuck, internal grinding attachment, wet grinding attachment, surface grinding attachment, collet chuck, magnetic chuck, index centers, end mill sharpening attachment, and many convenient accessories commonly used in conjunction with cutter sharpening. With the surface grinding attachment, the machine may be used for surface grinding operations.

The principles involved in the operation of the universal and tool grinding machine are similar to those for the universal grinding machines, surface grinding machines, and cutter and tool grinding machines. Hence, study of the procedures used in performing these operations on other basic types of grinding machines, as outlined in the following units, will aid in learning to perform the same operations on the universal and tool grinding machine.

Gaging Ground Parts

Where a number of parts are to be ground to the same size on a cylindrical grinding machine, they may be rapidly checked for size with an indicating *grinding gage* or with a *snap gage*. A dial indicating grinding gage may be attached to a cylindrical grinding machine as shown in Fig. 13-10. This type gage indicates the size of the work directly, while the machine is running, and wheel wear can be compensated for.

Several types of dial indicating snap gages which may be used to gage the work while mounted in the machine are shown in Figs. 3-93, 3-95, and 3-97. These gages indicate size directly, whether oversize or undersize, and, therefore, are convenient for measuring work in the grinder.

Go and no-go snap gages also may be used, Figs. 3-138, 3-139, and 3-140. However, gages of this type show only whether the workpiece is within specified tolerances. They do not indicate the amount of variation from the basic size.

General Preliminary Procedure

Some of the possible grinding troubles which might occur while performing grinding operations on various types of grinders are listed in

Table 16, together with their probable causes. The following are general procedures which should be followed in preparation for grinding operations:

1. Make all settings and adjustments as explained in the units which follow.
2. Before starting the machine, see that all driving belts have proper tension. A V-belt is properly tensioned when it can be depressed about 1″ using only slight pressure. Excessive tension will cause belts to wear rapidly, and it may damage the spindle.

Table 16
Possible Grinding Troubles

Symptom	Probable Cause
Work Shows Chatter Finish	Grinding wheel out of balance or not clamped properly on the wheel sleeve. Grinding wheel dull, glazed, or loaded. Poor choice of wheel for material being ground. Work not effectively supported; centers worn or need lubrication. Not a sufficient number of back rests used, or back rests not properly adjusted. Too high a work speed or rate of table travel. Cut too heavy, caused by excessive cross feed. Unbalanced workpiece (for example, a crankshaft) running at a speed which is too high or running away from the driving dog (too much momentum). A worn or defective driving belt, check headstock, spindle, and table belts. Machine located on an insufficiently rigid floor or a floor which transmits vibration to the machine.
Scratches on the Work	Using a dirty coolant. Grinding wheel not trued properly. Truing diamond dull, cracked, or broken; or not held rigidly in the holder; not clamped securely in the truing fixture; the fixture not rigidly clamped in position; or footstock spindle not clamped. Too rapid table feed, or a too deep cut when truing or dressing the wheel. Wheel too coarse for the work.
Spiral Marks on the Work	Point of truing diamond too high. The wheel should be trued with the diamond point as near the heights of the work centers as possible.
Wheel Burning the Work	Insufficient coolant used, or coolant not properly directed at the point of contact of the wheel and the work. Grinding wheel dull, glazed, or loaded; needs dressing. Wheel too hard, wheel speed too high, or work speed too low. Excessive cross feed.
Work Not Ground Parallel	Swivel table not set accurately at zero. Swivel table pivot shoe may need adjusting. Headstock or footstock not seated properly on the table. Centers not seated properly in the spindle, or center points worn out of round. Center holes in workpiece dirty, out of round, or do not fit the centers properly. Radial play in the footstock spindle. Spindle clamp not properly adjusted. Back rests needed, or if used, not properly adjusted.
Work Not Sizing Uniformly	Wheel Slide Rapid Travel Arrangement motor brake needs adjusting. Cross-feed screw thrust bearing needs adjusting.
Wheel Spindle Runs Too Hot or Stalls	Insufficient oil in spindle reservoir, or wrong kind of oil. Cross feed too heavy, beyond capacity of the machine. Spindle driving belts too tight.

3. Make certain that all guards are in working condition and in place. See that the machine is properly lubricated.

4. Before starting a grinding operation, run the machine for about fifteen minutes. This will bring the machine to running temperature and thus eliminate variations due to expansion of machine parts.

<blockquote>
UNIT

114
</blockquote>

How To Operate Surface Grinding Machines

As indicated in Unit 113, several different basic types of surface grinding machines may be used for grinding flat surfaces. Since horizontal-spindle surface grinding machines are the type which are used most widely in schools, toolrooms, and small commercial shops, this unit is concerned with these machines and their operation.

Machine Features

Although the design and the control mechanisms may vary some with different manufacturers, the principles involved are similar.

Machine Size: The size or capacity for horizontal-spindle machines usually is designated by the size of the working area of the table or of the chuck mounted on the table. Thus a 6 x 18 machine has a working area at least 6" x 18", that is, it has transverse (cross feed) table travel of at least 6" and longitudinal table travel of 18". On most machines, the amount of table travel is slightly more than the designated size of the working area.

The distance from the center of the wheel to the top of the working surface also is a factor in determining the maximum height of parts which may be ground on the machine; this distance, minus the radius of the grinding wheel, determines the maximum height of parts which may be surface ground.

The machine in Fig. 13-15 has a table work area of 5" x 11". The machine in Fig. 13-16 has a table work area of 6" x 18". Machines of these sizes and capacities commonly are used in schools.

Feed: Surface grinders of the horizontal-spindle type are available with either hand feed or power feed. The power feed, available for either or both longitudinal and cross

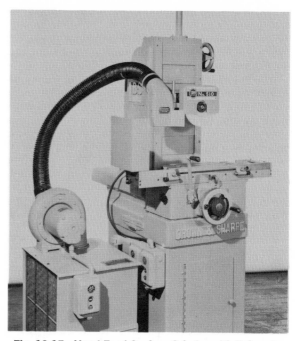

Fig. 13-15. Hand-Feed Surface Grinder with Exhaust Attachment (Brown & Sharpe)

feeds, may be a mechanical-type feed mechanism or a hydraulically operated feed mechanism. The machine in Fig. 13-15 is the hand-feed type; that in Fig. 13-16 has hydraulic power feed for both longitudinal and cross feed.

The vertical-feed handwheel and cross-feed handwheel, as in Fig. 13-17, have 0.0002"

graduations for accurate adjustments. An auxiliary adjusting knob for fine feed (Fig. 13-29) provides for vertical adjustments of the wheel elevation in 0.0001" graduations.

Wet or Dry Attachments: For dry grinding, an exhaust attachment is recommended. See Fig. 13-15. This attachment removes grit and dust from the area of the grinding operation, leaving the air clean. For wet grinding, a wet-grinding attachment, Fig. 13-18, is used. This attachment, which in-

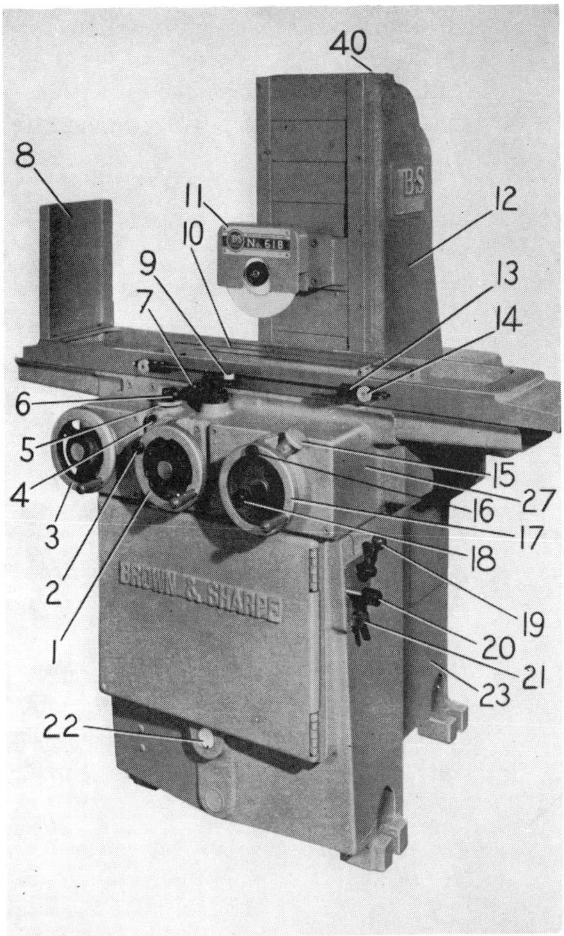

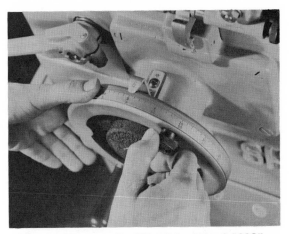

**Fig. 13-17. Cross-Feed Handwheel Has 0.0002"
Graduations** (Brown & Sharpe)

**Fig. 13-16. 6" x 18" Surface Grinding Machine with
Hydraulic and Hand Feeds** (Brown & Sharpe)
(1) Cross-feed handwheel; (2) Dial locknut, cross-feed handwheel; (3) Table handwheel; (4) Set screw, throttle adjustment bushing; (5) Throttle adjustment bushing; (6) Table throttle lever; (7) Table reversing lever; (8) Dust deflector; (9) Reversing lever contact roller; (10) Tables; (11) Wheel guard; (12) Upright; (13) Table dog; (14) Carrier locknut; (15) Fine-feed adjustment knob; (16) Dial locknut, elevating handwheel; (17) Elevating handwheel; (18) Fine-feed locknut; (19) Cross-feed directional lever; (20) Cross-feed regulating screw; (21) Wheel truing and rapid positioning lever; (22) Oil level sight glass; (23) Base; (27) Bed; and (40) Elevating screw guard, upper.

**Fig. 13-18. Hand-Feed Surface Grinder with
Wet-Grinding Attachment** (Brown & Sharpe)

cludes a pump, liquid container, and splash guards, provides a flow of cutting fluid in the grinding area. The cutting fluid reduces heat and, therefore, increases the rate at which metal may be removed. It also improves surface finish. When a considerable amount of metal is to be removed, roughing cuts should be made first, followed by finishing cuts. Roughing cuts generally may vary from 0.001″ to 0.003″ in depth, depending on the rigidity of the machine, whether a coolant is used, and the rate of feed. Finishing cuts generally should be 0.001″ or less in depth.

Accessories: Numerous accessories, in addition to the exhaust attachment and the wet-grinding attachment, are available for horizontal-spindle surface grinding machines. The accessories are designed for making various types of work setups; they are described later in conjunction with the methods employed for making setups. A radius and wheel truing attachment also is available, Fig. 13-39.

General Procedure

1. Select a grinding wheel suited to the work to be performed, and mount it on the wheel spindle. (See Unit 115.) Be sure the wheel is sound. Test it by striking it a light blow with a hammer; a clear ring indicates a sound wheel.

CAUTION: *If the wheel is changed, it will be necessary to true and balance the new wheel before attempting to grind a workpiece. (See Unit 115.) If the workpiece is to be form-ground, it will be necessary to shape the wheel accordingly. (See Unit 117.) In dry-grinding operations, a means of protecting the operator and the machine from grit and dust should be employed. The recommended means is either a central exhaust system or an exhaust attachment such as illustrated in Fig. 13-15.*

2. If available, connect the machine with the exhaust system, unless already connected.
3. Secure suitable clamps, vise, chuck, or other means of holding the work.
4. Mount the work on the table of the machine:
   A. *By Clamping:* Position, align, and clamp the workpiece, for example, as in Fig. 13-19.
   B. *By Using a Vise:* Position and mount the vise on the table; then support and grip the work as illustrated in Fig. 13-20. Use an indicator or surface gage to test that the surface to be ground is in a horizontal plane.
   C. *By Using an Adjustable Swivel Vise:* Position the vise; then grip the work as illustrated in Fig. 13-21.
   D. *By Using a Permanent Magnetic Chuck:* Mount the chuck on the table and clamp it in position. Place the workpiece or pieces on the chuck,

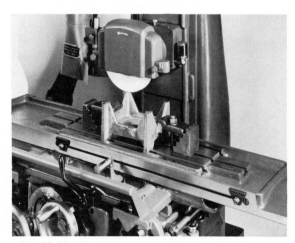

Fig. 13-19. Workpiece Held in Position with Clamps
(Brown & Sharpe)

Fig. 13-20. Workpiece Held in a Vise (Brown & Sharpe)

as illustrated in Figs. 13-22 and 13-23. With the work in position, move the control lever 180° to the right. Use back or end stops if the workpiece has only small contact with the chuck. Flat pieces of metal make good stops.

E. *By Using Index Centers:* Mount the index head and footstock on the table of the machine, aligning them by means of the tongues on their bases. Clamp in position. Place a driving dog on the work; then place it between centers and position it with respect to the grinding wheel, as in Fig. 13-24.

F. *By Using a Sine Plate:* A sine plate, Fig. 3-154, may be used when work-

pieces are to be ground to very precise angles. The sine plate is fastened to the grinder table. The work is attached to the sine plate by bolting or clamping.

G. *By Using a Perma Sine:* A perma sine, Fig. 3-155, is especially useful for precision grinding of angles or bevels. The perma sine is fastened to the grinder table, and workpieces are mounted on the perma sine at the desired angle.

Fig. 13-21. Workpiece Held in an Adjustable Swivel Vise (Brown & Sharpe)

Fig. 13-23. Grinding a Slot with Workpiece Mounted on Magnetic Chuck (Brown & Sharpe)

Fig. 13-22. Workpiece Held on a Permanent Magnetic Chuck (Brown & Sharpe)

Fig. 13-24. Workpiece Held Between Index Centers (Brown & Sharpe)

H. *By Using V-Blocks:* Round workpieces may be mounted in V-blocks on a magnetic chuck, as illustrated in Fig. 13-25. They also may be clamped to the machine table as in Fig. 13-26.

I. *By Using a Precision Vise:* Workpieces may be mounted in a precision vise (Fig. 13-27), and the vise mounted on a magnetic chuck. This arrangement works well for parts of small cross-sectional area.

J. *By Using an Adjustable Vise:* This type of vise may be adjusted at various angles and may be mounted on a magnetic chuck, as shown in Fig. 13-28. In this illustration, the surfaces on the part are being ground with the sides of the grinding wheel.

5. Properly lubricate the machine before starting it. If the machine has been idle for some time, alternately press the start and stop push buttons in rapid succession three or four times before running the machine at operating speed.

6. Protect eyes by wearing properly fitted goggles. Clothing should be protected with suitable coveralls.

Procedure for Manual Feed

1. Mount the work on the table of the machine in a suitable manner.

2. With the table handwheel, move the work under the grinding wheel. Then lower the wheel by means of the vertical-adjustment (elevating) handwheel, Fig. 13-29, until it almost touches the workpiece.

Fig. 13-27. Precision Vise for Use on Magnetic Chuck

Fig. 13-25. Work Mounted in V-Blocks on Magnetic Chuck (L.S. Starrett)

Fig. 13-26. V-Blocks Clamped to Machine Table (Brown & Sharpe)

Fig. 13-28. Grinding Workpiece Mounted in Adjustable Vise (Brown & Sharpe)

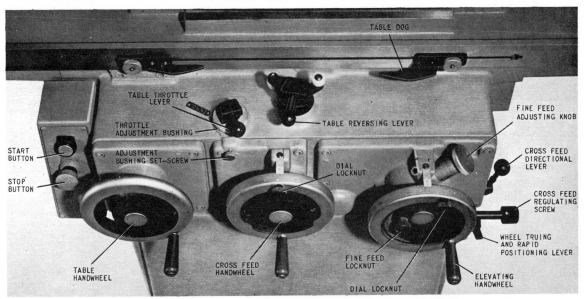

Fig. 13-29. Front Operating Controls on No. 618 Surface Grinding Machine (Brown & Sharpe)

3. With the cross-feed handwheel, move the table outward until the far side of the wheel projects beyond the farthest edge of the workpiece a distance equal to three-fourths the width of the face of the wheel.

4. Move the table to the right until the wheel clears the work by several inches.

On the machine illustrated, the power feed mechanism should be disengaged whenever continuous manual operation is desired. This is accomplished by turning the table throttle lever, Fig. 13-29, to the off position. The table handwheel always is engaged for manual operation. It is disengaged automatically when power table travel is engaged.

5. Turn the vertical-adjustment handwheel clockwise through sufficient graduations to produce a cut of .001″ to .003″. Lock the grinding head in position by tightening the clamping screw, if the machine is so equipped.

CAUTION: *When dry grinding a flat surface, considerable heat will be generated, particularly if a heavy feed is used. Overheating should be guarded against by using a light feed, and, where possible, a coolant.*

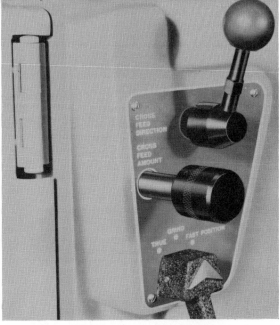

Fig. 13-30. Cross-Feed Controls on No. 618 Surface Grinding Machine (Brown & Sharpe)

6. Start the machine; then, with the table handwheel, advance the wheel steadily across the surface of the work. Move the wheel past the end of the work a sufficient distance to allow adjustment of the cross feed before reversing the table.

CAUTION: *Be sure the wheel guard is fastened securely in position.*

7. When the grinding wheel has cleared the end of the workpiece, move the table inward by turning the cross-feed handwheel clockwise one complete turn. This will give 0.100″ feed. With experience, a heavier feed may be taken.

8. Continue as in steps 6 and 7 until the entire surface has been rough ground.

9. When rough grinding has been completed, move the grinding wheel back to the starting point. Lower the grinding head sufficiently to make the finishing cut, usually .001″ or less.

Procedure for Power Feed

1. Proceed as in steps 1 through 6 under "General Procedure."

2. Mount the work on the table of the grinding machine in a suitable manner.

3. With the table handwheel (Fig. 13-29), move the work under the grinding wheel. Then lower the wheel by means of the vertical-adjustment (elevating) handwheel until it barely touches the surface of the workpiece.

4. Move the table to the left until the work clears the wheel by at least 1″ (more if necessary).

5. Bring the right-hand reversing dog against the right side of the reversing

Fig. 13-31. High-Speed Surface-Grinding Attachment
(Brown & Sharpe)

lever. Fasten it in position by tightening the clamping bolt.

6. Move the table to the right until the grinding wheel clears the end of the work by at least 1″ (more if necessary).

7. Bring the left-hand reversing dog against the left side of the reversing lever, and clamp it in position.

CAUTION: *When setting the table dogs for automatic reversing, be sure to allow sufficient over-travel of the work in both directions for completion of the cross-feed action before the work comes back under the wheel.*

Procedure for Power Cross Feed

The procedure for adjusting the power cross-feed mechanism varies for different makes of machines. Therefore, before using the machine, it is good practice to read the operator's handbook, which usually is supplied with the machine. The procedure which follows is for the Brown and Sharpe No. 618 machine, Figs. 13-16, 13-29, and 13-30.

By setting the cross-feed regulating screw, Figs. 13-29 and 13-30, any cross feed from 0.010″ to 0.250″ may be obtained at each reversal of the power longitudinal table travel. A continuous cross feed of 10″ per minute also is provided for wheel truing. The wheel also may be positioned rapidly over long distances, at a rate of 12 feet per minute, by using the selector lever provided, Fig. 13-30.

1. In starting the intermittant cross feed, first turn the selector lever, Fig. 13-30, to the *grind* position. Next, turn the cross-feed direction lever for the desired direction of cross feed, for example, *inward* or toward the rear of the machine.

2. Determine the amount of cross feed desired. Cross feed should be set in accordance with the width of the wheel, the depth of cut, and the finish desired. A cut in excess of one-half the width of the wheel's face never should be used, even for extremely coarse feeds. With a lower rate of cross feed for a given width of wheel, a deeper cut may be taken. For a high-quality finish, lower-than-average cross feeds should be taken. For average

cuts, a cross feed from 0.050″ to 0.100″ is satisfactory. With experience, the rate may be increased.

3. Start the table travel with the table throttle lever, Fig. 13-29. Then adjust the cross-feed knob, Fig. 13-30, to the desired amount of cross feed for each stroke of the table.

Some machines are equipped with trip dogs which can be positioned so that a cut automatically may be started or stopped at a particular point on the surface of the workpiece. After the cross feed of the table has been stopped by a trip dog, the cross-feed selector lever must be moved to change the direction of cross feed before again starting the table. Furthermore, the starting lever must be held in the engaged position until the trip dog has moved off the plunger sufficiently to permit the knob to remain engaged.

CAUTION: *When using cross-feed stop dogs, under no circumstances attempt to force the machine to grind beyond the maximum permitted in either direction by the dogs.*

4. With the grinding wheel at the right end of the workpiece and clear of the work, stop the table travel with the table throttle lever.

5. With the cross-feed wheel, position the work clear of the wheel.

Procedure for Cutting

1. Turn the vertical-adjustment handwheel through sufficient graduations to produce a cut of .002″ to .003″. Lock the grinding head in position by the clamping screw, if the machine is so equipped.

2. With the workpiece in position and the longitudinal table travel and cross feeds properly adjusted, engage the table throttle lever and make the cut.

3. When the roughing cut is completed, adjust the machine to take a finishing cut, about .0001″ to .001″, as desired.

High-Speed Attachments

By means of a high-speed surface-grinding attachment that can be mounted in the machine spindle of some machines, slots and semi-enclosed surfaces may be ground with wheels of appropriate size and shape. This attachment is illustrated in Fig. 13-31.

How To Change and Balance Grinding Wheels

A grinding wheel should fit easily, yet snugly, on the wheel sleeve. A loose wheel cannot be centered accurately and, consequently, will be out of balance. Such a wheel should not be used unless the core is recast. Neither should a wheel be used that has to be forced on the sleeve. Applying force may crack the wheel and thus make it unsafe for use. If the hole is only slightly too small, it may be enlarged by means of a half-round file of appropriate size. Simply remove a little metal uniformly around the hole. If the wheel is lead-bushed, sufficient metal may be removed by scraping with a pocket knife.

On some machines, the wheel is mounted permanently on a sleeve which, when change of wheel is made, is removed as a unit and a new unit of sleeve and wheel is installed. This practice saves time, as the wheel need not be removed from the sleeve until a change is necessary due to wear or development of a flaw.

Procedure for Removing a Wheel and Sleeve Unit

1. Secure an appropriate wheel sleeve puller and a pin wrench.
2. With the wrench supplied with the machine, loosen the spindle nut (Fig. 13-33) by turning it clockwise. The nut has a left-hand thread.
3. Thread the outer member of the wheel sleeve puller into the sleeve. Then tighten the cap screw, Fig. 13-34, against the end of the spindle, thus loosening the wheel sleeve from the spindle.

   On the No. 5 Brown and Sharpe plain grinding machine, a special T-handled wrench supplied with the machine has a threaded end intended for use as a wheel puller. To loosen the sleeve, tap the handle of the wrench with a hammer.

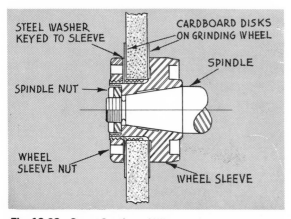

Fig. 13-33. Cross Section of Wheel Mounted on Arbor

Fig. 13-34. Cap Screw (Brown & Sharpe)

Procedure for Removing the Wheel from the Sleeve

1. With a pin wrench, loosen the wheel sleeve nut, Fig. 13-33.
2. Support the wheel on parallels or blocks of wood; then with the fingers, press the sleeve of the wheel. If force is required, use a rawhide or wooden mallet, tapping the sleeve very gently.

Procedure for Mounting the Wheel on the Sleeve

1. Secure a wheel suitable to the work to be performed.
2. Insert a finger in the spindle hole and suspend the wheel in the air. Very lightly tap the edge of the wheel with a hammer. If the wheel is sound, a clear ring will be heard. If no ring is heard, the wheel probably is cracked and should not be used.
3. Insert a rubber, leather, or blotting-paper washer between the wheel and each of the clamping flanges. Many makes of grinding wheels come with a heavy ring of blotting paper attached to each side of the wheel. Nevertheless, to provide greater protection for the wheel, it is good practice to use an additional ring or washer.
4. Screw the outer flange or sleeve nut onto the wheel sleeve, and tighten it with the wrench supplied for that purpose. Avoid exerting too much pressure.
5. Observe the condition of the spindle hole in the wheel and the end of the wheel spindle. They should be clean. If necessary, wipe each with a cloth.
6. Slide the wheel sleeve onto the spindle, and seat it by hand, aligning the keyway with the key in the spindle.
7. Draw the sleeve tight on the spindle by means of the spindle nut and wrench. The clamping nut should be tightened just enough to hold the wheel securely. Avoid too much pressure.

Procedure for Mounting a Wheel and Sleeve Unit

1. Secure a wheel and sleeve unit suitable to the work to be performed.

2. See that the hole in the wheel and the end of the spindle are clean. If necessary, wipe each with a clean cloth.

3. Slide the sleeve unit onto the spindle, and seat it by hand, aligning the keyway with the key in the spindle.

4. Draw the sleeve tight on the spindle by means of the spindle nut and wrench. The clamping nut should be tightened just enough to hold the wheel securely in place. Too much pressure may crack the wheel.

Procedure for Balancing

To avoid excessive vibration, it is essential that a grinding wheel be balanced. Most manufacturers balance their wheels before issuing them. Consequently, wheels 10″ or less in diameter rarely need further balancing. Larger wheels may need to be balanced because of wear and changes which may have developed within the wheel.

Balance may be achieved by: (1) Adding weight in the form of lead to the light side. This may be accomplished by removing small amounts of the wheel beneath the flanges and then filling the holes thus made with lead. (2) On some wheel units, balance is achieved by adjustment of segments attached to the inner sleeve flange, as in Fig. 13-35.

By Adding Lead:

1. Remove some of the abrasive material beneath the flanges on the light side of the wheel. Avoid removing too much material in one spot. It is better to make two or three small cavities rather than one large one. Cavities should be placed a short distance apart so as to distribute the added weight.

2. Fill the holes thus made with melted lead.

3. Remove excess lead so that the flanges will fit properly against the sides of the wheel.

4. Mount the wheel on a tapered mandrel; then place the mandrel on a support such as shown in Fig. 13-35. Locate the mandrel midway of the support.

5. Give the wheel a slight push, and allow it to roll back and forth until it comes to rest, which it will do with the heavy portion of the wheel at the bottom.

6. Continue adding or removing weight until the wheel is balanced. This will be evident when the wheel rolls to a gentle stop with no apparent tendency to roll backward, regardless of what portion of the wheel was at the bottom when it started to roll.

Using Balancing Segments:

1. Mount the wheel on a tapered mandrel; then place the mandrel on a support such as illustrated in Fig. 13-35. Locate the mandrel about midway of the support.

2. Give the wheel a very slight push, and allow it to roll back and forth until it comes to rest, which it will do with the heavy portion of the wheel at the bottom.

3. Move the balancing segments in the direction of the light side of the wheel; then test as before.

4. Continue adjusting the balancing segments until the wheel is balanced. This will be evident when the wheel rolls to a gentle stop with no apparent tendency to roll backward, regardless of what portion of the wheel was at the bottom when it started to roll.

Fig. 13-35. Wheel Balanced with Segments
(Brown & Sharpe)

443

UNIT
116   How To True or Dress Wheels on Surface Grinders

A grinding wheel should be trued each time it is put on the spindle, and dressed whenever it becomes dull, loaded, or glazed.

Truing refers to correcting eccentricity or an out-of-round condition by removing particles of the abrasive from the high part of the wheel, using a diamond tool. It also refers to forming the wheel concentrically to a particular shape, such as a concave or a convex face. To be in good condition, the wheel must be sharp and run true both on the periphery and on the sides.

Dressing produces a sharp grinding surface. A diamond tool is used to remove the dull or loaded surface of the wheel, thus presenting new and sharp cutting particles of abrasive. Dressing is necessary whenever the wheel cuts very slowly, indicating that it is dull, or when the spaces between the pieces of abrasive become filled with particles of metal, usually non-ferrous metal.

Fig. 13-36. Truing a Wheel on a Surface Grinder
(Brown & Sharpe)

Procedure for Truing

1. Protect the eyes by wearing properly fitted goggles, and protect clothing by wearing suitable coveralls.

2. Mount the wheel on the spindle as instructed in Unit 115.

3. Secure a wheel truing fixture such as that shown in Fig. 13-36.

4. Position the fixture on the table of the machine so that the diamond tool may be applied to the face of the wheel, as shown in Fig. 13-36. In the illustration, the contact point of the diamond tool is slightly ahead of the vertical center of the wheel and is inclined slightly in the direction of wheel travel. This will prevent gouging and tendency to chatter.

5. Clamp the fixture in position; then start the machine. With the vertical-adjustment handwheel, lower the grinding head until the wheel is lightly in contact with the diamond tool.

   CAUTION: *Be sure the wheel guard is fastened securely in position.*

6. With the cross feed, move the table so that the diamond tool clears the wheel. Then lower the grinding head about .0005".

   To prevent chipping the edges of the wheel, it is good practice to round the corners of the wheel slightly before truing the face. To do this, bring the diamond tool into contact with the corner of the wheel; then, by manipulating the cross and vertical feeds, remove a small amount of material from each corner of the wheel.

7. Start the machine. With the cross feed, pass the diamond tool across the face of the wheel two or more times. If a coolant is available, use it freely.

8. At the end of the second or third stroke, lower the head another .0005″, and take another stroke.
9. Continue as in steps 6 and 7 until the wheel is running true.
10. On rare occasions, it is necessary to true the sides of the wheel. To perform this operation, position the fixture so that a cut may be taken on respective sides of the wheel. Then taking a light cut, feed the grinding head downward. Continue with repeated cuts until the sides of the wheel are true.
11. When the truing operation is completed, remove the truing fixture. Thoroughly clean both it and the machine.

Procedure for Dressing

1. Proceed as in steps 2 through 9 inclusive under truing.

How To Shape Grinding Wheels on Surface Grinders

Often it is necessary to surface grind rounded fillets, grooves, or irregular surfaces. In these cases, the grinding wheel must be shaped according to the surface to be ground, whether it be in the form of a radius, an angle, a convex curve, a concave curve, or some other shape. In Fig. 13-37, a V-shaped wheel is being used to grind a V-shaped recess. A concave groove is being ground with a wheel which has a convex shape in Fig. 13-20.

Procedure

1. Secure a wheel suited to the work to be performed.
2. Mount the wheel on the spindle, and true it in the usual manner, Unit 116.
3. Mount a radius and wheel truing attachment on the table of the machine, and clamp it in position, Fig. 13-38.
4. Mount a diamond tool in the toolholder at right angles to the slide, as in Fig. 13-38.
5. Loosen the clamping screw in the front of the base of the fixture. Then swivel the slide to the angle required (for example, 60°), as indicated by the graduations on the base. Clamp the slide in position by tightening the screw.

6. With the vertical feed, lower the wheel until the tool contacts the wheel slightly below the axis.
7. With longitudinal and cross-feed handwheels, position the tool to make the cut.
8. Start the machine. Then with the handwheel at the rear of the attachment, move the diamond tool across the edge of the wheel, taking a cut of about .0005″. Take two or three passes before advancing the tool.

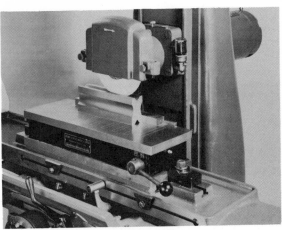

Fig. 13-37. Grinding a V-Shaped Recess
(Brown & Sharpe)

445

Fig. 13-38. Tool Mounted at Right Angles to Slide
(Brown & Sharpe)

9. With the longitudinal table feed, advance the tool for a second cut; again take at least two passes.
10. Continue as in steps 7 and 8 until the wheel has the desired shape, except for a light finishing cut.

Fig. 13-39. Shaping Convex Surface on a Wheel
(Brown & Sharpe)

CAUTION: *Do not advance the tool more than about .0005" at any advancement.*

11. Finish grinding with light cuts.
12. When the operation has been completed, remove the attachment and return to the place where kept when not in use.

Fig. 13-39 illustrates a radius and wheel truing attachment positioned for grinding a convex surface on the face of the wheel.

UNIT 118 — How To True or Dress Wheels on Universal or Plain Grinders

Procedure for Truing a Wheel on Footstock Fixture

1. Secure and mount on the footstock, a footstock type of wheel-truing fixture, as in Fig. 13-40.

   If preferred, a table fixture (Fig. 13-41) may be clamped to the table of a plain grinding machine.

2. Position the grinding wheel so that it will clear the footstock as the table is traversed (moved back and forth), carrying the diamond tool across the face of the wheel.

3. Secure a diamond tool, and clamp it in the fixture as shown in Fig. 13-40. The point of the diamond should touch the center

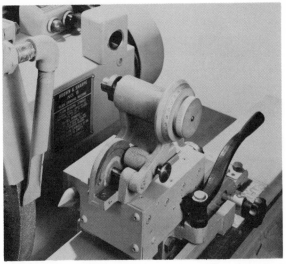

Fig. 13-40. Wheel-Truing Fixture Mounted on Footstock
(Brown & Sharpe)

Fig. 13-41. Table Wheel-Truing Fixture
(Brown & Sharpe)

of the face of the wheel, which usually is the high part. The diamond tool should contact the wheel very slightly below the axis of the wheel. This will prevent gouging and possible chattering. With the tool in position, tighten the footstock clamp.

NOTE: Because a diamond wears through use, it is important that the tool always be positioned in a manner that will present a sharp edge to the face of the wheel. When the diamond has become cone-shaped, turn it in the holder so as to present it at a new angle to the wheel.

4. Position and adjust reversing dogs so that power table travel can be used. Be sure to provide for passing the truing tool a short distance beyond the edge of the wheel on each stroke.
5. Adjust the table travel for a moderately rapid rate for the roughing cut.
6. Set the grind-true switch at true. This will assure a constant flow of coolant.
7. Start the machine, and position the sliding table so that the diamond tool is in contact with one edge of the wheel. Round the corner of the wheel slightly by manipulating the cross and longitudinal hand feeds.

CAUTION: *Be sure the wheel guard is in position and fastened securely.*

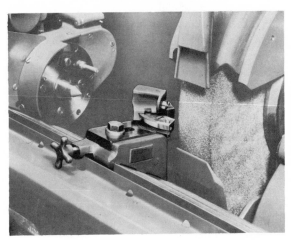

Fig. 13-42. Radius Wheel-Truing Attachment
(Brown & Sharpe)

Slight rounding of the corners prevents chipping the edges of the wheel when the tool is fed straight across its face.

8. Round the other corner of the wheel in like manner.

If preferred, the edges of the wheel may be slightly rounded with a hand-held diamond tool or a radius wheel-truing attachment such as illustrated in Fig. 13-42.

9. Start the table travel by pulling the start-stop lever.
10. Advance the wheel to take a cut of .0005" to .001".

11. Continue passing the tool across the face of the wheel until the wheel is running true. Then reduce the speed of table travel, and take finishing cuts of .0005″, followed by one or two of .0001″ or .00025″.

12. When through truing (or dressing) a wheel, remove the truing attachment, and thoroughly clean the machine to remove grit and other foreign matter. Return attachment and other tools to the place where kept when not in use.

Procedure for Dressing a Wheel

1. Proceed as in steps 1 through 12 inclusive, above.

Procedure for Truing the Radius

Radius truing is the process of rounding the corners of the wheel for the purpose of grinding up to shoulders where a fillet is required. It is accomplished by means of a *radius wheel-truing attachment*, Fig. 13-42. This device provides a convenient means of shaping either the right-hand or left-hand corner of the grinding wheel within radius limits of zero and ½″.

1. Secure, mount, and position a radius wheel-truing attachment on the swivel table, Fig. 13-42. Clamp the attachment in position with the knob at the front of the attachment.

2. With the cross feed, bring the wheel to within a short distance of the radius attachment.

3. Determine the radial setting of the diamond tool by subtracting the desired radius from the figures stamped on the back

face of the toolholder. These figures show the exact radial distance from that surface to the center about which the diamond tool is rotated.

4. Using a micrometer or gage, set the tool at the determined radial distance.

5. Swing the diamond-tool holder to its forward position (at right angles to the wheel spindle); then loosen the clamping bolt at the front of the traverse adjustment slide, and move the attachment forward until the diamond touches the face of the wheel. Clamp the slide in position by tightening the nut on the clamping bolt.

6. Move the table sufficiently for the diamond tool to clear the wheel; then swivel the holder until the tool is at right angles to the side of the wheel. With the table handwheel, move the table forward until the diamond touches the wheel. The attachment is now correctly positioned to form the desired radius.

7. Withdraw the table slightly, so that when the diamond-tool holder is swiveled on the segment, the tools will cut a small amount of material from the corner of the wheel. Swivel the holder back and forth around the segment, removing a small amount of the wheel at each pass. Keep the diamond advancing toward the wheel by moving the table of the machine a small amount after each stroke.

8. When the operation has been completed, remove the attachment, and thoroughly clean both it and the machine. Return the attachment and other tools to the place where kept when not in use.

UNIT

119   How To Shape Wheels on Plain or Universal Grinders

In the manufacture of metals and other hard substances, it frequently is necessary to grind one or more surfaces at an angle, a radial shape, or a combination of these. This is accomplished by appropriately shaping the face of the grinding wheel.

General Procedure

1. True the grinding wheel, Unit 118. Be sure to protect the eyes with properly fitted goggles. Also be sure that the wheel guard is fastened securely in position.
2. Secure a *radius and angle wheel-truing attachment*, such as that shown in Fig. 13-43. When appropriately adjusted, this attachment will form accurate convex or concave faces on wheels, as desired, up to 1″ radius.

A second type of radius wheel-truing attachment is shown in Figs. 13-44 and 13-45. A second type of angle-truing attachment is shown in Fig. 13-46. Both of these attachments may be used on universal grinders.

3. Position the fixture on the table of the machine; then tighten the clamping bolts.

Fig. 13-43. Radius and Angle Wheel-Truing Attachment (Brown & Sharpe)

Fig. 13-45. Radius Wheel-Truing Attachment for Concave Radius (Brown & Sharpe)

Fig. 13-44. Radius Wheel-Truing Attachment Arranged for Convex Radius (Brown & Sharpe)

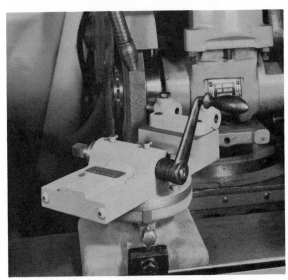

Fig. 13-46. Angle Wheel-Truing Attachment (Brown & Sharpe)

449

Procedure for a Convex Face

1. Select a wheel appropriate to the work to be done and with the same face width as the radius to be formed. Mount the wheel on the spindle.

2. Proceed as in steps 1 through 3 in "Procedure for Truing the Radius," Unit 118.

3. Place a diamond tool in the toolholder parallel with the slide, as in Fig. 13-43. The diamond tool should contact the wheel slightly below the axis of the wheel. This will prevent gouging and possible chattering. Position the diamond point by means of the setting gage at the front of the toolholder. Clamp the tool in position.

4. Adjust the slide by means of the hand-wheel, withdrawing it to the right of center, by the scale on the slide, until the radius desired registers (for example, ¾″). Then tighten the clamping screw at the back of the slide.

5. With the longitudinal table feed, position the fixture so that the axis of the diamond tool is centered with respect to the center of the face of the wheel.

6. Start the machine. With the cross feed, advance the wheel toward the tool. At the same time, swivel the attachment on its base. Be careful to avoid a heavy first cut at the edges of the wheel.

7. Pass the tool across the face of the wheel two or more times by swiveling the fixture on its base. Then, with the cross feed, advance the wheel about .0005″, and again take two or more strokes.

8. Continue with repeated strokes and wheel adjustments until the face of the wheel has the desired radius (shape), leaving about .0005″ or .001″ for finishing.

   CAUTION: *Do not advance the wheel more than about .0005″ at any single advancement.*

9. Finish grinding with a series of light cuts, using a feed of about .00025″.

10. When the operation has been completed, remove the attachment and thoroughly clean both it and the machine. Return the attachment and tools to the place where kept when not in use.

Procedure for a Concave Face

1. Proceed as in steps 1 through 3, "General Procedure."

2. To form a concave face on the wheel, clamp the diamond tool in the toolholder *parallel to the slide*, as in Fig. 13-43. Position the diamond point by means of the setting gage at the front of the toolholder. Clamp the tool in position.

3. Adjust the slide by means of the hand-wheel, advancing it to the left of center by the scale on the slide until the radius desired registers (for example, ⅝″). Then tighten the clamping screw at the back of the slide.

4. With the longitudinal table feed, position the fixture so that the axis of the diamond tool is centered with respect to the center of the face of the wheel.

5. Start the machine. Then with the cross feed, bring the wheel into contact with the tool.

6. Pass the tool across the face of the wheel by swiveling the attachment on its base. Take two or more strokes. Then by means of the cross feed, advance the wheel toward the tool .0005″.

7. Continue with repeated strokes and wheel adjustments until the desired shape has been achieved, except for a small amount of stock for finishing, about .0005″ or .001″.

   CAUTION: *Do not advance the wheel more than about .0005″ at any single advancement.*

8. Finish grinding with a series of light cuts, using a feed of about .00025″.

9. When the operation has been completed, remove the attachment and thoroughly clean both it and the table of the machine. Return the attachment and tools to the place where kept when not in use.

Procedure for an Angular Face

1. Select a wheel suited to the work to be done.

2. Mount the wheel on the spindle, Unit 115.

3. Secure an angle wheel-truing attachment, Fig. 13-46. Position and clamp the attachment on the table of the machine.

4. Swivel the attachment to the desired angle on its swivel base.

5. With the longitudinal table feed and the cross feed, position the wheel so that it just clears the diamond point.

6. With the table feed, traverse the diamond toward the wheel for a light cut, about 0.0005″. The table remains stationary while the cut is being made.

7. Start the machine. With the crank provided on the angle wheel-truing attachment, traverse the diamond across the wheel at the desired angle, Fig. 13-46.

8. Continue as in steps 6 and 7 until the wheel is formed to the proper angle and depth. In Fig. 13-47, a wheel is shaped with an angular face for grinding a diameter and a slight shoulder.

9. When the operation is completed, remove the attachment and thoroughly clean the machine. Return the attachment and other tools to the place where kept when not in use.

Fig. 13-47. Grinding a Diameter and a Slight Shoulder
(Brown & Sharpe)

How To Grind Centers

UNIT

120

To produce accurate work when grinding stock held between centers, the centers themselves must be as accurate as the operator can make them. Through constant use, centers lose their accuracy and must be reconditioned. This may be done by activating the live center on a machine equipped for this purpose. The method of truing the center is similar to that of grinding an angle or taper, as described in Units 124 and 128.

When the headstock center cannot be activated, use a special attachment as in Fig. 13-48.

Fig. 13-48. Grinding a Center Using a Special Attachment (Brown & Sharpe)

Procedure

1. Secure a center grinding attachment, and place on the swivel table of the machine.

2. With a clean cloth, wipe the body of the center and the hole in the attachment. Both must be clean.

3. Insert the center in the hole in the attachment. Be sure it is firmly seated.

4. Advance the grinding wheel to a forward position. Then approximately position the grinding attachment, and fasten it in position with the clamping bolt, as in Fig. 13-48.

5. Protect the eyes by wearing properly fitted goggles.

6. Set the grind-true switch at "true." This will give a constant flow of coolant.

7. Start the machine. Advance the wheel against the workpiece (center), and, at the same time, rotate the center in the attachment by means of the handwheel at the rear of the attachment, Fig. 13-48.

   CAUTION: *Be sure the wheel guard is fastened securely in position.*

8. Continue grinding until the center is true and smooth.

9. When the operation is completed, remove the center from the attachment, using a knockout rod, if necessary. Then remove the attachment and thoroughly clean both it and the machine. Return the attachment to its proper place.

UNIT

121   Grinding Cutting Speeds and Feeds

When setting up a grinding machine, it is necessary to consider wheel speed, work speed, and table travel.

Wheel Speed

The recommended surface speeds for most vitrified-bonded grinding wheels range from 4000 to 6500 feet per minute (fpm). For cylindrical grinding, the speeds generally range from 5500 to 6500 fpm. Speeds above 6500 fpm are dangerous and should not be used. Speeds below 5500 fpm are used when a soft wheel action is desired.

Surface wheel speed must not be confused with revolutions per minute (rpm). As the diameter of the wheel is decreased, the rpm of the wheel may be increased. When the diameter of the wheel is increased, the rpm should be decreased an amount sufficient to keep the surface speed below the maximum of 6500 fpm.

To determine the rpm necessary to produce a surface speed which will not exceed 6500 fpm, one must first find the circumference of the wheel in feet, and then divide the surface speed desired by this circumference. For example, the circumference of an 11″ wheel =

$$\frac{11'' \times 3.1416}{12''} = 2.88 \text{ feet circumference}$$

Then:

$$\text{rpm} = \frac{\text{Surface speed}}{\text{Circumference of wheel}} = \frac{6500}{2.88}$$
$$= 2257 \text{ rpm}$$

The large pulley on a typical cylindrical grinder will produce a spindle speed of about 2077 rpm. With an 11″ wheel, this will produce a surface speed of 5828 fpm:

Surface speed = rpm of spindle × circumference of wheel in feet.

Example: Surface speed $= 2077 \times 2.88$
$\qquad\qquad = 5828$ fpm

This speed is within the 5500 to 6500 fpm limit recommended, and, assuming the appropriate type of wheel has been selected, it should produce work of a good quality.

A higher surface speed may be achieved by using a larger wheel, for example, a 12″ wheel.

Example: $\dfrac{12 \times 3.1416}{12} = 3.1416$ circumference of wheel

Surface speed $= 1772 \times 3.14 = 5564$ fpm
$\qquad\qquad\qquad\qquad\qquad$ ence of wheel

When rpm $= 2077$, *then,*

Surface speed $= 2077 \times 3.14 = 6512$ fpm

This produces a speed in excess of that recommended as a maximum. Therefore, a lower rpm should be used, for example, 1772 rpm.

Then,

Surface speed $= 1772 \times 3.14 = 5564$ fpm

This is only a little above the minimum recommended, but it is a safer operating speed.

Work Surface Speed

Recommended work speed for cylindrical grinding is from 50 to 100 fpm for most materials. Aluminum, brass, and other soft material may be ground at the rate of 200 fpm. A work speed of from 50 to 70 fpm will produce good results. The slower the workpiece revolves, the harder will be the wheel reaction. On the other hand, too much speed will not accomplish more work and is likely to cause excessive wear and possible damage to the machine. Consequently, the work speed should not be lower than the minimum nor above the maximum recommended. For finishing cuts, work speed usually is increased by about 33 percent.

On most plain grinding machines, changes in work speed are made by a four-step pulley on the headstock of the grinder. On many universal grinding machines, changes are accomplished by setting the headstock speed-selector dial to the desired rpm.

Example: Assume the diameter of the workpiece is ¾″ and a work speed of no more than 70 fpm is required. Find the rpm of the headstock, by applying the following formula:

$$\text{rpm} = \frac{\text{Work speed in feet} \times 12}{\text{Circumference of work in inches}}$$

Then:

$$\text{rpm} = \frac{\text{Work speed} \times 12}{3.14 \times \text{Dia. of work}}$$

$$\frac{70 \times 12}{3.1416 \times .75} = \frac{70}{.1950} = 354 \text{ rpm}$$
$$.26$$

Setting the work to revolve at 319 rpm will produce a satisfactory work speed.

Table Travel

The maximum recommended rate of table travel for rough grinding is about two-thirds of the width of the grinding wheel per revolution of the workpiece. For finish grinding, a rate of travel equal to approximately one-third or less of the width of the face of the wheel will produce good results. When a very smooth finish is desired, the rate of travel may be as low as one-eighth of the width of the wheel.

To determine the rate of travel in inches, multiply the desired work speed in revolutions per minute by the distance in inches the workpiece should travel per revolution.

Example: Given a 1″ wheel, a work speed of 319 rpm, and a table travel per revolution of two-thirds the width of wheel, the rate of table travel in inches per minute (ipm) equals:

Table travel $= \text{rpm} \times \tfrac{2}{3}$ width of wheel.

Table travel $= 319 \times .66 = 210$ ipm.

Table travel rates generally may be set from 3 to 150 ipm.

In the example given, the highest rate of travel available would be used, and, if necessary, the rpm of the work would be reduced. Changes in longitudinal table travel are made by means of the table speed-selector knob. On some grinding machines, the rate of travel may be changed while the table is traveling.

Depth of Feed

Assuming that a suitable wheel, correct wheel and work speeds, and proper table travel have been selected, then the depth of the cut is a matter of adapting the cutting load to the nature of the material and the power of the machine.

When making roughing cuts, beginners tend to take a series of light cuts instead of a heavy cut which will remove a major part of the material at a single pass. Experienced operators usually take a heavy roughing cut. Ordinarily a roughing cut should be from .001″ to .004″ (thousandths), and a finishing cut from .0002″ to .0010″ (ten thousandths). The amount of stock left for grinding depends upon the character of work and the nature of the material. On some materials or workpieces, as little as .005″ might suffice, while on others, as much as .04″ should be left.

Through experience, an operator can determine whether a cut is heavy or light by the volume of sparks that flow from the cut. A heavy volume indicates a heavy cut, and vice versa.

The Universal Grinding Machine

The universal grinding machine, its principal parts, and the operations which it is capable of performing were explained briefly in Unit 113. This unit, however, is concerned with a more detailed study of the universal grinder, including its principle parts, operational controls, and machine accessories. The operator must be acquainted with this information, before he attempts to set up and operate the machine.

Principal Parts

The principal parts and the operational controls for a No. 1 Brown and Sharpe universal grinding machine are shown in Figs. 13-52 and 13-53. Although the particular controls and their locations may vary with different makes, the principles involved in their operation are similar. Nevertheless, it is advisable to study the operator's handbook supplied with the machine, before attempting to operate the machine.

Wheel Stand: The wheel stand unit includes the *external grinding spindle*, which is shown in position for external grinding, Fig. 13-54. The *internal grinding spindle* is located immediately above the external spindle, and it is in a retracted position. For internal grinding operations, this spindle is brought forward and fastened in position as shown in Fig. 13-69. The external spindle is driven by a V-belt from its motor, while the internal spindle is driven with a flat belt from an independent motor.

The *wheel spindle head*, Fig. 13-54, supports both grinding spindles. It may be swiveled 90° in either direction from zero, as indicated by the scale graduated in degrees. The wheel spindle head, universal turret, and wheel slide are held secure by a single bolt. The head of the bolt is located directly below the internal grinding motor.

The *universal turret* may be swiveled and locked in four different angular positions, each 90° apart. In these positions, the wheel may be located closer or further away from the sliding table, as desired. Each 90° position provides for a 2″ difference in location of the wheel spindle head. This adjustment, together with the 5″ maximum traverse movement along the *wheel slide*, makes it possible to properly locate the wheel for large- or small-diameter workpieces. Cross feed of the grinding wheel may be operated manually with the cross-feed handwheel or automatically with a cross-feed mechanism.

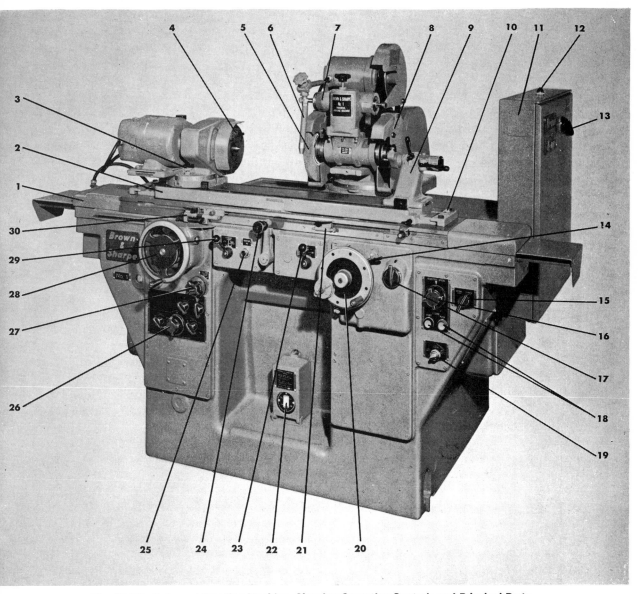

Fig. 13-52. Universal Grinding Machine, Showing Operating Controls and Principal Parts
(Front View) (Brown & Sharpe)

(1) Sliding table; (2) Swivel table; (3) Headstock; (4) Work driving plate; (5) External grinding wheel; (6) Coolant nozzle; (7) Internal grinding spindle unit; (8) Wheel guard, right; (9) Footstock; (10) Swivel table adjustment scale; (11) Electrical control compartment; (12) Disconnect switch indicator light; (13) Disconnect switch; (14) Switch operating slide throw-out lever; disengages cross-feed positive stop to permit continuous rotation of cross-feed handwheel; (15) Internal-external grinding motor selector switch; (16) Headstock speed control knob; (17) Cross-feed gear shifting knob; (18) Machine start and stop push buttons; (19) Lever-handwheel selector switch; (20) Cross-feed handwheel; (21) Table dog, right; (22) Hydraulic tank filler opening and gage; (23) Cross-feed control lever; (24) Table reverse lever; (25) Headstock jog button; (26) Cross-feed control knobs; (27) Table speed selector knob; (28) Table handwheel; (29) Headstock and table control lever; (30) Table dog, left.

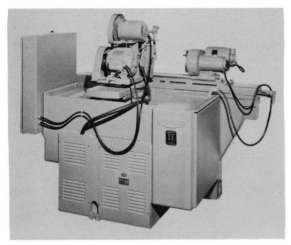

Fig. 13-53. Universal Grinding Machine (Rear View) (Brown & Sharpe)

The *wheel slide base* has ways (bearing surfaces) on which the wheel slide traverses. This base may be swiveled up to 90° to either side of zero for face grinding or for grinding steep angles, Figs. 13-64 and 13-65. The base must be clamped securely in position for all grinding operations.

Headstock Unit: The headstock unit, Fig. 13-55, is a self-contained unit including the headstock spindle, driving motor, work-driving plate with driving arm, and headstock base. The headstock may be swiveled up to 180° on the base which is graduated in degrees. It is swiveled for face grinding or for steep angular grinding of workpieces which are mounted on the headstock spindle or in a chuck, Fig. 13-67.

The headstock unit is aligned on the swivel table by a lip at the rear of the base. Two

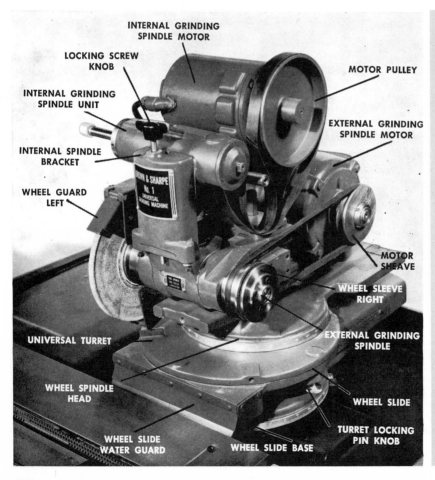

Fig. 13-54. Wheel Stand Unit (with Belt Guards Removed) (Brown & Sharpe) Note that the external grinding spindle is in grinding position.

clamp bolts at the front of the base hold the unit securely in position. The table surfaces should be clean and free from nicks or dents when the unit is clamped in place. A variable-speed motor provides speeds ranging from about 60 to 600 rpm. Headstock speeds are controlled by the headstock speed-control knob, Fig. 13-56.

Headstock spindle rotation on the machine in Fig. 13-52 may be controlled with a *lever control* or a *handwheel control*. When the *lever-handwheel selector-switch knob* (Fig. 13-56) is set at lever control, headstock spindle rotation is started and stopped with the *headstock and table control lever*, Fig. 13-57. With this lever at *headstock running*, the spindle rotates and coolant flows; then when the lever is moved to *table running*, the table travels. When the lever-handwheel selector-switch knob is set for *handwheel control*, the headstock spindle is started and stopped by a switch which is controlled by the cross-feed handwheel (to be explained shortly).

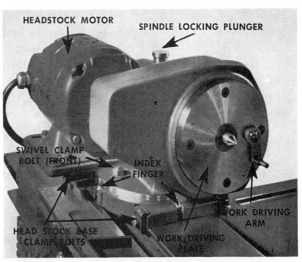

Fig. 13-55. Headstock Unit with Work-Driving Plate in Position (Splash Guard Removed) (Brown & Sharpe)

table travel. For convenience in wheel truing, the knob on the table reverse lever may be pulled forward to permit the table to be traversed beyond the limit of the dogs.

Longitudinal Table Travel

The sliding table may be traversed manually with the table handwheel or automatically by a power-actuated hydraulic system. For power table travel, the *lever-handwheel selector switch*, Fig. 13-56, first is set at *lever control*. The table then is started or stopped with the headstock and table control lever; with the headstock spindle running, the table starts to travel when the lever is turned to the *table running* position. Table travel rates from 3″ to 150″ per minute, as desired, may be selected with the *table speed-selector knob*, Fig. 13-57.

Table Dwell: The table may be set to dwell for a period of 0 to 2½ seconds at one or at both ends of the work for each table reversal. Two knobs located near the table speed selector, Fig. 13-57, are used for this purpose.

Table reversal may be controlled manually or automatically with the *table reverse lever*, Fig. 13-57. For automatic operation, the *adjustable table dogs* may be set to actuate the table reverse lever for any desired length of

Cross-Feed Mechanism

The cross feed of the grinding wheel may be operated manually or by power, as determined by the position of the *cross-feed control lever*, Fig. 13-58. For power operation, the cross-feed handwheel is rotated slightly to the left, in order to release the *switch operating slide*. The feed is then engaged by throwing the cross-feed control lever to *start*. When grinding is complete, a fixed pin in the back of the cross-feed wheel contacts the switch operating slide, thus stopping the cross feed. The cross-feed control lever is then thrown to *stop*, and the wheel is withdrawn by rotating the handwheel to its starting position. The cross-feed control lever must be in the *start* position in order to start the cross-feed mechanism in operation, in either handwheel or lever control. This movement may be stopped by turning the cross-feed control lever to the *stop* position.

For automatic operation, the *switch operating slide throw-out lever* must always be in its lower position. For hand cross feed over the complete range of wheel slide travel, this lever should be in its upper position.

Selecting Amount of Cross Feed: The cross-feed handwheel has 200 graduations, each representing 0.0005″. Hence, one complete revolution of the handwheel represents 0.100″ on the diameter of the workpiece. Fine adjustments may be made with the index dial which has 0.0001″ graduations. Thus, one complete turn of this dial represents 0.004″ on the diameter of the work.

The amount of automatic cross feed is set with the cross-feed knob, Fig. 13-57. Cross-feed rates may be set for each or alternate table reversal in amounts ranging from 0.0001″ to 0.003″ on work diameter.

The *internal-external grinding selector knob*, Fig. 13-56, should be set for the type of grinding operation being performed. By setting the knob at the internal position for internal grinding, the handwheel may be turned counterclockwise for advancing the grinding wheel into the work, the same as for external grinding; the grinding wheel then is positioned at the rear of the hole so that it may be easily observed by the operator, Fig. 13-70. The

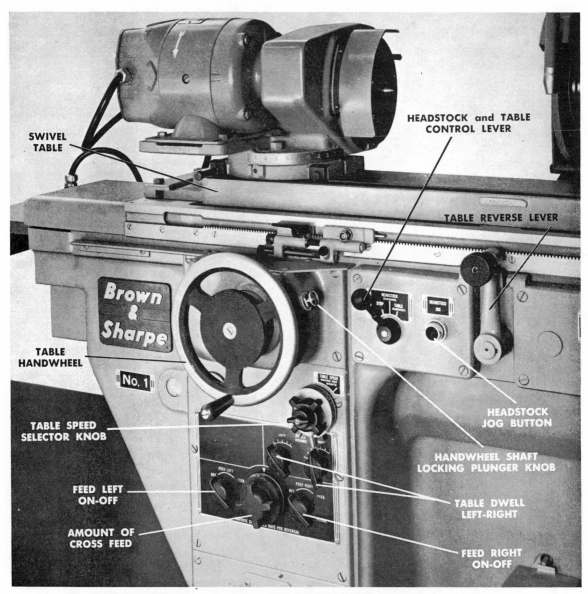

Fig. 13-57. Handwheel for Longitudinal Table Travel and Controls at Left Front of Machine
(Brown & Sharpe)

458

handwheel graduations and positive stop then are used in the same manner as they are for external grinding.

Setting Cross-Feed Positive Stop

Universal grinding machines generally are provided with some type of cross-feed *positive-stop* mechanism. This mechanism may be set to cause further cross feeding to cease when the work is ground to the desired diameter. The particular method for setting the positive-stop mechanism may vary with different machines, but the principles involved are similar.

The procedure for setting the positive-stop mechanism, Fig. 13-58, for a Brown and Sharpe universal grinding machine (Fig. 13-52) will be described. The pin, located behind the index dial on the cross-feed handwheel, comes

in contact with the right-hand side of the switch operating slide when the grinding wheel advances to the desired work diameter; this provides a positive stop for the cross feed when the handwheel is at zero. The stopping point for the positive stop is set for the desired work diameter in the following manner:

1. With a workpiece mounted between centers and with all other setup adjustments made, use the cross-feed handwheel to bring the grinding wheel forward until it just touches the work.

2. Pull out the disengagement knob, thus freeing the handwheel. Turn the handwheel until the fixed stop pin comes in contact with the right side of the switch operating slide.

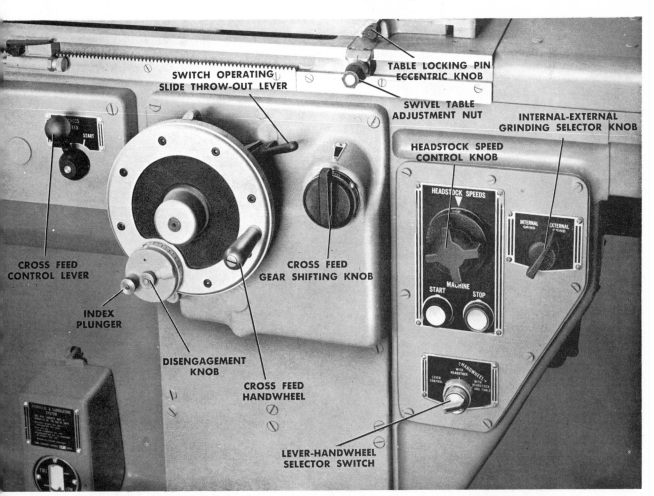

Fig. 13-56. Cross-Feed Handwheel and Controls at Right Front of Machine (Brown & Sharpe)

3. Again engage the engagement knob. Engage the cross feed, and allow the work to be ground to the size permitted by the stop. When the grinding wheel has sparked out at the footstock end, disengage the cross feed, and turn the handwheel back to its starting point.

4. Carefully measure the work diameter, and set the index dial for the amount of stock still to be removed. When the index dial is turned clockwise, the diameter of the work is reduced. To avoid grinding the work undersize, set the stop to grind one or two thousandths oversize for this stage of the initial setup.

5. Engage the cross feed, and again grind the work until cross feed is stopped by the positive stop. When the wheel has sparked out at the footstock end, disengage the cross feed.

6. Measure the diameter of the work, and make a final setting of the index dial for the amount of stock to be removed. As a final check, run through the grinding cycle again and measure the work. If further adjustments are necessary, make them as described under this step.

Accessories

Several accessory items are available for use on universal grinding machines. These include universal back rests for supporting long workpieces, Fig. 13-63; angle wheel-truing attachment, Fig. 13-46; radius wheel-truing attachment, Figs. 13-44 and 13-45; 3-jaw universal chuck, Fig. 13-81; and a collet attachment, Fig. 13-80. Chucks and collets are used for internal grinding operations as shown in Fig. 13-70. They also are used for face-grinding operations as shown in Fig. 13-67.

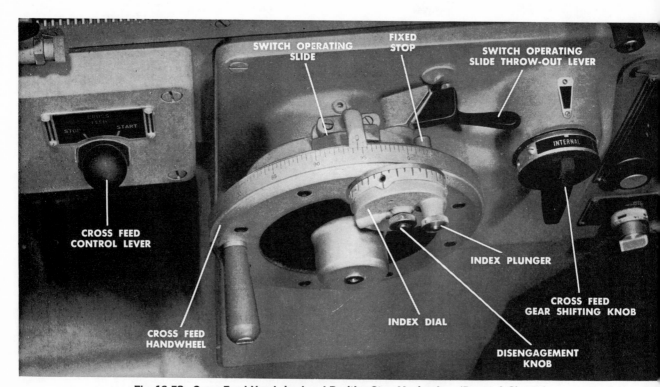

Fig. 13-58. Cross-Feed Handwheel and Positive Stop Mechanism (Brown & Sharpe)

How To Operate Universal Grinders—Cylindrical Work

The procedure described in this unit is that of setting up a standard universal grinding machine to grind the exterior of straight cylindrical work. In general, the procedure is applicable to standard makes of universal grinding machines.

CAUTION: *To produce accurate work, care and precision must be exercised in setting up a grinding machine. For the same reason, the machine should be properly lubricated and warmed up before starting to grind.*

When starting a universal grinding machine for the first time after it has been idle for several hours, press the start button; then almost immediately, push the stop button. Repeat this three or four times so that the bearings of the spindle will be well lubricated before running the spindle at operating speed.

General Procedure

1. Select a wheel suited to the work to be performed, and mount it on the wheel spindle. (See Unit 115.) Be sure the wheel is sound. Support the wheel by inserting the forefinger in the spindle hole; then test by striking it a light blow on the edge with a hammer or some hard substance. A clear ring indicates a sound wheel.

   If the wheel is changed, it will be necessary to true, and possibly balance, the new wheel before attempting to grind a workpiece. (See Unit 115.)

2. Determine a desirable work surface speed. (See Unit 121.) Set the headstock speed-selector dial accordingly.

3. Determine desirable wheel surface speed. If necessary change the sheave on the spindle motor shaft.

4. Examine all driving-belt tensions. A V-belt is properly tensioned when a light pressure will depress the belt slightly. Adjustment of the wheel spindle drive belt is made as directed in the operator's handbook provided with the machine.

5. Determine the rate of table travel, if any. The rate may vary from about 3″ to 150″ per minute. When the surface to be ground is the same width or is narrower than the width of the wheel, no table travel is necessary. The same holds true when plunge or straight-in grinding a narrow recess.

6. Check to make sure that the swivel table is set at zero. If adjustment is necessary, loosen the clamping bolts at each end of the table. Then make the adjustment by means of the adjusting nut at the front of the machine. See Fig. 13-59. Verify the setting by a trial cut at each end of the workpiece.

7. Thoroughly clean the table and ways; then position the headstock and footstock to receive the workpiece. To avoid excessive wear at either end of the ways, the headstock and footstock should be an equal distance from the respective ends of the table. Align the headstock by means of the flange on the base, Fig. 13-55.

Fig. 13-59. Table Swiveled for Grinding a Taper
(Brown & Sharpe)

8. Examine the centers of the grinding machine to determine that they are clean, smooth, and ground at the correct angle. Test with a center gage. If the centers are not ground with an inclusive angle of 60°, the angle should be corrected by regrinding. See Unit 120.

9. Before starting to grind, attach table water guards, and position the coolant piping and nozzle.

Procedure for Mounting Stock

1. Secure a workpiece; make certain that the center holes are clean, of the correct shape and depth, and well oiled.

2. Secure a suitable driving dog, and place it on one end of the workpiece.

3. With the cross-feed handwheel, move the wheel slide back and forth. The universal turret should be so positioned that the wheel will come far enough forward to grind the work, yet will give sufficient clearance for inserting the workpiece between centers. If necessary to adjust the universal turret, loosen the clamping bolt; then make the adjustment and re-clamp, Fig. 13-54.

4. For straight cylindrical grinding, the wheel slide should be at right angles to the sliding table. The grinding wheel spindle should be parallel with the sliding table.

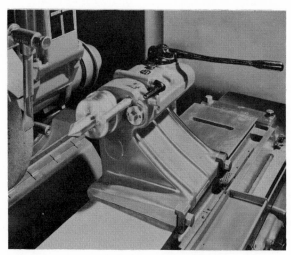

Fig. 13-60. Footstock of the Universal Grinder
(Brown & Sharpe)

5. Place the drive end of the workpiece on the headstock center; then slide the footstock forward until it supports the other end of the workpiece. Draw the operating lever (Fig. 13-60) forward about a third of the way to withdraw the footstock center from the workpiece. Hold the operating lever in the above position by tightening the spindle clamp (Fig. 13-60). Now move the footstock forward until the center is seated in the center hole of the workpiece. Align the lip on the footstock with the edge of the swivel table, and fasten the footstock in position by tightening the clamping bolts. Release the spindle clamp to permit the spring at the rear of the spindle to push the center firmly against the workpiece.

CAUTION: *Be sure the pressure of the spring is great enough to hold the center firmly against the work. Avoid excessive pressure.*

6. With the cross-feed handwheel, Fig. 13-56, advance the grinding wheel until it is within ¼″ of the workpiece.

Procedure for Setting Table Travel

Table travel may be accomplished by hand or power feed. When power feed is employed, stop dogs (Fig. 13-61) should be used. Stop dogs may be used with hand feed at the option of the operator.

1. To set the table reverse dogs, first move the table to the left until the right-hand edge of the grinding wheel is one-third of its width to the right of the end of the workpiece, which usually is an open end.

2. Push the table reverse lever to the left as far as it will go.

3. Move the right-hand dog along the rack until it comes against the table reverse lever. Then clamp the dog in position.

4. With the handwheel, move the table to the right until the wheel is located at the position where the cut is to stop; for example, within ¾″ of the driving dog or against a shoulder. Set the left stop dog.

5. Back the wheel at least 1″ away from the work. This will allow the wheel to clear the work and the work driving dog, in

case the table reversing dogs require further adjustment after the grinder is started.

Procedure for Manual Cross Feed

1. To feed the wheel manually over the complete range of wheel slide travel, turn the switch operating slide throw-out lever, Fig. 13-58, to its upper position.

2. Start the machine and engage the longitudinal table travel at the proper rate. The rate may range from 3″ to 150″ per minute. Set the table dwell knobs to cause the table to dwell at each reversal. Usually it may be set between 0 and 2½ seconds.

   Note whether the table stop dogs need further adjustment. If necessary, stop the machine and adjust. The wheel should clear any work shoulders, the driving dog, and the tailstock spindle.

3. With the cross-feed handwheel, advance the grinding wheel to the workpiece, taking a moderate feed. (See Unit 121.) Then engage the table travel.

   CAUTION: *Before starting to grind, the operator should protect his eyes by wearing properly fitted safety goggles.*

4. When the wheel has sparked out at the footstock end of the work, stop the table travel and rotation of the work. Then, without withdrawing the wheel, accurately measure the diameter of the work. Calculate the number of whole thousandths, plus the number of ten-thousandths (0.0001) of an inch still to be removed. Set the positive-stop mechanism so that further feeding will cease when the diameter is reduced to allow at least 0.001″ oversize. Unit 122 includes the procedure for engaging the positive-stop mechanism.

   Since these mechanisms vary in design, it may be necessary to consult the operator's handbook for the specific machine in order to determine how to set the mechanism properly.

5. Engage the headstock spindle rotation, and advance the grinding wheel for the desired depth of cut with the cross-feed handwheel. Then engage the table travel for completion of the cut. When the wheel sparks out at the end of the workpiece, disengage the table travel. Continue this procedure, using manual cross feed, until the work has been reduced several thousandths of an inch, but not down to the positive-stop setting. Stop the table travel and work rotation when the wheel sparks out at the footstock end of the work.

6. Accurately measure the workpiece to determine the number of thousandths plus ten-thousandths of stock still to be removed. Check to see that the positive-stop mechanism is still set to cease feeding when the work is at least 0.001″ oversize. Readjust the positive stop if necessary.

7. Start the machine, advance the wheel, and continue grinding until further feeding is ceased by the positive-stop mechanism. When the wheel sparks out at the footstock end of the work, free of the work, stop the table travel and work rotation.

8. Measure the work diameter to see that it is down to about 0.001″ oversize. If it is significantly more than this, reset the positive-stop mechanism accordingly and grind to 0.001″ oversize as in steps 6 and 7.

9. Accurately measure the work to determine the number of ten-thousandths (0.0001) of an inch still to be removed.

Fig. 13-61. Table Reversing Lever and Dog
(Brown & Sharpe)

10. Start the work rotating, and with the ten-thousandths hand-feed dial, set the feed for several ten-thousandths of one inch, if it is certain that this much material is to be removed. It is better to take several very light feeds than to grind the work undersize. Engage the table travel, and complete the cut.

11. When the wheel sparks out (with the wheel at the footstock end of the work, and clear of the work), stop the table travel and work rotation. Accurately measure the size. If more material must be removed, proceed as in step 10. When the work is ground to the specified dimension, back the wheel away from the work. Then remove the workpiece. Long pieces should be supported by one or more back rests, Fig. 13-62.

Procedure for Automatic Cross Feed

1. Mount a workpiece between centers as in steps 1 through 5, "Procedure for Mounting Stock."

2. Set the table travel as in steps 1 through 5 under "Procedure for Setting Table Travel."

3. Start the machine, engage the table traverse, and then advance the grinding wheel by means of the cross-feed handwheel. Take a moderate cut.

Fig. 13-62. Universal Back Rests in Position
(Brown & Sharpe)

CAUTION: *Before starting to grind, protect the eyes by wearing properly fitted safety glasses.*

4. Stop table travel and work rotation when the wheel has sparked out at the footstock end. Then, without withdrawing the wheel, accurately measure the diameter of the work. Calculate the number of whole thousandths, plus ten-thousandths (0.0001), of an inch still to be removed. Set the positive-stop mechanism so that further feeding will cease when the diameter is reduced to allow at least 0.001″ oversize.

   Since positive-stop mechanisms vary, it may be necessary to consult the operator's handbook for the specific machine in order to determine how to set the mechanism properly.

5. Set the rate of power cross feed desired with the power cross-feed selector. Rates usually vary from 0.0001″ to 0.003″.

6. Set the knobs which determine whether the cross feed is to be operative at each table reversal or at alternate reversals. When operative at each reversal, the wheel wears more evenly.

7. Set the knobs which determine the amount of table dwell at each end of the work. The dwell period usually may vary from 0 to 2½ seconds at each table reversal.

8. Engage the table travel, engage the power cross-feed lever, and grind the work until it has been reduced several thousandths of an inch, but not down to the positive stop.

9. When the wheel sparks out at the footstock end, disengage the power cross feed, table travel, and work rotation. Accurately measure the workpiece to determine the number of thousandths, plus ten-thousandths, of stock still to be removed. Check that the positive-stop mechanism still is set to allow at least 0.001″ oversize. Adjust the positive stop if necessary.

10. Engage the power cross feed and the table travel. Continue grinding until further cross feeding is ceased by the positive-stop mechanism. When the wheel

sparks out at the footstock end of the work, free of the work, disengage the power cross feed, table travel, and work rotation.

11. Accurately measure the work to determine the number of ten-thousandths (0.0001) of an inch still to be removed.

12. Engage the table travel, and, with the ten-thousandths hand feed dial, set the feed to remove several ten-thousandths of an inch.

13. When the wheel sparks out at the footstock end of the work, disengage the table travel and work rotation. Accurately measure the work. If more material is to be removed, proceed as in step 12. When the work is ground to the specified size, back the wheel away from the work and remove the workpiece.

NOTE: When grinding subsequent workpieces to the same size, mount the work in the usual manner. Grind with the use of the automatic cross feed until further cross feeding is stopped by the positive-stop mechanism. Any error in finish size will be due to wheel wear and may be compensated for by hand feeding to finish dimension with the ten-thousandth hand-feed dial.

When a grinding gage, Fig. 13-10, is used, the workpiece may be ground directly to finished dimension with the use of automatic cross feed. When the workpiece is ground to the correct finished size, the power cross feed is disengaged. The machine is stopped in the usual manner, and the workpiece is removed.

How To Set Up Universal Grinders—External Tapers

The universal grinding machine may be set up for grinding either slight or steep external tapers. Whenever practicable, grind a taper with the wheel pressure toward the headstock.

Procedure for Slight Tapers

Tapers up to 8° usually are ground by swiveling the swivel table, as in Fig. 13-63.

1. Swivel the table to the position required. Fasten it by tightening the clamping bolts at each end. (See Fig. 13-59.)

2. Secure, change, and true the grinding wheel, if necessary.

3. Secure a workpiece, and mount it between centers.

4. Determine the work and spindle speeds required. Make the necessary adjustments.

5. Set table feed stop dogs in the usual manner, if used. (See Unit 122.)

6. Protect the eyes with properly fitted goggles.

7. Be sure the wheel guard is fastened securely in position.

8. Attach the table water guards, adjust coolant piping and nozzle, and turn on coolant.

9. Start the machine, and grind in the usual manner. (See Unit 122.)

10. When grinding has been completed, clean and restore the machine to normal working condition.

Procedure for Steep Tapers

Steep or sharp tapers may be ground by using several different kinds of setups. One common method involves swiveling the wheel spindle head on its base to the required angle; this method works well if the surface to

465

be ground is not wider than the wheel face. A second common method is to swivel the wheel spindle head 90° and, in addition, swivel the wheel stand slide base to the angle of the taper, Figs. 13-64 and 13-65. A third method

Fig. 13-63. Grinding a Taper with Table Swiveled
(Brown & Sharpe)
Long pieces are supported with one or more universal back rests.

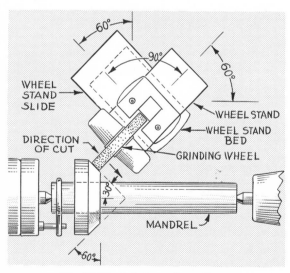

Fig. 13-64. Grinding a Steep Taper

involves mounting the work on the headstock spindle with a chuck or other suitable device; the headstock then is swiveled to the desired angle of taper, as in Fig. 13-66. The latter method also may be employed for face grinding a workpiece; however, the headstock must then be swiveled 90°, as shown in Fig. 13-67.

The following procedure for grinding steep or sharp external tapers is for the second method, which involves swiveling the wheel head and the wheel stand slide base as illustrated in Fig. 13-64.

1. Determine the angle of the taper, for example, 30°.
2. Loosen the clamping bolts, and set the wheel stand slide base at 60° (90° — 30°). This will put the wheel in position to

Fig. 13-65. Grinding a Steep Taper with Wheel Slide Swiveled (Brown & Sharpe)

Fig. 13-66. Grinding a Steep Taper with Headstock Swiveled (Brown & Sharpe)

grind a 30° angle on the work surface. (See Fig. 13-64.) Next turn the wheel head so that the spindle is parallel with the slide base; then clamp the slide and spindle head in position by tightening the bolts.

3. Secure a suitable wheel; change and dress it, if necessary.

4. Mount the workpiece in a chuck or other suitable holding device.

5. Adjust headstock for revolving spindle grinding.

6. Determine the work and wheel speeds required. Make necessary adjustments.

7. Set the machine for the correct work speed.

8. Protect the eyes with properly fitted goggles.

9. Be sure the wheel guard is fastened securely in position.

10. Attach the table water guards, adjust coolant piping and nozzle, and then turn on coolant.

11. Start the machine. Then with hand table feed, bring the work into contact with the revolving wheel. Pass the wheel across the face of the work with the cross-feed handwheel.

    If the face of the wheel is the same width as, or wider than, the surface to be

Fig. 13-67. Headstock Swiveled 90° for Face Grinding
(Brown & Sharpe)

ground, no movement of the cross feed is necessary.

12. At the end of the first cut, advance the work slightly by moving the sliding table forward sufficiently for a cut about 0.001″ or more, depending upon the amount of stock to be removed.

13. Continue with repeated cuts until the work is reduced to size.

14. When the operation has been completed, clean and restore the machine to normal working condition.

How To Set Up Universal Grinders—Internal Grinding

The procedure described in this unit is for setting up standard universal grinding machines for straight internal grinding. With some machines, the procedure may differ somewhat, but the principles are essentially the same.

Some universal grinding machines are provided with internal grinding fixtures as stan-

dard equipment, Fig. 13-54. This type of fixture is mounted on a hinged bracket which rests at the top of the wheel when not in use. It can be moved instantly into operating position, Fig. 13-69, and is locked in position with a screw knob. This type of spindle is driven with a flat belt from an independent motor, without disturbing the external spindle.

When the internal grinding fixture is used, the operator sets the cross-feed selector knob to the internal grinding position; this permits the cross-feed handwheel to be turned counterclockwise to advance the grinding wheel into the work, toward the rear of the hole. Thus the grinding action may be easily observed by the operator. The internal setting on the selector knob also permits using power feeds, handwheel graduations, and the positive-stop mechanism, in the same manner as for external grinding.

Some other types of universal grinders are equipped with an internal grinding fixture

Fig. 13-69. Internal Grinding Spindle in Position for Use
(Brown & Sharpe)

Fig. 13-70. Grinding the Internal Surface of a Part
(Brown & Sharpe)

which may be attached to the wheel head of the machine as an independent accessory. This type fixture usually is driven by the external grinding wheel motor, with a flat belt; consequently, it is necessary to remove the V-belt guard and V-belts from the sheaves of the motor. The flat belt to the internal grinding fixture is then placed on the flat motor pulley which is provided for this purpose.

The operator's handbook supplied with the machine explains how the fixture is mounted, as well as the procedure for changing and adjusting any necessary belts.

Procedure for a Straight Cylinder

1. Secure a workpiece and a suitable chuck.
2. Mount the chuck on the nose of the headstock spindle.
3. Determine desirable work surface speed, and make necessary adjustments. (See Unit 121.)
4. Determine desirable wheel surface speed, and make necessary adjustments. (See Unit 121.)
5. Determine desirable rate of table travel, if any. Make adjustments accordingly. (See Unit 121.)
6. Position the internal grinding fixture, and clamp or bolt securely. (Refer to the operator's handbook, if necessary.)
7. Mount the flat belt from the motor to the internal grinding fixtures. On some machines, it may be necessary to remove the V-belt guard and V-belts, as described above.
8. On machines equipped with a motor selector knob, turn the knob to the *internal* position, so that the internal grinding motor will be operative.
9. On machines equipped with an internal-external grinding selector knob, turn the knob to the *internal* grinding position.
10. Disengage the power cross-feed control lever. For the beginning operator, hand cross feeding is recommended.
11. Be sure the swivel table and the headstock are set at zero degrees.
12. Mount the workpiece in the chuck. Be sure it is centered accurately; if necessary, test with a dial indicator.

13. Adjust the machine for table travel, if desired. When used, the table dogs should be so positioned that the wheel will pass only partly off the work at the beginning and end of the stroke.

CAUTION: *If the workpiece has an internal shoulder or a closed end against which the wheel will come, the table stop dog at that point must be so positioned that table travel will stop just as the wheel reaches the spot.*

14. Protect the eyes by wearing properly fitted goggles.
15. Start the machine. Then run the wheel into the opening by hand, and, at the same time, advance the wheel against the rear of the hole with the hand cross feed, as in Fig. 13-70, taking a light cut. At the end of the cut, withdraw the wheel.

When power table travel is being used and grinding has been completed, the wheel may be brought clear of the work by releasing the right-hand stop dog.

16. Make repeated cuts in a similar manner.
17. When changing for subsequent workpieces, loosen only two adjacent chuck jaws; then remove the finished piece and insert a new piece.

CAUTION: *When grinding long pieces, the outer end should be supported by a center rest or other suitable device.*

18. When through, clean and restore the machine to its normal condition. Return any special equipment to the place where it is kept when not in use.

How To Set Up Universal Grinders—Internal Tapers

Either slight or steep internal tapers may be ground with a universal grinder.

Procedure for Slight Tapers

1. Determine the angle of taper required.
2. Make certain that the wheel stand is set at zero. Then bring the internal grinding fixture into position, and clamp it securely, Fig. 13-69.
3. Mount the belt for the internal grinding fixture, as described in Unit 125. Tension the belt properly.
4. Mount the workpiece in a chuck or other suitable device. Be sure it is centered accurately. If necessary, test with a dial indicator.
5. Make certain that the headstock is set at zero degrees.

6. Swivel the table through the required number of degrees, for example, 5°. Clamp it in position.
7. On machines equipped with a motor selector knob, turn the knob to the *internal* position so that the internal grinding motor will be operative.
8. Protect the eyes by wearing properly fitted safety glasses.
9. Determine desirable wheel surface speed, and make any necessary adjustments, if possible. (See Unit 121.)
10. Determine desirable work surface speed, and set the headstock speed-selector dial accordingly. (See Unit 121.)
11. Determine the desirable rate of table travel, if any. Make adjustments accordingly. (See Unit 121.)

469

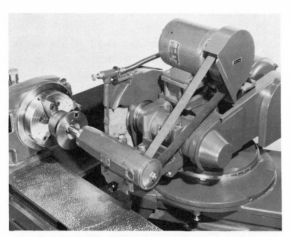

Fig. 13-71. Grinding a Steep Internal Taper with Wheel Slide Base Swiveled (Brown & Sharpe)

12. True and dress the grinding wheel, if necessary.
13. Set the table stop dogs, if desired.
14. Start the machine; then run the wheel into the opening by means of the hand table feed. At the same time, bring the wheel lightly into contact with the workpiece by turning the cross-feed handwheel. Advance the wheel into the opening by turning the table-feed handwheel counterclockwise.
15. At the end of the cut, bring the wheel back to the starting point. Then advance the wheel a small amount, and take a second cut.
16. Continue with repeated cuts until the work is brought to size.
17. When the operation has been completed, clean and restore the machine to its normal condition. Clean any special equipment, and return it to the place where kept when not in use.

Procedure for Steep Tapers

Steep internal tapers generally are ground by swiveling the headstock on its base to the required angle.

1. Proceed as in steps 1 through 4, above.
2. Make certain that the swivel table is set at the zero position.
3. Loosen the bolts which fasten the headstock to the base. Swivel the headstock to the desired angle, for example, 20°. Tighten the bolts.
4. Proceed as in steps 7 through 17, above.

A second method for grinding steep internal tapers can be used. In this, the wheel slide base, Fig. 13-54, is swiveled to the desired angle of taper, Fig. 13-71. The wheel spindle head then is swiveled so that the internal grinding spindle is parallel with the sliding table, Fig. 13-71. Finally, the grinding wheel is fed along the tapered surface with the cross-feed handwheel, or by power cross feed, as desired.

UNIT 127

How To Sharpen Cutters on a Universal Grinding Machine

Plain milling cutters with straight teeth can be ground on a universal grinding machine. Usually such work is mounted on a mandrel, as in Fig. 13-72. This operation also can be performed on a plain cylindrical grinding machine or on a cutter and tool grinding machine.

Procedure

1. Set the machine as for straight cylindrical grinding.

2. Protect the eyes with properly fitted goggles.

3. Mount the cutter on a suitable mandrel, and place it between the centers of the machine, using dead-center grinding.

   True the face of the wheel. Usually only a small amount of the face comes in contact with the work; the remainder of the wheel face is dressed back sufficiently to prevent contact.

4. Fasten the tooth rest bracket on the swivel table, and adjust the tooth rest. The rest must be set below the center of the wheel spindle enough to grind clearance on the back of the tooth of from 4° to 7°, depending upon size.

   The tooth rest must be the swivel type or the spring type which permits the cutter to be rotated from one tooth to the next, without removing the cutter from its location between centers.

5. Hold the first tooth to be sharpened down on the tooth rest. Then bring the wheel into contact with the cutter for a light cut, about 0.002″ deep. With the table hand feed, move the cutter back and forth across the face of the wheel until the wheel sparks out.

6. Move the cutter past the wheel far enough to clear the wheel while the cutter is rotated over the flexible tooth rest, to the

Fig. 13-72. Grinding a Cutter Mounted on a Mandrel
(Brown & Sharpe)

next tooth to be ground. Rotate the cutter upward to the next tooth.

7. Continue as in steps 5 and 6 until all teeth have been ground.

8. If the teeth require more grinding to become sharp, advance the wheel for a second cut, usually from 0.001″ to 0.002″.

9. Proceed as in steps 5 and 6 until all teeth have been ground sharp.

How To Operate Plain Grinders—Cylindrical Grinding

The procedure described in this unit is that of setting up a standard plain cylindrical grinding machine, of the type shown in Fig. 13-73, to grind the exterior of cylindrical work. With different makes of machines, the procedure may vary somewhat, but the same principles apply.

Orientation to the Machine

Plain cylindrical grinding machines are used for grinding straight cylindrical surfaces, taper surfaces, shoulders, and fillets. They also may be used for form grinding by dressing and shaping the desired contour on the grinding wheel.

Fig. 13-73. Plain Grinding Machine (Brown & Sharpe)

(1) Sight indicator for automatic oiling system; (2) Table speed selector lever; (3) Sliding table; (4) Table handwheel; (5) Table start-stop lever; (6) Swivel table; (7) Headstock belt guard; (8) Headstock motor; (9) Table reverse dog; (10) Table reverse lever; (11) Work tray; (12) Coolant valve; (13) Wheel guard; (14) Cartridge-type wheel spindle; (15) Spindle motor; (16) Constant level spindle oiler (for plain bearing only); (17) Telltale; (18) Spindle belt guard; (19) Footstock operating lever; (20) Footstock; (21) Swivel table adjustment knob; (22) Switch operating slide throwout lever; (23) Index dial; (24) Cross-feed pawl lever; (25) Main line disconnect switch; (26) Cross-feed handwheel; (27) Mechanism for setting amount of automatic cross-feed; (28) Grind-true switch; (29) Off-on switch for wheel slide rapid travel; (30) Machine start-stop buttons; (31) Electrical control compartment; and (35) Pocket for hoisting hook.

Knowledge of the cross-feed mechanism and the wheel-slide rapid-travel mechanism on the machine in Fig. 13-73 will aid in understanding the operational procedures to follow. These features are explained briefly.

Cross-Feed Controls: The cross feed may be operated by hand or automatically with power. The index dial on the cross-feed handwheel (Figs. 13-75 and 13-79, pages 475 and 478) is graduated in increments of 0.0001″. It also is further graduated to increments of 0.000 020″ (20 millionths or 20 microinches). Thus the hand or the power cross feed can be set to 0.000 020″ on work diameter. Accuracy to within 0.0001″ is common practice with cylindrical grinding.

The cross-feed mechanism provides for either hand or power cross feed to a *positive stop*. The positive stop is used for grinding to a predetermined diameter; when the work is reduced to this diameter, cross feeding will cease. For further cross feeding, the index dial must be reset.

The work may be ground to finish size with manual or automatic cross feed. The *amount of automatic cross feed* is established by setting the variable-radius crank mechanism, Fig. 13-79. It may be set for automatic reduction of the work diameter at each reversal in steps of 0.000 25″, from 0.000 25″ to 0.0045″.

Wheel-Slide Rapid Travel: The wheel-slide rapid-travel mechanism is a standard feature of the plain grinder in Fig. 13-73. It provides for rapid advance of the grinding wheel to the starting position and for rapid withdrawal of the wheel at the completion of the grinding cycle. In this way, the workpiece may be inserted or removed rapidly and safely without backing the wheel off manually. The wheel slide travels 1″ within a period of about 1 second during rapid advance or withdrawal.

The grinding wheel is brought forward to the end of the 1″ rapid movement, and the wheel-slide rapid travel is engaged with an on-off switch, Fig. 13-73. When engaged, it may be controlled through the rotation of the cross-feed handwheel. The grinding wheel advances automatically when the grinding cycle is started, and it is withdrawn automatically when the grinding is completed. The forward movement of the wheel can be stopped at any time with a slight rotation of the cross-feed wheel. A red light glows while the wheel is advancing — an amber one when the advance is complete. The use of the wheel-slide rapid travel may be cut out at any time with the off-on switch provided for the rapid-travel mechanism.

The initial starting position of the grinding wheel is established with the rapid-travel mechanism in the advanced position. The wheel is set in this position manually with the hand cross-feed wheel. This enables the rapid-advance mechanism to retract and again advance the wheel close to the work during the grinding cycle. At the end of the rapid advance, the wheel is fed into the work by the cross-feed mechanism, either manually or automatically, depending on the position of the cross-feed pawl lever.

The wheel may be withdrawn at any time during the grinding cycle, or at the end of a cut, by turning the cross-feed handwheel back to the starting position of the initial cut.

General Precautions: Several general precautions should be observed before starting the grinding machine.

CAUTION: *To produce accurate results, the machine should be warmed up before starting to grind. Ordinarily, a machine will reach optimum running temperature in about 15 minutes. If the spindle motor is started when the operator starts the process of setting up the machine, optimum running temperature will be achieved by the time he has completed the setup.*

Before starting to grind, always check that the machine is properly lubricated, that the supply of coolant is adequate for the work to be done, and that the coolant valve is set to deliver an adequate flow. Replenish the coolant whenever necessary.

When starting a grinding machine for the first time after it has been idle for several hours, press the start button; then, almost immediately, push the *stop* button. Repeat this three or four times so that the bearings of the spindle will be well lubricated.

The diameter of the finished work should be checked occasionally to determine wheel wear. To compensate for wheel wear and to produce accurate work, the operator must adjust the index dial on the cross feed, as necessary. When a grinding gage of the type shown in Fig. 13-10 is used, the work may be ground directly to size without compensation for wheel wear. However, the grinding gage must be set to gage size accurately, and it must be mounted securely on the machine.

When operating a grinding machine, the operator should always wear properly fitted goggles and suitable coveralls.

Procedure

1. Select a wheel suited to the work to be performed, and mount it on the wheel spindle. (See Unit 115.) Be sure the wheel is sound. Support the wheel by inserting the forefinger in the spindle hole; then test it by striking it a light blow on the edge with a hammer or some hard substance. A clear ring indicates a sound wheel.

Fig. 13-74. Headstock Drive Mechanism
(Brown & Sharpe)
Note that the headstock is aligned with the front lip of the base.

If the wheel is changed, it is necessary to true and, possibly, balance the new wheel before attempting to grind a workpiece. (See Unit 115.)

2. Determine the work surface speed. (See Unit 121.) If necessary, change the headstock "O" ring step pulley, Fig. 13-74.

3. Determine the wheel surface speed desired. If necessary, change the motor pulley, or by other means change the ratio of motor and wheel spindle speed.

4. Determine the rate of table travel, if any.

    When the surface to be ground is the same width or is narrower than the wheel, no table travel is necessary; the same is true when plunge or straight-in grinding a narrow recess.

5. Check the setting of the swivel table. If adjustment is necessary, loosen the clamping bolts at each end of the table; then make the adjustment by means of the knob and scale provided. This is an approximate setting which must be verified by a trial cut at each end of the workpiece.

6. Thoroughly clean the table and ways; then position the headstock and footstock to receive the workpiece. To avoid excessive wear at either end of the ways, the headstock and footstock should be located an equal distance from the respective ends of the table. Align the headstock by means of the front lip of the base. (See Fig. 13-74.) Then fasten it in position by tightening the clamping bolts.

7. Be sure that the grinding wheel is set back far enough to permit putting a workpiece between centers. If the wheel is too far advanced, depress the switch operating slide by means of the throwout lever, Fig. 13-75; then move the wheel back the distance desired.

    CAUTION: *For the machine in Fig. 13-73: Because of the wheel-slide rapid-travel mechanism, the grinding wheel first must be brought forward to the end of the 1" rapid movement, until the light changes from red to amber. If the wheel is then too far forward, set the grind-true switch at* true *before disengaging the switch operating slide; this holds the rapid-travel mechanism in the forward position.*

Move the wheel back clear of the work. Using the cross feed thus established, push the grind-true switch to the *grind* position; this will stop the headstock and the coolant, and will cause the wheel to be withdrawn 1″ by rapid travel.

To prevent undesired rapid advance of the wheel while setting up or truing the wheel, shut off the wheel-slide rapid-travel switch at the right of the machine.

8. Examine the centers of the grinding machine to determine that they are clean, smooth, and ground at the correct angle; test with a center gage. If the centers are not ground with an inclusive angle of 60°, correct by regrinding. (See Unit 120.)

9. Secure a workpiece; make certain that the center holes are clean, of the correct shape and depth, and well oiled.

10. Secure a suitable driving dog, and place it on one end of the workpiece.

11. Place the workpiece on the headstock center. Then draw the footstock spindle operating lever, Fig. 13-76, about a third of the way forward, to the left; at the same time, push the footstock forward until its center is seated in the workpiece. Align the footstock with the front lip on its base, and clamp the footstock securely with the clamping bolt.

If necessary to increase the spring pressure on the spindle, turn the spring pressure adjusting nut at the rear of the footstock. (See Fig. 13-76.) The pressure should be great enough to hold the center firmly in the work, but not great enough to cause the work to spring or prevent it from turning freely.

12. With the cross-feed handwheel, Fig. 13-75, advance the grinding wheel until it is within ¼″ of the workpiece.

13. To set the table reverse dogs, first move the table to the left until the right-hand edge of the grinding wheel is one-third of its width to the right of the end of the workpiece.

14. Turn the dog adjusting screws, Fig. 13-77, inward as far as they will go; then loosen the dog clamping bolts.

15. Push the table reverse lever to the left until it strikes the left positive stop. (See Fig. 13-77.) Bring the right-hand dog into contact with the reversing lever; then, with the handwheel, move the table 3″ or 4″ to the right without changing the position of the dog in the T-slot. Tighten the dog clamping bolt.

16. With the hand feed, move the table to the right until the left side of the grinding wheel is within ½″ or so of the driving dog.

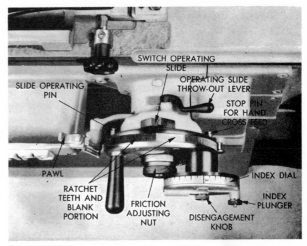

Fig. 13-75. Cross-Feed Handwheel and Control Mechanisms (Brown & Sharpe)

Fig. 13-76. Footstock Showing Operating Levers (Brown & Sharpe)

17. Push the table reverse lever to the right until it strikes the right-hand positive stop; then proceed as when setting the right-hand dog.

18. With the wheel-slide rapid-travel switch in off position, start the machine, and engage the power table travel by pulling the start-stop lever forward, Fig. 13-78. Then back off the right-hand adjusting screw, Fig. 13-77, until the table reverses exactly at the position desired. Make a similar adjustment at the left-hand point of reversal; then tighten the check nuts on the dog adjusting screws.

> NOTE: When grinding to the end of a piece, allow the end to run approximately half way across the face of the wheel before reversing.

Fig. 13-77. Table Reversing Lever and Dogs (Front of Grinder) (Brown & Sharpe)

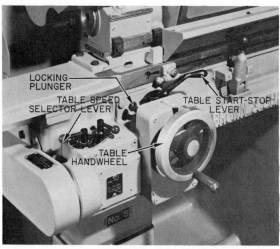

Fig. 13-78. Controls for Longitudinal Table Travel (Brown & Sharpe)

19. With the cross-feed handwheel, return the grinding wheel to the starting or normal inactive position.

The grinding wheel may be brought into contact with the workpiece by advancing the wheel with the manual or hand-operated cross feed or by automatic cross feed. Observe the caution indicated under step 7 above.

Procedure for Manual Cross Feed

Hand-operated cross feed on machines of the type shown in Fig. 13-73 is used mainly for plunge-cut grinding where the machine table remains stationary. However, it also may be used with grinding operations which involve longitudinal table travel.

The correct amount of feed for a given piece of work depends upon the kind of material, the length and diameter of the workpiece, surface speed of the wheel and work, table speed, wheel characteristics, and finish requirements. Ordinarily for traverse (longitudinal) grinding, a feed of .001″ to .0015″ is a good starting feed. For plunge-cut grinding, .001″ is satisfactory. Experience and experimentation will suggest variations that may safely be made in both speeds and feeds.

1. With a workpiece mounted between centers and other adjustments completed as previously described, bring the grinding wheel forward until it just touches the workpiece.

2. Loosen the cross-feed handwheel friction adjusting nut located at the center of the wheel, Fig. 13-75. This permits the handwheel to be turned without turning the cross-feed screw, and, consequently, without changing the position of the grinding wheel in relation to the workpiece.

3. Examine the position of the pins at the back of the handwheel. If either one is in contact with the switch operating slide, turn the handwheel until both are in the same relative position with respect to the slide, as shown in Fig. 13-75.

4. Pull out the index plunger, Fig. 13-75. Then grasp the index dial, and gently rotate it counterclockwise about its own center, until the permanently located stop

pin behind the dial is nearly in contact with the right-hand side of the switch operating slide, Fig. 13-75.

CAUTION: *Do not hold the handwheel while rotating the dial.*

5. Engage the index dial plunger, and throw the starting switch. Then turn the handwheel counterclockwise, bringing the stop pin against the switch operating slide, Fig. 13-75. Continue grinding until the work has sparked out the amount desired; then turn the handwheel clockwise, thus bringing the wheel back to the starting point. *Be sure the wheel guard is fastened securely in position.*

CAUTION: *Whenever there is likelihood that contact of the grinding wheel with the workpiece will cause the piece to vibrate or spring away from the wheel, the work should be stabilized by means of a back rest, similar to that shown in Fig. 13-63. For procedure in setting up and adjusting a back rest, see Unit 130.*

6. With a micrometer or other suitable means, carefully measure the diameter of the ground portion of the work, and determine the amount it is to be reduced. Then turn the handwheel so as to bring the index dial near the top where it can be read easily. Now turn the dial clockwise so that the advance of the wheel will be stopped at the point desired, for example, when the wheel reduces the diameter of the work by .002″.

CAUTION: *When making this adjustment, remember that turning the dial through one of the graduations which appear on the rim of the dial will permit advancement of the wheel by .0001″. Moving the dial clockwise through one graduation will reduce the diameter of the work .0001″. A complete revolution of the dial clockwise will reduce the diameter of the work .004″.*

To avoid the risk of grinding the workpiece too small, set the stopping point about .002″ oversize.

7. Advance the wheel, and further reduce the work. Again, measure the diameter of the ground portion; then make final adjustment of the index dial. Check this setting, using a second workpiece and comparing the measurements of the ground surfaces. When the machine has been set up for rough grinding, the left-hand pin at the back of the cross-feed handwheel should be relocated, if necessary, so that only a relatively small movement of the handwheel will be necessary to bring the grinding wheel into contact with the work.

8. Place another workpiece between centers; then advance the wheel, and engage the longitudinal table travel. When the workpiece has been reduced to size, remove it from between centers. Then move the driving dog to the opposite end, and again mount the workpiece between centers and complete grinding.

9. When all workpieces have been rough ground, set the machine to make the finishing cut, usually between .00025″ and .0005″ at each reversal of table travel. Proceed to make the finishing cut or cuts in the usual manner.

Procedure for Automatic Cross Feed

1. Mount a workpiece between centers, and complete other adjustments as previously described.

2. Determine the amount of cross feed desired at each reversal of the table, for example, .0015″.

3. Automatic cross feed is accomplished by means of an adjustable-radius crank mechanism, such as illustrated in Fig. 13-79. To set the mechanism for a feed of .0015″, first disengage the pawl, Fig. 13-75; then loosen the wheel feed adjusting slide clamp, Fig. 13-79, move the slide to the setting desired, and securely tighten the clamp screw.

NOTE: The scale on the Brown and Sharpe plain grinding machine, Fig. 13-79, shows the settings for feeds from .00025″ to .0045″ on the

Fig. 13-79. Mechanism for Adjusting Automatic Cross-Feed (Brown & Sharpe)

work diameter by quarter thousandths of an inch; the figures 1, 2, 3, and 4 indicate thousandths.

4. Start the table (except for a plunge cut). In order to bring the wheel to the advanced position of the rapid movement, raise the switch operating slide. Then set the grind-true switch to true, depress the switch operating slide, and bring the wheel forward until it just touches the work.

5. Raise the switch operating slide, set the grind-true switch to grind, and take a light cut.

6. Stop the table, withdraw the wheel, and carefully measure the diameter of the work at both ends of the surface being ground. Correct the angular setting of the table, if necessary.

7. Set the stopping point of the automatic cross feed. To do this, loosen the hand-

wheel adjusting nut, Fig. 13-75. Then, with the index dial mechanism, turn the handwheel so that when the pawl is engaged, there will be six or seven ratchet teeth between the pawl and the non-toothed section on the rim of the wheel, Fig. 13-75.

8. Moderately tighten the friction adjusting nut, but do not force it; then start the table, engage the pawl, and let the machine run until the cross feed has stopped. This will occur when the pawl strikes the smooth section of the handwheel.

9. As soon as the cross feed stops, disengage the pawl when the wheel reaches the footstock end of the workpiece. At the same time, withdraw the grinding wheel to the starting position.

10. With a micrometer or other suitable means, carefully measure the ground portions of the work, and determine the amount the piece is to be reduced.

11. Advance the grinding wheel until it just touches the work; then turn the dial clockwise sufficiently to advance the wheel the amount desired, for example, .0005″. Remember that a revolution of one graduation on the dial will advance the wheel enough to reduce the work .0001″.

12. Engage the pawl, and let the machine run until the cross feed again stops; then again measure the work and make necessary adjustments.

13. After the first workpiece has been rough ground as far as the point of reversal, stop the machine, change the driving dog to the finished end of the work, and complete rough grinding the piece.

   When the machine has been set up for rough grinding, the left-hand pin at the back of the cross-feed handwheel should be relocated, if necessary, so that only a relatively small movement of the handwheel will be necessary to bring the grinding wheel into contact with the work.

14. When all pieces have been rough ground, set the machine to make the finishing cut, usually between .00025″ and .0005″ at each reversal of the table. Proceed as when making a rough cut.

How To Make Taper and Angular Cuts with Plain Grinders

For the purpose of grinding tapered work, the swivel table on a plain cylindrical grinding machine may be turned about 8° from its normal position parallel with the sliding table. Most plain grinding machines are designed for external grinding of straight cylindrical parts, or cylindrical parts with tapers up to about 8°. However, on some plain grinding machines, as in Fig. 13-73, the headstock is so designed that it may be swiveled up to about 45° for grinding steep tapers or angles.

With the headstock swiveled, the work may be held with collets as shown in Fig. 13-80. Work also may be held in a 3-jaw universal chuck, Fig. 13-81.

Procedure for Tapered Cuts

1. Determine the angle at which the table is to be swiveled and, likewise, the direction of swivel. Ordinarily, the work is mounted between centers with the small end toward the footstock.
2. Loosen the clamping bolts at both ends of the swivel table. Then by means of the swivel-table adjusting knob, swivel the table until the indicator registers the desired amount of taper on the scale, for example $\frac{5}{16}''$ taper per foot. This method of setting frequently is slightly inaccurate, and the setting must be corrected after a trial cut has been taken.
3. Tighten the clamping bolts; then set up the machine as for a normal grinding operation.
4. With the hand cross feed, advance the wheel until it just touches the workpiece at the small end. Then, without further advancing the wheel, move the sliding table to the right, and observe the relative positions of the wheel and workpiece. If a noticeable difference exists, correct the angular setting of the swivel table by just barely loosening the clamping bolts; then turn the adjusting knob in the direction which will correct the error. Tighten the clamping bolts.

Fig. 13-80. Wheel Head in Swiveled Position, with Collet Attachment (Brown & Sharpe)

Fig. 13-81. 3-Jaw Universal Scroll Chuck Mounted on Headstock Spindle (Brown & Sharpe)

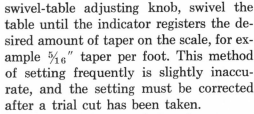

5. Adjust the cross feed so that there will be sufficient excess stock remaining for a second cut.

6. Start the machine, and make the cut in the usual manner.

CAUTION: *Be sure the wheel guard is fastened securely in position.*

7. At the conclusion of the first cut, test the angularity of the ground surface. Tapered work usually is tested by means of a cylindrical taper gage.

8. Make correction in the angular setting of the swivel table, if necessary; then grind in the usual manner.

Because of the angle or taper of the workpiece, the relation between the cross feed and the work is not constant unless the center holes are held in positive relation with the length of the workpiece. To assure accuracy of taper of a number of pieces, it is recommended that two cuts be taken and the work tested after the first.

Procedure for Angular Cuts

In machine shop practice, an angular cut is considered to be one having a taper greater than about 8°.

1. Mount the work in a suitable chuck.

2. Loosen the clamping bolts on the headstock, swivel the headstock to the desired angle, and tighten the clamping bolts, Fig. 13-80.

3. Set up the machine as for normal grinding operation. (See Unit 128.) For long angular cuts, the work is traversed across the wheel by means of longitudinal table travel. Set the table dogs if the width of the angle requires table travel across the wheel, and if automatic table travel is to be used.

4. With the table handwheel and the cross-feed wheel, advance the wheel until it is just clear of the work.

5. Adjust the cross feed so that there will be sufficient excess stock remaining for a second cut.

6. Start the machine, and make the cut in the usual manner.

CAUTION: *Be sure the wheel guard is fastened securely in position. Wear appropriate safety goggles.*

7. At the conclusion of the first cut, test the angularity of the work. Make a correction in the angular setting of the headstock if necessary.

8. Proceed with additional cuts as necessary. Allow sufficient material for a finishing cut (or cuts).

9. Adjust the feed for a finishing cut.

10. Make the finishing cut (or cuts) in the usual manner.

UNIT 130

How To Use a Spring Back Rest for Cylindrical Grinding

Whenever work is slender and has a tendency to spring away from the grinding wheel, it should be supported by means of a back rest or steady-rest. Devices of this type may be used on either plain or universal cylindrical grinding machines. See Figs. 13-62 and 13-63. The rest shown in Fig. 13-82 will accommodate work up to 1″ in diameter. Bronze shoes for the attachment are available for work from ⅛″ to 1″ in diameter, by sixteenths. The shoe follows the work automatically, giving constant support and releasing its pressure when the work reaches the required size.

Procedure

1. Secure a back rest, mount it on the sliding table, and clamp it in position with the clamping bolts.

   When grinding long, slender pieces, support should be given every few inches. For example, a piece ½″ in diameter should be supported every four or five inches of its length, measured from the machine centers.

2. Place a workpiece between centers.

3. Back off the shoe adjusting screws, until the shoe is clear of the workpiece.

4. Fit the shoe to the workpiece by hand, and hold the shoe in that position while turning the adjusting screws until they just bear against the shoe. The upper screw acts upon the shoe through the lever shown in Fig. 13-83.

5. Start the machine, advance the wheel, and take a light cut. As the wheel advances, turn the shoe adjusting screws just enough to keep the shoe in contact with the workpiece.

   If more than one back rest is used, correction of the adjusting screws must be made on each rest.

6. With a micrometer, measure the diameter of the work at two or more points. If variation of size is found, correct it by slightly advancing the lower shoe adjusting screw at the large end of the work; then grind as in step 5.

7. Again measure the work. Make adjustments as in step 6 until the workpiece is of the same diameter throughout its length.

8. Take a finishing cut of the required depth. As the wheel progresses, advance the shoe adjusting screws sufficiently to keep the shoe in contact with the workpiece.

9. With the workpiece reduced to size and the shoe in contact with the finished piece, each sliding nut (Fig. 13-83) will be seated against its positive stop.

10. With the shoe in contact with the work and the sliding nuts in position, tighten the clamping screws on both clamp collars.

11. Adjust the pressure on the shoe as necessary by means of the spring adjusting screws. The combined pressure of the two springs should be no greater than necessary to prevent chatter or springing of the work while it is being ground.

12. When a new workpiece is placed between centers, the back-rest springs will be compressed and the shoe (or shoes) held against the work to support it.

The type of spring back rest illustrated may be used as a solid type merely by tightening the spring adjusting screws until the springs are fully compressed.

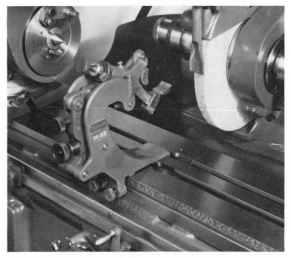

Fig. 13-82. **Back Rest or Work Support**
(Brown & Sharpe)

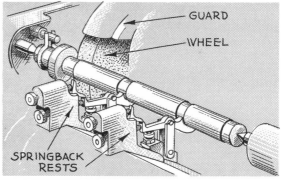

Fig. 13-83. **Spring-Type Back Rests in Position**

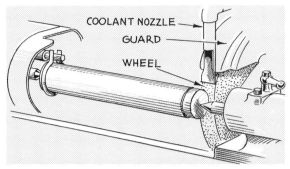

Fig. 13-84. Spot Grinding One End of a Workpiece

When used as a solid back rest, the shoe must be lowered to permit placing the work between centers. This is accomplished by withdrawing the upper shoe adjusting screw. (See Fig. 13-83.) During the grinding operation, the shoe is kept in contact with the work by advancing the upper adjusting screw as the work is reduced in diameter.

Some operators spot grind the work when using either a solid or compensating type of back rest. When this procedure is used, short sections of the workpiece are ground straight in — to within about .002″ of the finished diameter. See Fig. 13-84.

Test Your Knowledge of Section 13

Unit 113: Grinding and Grinding Machines

1. To what dimensional tolerance are grinding operations frequently performed?
2. In addition to the close tolerances possible, list a second distinct advantage of grinding as compared with other methods of machining.
3. List several examples of precision-ground parts in a modern automobile engine.
4. Compare the cutting action of a grinding wheel with the cutting action of a lathe tool or milling cutter.
5. Explain the difference between surface grinding and cylindrical grinding.
6. List two common types of grinding machines which perform cylindrical grinding operations.
7. List three kinds of machines or methods which may be used to perform internal grinding operations.
8. Define the meaning of form grinding, and list three kinds of machines on which form grinding may be done.
9. Give an example of an object which is ground by the plunge grinding method.
10. Explain how centerless grinding is performed, and list several kinds of items which are ground by this method.
11. List several kinds of tools which are commonly ground on a cutter and tool grinder.
12. What is meant by offhand grinding?
13. For what basic types of operations are surface grinding machines used?
14. List two general types of surface grinding machines, and indicate the principal differences between them.
15. What basic type of surface grinding machine is commonly used in tool and die shops, toolrooms, maintenance shops, and school shops?
16. Why is a vertical-spindle surface grinder often used for production purposes?
17. What kinds of operations are generally performed on a plain grinding machine?
18. List several of the principal parts or mechanisms on a plain grinding machine.
19. What kinds of operations can be performed on a universal grinding machine?
20. List several grinding operations which can be performed on a universal grinder, but which cannot normally be performed on a plain grinder.
21. List several important parts or mechanisms on a universal grinding machine.
22. Explain how short workpieces generally are mounted in a universal grinder for either face or angular grinding.
23. What kinds of operations may be performed on a *universal and tool* grinding machine?

482

24. List several kinds of accessories which are available for a universal and tool grinding machine.
25. Explain how an *indicating grinding gage* is used on cylindrical grinding machines.
26. Explain how indicating snap gages are used for checking the size of parts being ground on cylindrical grinding machines.
27. Explain how *go and no go* gages are used for checking the size of ground parts.
28. List several possible causes for a chatter finish while grinding.
29. List several possible causes for burning the work while grinding.
30. List several possible causes for the wheel spindle running too hot on a grinding machine.

Unit 121: Grinding Cutting Speeds and Feeds

1. What is the range of wheel surface speeds recommended for grinding with most vitrified grinding wheels?
2. What range of wheel surface speed, or cutting speed, is generally recommended for most cylindrical grinding operations?
3. Explain the basic difference between wheel surface cutting speed and rpm of a grinding wheel.
4. Give the formula which may be used to calculate the surface speed of a grinding wheel when the spindle speed of the machine is known.
5. What is the recommended work-speed range for cylindrical grinding of most materials?
6. How do work speeds for finishing cuts compare with those recommended for roughing cuts on a cylindrical grinder?
7. Calculate the work rpm necessary for cylindrical grinding of a workpiece $1\frac{1}{4}''$ in diameter at a work speed of 60 fpm.
8. What is the maximum rate of table travel, per revolution of the work, for rough cylindrical grinding?
9. What is a recommended rate of table travel, per revolution of the work, for finish cylindrical grinding?
10. What is the range in depth of cut recommended for rough grinding cuts?
11. What is the range in depth of cut recommended for finish grinding cuts?

Unit 122: The Universal Grinding Machine

1. List the principal parts of the wheel stand unit on a universal grinding machine.
2. For what operations would it be necessary to swivel the wheel spindle head on a universal grinding machine?
3. For what purpose would it be necessary to swivel the headstock on a universal grinding machine?
4. What range of table travel speed generally is available on a universal grinding machine?
5. What devices are provided on a universal grinder for automatic control of the length of table travel?
6. For what purpose is a cross-feed positive-stop mechanism used on a universal grinding machine?
7. List four or five accessories which may be used on a universal grinding machine.
8. For what purposes are chucks or collets used on universal grinding machines?
9. For what purpose are universal back rests used on cylindrical grinding machines?

Sophisticated Sensitivity — Measuring Smoothness
(AIL Div. — Cutler-Hammer)

Surface Texture

Surface Texture Specifications

Control of Surface Texture

The quality or texture of a machined surface may be controlled by careful consideration of many factors involved in the machining process. Some of the most significant of these include: type of machine used, rigidness of the machine and setup, type of material, selection of the cutting tool, depth of cut, feed, cutting speed, cutting fluid, and skill of the operator.

The type of surface to be produced on a given product is determined by the designer, and it is indicated on the drawing with standard symbols. Such items as bearings, gear teeth, and pistons frequently must have controlled surface quality. For example, a surface on a bearing can be excessively rough or smooth. If it is too rough, it will wear rapidly, resulting in limited life. If it is too smooth, it will not have adequate provision for oil pockets and will be difficult to keep lubricated, thus again resulting in limited life.

To require a high surface quality where it is not necessary is expensive and unprofitable. It may also result in lack of attention to surface quality where it is necessary for adequate performance. Where detailed specifications concerning surface quality are not indicated, it means that the surface produced by the particular machine operation is adequate.

The machinist must produce machined surfaces which meet specified standards of quality. He must be able to interpret the surface quality specifications indicated on drawings and blueprints. (See Fig. 14-6.) He also must know how to measure or determine whether machined surfaces meet surface quality specifications.

All machined surfaces, including those which appear to be very flat and smooth, have surface irregularities. Under high magnification, scratches or grooves in the form of peaks and valleys are revealed. These irregularities may or may not be superimposed on larger waves. Such complex factors as height, width, and direction of surface irregularities determine surface texture. They are specified with standard symbols on drawings.

Surface Texture Standards Unified

In 1961, after several years of cooperative effort, delegates of the United States, Great Britain, and Canada reached substantial

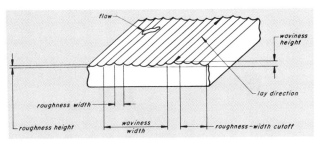

Fig. 14-1. Surface Characteristics (ASA B46.1-1962)

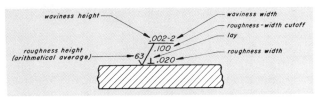

Fig. 14-2. Symbol Designating Surface Characteristics
(ASA B46.1-1962)

agreement on surface quality standards. In 1962 these standards were approved by the American Standards Association and were designated an American Standard, *Surface Texture*, ASA B46.1-1962.* This is a unified standard concerned with terms, ratings, and symbols related to surface quality. It includes information necessary for specifying and determining surface quality. The standard is concerned with surfaces produced by machining, casting, molding, forging, rolling, plating, etc.

Some of the content and several of the illustrations used in this unit have been extracted from *Surface Texture*, (ASA B46.1-1962), with the permission of the publisher.*

Terms Related to Surface Texture

The following terms related to surface texture have been defined by the American Standards Association and have been extracted from ASA B46.1-1962 with the permission of the publisher:

Surface Texture. Repetitive or random deviations from the nominal surface which form the pattern of the surface. Surface texture includes roughness, waviness, lay, and flaws.

Surface. The surface of an object is the boundary which separates that object from another object, substance, or space.

Profile. The profile is the contour of a surface in a plane perpendicular to the surface, unless some other angle is specified.

Center Line. The center line is the line about which roughness is measured and is a line parallel to the general direction of the profile within the limits of the roughness-width cutoff, such that the sums of the areas contained between it and those parts of the profile which lie on either side of it are equal. See Fig. 14-3.

Microinch. A microinch is one millionth of an inch (0.000 001 inch) . . . microinches may be abbreviated as MU inch.

Roughness. Roughness consists of the finer irregularities in the surface texture usually including those irregularities which result from the inherent action of the production process. These are considered to include traverse feed marks and other irregularities within the limits of the roughness-width cutoff. See Fig. 14-1.

Roughness Height. For the purpose of this standard, roughness height is rated as the arithmetical average deviation expressed in microinches measured normal to the center line. The preferred series of roughness height values is given in Table 17.

Arithmetical Average . . . An approximation of the average roughness may be obtained by adding the y increments shown in Fig. 14-3 without regard to sign and dividing the sum by the number of increments taken:

$$Y = \frac{y_a + y_b + y_c + y_d + y_e \ldots\ldots\ldots\ldots + y_n}{n}$$

. . . On most surfaces the total profile height of the surface roughness will be approximately four times the measured surface roughness in microinches. This factor will vary somewhat with the character of the surface under consideration, but the value of four is useful to establish approximate profile heights.

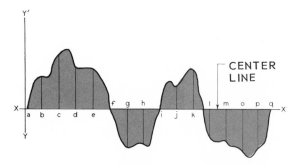

Fig. 14-3. Short Section of Hypothetical Profile Divided into Increments (ASA B46.1-1962)

*American Standards Association. *Surface Texture,* ASA B46.1-1962. The American Society of Mechanical Engineers. United Engineering Center, 345 East 47th Street, New York. (Supersedes ASA B46.1-1955)

Table 17 Standard Surface Texture Values			
Preferred Series Roughness Height Values (Microinches)			
5	20	80	320
6	25	100	400
1 8	32	125	**500**
2 10	40	160	600
3 13	50	200	800
4 16	63	250	**1000**
(Usage of bold face values is recommended)			

Standard Roughness Cutoff Values (Inches)					
0.003	0.010	**0.030**	0.100	0.300	1.000

Preferred Series Waviness Height Values (Inches)					
0.00002	0.00008	0.0003	0.001	0.005	0.015
0.00003	0.0001	0.0005	0.002	0.008	0.020
0.00005	0.0002	0.0008	0.003	0.010	0.030
				(ASA B46.1 — 1962)	

Roughness Width. Roughness width is the distance parallel to the nominal surface between successive peaks or ridges which constitute the predominant pattern of the roughness. Roughness width is rated in inches. See Fig. 14-1.

Roughness-Width Cutoff. The greatest spacing of repetitive surface irregularities to be included in the measurement of average roughness height . . . Roughness-width cutoff is rated in inches. Standard values are given in Table 17. Roughness-width cutoff must always be greater than the roughness width in order to obtain the total roughness height rating. See Fig. 14-1 . . . When no value is specified, the value 0.030 is assumed.

Waviness. Waviness is the usually widely-spaced component of surface texture and is generally of wider spacing than the roughness-width cutoff. Waviness may result from such factors as machine or work deflections, vibration, chatter, heat treatment or warping strains. Roughness may be considered as superimposed on a "wavy" surface. See Fig. 14-1.

Waviness Height. Waviness height is rated in inches as the peak to valley distance, Fig. 14-1. The preferred series of maximum waviness height is given in Table 17.

Waviness Width. Waviness width is rated in inches as the spacing of successive wave peaks or successive wave valleys. When specified, the values shall be the maximum permissible, Fig. 14-1.

Lay. The direction of the predominant surface pattern, ordinarily determined by the production method used, Fig. 14-1. Lay symbols shall be as . . . . shown in Fig. 14-5.

Flaws. Flaws are irregularities which occur at one place or at relatively infrequent or widely varying intervals in a surface, Fig. 14-1. Flaws include such defects as cracks, blow holes, checks, ridges, scratches, etc. Unless otherwise specified, the effect of flaws shall not be included in the roughness height measurements.

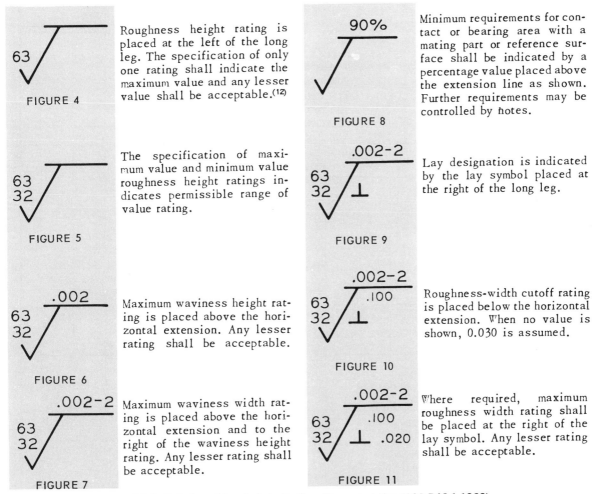

FIGURE 4 — Roughness height rating is placed at the left of the long leg. The specification of only one rating shall indicate the maximum value and any lesser value shall be acceptable.[12]

FIGURE 5 — The specification of maximum value and minimum value roughness height ratings indicates permissible range of value rating.

FIGURE 6 — Maximum waviness height rating is placed above the horizontal extension. Any lesser rating shall be acceptable.

FIGURE 7 — Maximum waviness width rating is placed above the horizontal extension and to the right of the waviness height rating. Any lesser rating shall be acceptable.

FIGURE 8 — Minimum requirements for contact or bearing area with a mating part or reference surface shall be indicated by a percentage value placed above the extension line as shown. Further requirements may be controlled by notes.

FIGURE 9 — Lay designation is indicated by the lay symbol placed at the right of the long leg.

FIGURE 10 — Roughness-width cutoff rating is placed below the horizontal extension. When no value is shown, 0.030 is assumed.

FIGURE 11 — Where required, maximum roughness width rating shall be placed at the right of the lay symbol. Any lesser rating shall be acceptable.

Fig. 14-4. Relation of Symbols to Surface Characteristics (ASA B46.1-1962)

Contact Area. Contact area is the area of the surface required to effect contact with its mating surface. Unless otherwise specified, contact area shall be distributed over the surface with approximate uniformity. Contact area shall be specified as shown in Fig. 14-4E.

Application of Surface Symbols

Surface quality is designated with a surface symbol and ratings. The symbol is similar to a check mark, but with a horizontal extension line added, Fig. 14-2. The long leg of the check-like symbol is to the right as the drawing is read. If only the roughness height is designated, the horizontal extension line may be omitted. Where no specifications or ratings are included with the surface symbol, it is assumed that the surface produced by the particular operation or process will be satisfactory.

The point of the surface symbol is located on the line indicating the surface specified. It also may be located on an extension line or leader pointing to the surface specified, as in Fig. 14-6. Symbols used with the surface symbol to indicate lay are shown in Fig. 14-5.

Surface quality ratings for various characteristics such as roughness, waviness, and lay are positioned specifically in relation to the surface symbol. The relative location of these specifications and ratings is indicated in Fig.

Table 18
Surface Roughness Produced by Common Production Methods[*]

Process	Roughness Height (Microinches)												
	2000	1000	500	250	125	63	32	16	8	4	2	1	0.5
Flame cutting													
Snagging													
Sawing													
Planing, Shaping													
Drilling													
Chemical Milling													
Electrical Discharge Machining													
Milling													
Broaching													
Reaming													
Boring, Turning													
Barrel Finishing													
Electrolytic Grinding													
Roller Burnishing													
Grinding													
Honing													
Polishing													
Lapping													
Superfinishing													
Sand Casting													
Hot Rolling													
Forging													
Permanent Mold Casting													
Investment Casting													
Extruding													
Cold Rolling, Drawing													
Die Casting													

Key

▬▬▬ Average Application

▨▨▨ Less Frequent Application

The ranges shown above are typical of the processes listed.
Higher or lower values may be obtained under special conditions.

(*ASA B46.1 — 1962)

LAY SYMBOL	DESIGNATION	EXAMPLE
‖	Lay parallel to the line representing the surface to which the symbol is applied.	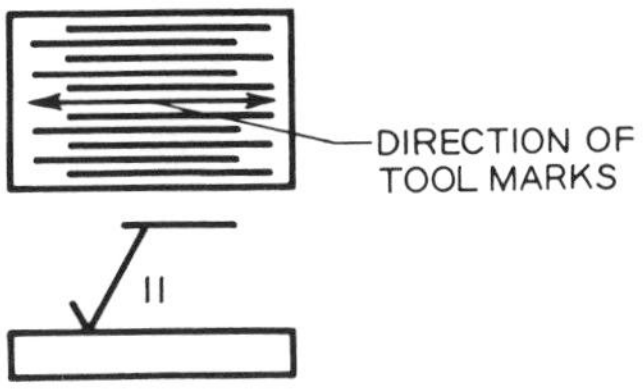 DIRECTION OF TOOL MARKS
⊥	Lay perpendicular to the line representing the surface to which the symbol is applied.	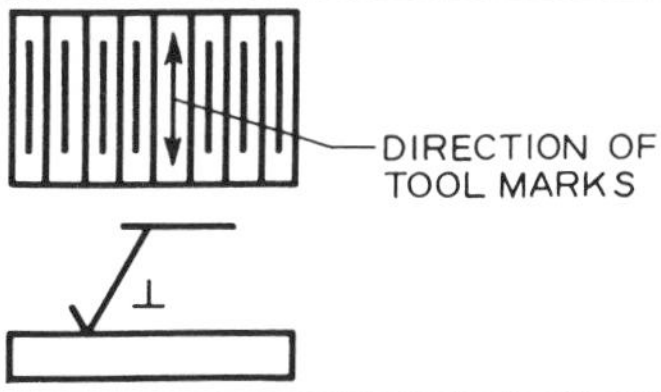 DIRECTION OF TOOL MARKS
X	Lay angular in both directions to line representing the surface to which symbol is applied.	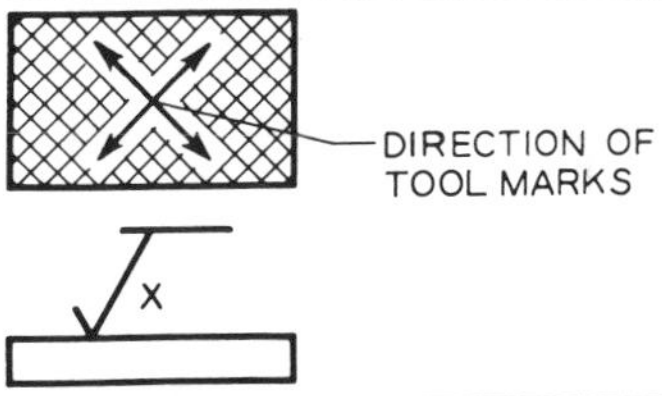 DIRECTION OF TOOL MARKS
M	Lay multidirectional	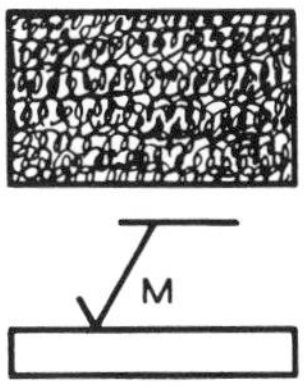
C	Lay approximately circular relative to the center of the surface to which the symbol is applied.	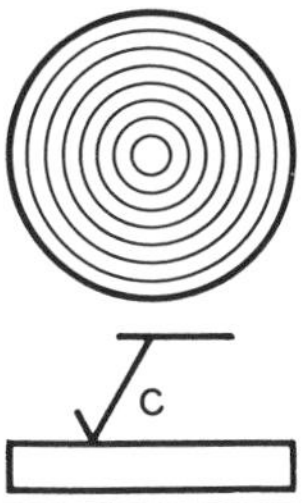
R	Lay approximately radial relative to the center of the surface to which the symbol is applied.	

Fig. 14-5. Lay Symbols (ASA B46.1-1962)

491

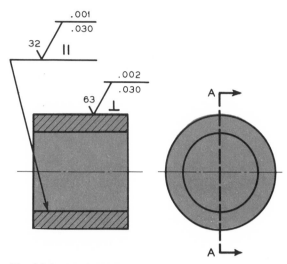

Fig. 14-6. Application of Surface Roughness Symbols
(ASA B46.1-1962)
Section AA Interpretation:

Roughness Height (OD) . . . . 63 Mu. in.
Roughness Height (ID) . . . . 32 Mu. in.
Roughness-Width Cutoff 030
Waviness Height (OD) 002
Waviness Height (ID) 001
Lay (OD) . . . . Circumferential
Lay (ID) . . . . Axial

14-4. An example of surface quality symbols with specifications is shown and interpreted in Fig. 14-6.

The quality of a surface is determined to a large extent by the machining or production method used to produce the surface. The range of surface roughness made by various production methods is illustrated in Table 18. A wide range may be achieved for a given method. For example, the range of roughness for turning may vary from 2 to 1000 microinches, depending on various machining factors, such as type of material, rate of feed, depth of cut, etc. Where a specific surface quality is desired for a given job, the method which will produce the desired surface most economically generally is selected.

Checking Surface Texture

The quality of a surface may be determined in several ways, depending on the type of equipment available. Surface irregularities are checked or measured by various types of measuring instruments used in research laboratories and by inspectors or machinists on production lines. Comparison specimens also may be used.

Comparison Specimens

Comparison specimens are used to check or determine surface quality through the sense of sight and touch. A standard specimen with the surface quality desired, checked previously with a reliable surface measuring instrument, may be used. The surface being checked is compared with the specimen by dragging the fingernail over both surfaces. Although this is not as reliable and accurate as other methods, it is economical and satisfactory for checking those surfaces which do not require extremely close tolerances.

Commercial comparison specimens, also called *master standards*, are available in sets, Fig. 14-7. The sets include blocks with various types of lay and with surface qualities ranging from rough to very smooth. They are available in various materials, including stainless steel, nickel alloys, aluminum alloys, and hard black plastic. The black plastic aids in elimination of possible error in judgment which may result in comparing bright specimens with less brilliant materials. An example of a specimen set complete in one solid piece is the microfinish comparator shown in Fig. 14-8.

Surface Roughness Indicator

The roughness of a surface may be determined with several types of special instruments. However, the most widely used is an electrical instrument of the *stylus type*. As the stylus passes over an irregular surface, perpendicular to the surface, its motion is amplified, and the average roughness of the surface is indicated in microinches. An instrument of this type is shown in Fig. 14-9.

Surface measuring instruments of the stylus type are available for either hand- or machine-powered movement of the stylus. More accurate readings are obtained with the power-driven stylus. If the surface being measured has a high degree of waviness, and if the specifications require an accurate roughness-width-cutoff setting, hand-guided operation of the tracer head and stylus is not recommended.

Stylus instruments are available with several roughness height ranges, usually for 3, 10, 30, 100, and 300 average microinches. See knob at lower right, Fig. 14-9. The instrument also may be provided with several roughness-width-

cutoff ranges, including 0.003″, 0.010″, and 0.030″, lower left of Fig. 14-9. Unless otherwise specified on the drawing, a roughness-width cutoff of 0.030″ should be selected. With this wider cutoff range, a more accurate average reading of surface irregularities may be determined.

Designations for Roughness Height

The roughness height, according to the 1962 ASA standard, is expressed in microinches as the simple *arithmetical average* (AA) deviation, measured normal to the center line. The center line through the profile of a rough sur-

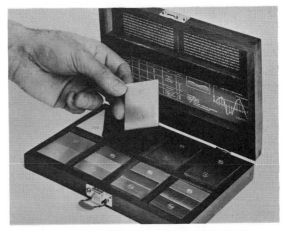

Fig. 14-7. Surface Finish Master Standards
(GAR Div. — Heli-Coil)

Fig. 14-8. S-22 Microfinish Comparator (GAR Div. — Heli-Coil)

Fig. 14-9. Surface Roughness Indicator
(AIL Div. — Cutler-Hammer)
(A) Indicator; (B) Being used at the bench; (C) Being used at the machine.

face is shown in Fig. 14-3. In previous standards, the roughness height was expressed in microinches as the *root mean square average* (RMS) deviation, measured normal to the center line.

Some older measuring instruments may be calibrated to indicate surface roughness according to the RMS average instead of the newer unified AA reading. Certain instruments are equipped with a selector switch for selecting either the RMS or the AA reading. In addition, some drawings also may use the older RMS roughness figure rather than the newer AA figure.

Roughness measuring instruments calibrated for AA values will indicate approximately 11 percent lower for a given surface than those calibrated for RMS average values. Continued use of drawings originally specified with the RMS average values and measurement of the corresponding surfaces with instruments calibrated with AA values will result in acceptance of surfaces with up to 11 percent greater roughness than intended. However, because the absolute limit of roughness for satisfactory functioning of a surface is indefinite, many manufacturers adopt AA ratings without changing the RMS values indicated on older drawings. For most surface measurement applications, the difference between the two values is of no consequence.

In order to eliminate error or confusion in the use of various stylus instruments, standards are included in ASA B46.1-1962. The stylus must be a specified size and shape. For instruments indicating a numerical value only, a spherical-tip stylus with a 500 microinch (0.0005″) radius tip is standard. Stylus tips of other sizes may be preferred for profile recording instruments. The performance of an instrument for measuring surface roughness should be checked by measuring a precision reference specimen. For further details concerning standards for stylus instruments, the above standard should be consulted.

Test Your Knowledge of Section 14

Unit 136: Surface Texture Specifications

1. List several factors which determine the quality of a machined surface.
2. Who determines what type of surface is to be produced on a machined part?
3. Why should some machined surfaces be very smooth?
4. Why should a designer avoid requiring a high-quality surface when a surface of lesser quality would be satisfactory?
5. Why should the machinist know about surface texture specifications?
6. What is meant by *surface texture*?
7. What is meant by a *microinch*?
8. Explain the meaning of *roughness height*.
9. Explain the meaning of *roughness-width cutoff*.
10. What is the meaning of *waviness*?
11. Explain the meaning of *waviness width*.
12. Explain the meaning of *lay*.
13. Describe the shape of a surface symbol, and explain where it is used.
14. When a surface symbol is used without specifications, what is its meaning?
15. What are the average roughness height ranges produced by the following machining operations: (a) drilling, (b) milling, (c) grinding, (d) polishing, (e) super-finishing?
16. What factors determine the quality of surface texture produced by an operation such as turning?

Unit 137: Checking Surface Texture

1. Explain what comparison specimens are and how they are used to check surface texture.
2. Explain how a surface roughness indicator of the stylus type is used to check surface texture.
3. What roughness height ranges often are available for use on surface roughness measuring instruments?
4. What is the advantage in using a surface roughness indicator which has a power-operated stylus?
5. What *roughness-width-cutoff* rating should be selected for measuring with a stylus instrument when no specific figure is indicated with the surface texture symbol?
6. From what source can one secure additional special information concerning standards for the use of stylus surface roughness indicators?

Decrease, Dissipate, Disperse — Friction, Heat, Chips

(Texaco)

Cutting Action and Cutting Fluids

The Action of a Cutting Tool on Metal

Machine tools produce metal chips of various kinds and shapes. Some chips are short and tend to flake off, some are in the form of long coils, and some are short, bent parts of a coil. The type of chip formation is a factor in determining how rapidly metal may be removed from the workpiece, and it influences the texture of the machined surface.

The type of chip formed at the cutting edge is determined largely by the type of material being cut and the shape of the cutting tool. Since the type of material machined for a particular purpose is constant, the form of the chip may be changed by changing the shape of the cutting tool through grinding. The machinist can determine whether a cutting tool has the proper shape for cutting a given material by knowing the properties of the material and by observing the type of chip which is formed.

How the Tool Cuts

One can understand metal chip formation more readily by understanding the action of the metal at the cutting edge of the tool as the material is being cut.

All metals in the solid state have a characteristic *crystalline* structure, frequently referred to as the *grain structure*. The *crystals* or grains may vary in size from very fine to very coarse, depending on the type of metal and whether or not it has been *heat-treated*. Each crystal is composed of groups of *atoms* or *molecules* clustered together. The crystals of a pure metal such as pure copper are composed of large clusters of atoms. The crystals

of an alloy such as steel, which may be composed of several metallic or nonmetallic elements, have large clusters of either atoms or molecules.

Fig. 15-1 is a diagram of a cutting tool, such as a shaper tool bit, forming a chip on a metal workpiece. As the tool advances against the workpiece, great forces are exerted on the crystalline metallic grains in front of the tool face; these grains, in turn, exert similar pressures on the grains ahead of them, in the direction of the cut. As the tool continues to advance, the material at point *A* is sheared by the cutting edge of the tool, or it may be torn loose by the action of the bending chip which is being formed. As the chip is formed, maximum stress is exerted along line *AB*, which is called the *shear plane*. This plane is approximately perpendicular to the cutting face of the tool. When the force of the tool exceeds the strength of the material at the shear plane, rupture or

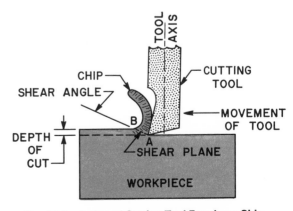

Fig. 15-1. Action of Cutting Tool Forming a Chip

499

slippage of the crystalline grain structure occurs, thus forming the metal chip (or chips). The cutting edge of the tool tends to scrape or smooth the machined surface. This cycle is repeated continuously as the tool advances further along the workpiece.

The type of chip formed in Fig. 15-1 is typical of that formed from ductile materials such as free-machining steel or certain aluminum alloys. This type of chip escapes along the tool face by a process known as *plastic flow*. A material is said to be *plastic* if it can be permanently deformed without rupture or breaking. Some metals have more *plasticity* than others. Modeling clay has excellent plasticity since it can be molded to any shape without breaking or returning to its original shape. Likewise, aluminum and free-machining steel have high plasticity, when compared to cast iron, which has little or no plasticity.

Types of Chips

Cutting tools form three basic types of chips, depending on the type of material being cut. The type of chip influences the amount of tool wear and determines the quality of surface finish.

Discontinuous Chip: When a brittle metal such as cast iron or bronze is machined, the chips are broken up in the form of flakes along the shear plane and ahead of the cutting edge of the tool, as in Figs. 15-2 and 15-3. This type of chip is called the discontinuous chip or segmental chip. Brit-

tle metals have small, irregularly-shaped grains which are held together with a brittle glass-like bond. Since the grains are so hard, pres-

Fig. 15-3. Formation of Typical Discontinuous Chip (Magnification About 5×) (Cincinnati Milling Machine)

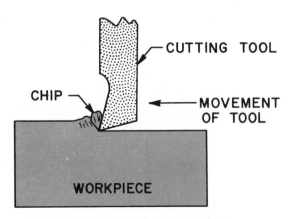

Fig. 15-2. Discontinuous-Type Chip

500

sure from the tool transfers easily from one grain to another ahead of the tool. This causes the metal to fracture into short chips, which escape freely along the tool face and clear the cutting zone easily. This type chip, however, causes considerable tool wear and rounding of the cutting edge.

Factors which contribute to the formation of discontinuous type chips are: a small rake angle on the cutting tool, low cutting speeds, thick chips, and vibration of the cutting tool.

Continuous Chip: The continuous chip is formed when ductile metals such as aluminum or free-machining steel are machined, Fig. 15-4. The chip has the form of a continuous coiled ribbon. It is formed at the cutting edge of the tool by the shearing action of the tool.

Ductile metals usually have a larger grain size and good plasticity, thus enabling the grains to withstand considerable distortion without fracture. As the tool advances, the metal ahead of the cutting edge is compressed. This compressed metal becomes *work-hardened* as it starts to form a chip. The hardened chip resists further compression and escapes along the tool face in the form of a continuous chip. This cycle repeats itself continuously as the tool proceeds with the cut. The tool edge tends to smooth the surface which remains relatively soft.

The continuous chip is the ideal way of machining metal. It produces a good finish, causes less friction, and requires less power to remove a given amount of metal. Factors which tend to cause continuous chips on ductile materials are large rake angles on the tool, high cutting speeds, a sharp cutting edge with a highly-polished tool face, and the use of a good cutting oil to reduce friction.

Continuous Chip with Built-Up Edge: The continuous chip with a built-up edge frequently is formed on tough metals such as medium-carbon steels, tool steels, and alloy steels. This type of chip (illustrated in Fig. 15-5) takes the form of a "somewhat-continuous" ribbon, or short pieces of ribbon which break off frequently.

The crystalline grains of tough, ductile metals usually are moderate in size and are held together with a strong bond. As the tool compresses the metal ahead of the cutting edge, the metallic grains become work-hardened, resist further compression, and start to escape along the tool face in the form of a chip. However, some of the tough, highly-compressed metal thoroughly cleans the tool face and forms a weld-like bond along the cutting edge and on the tool face. The metal bonded to the tool is called a *built-up edge*. As the chips slide over the tool face, the built-up edge slides off, and the cycle repeats itself.

Some of the metal immediately ahead of the tool, and ahead of the built-up edge on the tool, tends to fracture or tear apart at the shear plane. It then slides under the cutting edge of the tool, thus causing a rough surface

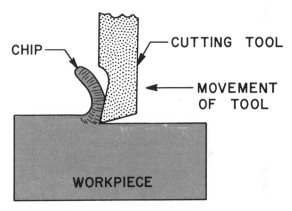

Fig. 15-4. Continuous-Type Chip

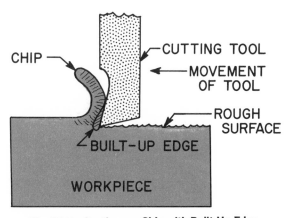

Fig. 15-5. Continuous Chip with Built-Up Edge

501

CUTTING ACTION:

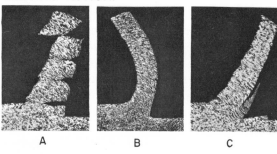

Fig. 15-6. Basic Types of Chips (Magnification About 15×) (Cincinnati Milling Machine) (A) Discontinuous; (B) Continuous; (C) Continuous, with built-up edge.

which often is considerably work-hardened. This type of chip causes increased friction and increased heat, and it requires much more power for removal of a given amount of metal.

Factors which tend to minimize the formation of chips with a built-up edge are: proper rake angles on the tool, a sharp cutting edge, a polished tool face, correct cutting speed and feed, and the use of a good cutting fluid.

A comparison of the three basic types of chips may be made by observing Fig. 15-6. The principles involved in the action of the cutting tool in forming the three types of chips described applies to the cutting action of many basic metal-cutting tools including: (1) single-point tools, such as shaper tool bits, planer tool bits, boring tool bits, and threading tool bits; and (2) tools with multiple cutting edges, such as drills, milling cutters, reamers, taps, threading dies, broaches, and other specialized cutting tools.

139 Cutting Fluids

In addition to the proper feed, cutting speed, and shape of the cutting tool, careful attention should be given to the selection and use of the proper cutting fluid. Cutting fluids prolong tool life, increase the length of time between tool sharpening, increase the rate of metal

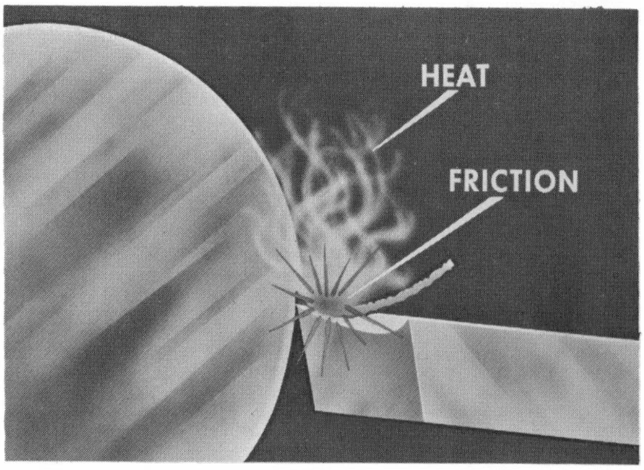

Fig. 15-7. Heat Generated at Cutting Edge (Texaco)

removal, aid in producing a finer finish, and enable machining to closer tolerances.

The term *cutting fluid* includes *cutting oils, cutting coolants,* and certain *synthetic* cutting *fluids* which are not oils. Each of the basic cutting fluids is developed for certain machining applications. Therefore, in order to select the proper cutting fluid for a particular machining application, one must understand the purposes of cutting fluids, the properties and classification of cutting fluids, and the factors which should be considered in selecting cutting fluids.

What Cutting Fluids Do

The principal functions of cutting fluids include *cooling* the cutting tool and the work and *lubricating* the face of the tool and the chip. The lubricating action *prevents adhesion,* which forms a built-up edge on the tool, and *reduces tool wear.* In addition to these functions, cutting fluids should also: provide a flushing action for chip removal, leave no stain or discoloration on the work, leave minimum sediment deposit on the machine, prevent or inhibit rusting of the machine and the work, resist smoking and fogging over the work, resist bacterial growth, and resist the development of an unpleasant odor as the fluid ages or becomes contaminated.

Coolant: Approximately 90% of the energy used in metal cutting is converted into heat. The heat is developed in the workpiece at the cutting edge of the tool. It results from the compression and friction generated as the metal chip is formed and escapes over the face of the cutting tool, Fig. 15-7. When the cutting speed and depth of cut are increased, the amount of heat developed also increases. A cutting fluid with good coolant properties is used to cool the workpiece and the cutting tool, when heavy cuts are made at high speeds.

Lubricant: A cutting fluid with good lubricating properties is used as an aid in the prevention of a built-up edge on the cutting tool. Such an edge frequently is caused by machining tough, ductile materials at a cutting speed which is too low. High pressures and resultant friction at the edge of the tool cause the freshly-cut metal to adhere or pressure-weld to the tool face, Figs. 15-8 and 15-9. As the metal is piled up, it slides off along the tool face, and the cycle repeats itself again and again. The work-hardened chip, while forming the built-up edge of the tool, leaves a rough surface on the workpiece and rapidly wears the flank of the tool. Low cutting speeds tend to promote the development of the built-up edge. A cutting fluid with good lubricity and anti-weld characteristics retards this development.

Reduces Tool Wear: High cutting speeds, with increased friction and heat, result in rapid wear at the cutting edge of the tool; in some cases, complete tool breakdown results, Fig. 15-10. The work-hardened chip moves over the face of the tool too rapidly to weld to the tool face. High heat causes the tool to soften and wear. With increased tool wear, the tool fractures easily.

The following tool materials begin to soften in the indicated heat ranges: carbon tool steel at 400° to 500° F.; high-speed steel at 1000° to 1100° F.; cast alloys at 1200° to 1500° F.; and cemented carbides at 1500° to 1700° F. Therefore, the principal purposes of a cutting

Fig. 15-8. Built-Up Edge on Tool Face (Texaco)

Fig. 15-9. Chip Welded to Tool Face (Texaco)

Fig. 15-10. Complete Breakdown of Tool (Texaco)

fluid at high speeds are to cool the tool and the work, to lubricate the tool face and the chip, and to resist tool wear and the formation of a built-up edge on the tool.

Function in Grinding: Cutting fluids also are recommended for many grinding operations. A fluid with good cooling properties is necessary to prevent distortion of the work due to heat developed with heavy grinding. On light grinding, proper lubrication prevents wheel clogging and improves

Fig. 15-11. Emulsifiable Oil Cutting Fluid (Texaco)

Fig. 15-12. Use of Soluble Oil Solutions (Texaco)
Note the cloudy white color.

the smoothness of the finish. Cutting fluids also increase the life of the grinding wheel by reducing the frequency of wheel dressing.

Classification of Cutting Fluids

There are numerous cutting fluids available under different trade names. However, most of the commercial cutting fluids can be classified within two groups — the cutting oils and the emulsifiable oils. *Cutting oils* also are frequently referred to as *straight oils*. Their principal ingredient is petroleum mineral oil. Other ingredients are added to provide the properties desired.

Emulsifiable oils, also called *soluble oils* or *water-soluble oils*, are composed of emulsifiable mineral oil and water. An emulsifying agent in the oil causes it to disperse evenly in tiny droplets throughout the solution, Fig. 15-11. For certain desired properties, other additives are compounded with the oil. The cutting solutions are usually cloudy or milky-white, Fig. 15-12.

Cutting Oils: Lard oil, derived from animal fats, is a good cutting oil for many machining applications at lower cutting speeds. However, it is relatively expensive when used undiluted in large quantities. Mineral oil may be added, and, when so diluted, it commonly is classified as mineral-lard oil — one of the basic straight mineral cutting oils.

There are several basic mineral cutting oils. Each type acquires its special characteristics or properties through additives, including fatty

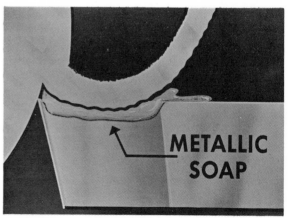

Fig. 15-13. Fatty Oil Additives Produce Metallic Soap Film (Texaco)

oils, fatty acids, sulfur, chlorine, phosphorous, and certain other chemicals. The basic ingredient, mineral oil, provides for the cooling property of the oil. It also provides for some lubrication of the cutting tool and the chip.

Lubrication properties are improved when fatty oils or fatty acids are added to mineral oil. The fatty oils include such oils as lard oil, sperm oil, or fish oil. These improve the *wetability* or *oiliness* of the cutting fluid, by enabling the oil to disperse evenly and cling to the cutting tool. Under the heat and pressure developed while cutting, the fatty oils combine to form a metallic soap between the cutting tool and the chip, thus reducing friction, Fig. 15-13. Reduced friction results in improved tool wear, reduction in power, and improved surface finish.

Anti-weld properties of mineral cutting oils are provided through the addition of sulfur, chlorine, or both sulfur and chlorine. When a clean metal chip, under heat of friction, is coated with a cutting fluid containing sulfur (or chlorine), a chemical reaction takes place between the surface of the tool and the chip, forming a sulfide (or chloride) film. This film has a lower shear strength than the metal being cut, thus reducing friction at the cutting edge of the tool. The film also aids in preventing the formation of a built-up edge on the tool. The chemical additives provide for anti-weld properties at a higher temperature than can be provided for with the addition of fatty oils alone. The chemical reaction of the chlorine takes place at temperatures lower than that required for the sulfur reaction. Therefore, sulfur additives in cutting oils usually are recommended for heavy-duty machining operations where high heats are developed. Through various combinations of additives, a wide variety of cutting oils are produced for use in machining different metals under different conditions.

When heavily compounded cutting oils were first developed, they were usually very dark, as in Fig. 15-14. These dark oils still are available. Through modern oil chemistry, *transparent* compounded cutting oils also are available and widely used today. The cutting tool and the work can be observed clearly through the transparent oils (Fig.15-15); shop

cleanliness and working conditions also are improved through their use.

Active and Inactive Cutting Oils. There are two basic types of mineral cutting oils — active and inactive. The *active* oils usually are recommended for use with ferrous metals on heavy-duty operations requiring extreme pressures. They cause discoloration of many copper alloys, including bronze bearings, due to the chemical reaction of additives, mainly sulfur. See Fig. 15-16.

Fig. 15-14. Highly Compounded Dark Cutting Oil
(Texaco)

Fig. 15-15. Transparent Cutting Oil (Texaco)

**Fig. 15-16. Cooper Strips from Corrosion Test
at 212°F.** (Texaco)
**Oil represented by strip on left contains no active
sulfur; that on right contains active sulfur.**

The *inactive* cutting oils do not cause any discoloration of metal, and so can be used with machines which have bronze bearings or bushings They are recommended for machining the nonferrous metals.

Both the active and the inactive types are available as transparent oils. These rapidly are replacing the dark oils, particularly on medium- and light-duty machining applications. Certain inactive, transparent cutting oils have been developed which are "tri-purpose" oils, *i.e.*, they can be used as a cutting fluid, as a lubricant for the machine, and in the hydraulic system of the machine. Hence, there is then no problem of one oil contaminating the other where leaks or other forms of mixing occur.

Emulsifiable Oils: The emulsifiable oils, which were previously mentioned in this unit, also are known widely as *soluble oils*. However, they are not really soluble, since oil does not dissolve in water. Because of an emulsifying base, usually in the form of a soap, the oil is dispersed in fine droplets throughout the water (Fig. 15-11). These oils are mixed in various proportions according to the machinability of the metal and the severity of the operation. The mixtures vary from 10:1 (10 parts water to 1 part oil) for severe operations on metals of low machinability, to 50:1 for grinding operations.

The emulsified oil solutions have better coolant properties than the cutting oils. Actually, water is one of the best coolants known. However, water has little lubrication value, and it reacts readily with the work surfaces and machine surfaces causing rust. Therefore, rust inhibitors are compounded with the oil for prevention of such corrosion.

Other additives are compounded with emulsifiable oils to develop desired properties. Lubrication properties are developed through the compounding of fatty oils or fatty acids. Antiweld properties are provided for through the compounding of sulfur, chlorine, or both, depending on the characteristics desired.

Emulsified oil solutions have limited working life. They should be replaced periodically, and the machine should be thoroughly cleaned before the new solution is used. Emulsifiable oils are sterile as manufactured, and they frequently have germicidal substances compounded in the oil to combat bacterial growth. However, with age and heavy use, they become rancid and develop an unpleasant odor. The solution should then be replaced.

When mixing emulsified oil solutions, *the oil always should be added to the water* (rather than water to oil) in order to form a proper solution. Soft water should be used when possible. If unavailable, an emulsifiable oil specially prepared for use in hard water should be used.

Mixing Emulsifiable Oil Solutions. The proportion of oil mixed with water in preparing an emulsified oil solution varies according to the machinability of the metal and the severity of the operation. For a list of the common metals and their approximate machinability ratings, see Table 30, appendix. Various machining operations are listed according to severity in Table 43, appendix.

When oil manufacturer's recommendations are available, they should be followed. In their absence, however, the following general recommendations may be used as a guide:

(Metal Machinability)	(Type of Operation)	(Dilution Water to Oil)
1. Low machinability	medium severity	10:1
2. Low machinability	low severity	20:1
3. Medium machinability	medium severity	15:1
4. Medium machinability	low severity	30:1
5. High machinability	medium severity	30:1
6. High machinability	low severity	30:1
7. Average cylindrical and surface grinding operations		30:1
8. Very-fine-finish grinding operations (thread grinding)		40:1 or 50:1

Dermatitis is an inflammation of the skin. Some people acquire dermatitis when in contact with emulsifiable cutting oils, particularly when the skin is dirty or contaminated. Therefore, hands should be kept clean by thorough washing with soap and warm water before and after working with cutting oils. Clothing also should be kept clean and free of cutting oil.

The emulsifiable oil solutions are the most widely used of all the cutting fluids. They have wide application and may be used on most metals for all except the most severe operations; see Table 43, appendix. These oils usually are the most economical cutting fluids for use where they are recommended.

Synthetic Emulsified Cutting Fluids. A second group of cutting fluids composed of an emulsifiable solution is the *synthetic* group. These fluids are diluted solutions of water and water-soluble chemical compounds. The chemicals are used instead of oils in providing lubricant and anti-weld properties. These solutions may be clear, or they may be very fine emulsions. They form one of the most recently developed groups of cutting fluids. Synthetic cutting fluids may seem expensive at first thought, but they may be diluted as highly as 275 parts water to one part compound. These solutions gradually are replacing straight cutting oils and emulsified oils for many applications. The manufacturer's recommendations should be consulted before using them, since there are several types available.

Other Cutting Fluids and Coolants: Several other types of cutting fluids or coolants may be used in machining metals:

Kerosene may be used on aluminum, aluminum alloys, and brass for machining operations of low severity. It has satisfactory cooling properties, and some lubricant properties for chip removal. It also may be mixed with lard oil as a cutting fluid for more severe applications on these materials. Nevertheless, the other cutting fluids listed in Table 43, appendix, usually are considered superior to kerosene.

Compressed air sometimes is used as a coolant and for the purpose of removing chips when machining cast iron. Cast iron contains graphite, which tends to serve as a lubricant at the edge and face of the cutting tool. Cast iron usually is machined dry.

Cutting wax fluids have been developed for use as cutting compounds. However, certain types also may be used as additives to be compounded with other cutting fluids, such as petroleum-based mineral cutting oils or emulsified oil solutions. The manufacturer's recommendations should be followed in mixing or using cutting waxes.

Selection of Cutting Fluids

There is no set rule which can be followed in the selection of a cutting fluid for a particular machining operation. The recommendations of suppliers for the use of cutting fluids are general, and their applications vary. It would be ideal if some physical property of the metal, such as its hardness, could be used to assign the metal a fixed *machinability rating* which would apply at all times in selecting a cutting fluid, but this is not possible. However, three principal factors can be used as a guide in selecting a cutting fluid for a particular application — (1) the machinability rating of the metal, (2) the severity of the operation being performed, and (3) the operating conditions.

Machinability: The term *machinability* has been much abused. It is difficult to define because its meaning is dependent on many factors, and not all authorities agree on its exact definition. In general, however, the term *machinability* means the ease with which

507

a metal may be machined. A metal with a high machinability rating frequently machines with comparatively low power consumption, has a high rate of metal removal, produces a good surface finish, and causes minimum tool wear. Some of the more important factors affecting the machinability rating of a metal include the following: the grain structure and hardness of the metal, the chemical composition of the metal, the type of machining operation, the tool shape and type of chip formed, the tool material, the rigidness of the work setup, and the cutting feed.

For the purpose of selecting proper cutting fluids, most of the commonly used metals have been classified in six groups according to their approximate machinability ratings as shown in Table 43, appendix. The machinability rating is expressed as a percentage, in comparison with A1S1 B1112 cold-drawn Bessemer Steel, which has a rating of 100 percent, Fig. 15-17. Metals which are more difficult to machine have a machinability rating of less than 100%, Fig. 15-18. Metals which machine more easily have a rating of more than 100%.

In most machining applications, as the machinability rating of the metal increases, cutting speeds may be increased. The relative machinability ratings of specific steels are indicated in Table 30, appendix. Machinability ratings are based on exact comparisons of various metals which are machined under scientifically controlled conditions, Fig. 15-19. With metals having low machinability ratings, the use of an active cutting oil with heavy-duty lubricant and anti-weld properties generally is recommended.

Severity of the Operation: The severity of the machining operation being performed is a significant factor in the selection of a cutting fluid. Various metal-cutting operations are rated in Table 43, appendix, according to numbers 1 through 10. Broaching (rated number 1) is the most severe, while sawing and grinding (rated num-

Fig. 15-17. Machinability Rating of B1112 Steel
(Texaco)
The machinability rating of metals is expressed as a percentage in comparison with B1112 steel, which is rated at 100 percent.

Fig. 15-18. Machinability Rating of Hard Cast Steel
(Texaco)

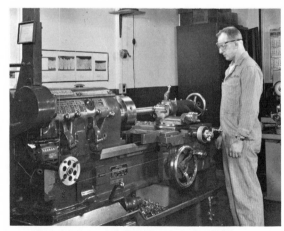

Fig. 15-19. Testing Machinability of Metals
(U.S. Steel)
Specially modified constant-pressure lathe is used to test the machinability of various steels.

ber 10) are the least severe. The heaviest-duty cutting fluids generally are recommended for the most severe machining operations.

Operating Conditions: Several operating conditions should be considered in the selection of cutting fluids. These include cutting speeds, feeds, depth of cut, tool geometry, tool material, heat treatment or work-hardness properties of the material, and rigidity of the work and the machine. Heavy cuts and slow speeds generally require excellent lubricating qualities. High speeds generally require greater coolant properties. High speeds, together with the high heat developed in machining steels of low machinability, generally require good lubricity, cooling, and anti-weld properties.

Selection Guide: In the selection of cutting fluids, Table 43, appendix, should be used as a general guide. Careful study of the table reveals that a specific cutting fluid often may give satisfactory results on several different metals of varying machinability rat-ings; it may also produce satisfactory results on several different operations.

Table 43, appendix, indicates the basic types of cutting fluids. Each of the several major oil companies produces cutting fluids which are similar or equivalent to the basic cutting fluids recommended in the table. Each company generally has a trade name for the equivalent oil. A review of the company literature and recommendations will aid further in accurately selecting the proper cutting fluid. In the selection of a synthetic cutting fluid, the manufacturers' recommendations should be reviewed carefully.

In summary, the following factors should be considered in the selection of a cutting fluid:

1. The machinability rating of the metal.
2. The severity of the operations being performed.
3. The operating conditions.
4. The properties of the cutting fluid.
5. The cost of the cutting fluid.
6. The recommendations of the manufacturer of the fluid.

Cutting Tool Materials

The properties of metal cutting tools are determined by the materials from which the tools are made. Such tools must possess a variety of different properties in order to cut the many different metals under varying conditions of severity. To meet these demands, tools have been produced from a variety of materials. In order to select the proper cutting tool for a given application, one must understand the basic properties required of cutting tools and the basic properties of each of the significant cutting-tool materials.

Properties of Cutting Tools

The most important properties of cutting tools are the following: hardness at high temperatures, wear resistance, and impact strength.

Hardness at High Temperatures: A cutting tool must be harder than the material which it is designed to cut. If it is too hard, it will be too brittle and will shatter easily. As the tool cuts, high heat is developed as a result of compression and friction at the cutting edge of the tool. All metal cutting tools begin to lose hardness to some degree when they are heated to temperatures which are sufficiently high. As the tool loses its hardness due to heat, it wears or breaks down at the cutting edge or face. (See Fig. 15-10.) Various cutting materials have different degrees of initial hardness, and they begin to lose their hardness at different temperatures. Hence, the hardness of the tool and the degree to which it retains its hardness at high temperatures are important in the selection of a cutting-tool material.

Wear Resistance: Cutting tools must be tough and wear-resistant. A cutting tool has toughness when it resists breaking or deforming under strains or heavy tool pressures. It is wear-resistant if it resists abrasion at the cutting edge and along the tool face. Wear usually takes place due to a lack of toughness. As indicated previously, wear resistance is related to heat. When the temperature level is attained at which the tool starts to lose its hardness significantly, the metal loses its toughness and wears more rapidly. See Fig. 15-10.

Strength: A cutting tool should have the kind of strength properties which give it impact resistance and resistance to vibration. It also must possess resilience, *i.e.*, be able to withstand shock. A cutting tool is resilient if it will return to its original shape after being slightly deformed from severe compressive strain. Strength in cutting-tool materials is not always proportional to hardness. Some of the hardest tool materials lack strength because they are too brittle.

No one cutting-tool material will satisfy conditions for machining all metals under all conditions. However, with careful study of the various materials, a cutting tool may be selected which will give satisfactory results on a wide variety of machining applications on several different metals.

Materials Used in Cutting Tools

The various materials from which most metal cutting tools are made can be classified under the following principal headings:
1. Carbon tool steel
2. High-speed steel
3. Cast alloys
4. Cemented carbides
5. Ceramics
6. Diamonds

Carbon Tool Steel Cutting Tools

Many cutting tools can be made from high-carbon tool steel. Some common examples include drills, reamers, center drills, forged boring bars, hand taps, and threading dies.

The chief advantage of carbon tool steel is its low cost in comparison with other cutting-tool materials. A principal disadvantage is its loss of hardness at relatively low temperatures. It begins to soften at 400° F. to 500° F. This temperature range is indicated by the heat-color range from brown to purple. When this range is exceeded, a blue or dark grey color appears, and the tool softens and wears rapidly.

Other properties of carbon tool steel include the following: a keen edge can be produced on the tool; it has good shock resistance; it can be machined in the annealed condition; tools should be used at temperatures below 400° F.; and the carbon content of the steel varies from .8% to approximately 1.25%. Carbon-steel tools generally should be operated at low cutting speeds, usually about one-half those recommended for high-speed steels. With lower cutting speeds, less heat is generated, and tool life is prolonged.

High-Speed Cutting Tools

The principal advantage of high-speed tool steels (HS steel) in comparison with high-carbon steel is their retention of hardness up through a dull red heat, ranging from approximately 1000° to 1100° F. They begin to soften due to tempering in this range, but they do not soften significantly until heated above this range. The property of tool steels to retain hardness to high heat or red heat is called *hot-hardness* or *red-hardness*.

The following are examples of tools which very frequently are made of high-speed steel: drills, reamers, end mills, center drills, counter bores, milling cutters, taps, and lathe centers. High-speed steel also is widely used for cutting tool bits used on lathes, shapers, and planers, Fig. 15-20. High-speed steel cutting tools generally will stay sharp for a much longer period of use than tools made of carbon tool steel.

The high-speed tool steels are the most heavily alloyed of all the steels. Their principal elements are tungsten and molybdenum. Other elements which also are alloyed with these steels in significant amounts are cobalt, vanadium, and chromium. Each of these elements imparts particular properties to the steel. Tungsten, molybdenum, chromium, and vanadium are carbide-forming elements, i.e., they combine with carbon to form carbides. The carbides cause the steel to resist softening at higher temperatures. They also impart high wear resistance to the steel. Cobalt is not a carbide former, but it combines with the iron in steel in a manner which increases the red-hardness of high-speed steels.

Types of High-Speed Steels: There are several different types of high-speed tool steels. The most common types may be classified in the following manner:

1. *Tungsten base steels:* This type of steel commonly is accepted as the standard for use in comparing the properties of other types of high-speed tool steels. One of the most commonly used steels of this type is the 18-4-1 steel (type T1). It is composed of 18% tungsten, 4% chromium, and 1% vanadium. Other tungsten steels with varying amounts of these elements are available.

2. *Molybdenum base steels:* One of the common steels of this type is 8% molybdenum, 4% chromium, and 2% vanadium (type M10). It has performance properties generally comparable to 18-4-1 tungsten steel.

3. *Tungsten-molybdenum base steels:* Steels of this class are similar to the tungsten steels, except that some of the tungsten is replaced with molybdenum. A common

steel of this type is 5% molybdenum, 6% tungsten, 4% chromium, and 2% vanadium (type M2). It has performance properties similar to 18-4-1 tungsten steels. The majority of the high-speed steels are of the tungsten-molybdenum type. They contain some of each of the four elements — tungsten, molybdenum, chromium, and vanadium.

4. *Cobalt steels:* Cobalt in amounts from 5% to 12% may be added to any of the above high-speed steels, Fig. 15-20. The cobalt increases the red-hardness of the steel significantly. High-speed steels which include a large percentage of cobalt are sometimes called *super high-speed steels.* The super HS steels frequently are used for tool bits or as tips on cutting tools. When the cobalt content is high, the hardness and wear resistance also are increased, but the impact toughness or resistance to shock generally is decreased.

When a particular cutting tool is available in several different types of high-speed steel, the manufacturer's recommendations should be considered in making the selection. Production efficiency is increased through understanding cutting-tool materials and selecting cutting tools accordingly.

Cast-Alloy Cutting Tools

A number of cast alloys have been developed for use as cutting-tool materials. Some common brand names are *Stellite, Rexalloy, Armaloy,* and *Tantung.* The cast alloys are used as brazed tips on tool shanks (Fig. 15-21), as removable tool bits, as inserts in toolholders, and as inserts in milling cutters (Fig. 15-22). The cast alloys are nonferrous materials with a cobalt base. They do not contain iron, except

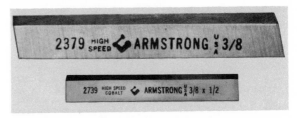

Fig. 15-20. High-Speed Steel Tool Bits (Armstrong)

that which is present in the form of an impurity in the raw materials used. Cast alloys used as cutting tools may contain various combinations of the following principal elements: cobalt 35% to 55%, chromium 25% to 35%, tungsten 10% to 20%, nickel 0% to 5%, and carbon 1.5% to 3%. Very small amounts of other elements sometimes are added. The cast alloys are cast slightly oversize and are ground to shape. They cannot be forged or machined successfully.

The principal advantage of the cast alloys, in comparison with high-speed steels, is their high red-hardness. Because of this property, higher cutting speeds may be used, and tool life

Fig. 15-21. Tool Bits with Brazed Cast-Alloy Tips
(Stellite Div. — Union Carbide)

is maintained at the resultant higher cutting temperature. Although the cast alloys begin to soften slightly at temperatures from 1200° to 1500° F., they are not seriously affected by temperatures below 1500° F. Any loss of hardness at these high temperatures is regained upon cooling. High-speed steels are slightly harder than the cast alloys at temperatures below 1100° F. Above this temperature, the cast alloys are harder and retain their hardness up to 1500° F. Thus, the cast alloys perform better for machining applications where temperatures ranging from 1100° to 1500° F. are developed. These applications usually will occur at cutting speeds which exist between the highest cutting speeds for high-speed steels and the lowest practical speeds for carbide tools. The cast-alloy tools generally perform best at high speeds. They may be operated at cutting speeds approximately 50% to 75% faster than the maximum for high-speed steel tools.

Most cast alloys are more brittle and generally will not stand the heavy shock or impact pressures which tool steels or high-speed steel will stand. They must, therefore, be well supported in a tool shank or toolholder.

Cast alloys are made by some manufacturers in several different grades which vary in impact-rupture strength. Certain grades of cast alloy have impact-rupture strength comparable to high-speed steel. These grades may be used in machining applications where extreme

Fig. 15-22. Milling Cutter with Cast-Alloy Insert Teeth
(Stellite Div. — Union Carbide)

Fig. 15-23. SAE 1137 Steel Machined at 460 sfpm with Carbide-Tooth Milling Cutter (Cincinnati Milling Machine)

shock conditions are encountered. It is best to follow the manufacturer's recommendation in selecting the grade of cast alloy used for a particular machining application.

Aluminum-oxide abrasive wheels are recommended for grinding or sharpening the cast alloys. They may be ground wet or dry, but they should not be quenched after grinding dry.

Cemented-Carbide Cutting Tools

Cemented-carbide cutting tools are used widely in modern production machining. Their principal advantages are high initial hardness, retention of hardness at red heats up through about 1700° F., and increased cutting speeds. Carbide cutting tools may be operated at speeds from two to four times the cutting speeds used for high-speed steel cutting tools. Fig. 15-23 shows SAE 1137 steel being machined at approximately 460 surface feet per minute with a milling cutter which has carbide teeth. It has been estimated that if carbide cutting tools became unavailable, the output of the nation's production lines would be reduced to about one-half the present rate.

The principal ingredients of the cemented carbides used for cutting tools are tungsten carbide and cobalt. Certain types of cemented carbides have titanium and tantalum carbides included to obtain specific properties. The carbide-tool materials are called *cemented carbides* because the carbide grains are cemented together during the manufacturing process with a binder, usually cobalt. Carbide tools are cast to shape and are very hard in the *as cast* condition. They do not require any further heat treatment. Carbides cannot be shaped by forging, but may be shaped by grinding.

Because of the initial high cost of cemented-carbide materials, carbide cutting tools frequently are used in the form of cutting tips brazed on the tool shank or on the body of a cutting tool as in Figs. 15-24 and 15-25. Carbide cutting tools often are used as tool inserts of the disposable type which may be rotated for use on each of the cutting edges or

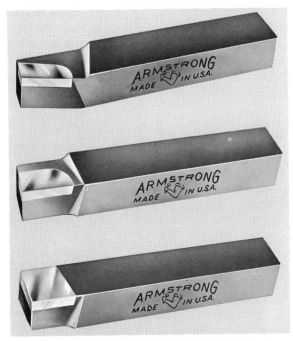

Fig. 15-24. Carbide-Tipped Tool Bits (Armstrong)

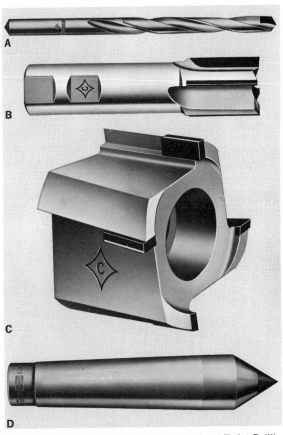

Fig. 15-25. Carbide-Tipped Tools (Cleveland Twist Drill) **(A) Straight-shank drill; (B) Straight-shank end mill; (C) Shell end mill; and (D) Lathe center.**

513

corners before they are thrown away. See Fig. 15-26. Carbides often are used for disposable chip breakers on shank toolholders, as in Fig. 15-25. Smaller cutting tools such as drills, reamers, center drills, and end mills are available in solid carbide form. See Fig. 15-27. Carbides also may be used as inserts on lathe or grinder centers, as in Fig. 15-25.

Cemented Carbide Groups: There are two basic groups of carbide materials used in cutting tools. *Group C* carbide is composed principally of tungsten carbide and cobalt, and it is used for machining cast iron and the nonferrous metals. *Group S* is composed principally of tungsten carbide tantalum carbide, titanium carbide, and cobalt. It is used for machining the various steels. If group *C* is used for machining steel, wear craters appear rapidly on the face of the tool. The titanium and tantalum carbide ingredients in group *S* carbides improve the wear-resistance qualities.

The amount of cobalt in either of the two groups of carbide affects the hardness of the cutting tool. As the amount of cobalt is increased, the tool becomes harder. With increased hardness, the carbide has increased wear resistance and tool life, together with decreased shock resistance due to brittleness. With decreased hardness, there is a decrease in wear resistance, but there also is a corresponding increase in shock resistance or impact toughness.

A second factor which influences the hardness, wear resistance, and impact toughness of the carbides is the grain structure. A fine grain structure increases hardness, while a coarse grain structure decreases hardness. The manufacturer can, therefore, control the hardness and toughness of carbides through control of the ingredients and the grain structure.

Cemented-Carbide Classifications: There are many different machining applications on which carbide cutting tools are used. These vary from roughing cuts to light finishing cuts on materials which may be very hard or soft. Different *grades* of carbide materials have been developed by tool manufacturers to meet the conditions demanded. Each grade is developed with certain properties for use on certain applications. Some grades of carbide are recommended for use on very specific applications, while others may be used on a broad range of general applications. Attention should be given to the selection of the right grade for the particular job or machining application.

The *Carbide Industry Classification System* may be used as an aid both in classifying machining applications and in selecting the proper grade of carbide cutting tool. Many carbide tool manufacturers recognize this classification system. Each manufacturer recommends one or more specific grades of carbide for use in each machining application. In some cases, one carbide grade may be selected which will

Fig. 15-26. Carbide Insert Tool Bit (Armstrong)
Note insert toolholder and disposable carbide cutting tool and carbide chip breaker.

Fig. 15-27. Solid Carbide Cutting Tools (Cleveland Twist Drill)
(A) Straight-shank drill; (B) Four-flute double end mill; and (C) Two-flute double end mill.

produce satisfactory results on several different machining applications. The following eight classifications are used in grouping machining applications for cemented-carbide cutting tools according to the Carbide Industry Classification System:

Cast iron and nonferrous materials
  C-1: Roughing cuts
  C-2: General-purpose cuts
  C-3: Light finishing cuts
  C-4: Precision boring cuts

Steel and steel alloys
  C-5: Roughing cuts
  C-6: General-purpose cuts
  C-7: Light finishing cuts
  C-8: Precision boring cuts

Included in this system are six additional classifications concerned with *wear applications* and *impact applications*. However, these are not within the scope of this unit.

In selecting a specific grade of carbide tool for one or more of the above machining classifications, the manufacturer's recommendations should be consulted. Such recommendations are available in tool supply catalogs and manufacturer's bulletins.

Each manufacturer uses his own numbering or identification system for each carbide grade. There also may be a variation in the properties and performance of the carbide grades recommended by several different carbide tool manufacturers for a particular machining application. Although these factors should be kept in mind, Table 19 may be used as an aid in the selection of carbide cutting tool materials. However, it is not recommended as a grade comparison chart.

Precautions in Use: Because of the special properties of carbide materials, particularly their hardness and brittleness, certain precautions should be observed with their use. Carbide tools must be rigidly supported in the toolholder or holding device. The machine and the work setup should be rigid and free from vibration. Interrupted cuts should be avoided when possible. The machine should not be stopped in the cut. Because of the pressure-welding characteristics of carbide tools at low speeds, they should be operated at the recommended cutting speeds, usually two to four times higher than those for high-speed steel tools. Proper cutting fluids also should be used.

Grinding Carbide Tools: Cemented-carbide cutting tools are very hard and cannot be ground on aluminum-oxide grinding wheels. They must be ground on harder abrasive wheels, either on silicon-carbide wheels or on diamond abrasive wheels as in Fig. 15-28. A 60-grit silicon-carbide abrasive wheel may be used for rough grinding on carbide cutting tools. A finer grit wheel, such as 100 grit, may be used for finish grinding. Silicon-carbide wheels used to grind cemented-carbide tools should have a soft bonding material. With a soft bond, dull abrasive grains break off readily, thus exposing sharp grains which reduce heat while grinding.

Diamond wheels are the best abrasive wheels for grinding cemented-carbide cutting tools. Although initially they are more expensive, they produce a better finish and cut faster, cooler, and with less wear. Diamond abrasive wheels should be used with special care; grinding speed should not exceed 5000 surface feet per minute, the proper cutting fluid should be used, and the proper grade of diamond wheel should be selected.

A more detailed description of diamond and other types of abrasive wheels is included in Unit 111. It is best to follow the manufacturer's recommendations concerning the use of diamond abrasives.

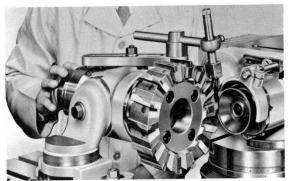

Fig. 15-28. Grinding Periphery of Tungsten-Carbide Face Mill with Diamond Abrasive Wheel
(Cincinnati Milling Machine)

Table 19
Selection Chart for Grades of Carbide Cutting Tools

(The grade references are furnished by the different carbide manufacturers, and are not intended to be a grade comparison chart.)

CHIP REMOVAL APPLICATIONS

C-1 Roughing Cuts — cast iron and non-ferrous materials
C-2 General Purpose — cast iron and non-ferrous materials
C-3 Light finishing — cast iron and non-ferrous materials
C-4 Precision boring — cast iron and non-ferrous materials
C-5 Roughing cuts — steel

C-5A Rough cuts and heavy feeds — steel
C-6 General purpose — steel
C-7 Finishing cuts — heavy feeds — steel
C-7A Finishing cuts — fine feeds — steel
C-8 Precision boring — steel

WEAR APPLICATIONS

C-9 Wear Surface — No Shock
C-10 Wear Surface — Light Shock
C-11 Wear Surface — Heavy Shock

IMPACT APPLICATIONS

C-12 Impact — Light
C-13 Impact — Medium
C-14 Impact — Heavy

MANUFACTURER'S NAME AND GRADE

Code	Adamas	Carmet	Carboloy	Firlomet	Firthite	Kenna Metal	Multi-Metals	New Comer	Sandvik Coromant	Sinter Cast	Talide	Tungsten Alloy	Unimet	Valenite	Vascoloy Ramet	Walmet	Wendt Sonis	Wesson	Willey
C-1	B	CA3	44A	FA-5	H	K1	OM1	NC4	H20	SF1	C89	9	U10	VC1	2A3 / 2A68	WA1	CQ12	GS	E8 / E13
C-2	A	CA4	883 / 860	FA-61 / FA-6	HA	K6	OM2	NC3 / C35 / N20	H20	SF2	C91	9H	U20	VC2	2A5	WA2	CQ2	G1	E6 / X3
C-3	AA	CA7	905	FA-7	HE	K8	OM3	NC2	H13	SF3	C93	9C	U30	VC3	2A7	WA3	CQ3	GA	E5
C-4	AAA	CA8	999	FA-8	HF	K11	OM4	NC2	H05	SF4	C95	9B	U40	VC4	2A7	WA4	CQ4	GF	E3
C-5	434	CA51	370	FT-3	T04 / NTA	KM / K21	3M5	NS65 / N50	S6	SF5	S88	11T	U53	VC125	AW-EE / VR77	WA5	CY15 / CY12	M / WS	945
C-5A	434	CA610	370 / 78B	FT-41 / FT-4	NTA / TXH	K21 / K2S	4M5	N50 / NS4	S6	SF5	S88	9S	U53	VC125	VR77	WA5	CY12 / CY15	HR	10A
C-6	D	CA720 / CA610	78B	FT-4 / FT-5	TXH / T22	K2S / K4H	3M6 / 4M6	NS3 / NS35 / N60	S4	SF6	S90	10T	U60	VC6	VR75 / EM	WA6	CY16 / CY5	26 / WM	8A
C-7	C	CA606	350 / 78	FT-62 / FT-6	T22 / TXL	K4H	3M7	NS2 / N70	S2	SF7	S900	9T	U70	VC7	VR73 / E	WA7	CY14 / CY2	WH	606
C-7A	548	CA711	78 / 350	FT-62 / FT-7	TXL / T31	K5H	4M7	NS15 / N80	S1P	SF7	S92	8T	U73	VC7	EH / VR65	WA7	CY2 / CY14	WH	6A
C-8	CC	CA604 / CA704	330 / 030	FT-7 / FT-71	T31 / WF	K7H / K165	3M8	NM95 / NM93	F1	SF8	S94	5S	U80	VC8	VR65 / VR97	WA8	CY31	HV	4A-509 / 3AT
C-9	A	CA4	883	FA-6	HA	K6	OM2				C99	9-9H / 9M	U20	VC9	2A5	WA9	CQ2	G1	E6
C-10	B	CA3	44A	FA-5	H	K1	OM1				C88	9	U10	VC10	2A3	WA10	CQ12	GS	E8
C-11	BB	CA10	55A	FA-3	HC	K1	OM11				C80	9A15 / 9A	U110	VC11	AW	WA11	CY4	M	E18
C-12	BB	CA10	55A / 44A	FB-5	DC2 / DC1	K96 / K94	IM12				C85	9M / 9	U135	VC12	2A3	WA12	CQ12	M	E13
C-13	HD15	CA11	55B / 55A	FB-4	DCX	K92	OM13				C80	9A15 / 9A	U130	VC13	AX	WA13	CY31	222	E18
C-14	HD20 / HD25	CA225	190	FB-3	DC4 / DC3	K90 / K91					C75	9A25 / 9A20	U140	VC14	AY	WA14	CY4	WP	E25

Ceramic Cutting Tools

Various ceramic tool materials have been developed for use in making cutting tools. These ceramics are cemented-oxide materials. They are composed of metal oxides which are cemented together by a bonding material after being sintered (*Sintering* is a process of fusing certain materials by heating them in a furnace at high temperatures.)

The principal ingredients used in ceramic tool materials are aluminum oxides, silicon oxides, and magnesium oxides. These materials may be used together or separately, with a binder. A common ceramic tool material may include 90% to 99% aluminum oxide together with a binder material. Aluminum oxide also is used commonly in grinding wheels.

Ceramic cutting tools, like cemented-carbide cutting tools, are used in the form of inserts or tool bits held in a toolholder mechanically. However, unlike carbide tools, they cannot be brazed. A ceramic cutting tool is illustrated in Fig. 15-29. Ceramic tool materials rank between sapphire and diamond in hardness; they are harder than cemented-carbide tools. They have a crystalline structure and are hard and brittle, and high in wear resistance, but they shatter quite easily because of low impact resistance or low rupture strength.

The hardness of ceramic tool materials is affected little by heat. Hot metal chips do not weld readily to the cutting tool when operated at the proper cutting speeds; therefore, cutting fluids generally are not needed. However, when coolants are needed to prevent distortion, the fluids should flow liberally over the cutting tool. A liberal flow will prevent intermittent cooling which may cause the tool to crack or shatter.

The principal advantages of ceramic cutting tools are increased cutting speeds and increased tool life per cutting edge. These tools also may be used for certain machining applications where it is necessary to cut heat-treated or very hard steel. Ceramic cutting tools may be operated at cutting speeds two to four times higher than those used for cemented-carbide tools. However, because of their low impact resistance, they generally should be used for fairly light finishing cuts at high speed. The high cutting speeds usually result in improved surface finish, which often eliminates the need for a ground finish.

Ceramic cutting tools should be sharpened by grinding on diamond abrasive wheels. When a replaceable tool insert is used, it may be rotated as each cutting edge becomes dull or worn. See Fig. 15-29.

Diamond Cutting Tools

Diamond is the hardest material known. It can be used at cutting speeds up to 5000 surface feet per minute. It will cut very hard materials and produce good finishes. Diamonds have been used on tools such as small boring bars for precision boring. However, diamonds are used more widely as abrasive wheels for grinding hard materials such as cemented-carbide tools, glass, stone, ceramic tools, and ceramic materials of all types. Because of the high initial cost of diamonds, they are recommended for uses where less-expensive materials will not perform well.

Those diamonds used for cutting tool applications are industrial diamonds — either natural or man-made (manufactured). The *natural* industrial types are impure, opaque diamonds which are relatively inexpensive when compared with diamonds used in jewelry.

Manufactured diamonds were produced after many years of research by several companies. The General Electric Company produced manufactured diamonds in 1955. Working independently, the Norton Company announced the development of man-made dia-

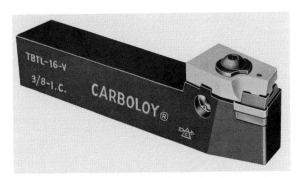

Fig. 15-29. Toolholder with Disposable Cemented-Oxide Tool Insert (Metallurgical Prod. Dept. — G.E.)

monds in 1960. Although the price of the diamonds was higher than that for natural diamonds when first produced, improvements in manufacturing techniques have eliminated the price differential. The development of manufactured diamonds insures a reliable supply for abrasives and other industrial uses when natural diamonds fluctuate in price or are in short supply.

Industrial diamonds may be used in the form of either chips or abrasive grains. A diamond chip may be mounted on the end of a cutting tool, such as on the abrasive-wheel dressing tool in Fig. 5-9. Diamond grains may be impregnated in steel, in cemented carbide, or in other types of bonding material to form a cutting tool such as a diamond-cluster nib used for truing an abrasive wheel, Fig. 15-30. Diamond abrasive grains also are used with an appropriate bonding material to form grinding wheels, as in Fig. 12-18. Diamond grinding wheels are discussed in more detail in Units 110 and 111.

Fig. 15-30. Diamond-Impregnated Cluster Nib for Dressing and Truing Grinding Wheels
(Desmond-Stephan)

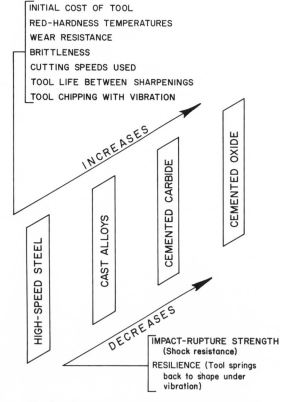

INITIAL COST OF TOOL
RED-HARDNESS TEMPERATURES
WEAR RESISTANCE
BRITTLENESS
CUTTING SPEEDS USED
TOOL LIFE BETWEEN SHARPENINGS
TOOL CHIPPING WITH VIBRATION

INCREASES

DECREASES

HIGH-SPEED STEEL
CAST ALLOYS
CEMENTED CARBIDE
CEMENTED OXIDE

IMPACT-RUPTURE STRENGTH
(Shock resistance)
RESILIENCE (Tool springs back to shape under vibration)

Fig. 15-31. General Characteristics of Various Cutting Tools

Comparative Cutting Speeds

There is no definite rule which can be used in recommending cutting speeds for cutting tools made from different materials. Recommended speeds will vary according to the following factors: the material being cut (including its hardness), the amount of feed, the depth of cut, the finish desired, the rigidness of the machine, the rigidness of the work set-up, the type of cutting tool, and the type of cutting fluid used.

Recommended cutting speeds vary considerably, according to the type of material used in the cutting tool and the type and machinability of the material being cut. In the absence of specific recommendations for each machining application, the following general rules may be used as a guide in selecting cutting speeds for cutting tools made of different materials.

1. High-speed steel cutting tools may be operated at speeds about twice those recommended for carbon-steel tools.

2. Cast-alloy cutting tools generally may be operated at speeds approximately 50% to 75% greater than the maximum speed recommended for high-speed steel tools; these speeds are approximately three times greater than those for carbon-steel tools.

3. Cemented-carbide cutting tools may be operated at cutting speeds from two to four times faster than those recommended for high-speed steel tools. Cutting fluids generally are required at the high end of this speed range.

4. Ceramic cutting tools may be operated on certain light machining operations at

speeds from two to four times greater than those recommended for the same application with carbide cutting tools.

General recommendations concerning cutting speeds for drilling, lathe work, shaper work, and milling are included in the sections of this book concerned with these machines and their operation. More specific recommendations for cutting speeds and feeds for various applications may be found in standard handbooks for machinists.

Summary

Cutting tools used for the machining of metals may be made of several basic types of tool materials. Each material used has certain characteristics which are necessary in particular machining applications. The best tool material for a specific operation, such as light-duty milling of steel at low speeds, may not be the recommended material for high-speed milling of the same material.

The general properties of four commonly used cutting-tool materials are summarized in Fig. 15-31.

Test Your Knowledge of Section 15

Unit 138: The Action of a Cutting Tool on Metal

1. What basic factors determine the type of metal chip which is formed by a metal cutting tool?
2. What is meant by the grain structure of metals?
3. Explain what is meant by the shear plane in chip formation.
4. Explain how a metal chip is formed at the cutting edge of a tool.
5. What is meant by plastic flow in chip formation?
6. Why should the machinist be concerned with the type of chip formed by a cutting tool?
7. What type of chip is formed when brittle metals (such as cast iron or bronze) are machined?
8. Describe the appearance of a continuous chip.

9. What type of metals usually form continuous chips?
10. How does compression of the metal at the cutting edge of the tool affect the hardness of the metal chip?
11. What type of chip formation is considered the ideal way of machining ductile metals? Why?
12. What factors tend to cause continuous chips to form on ductile metals?
13. What is meant by a continuous chip with a built-up edge?
14. On what types of materials does the continuous chip with a built-up edge form?
15. How does the built-up edge on a tool affect surface finish?
16. What factors tend to minimize the formation of a built-up edge on a cutting tool?
17. To what types of cutting tools do the principles of chip formation apply?

Unit 139: Cutting Fluids

1. What does the term "cutting fluids" include?
2. What are the principal functions of cutting fluids?
3. Why should a cutting fluid have a high cooling property?
4. Why should a cutting fluid have good lubricant properties?
5. How do good lubricant properties in a cutting fluid affect the formation of a built-up edge on the cutting tool?
6. How do high cutting speeds affect tool wear?
7. At what temperatures do the following tool materials begin to soften: carbon tool steel, high-speed steel, cast alloys, and cemented carbides?
8. What is the principal purpose in using a cutting fluid for grinding?
9. Under what two classifications are most commercial cutting fluids grouped?
10. What is the principal ingredient of most cutting oils?
11. Of what basic ingredients are emulsifiable oil solutions composed?

12. What is the general appearance of an emulsifiable oil solution?
13. What is lard oil, and what are its characteristics?
14. What are some of the additives which are compounded with mineral cutting oils?
15. Of what value are fatty oil additives in mineral cutting oils?
16. What is the purpose of sulfur or chlorine additives in cutting oil?
17. What additives are recommended for use in cutting oils used for heavy-duty machining applications, at high cutting speeds, on tough steels?
18. What are the principal advantages of the transparent cutting oils?
19. What are active cutting oils, and where are they generally used?
20. What is the advantage of tri-purpose cutting oils?
21. Explain how an emulsifiable oil solution is formed.
22. What determines the proportions of oil and water used in an emulsifiable oil solution?
23. What additives are compounded with emulsifiable oils?
24. What additive is compounded with emulsifiable oil to prevent bacterial growth?
25. What are the disadvantages of emulsifiable cutting oil solutions?
26. What are the advantages of emulsifiable oil solutions?
27. What procedure is used in mixing emulsifiable oil solutions?
28. What is dermatitis, and how can it be avoided?
29. What are synthetic emulsifiable cutting fluids?
30. On what materials may kerosene be used as a cutting fluid?
31. Are cutting fluids generally recommended for machining cast iron?
32. How are cutting wax fluids used?
33. What three principal factors should be used as a guide in selecting a cutting fluid for a particular job?
34. What is meant by the machinability of a metal?

35. What factors affect the machinability of a metal?
36. Explain how machinability ratings were developed for various metals.
37. Explain the rating system which is used to rate the severity of a machining operation.
38. What factors involving "operating conditions" should be considered in selecting a cutting fluid?
39. It is possible to select one cutting fluid which may be used for several different machining applications on several different materials. In what source can this information be found?
40. Summarize the factors which should be considered in selecting a cutting fluid for a particular application.

Unit 140: Cutting Tool Materials

1. What determines the properties of a metal cutting tool?
2. What are the most important properties which a cutting tool must possess?
3. How does high heat affect the hardness of a cutting tool?
4. What factors must be considered in selecting a cutting tool made of a particular tool material?
5. How is wear resistance affected by excessive heat at the cutting edge of a tool?
6. Explain what type of strength properties are desirable in cutting tools.
7. What is the principal advantage of carbon-steel tools?
8. At what temperature does carbon tool steel begin to soften?
9. List five metal cutting tools which may be made of high-carbon tool steel.
10. What are the principal advantages of high-speed steel cutting tools?
11. What is meant by the red-hardness, as applied to cutting tools?
12. What are the principal elements which are alloyed to produce high-speed steel?
13. What property does cobalt develop in HS steel?
14. List five types of cutting tools which commonly are made of HS steel.
15. List three basic types of HS steels used for cutting tools.

16. What general relationship usually exists between the hardness and the shock resistance of HS steel cutting tools?
17. What are the properties of cast-alloy cutting tools?
18. What are the principal advantages of cast-alloy cutting tools when compared with HS steel tools?
19. What are the principal elements from which cast-alloy tool materials are made?
20. Is there any advantage in using cast-alloy cutting tools at cutting temperatures below a red heat? Explain.
21. What type of abrasive wheel is recommended for grinding cast-alloy tools?
22. What are the principal advantages in using cemented-carbide cutting tools?
23. What are the principal ingredients in cemented-carbide cutting tools?
24. Why are carbide tools called "cemented carbides"?
25. In what forms are cemented-carbide cutting tools available?
26. How are the two basic groups of cemented-carbide cutting tools often classified?
27. What relationship usually exists between the hardness and the shock resistance of cemented-carbide cutting tools?
28. Explain the Carbide Industry Classification System of classifying machining applications.
29. How does one select a particular grade of carbide cutting tool for a particular application?
30. What precautions must be considered in machining with carbide cutting tools?
31. What types of grinding wheels may be used to grind carbide cutting tools?
32. What are the principal ingredients in ceramic cutting tool materials?
33. In what forms are ceramic cutting tools used?
34. What are the principal properties of ceramic cutting tools?
35. What type of grinding wheel should be used to sharpen ceramic cutting tools?
36. In what forms are diamonds used as cutting tools?
37. What materials often are ground with diamond grinding wheels?
38. What principal factors determine the cutting speeds used for a particular machining application, such as turning?
39. What comparative cutting speeds may be used with cemented-carbide cutting tools in comparison with HS steel cutting tools?
40. In what handbooks may one find specific recommendations concerning cutting speeds and feeds for use with each cutting tool material?
41. Summarize the properties of each of the basic cutting tool materials in comparison with HS steel.

Metallurgy — Exact Science Utilizing Other Sciences
(U. S. Steel)

Metals and Alloys

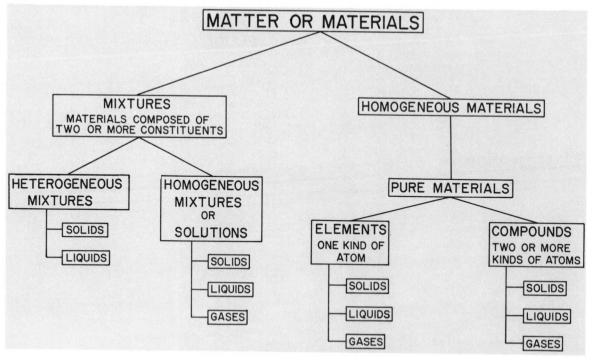

Fig. 16-1. Classification of Matter or Materials

This section includes nine units concerned with the nature, classification, and characteristics of metals and alloys. The characteristics of metals are called their *properties*.

A knowledge of the first six units is important to students of machining and metalworking at the introductory level. (These basic units are also necessary for the study of heat treatment, which is covered in Section 17.) The last three units of this section are concerned with alloy steels, nonferrous alloys, and cast iron. These units are more technical and should be reserved for advanced students.

Both the ferrous and the nonferrous metals are important. However, in this book, more emphasis is placed on the study of the ferrous metals because of their greater significance in relation to metal machining. The ferrous metals are those which contain iron. They include wrought iron, steel, and cast iron.

There are hundreds of different grades of steel and cast iron used in modern industry.

Hence a unit concerning the classification and identification systems used for these metals is included. These various grades were developed in order to secure metals which possess different properties, such as. strength, hardness, toughness, and machinability.

The properties of metals often depend largely upon how they are produced and processed. This is particularly true of the ferrous metals. For this reason, units concerning the production of iron and steel are included. The methods of production are closely related to the classification and identification systems used.

An understanding of various metals and their properties enables workers engaged in the machining of metals to perform their tasks more efficiently. A knowledge of metals and their properties also is important for the following types of workers: heat-treaters, metalwork technicians, metallurgists, tool designers, machine designers, mechanical engineers, welders, and foundry workers.

Classification of Metals

In the study of metals, it is necessary first to understand their basic classifications. When we speak of metals, we generally think of iron, steel, cast iron, copper, brass, bronze, and stainless steel. The modern automobile has more than one hundred different types of metal used in its manufacture. There are more than a thousand different metals used in modern industry.

The various metals may exist in the form of a *pure metallic element*. Examples include iron, copper, aluminum, tin, lead, and zinc. When two or more metallic elements are combined, they form a mixture classified as an *alloy*. Regardless of whether a metal is a pure metallic element or an alloy, it is referred to as *metal*.

Alloy

The term *alloy* can have several possible meanings, depending on whether it is used in a metallurgical sense or in the usual commercial sense.

As used in the study of metallurgy, an alloy is a substance which possesses metallic properties, and which is composed of a combination of two or more elements. One of the elements must be a metal; the others may be either metallic or nonmetallic elements. In this sense, plain carbon steel is basically an alloy of iron and carbon. It also includes certain other elements in the form of impurities.

However, for *commercial* purposes, plain carbon steel is seldom classified as an alloy

steel. Used in this sense, an alloy is a metallic substance composed of a combination of two or more metallic elements, one of which must be intentionally added. Nonmetallic elements also may be included in an alloy.

Alloys are further classified as ferrous alloys and nonferrous alloys. The *ferrous* alloys contain iron as the *base* metal, and one or more other metallic elements. Other nonmetallic elements also may be included. The base metal is generally the metal in largest proportion. For all steels, the base metal is iron. Examples of ferrous alloys include nickel steel, stainless steel, vanadium steel, and alloyed cast iron. All other steels which have metallic elements intentionally added to change their properties are ferrous alloys.

Nonferrous alloys do not contain iron, except in very small amounts in the form of impurities. Examples of nonferrous alloys include brass, bronze, and monel metal. Brass is a copper-base alloy which is composed largely of copper and zinc. Bronze is also a copper-base alloy, composed largely of copper and tin. Monel is a nickel-base alloy, composed largely of nickel and copper.

Composition of Alloys

The classifications of alloys and the properties of alloys depend largely on their composition. Alloys generally are composed of a *mixture* of several ingredients. The mixture may be composed of *elements* or *compounds*, or a combination of both elements and compounds.

Some alloys are called *homogeneous* mixtures because they are uniform or alike throughout. Other alloys are called *heterogeneous* mixtures because they are not uniform throughout. Similarly, many nonmetallic materials are mixtures.

Since a clear understanding of the terms just presented is important in understanding various metals and alloys, the terms will be reviewed briefly. They apply not only to metals and alloys, but also to all other materials. See Fig. 16-1.

Matter and material mean the same thing. *Material* is anything which occupies space and has mass (as measured by weight). Materials may exist in the form of solids, liquids, gases, or in any combination of these. Examples of common materials include wood, concrete, iron, rubber, water, and air.

Elements: All matter is made up of chemical *elements*. There are presently 103 known chemical elements; more may be discovered. About 85% of these are natural elements — *i.e.*, they occur in nature. The remaining elements are laboratory-produced.

The chemical elements form the building blocks from which all substances are composed. If all of the many thousands of substances or materials on earth were broken down into their chemical elements, they could be placed in individual piles of the natural elements which occur in nature.

The smallest particle of an element which can enter into a chemical combination to form a new substance is an *atom*. All elements are made up of atoms, and each element has atoms which are unlike those of another element. An atom is so small that it cannot be seen even with the most powerful microscope. However, through x-ray studies, scientists have determined that the largest atoms are about one twenty-five millionth of an inch in thickness. It would take about 25,000,000 atoms of this size placed side by side to form a line one inch in length. The smallest crystalline grain of metal which can be seen with a powerful metallurgical microscope is made up of an extremely large number of atoms.

The chemical elements are classified as *metallic* or *nonmetallic* elements, depending upon whether or not they possess recognized metallic properties. About three-fourths of the elements are classified as metals.

Metallic elements and other metallic materials possess many properties, but several are sufficient to distinguish between metallic and nonmetallic materials. The recognizable metallic properties include: metallic luster, good electrical and heat conductivity, some degree of malleability, and a crystalline structure while in the solid state. All of the metallic elements are in the solid state at room temperature, except mercury; it freezes (becomes a solid) at $-38°$ F.

Scientists determine whether an element is metallic or nonmetallic through the use of an *electrolysis test*. The element is dissolved in an acid, and an electric current is passed through the solution. The atoms of metallic elements show a positive charge and are attracted to the negative pole where the current enters the solution. Metals, therefore, may be scientifically defined as those elements which, in a pure state, in a solution, carry a positive charge and seek the negative pole in an electric cell. Hydrogen is a nonmetal which is an exception to this definition.

Compounds: Two or more elements may unite chemically to form a *compound*, which is a new substance. Water (H_2O) is a compound of hydrogen and oxygen. Ordinary table salt is sodium chloride ($NaCl$), a compound of sodium and chlorine. Iron and carbon unite to form *cementite*, which is iron carbide (Fe_3C), a compound. Cementite exists in some proportion in all types of steel and cast iron. In fact, through the control of the form and amount of cementite in steel and cast iron, the properties of these metals may be set at will.

A compound is a substance very different than the elements from which it is composed. Several examples will illustrate this important principle. Table salt is necessary for human consumption, yet the individual elements of which it is composed would be very harmful if consumed. Sodium is ordinarily dangerous to handle; chlorine is a poisonous gas.

A second example is water. Independently, hydrogen will burn, and oxygen will support combustion. However, when chemically combined as water, the compound will extinguish most fires.

A third example (one which is important in our study of iron and steel) is cementite. Pure iron is too soft for most practical applications, but when it is combined with carbon in the form of cementite, it is very hard.

The smallest particle of a compound which can exist to show its properties is a *molecule*. A molecule of water (H_2O) is made up of two atoms of hydrogen and one atom of oxygen. A molecule of common table salt (NaCl) is composed of one atom of sodium and one atom of chlorine. The atoms are combined in specific proportions in the molecules of all compounds. Molecules, like atoms, are too small to be seen with the most powerful microscope. Their existence has been determined by x-ray studies. There are many thousands of molecules in one tiny grain of table salt.

Pure Substances: All substances or materials which exist as a single element or a single compound are classified as *pure*, Fig. 16-1. Lead is a pure substance which exists as a single element. Pure water is a pure substance which exists as a pure compound.

Homogeneous Substances: Substances which are uniform in composition throughout are said to be *homogeneous*. All parts of a homogeneous substance are alike. Since all pure substances form in a consistent mathematical relationship, they are all homogeneous. Pure lead, pure iron, pure water, and pure oxygen are examples of solids, liquids, and gases which are homogeneous substances.

It may seem strange, but a substance need not be an element or a compound to be homogeneous. Solutions (such as salt water) are also homogeneous, Fig. 16-1. These will be explained a little later.

Many substances are not uniform throughout. Therefore they are *heterogeneous* substances. Heterogeneous has a meaning which is opposite from homogeneous.

Alloys Form as Mixtures

Not all substances exist as pure elements or compounds. Many substances exist as mixtures. Most metals which are produced for commercial purposes are alloys which form as mixtures. Mixtures may be of two types — heterogeneous mixtures and homogeneous mixtures. *Homogeneous mixtures* generally are called *solutions*. (These will be described later.) An understanding of mixtures will aid in understanding the properties of metals and alloys. It also will provide a good background for the study of heat-treatment processes.

Mixtures are composed of two or more ingredients which are mixed together without regard for specific proportions. The ingredients in a mixture do not unite chemically as in a compound. Rather, each retains its own identity. The individual ingredients in the mixture may be in the form of elements, compounds, or other mixtures.

Malleable cast iron is an example of a solid substance which is a mixture. A photomicrograph of the crystalline grain structure (magnified 100 times) of low-strength malleable cast iron is shown in Fig. 16-2. The light area

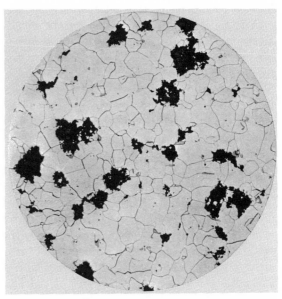

Fig. 16-2. Photomicrograph of Ferrite (Light Area) and Temper Carbon (Dark Area) in Low-Strength Malleable Cast Iron Magnified 100 times (100×)
(Precision Scientific)

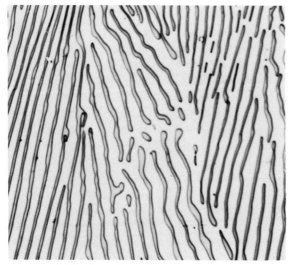

Fig. 16-3. Microscopic Structure Called Pearlite (2500×) (U.S. Steel)
Dark streaks are cementite (iron carbide) and light areas are ferrite (nearly pure iron).

shows ferrite grains (nearly pure iron). The dark areas show aggregates of temper carbon in the form of graphite. Actually there also may be small amounts of other constituents in the form of impurities which are mixed in with the ferrite. The impurities cannot be seen at the low magnification illustrated.

Pearlite is a mixture which exists in the crystalline grain structure of many types of steel and cast iron. It is composed of tiny layers of ferrite (nearly pure iron) and cementite (iron carbide). A photomicrograph of pearlite, as it appears through a metallurgical microscope at 2500 magnification, is shown in Fig. 16-3. Pearlite is so named because it resembles mother-of-pearl. Steel with a high proportion of pearlite is harder and stronger than steel with a low proportion of pearlite.

The cast iron and the pearlite described above are *heterogeneous mixtures* in the form of solids. They are heterogeneous because the parts are not all alike throughout. Such mixtures also frequently are called *mechanical mixtures.*

Most metals seldom are found in the pure state. They usually exist in nature as compounds or as mixtures. Iron is found in nature in the form of a mixture. The mixture is com-

posed of iron oxide, a compound, together with rock and other earthy materials.

Pure metals are not used widely because usually they do not possess properties which are necessary for most practical applications. Pure metals often are too soft, lack adequate strength, or rust too easily. Therefore, most metals are combined or mixed in some manner with one or more other metallic or nonmetallic substances in order to improve their characteristics or properties. Metals thus formed are called alloys. Carbon is alloyed with iron to make plain carbon steel (in the metallurgical sense). Tin is alloyed with copper to make bronze.

Some alloys form as heterogeneous mixtures, while others form as homogeneous mixtures. Homogeneous mixtures generally exist in the form of *solutions* in which the ingredients are uniformly distributed, Fig. 16-1.

Solutions: Many substances are in the form of a solution — *i.e.,* a homogeneous mixture of two or more substances whose proportions may vary within a wide range of limits. Normally we think of solutions as liquids. But there also are solid solutions and gaseous solutions. Since liquid solutions are most familiar, an example of this type will help describe the nature of solutions.

Liquid Solution. When sugar is added to water, the solid disappears. The sugar and water form a clear, homogeneous solution in which both ingredients are uniformly distributed. The sugar is called the *solute,* and the water is called the *solvent.* When only a small amount of sugar has been added and is dissolved, the solution is *dilute.* As more sugar is added, the solution becomes *concentrated.* When sugar is added to a point where it is no longer dissolved, but floats to the bottom, the solution is said to be *saturated.*

Solutions have several distinguishing characteristics. They are homogeneous mixtures. They are not chemical compounds, since they may form with the same ingredients in various proportions. They have properties of mixtures. However, the constituents differ from the aggregates which form heterogeneous mixtures, in that they are dissolved and are uniformly distributed. They remain uniformly distributed and do not settle out so long as the saturation point is not exceeded. Though solutions are not compounds, there is a loose chemical union between the solute and the solvent in most solutions.

Gaseous Solution. Air is an example of a gaseous solution. It is a homogeneous mixture of oxygen, nitrogen, water vapor, and small quantities of other gases.

Solid Solution. A solid solution is a solid substance which is a homogeneous mixture of two or more constituents. A number of alloys are of the solid solution type. An alloy may be formed where the alloying element or elements (solute) are dissolved in the base metal (solvent). The alloy thus formed is a solid solution. It is not chemically combined, yet it is alike throughout. The atomic arrangement of a solid solution is usually the same as that of the solvent.

Solid solutions may be formed with various proportions of solute and solvent. Some substances will dissolve in solids in very small proportions, and the saturation point will be reached. Other solid substances are mutually soluble in each other in all proportions.

A solid solution is formed in much the same manner in which sugar and water forms a liquid solution. Elements such as carbon, phosphorous, silicon, and manganese dissolve in iron in the unusually small proportions in which they are found in commercially pure iron. This form of iron is a solid solution.

Ferrite is nearly pure iron. Its composition is essentially the same as commercially pure iron. Ferrite exists in various proportions, at temperatures below 1330° F., within the grain structure of the following: wrought iron, plain carbon steels which have not been hardened, gray cast iron, and in many alloy steels.

The words *ferrite* and *ferrous* come from the Latin word *Ferrum*, which means iron. The chemical symbol *Fe*, for iron, also comes from the Latin word.

When sulfur is present in nearly pure iron, it combines with manganese to form manganese sulfide, a compound. The compound then exists as an inclusion in the iron. In this form, the iron alloy is a mechanical mixture of nearly pure iron and particles of manganese sulfide. The microscopic grain structure called

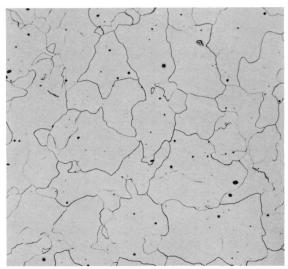

Fig. 16-4. Microscopic Structure Called Ferrite (Alpha Iron) (100×) (U.S. Steel)
All grains have the same composition. The dark spots are impurities in the form of inclusions.

ferrite is shown in Fig. 16-4. The tiny dark spots in the figure are inclusions in the form of impurities.

The following is a typical analysis for the constituents occurring in commercially pure iron: carbon 0.02%, manganese 0.01%, phosphorous 0.01%, silicon 0.01%, sulfur 0.02%, and iron 99.93%. Of course, the constituents may vary somewhat with different producers. Iron with a purity of 99.95% is available for use in chemistry laboratories.

Some alloying elements, such as nickel and copper, or gold and silver, are mutually soluble in each other. They dissolve in each other in all proportions in both the liquid and the solid states. The nickel-copper alloys and the gold-silver alloys are solid solutions.

Other alloying elements dissolve in the base metal in different proportions in the liquid and solid states. Furthermore, the proportion of the alloying element which remains in solid solutions may vary with the temperature and grain structure of the alloy formed. Carbon, the most significant alloying element in steel, behaves in this manner in steel.

Steel is basically an alloy of iron and carbon. Various heat-treatment processes are used in changing the properties of steel. These processes are possible largely because of the manner in which carbon is retained in solid solution with iron. The various heat-treatment processes are explained in the section of the book concerned with heat treatment of steel. You will be able to understand these processes more readily if you understand the classifications of materials, as described in this unit.

Numerous basic terms commonly used in the study of metals have been presented thus far.

Several of these terms will be used for review purposes to describe the composition of wrought iron in the following statements: Wrought iron is composed of a variety of different forms of *material*. The iron in wrought iron is usually in the form of a *solid solution*. The slag inclusions which are intentionally included in wrought iron are *compounds*. The slag and the solid solution of iron form a *mechanical mixture*. Thus, wrought iron is a mechanical mixture of nearly pure iron and slag.

UNIT

142   The Properties of Metals

More than one hundred different types of steel or other alloy metals are used in the typical modern automobile. Each particular metal is developed or selected because of its characteristics or properties in relation to its use. Typical properties which are considered in the selection and production of metal products include: weight, hardness, toughness, brittleness, corrosion resistance, response to heat treatment, and machinability. A basic knowledge of various metals and their properties is important for workers engaged in the design, machining, and maintenance of metal products.

Metals can be hardened, softened, bent, twisted, pulled apart, or fractured, depending on the properties which they possess. Also, the ease with which metal may be formed, shaped, or machined depends on its properties.

The properties of metals and other materials may be classified in three main groups as follows: (1) *Chemical properties* include characteristics concerned with the chemical composition and chemical reactions of materials. These are described in more detail at the end of this unit. (2) *Physical properties* include those characteristics used to describe a substance which is not being acted upon by external forces. It includes such items as color, density, heat conductivity, and electrical conductivity. (3) *Mechanical properties* include those characteristics which describe the behavior of metal which is being acted upon by external forces. It includes characteristics such as tensile strength, hardness, ductility, and machinability.

Mechanical Properties

In the area of metal machining, and in related areas of metalwork, an understanding of the *mechanical properties* of metals is most important. The following are some of the more significant mechanical properties which should be understood:

Hardness: Hardness may be defined as resistance to penetration. Hard metals resist denting or scratching. Of necessity, files and drills are made of metals which rank high in hardness. Various types of instruments are available for measuring the relative hardness of metals. This property may be increased or decreased in many metals by various methods of heat treatment. A drill is machined to shape while it is soft. It then is hardened by heat treatment so that it will cut other metals.

Hardenability: Hardenability is the property which enables a metal to harden completely through to its center when a heat-treatment method is used. Some metals rank low in hardenability. This means that they harden significantly on the surface layer only, while they remain relatively soft at the core or center. Metals which rank high in hardenability will harden through to the center.

Brittleness: Brittleness refers to the ease with which a metal or other material will crack or break apart without appreciable deformation. Gray cast iron is brittle in comparison with unhardened steel. Under a heavy blow, the cast iron will break apart like a cement block, while steel usually will bend instead of breaking. Brittleness is related to hardness in metals. Generally, as the hardness of a metal is increased, its brittleness also is increased. Similarly, as the hardness of the metal is reduced, the brittleness is reduced.

Ductility: Ductility is the property which enables a metal to be bent, twisted, drawn out, or changed in shape without breaking. Metals which rank high in ductility (such as copper, aluminum, and soft steel) can be drawn out into wire without breaking. Ductile metals fail or break gradually with increased stress or load. In contrast, brittle metals, such as cast iron, break abruptly by cracking when placed under increasing loads. Ductility usually is expressed as a *percentage of elongation* and as a percentage of *reduction in area*. These factors are derived from specimens on which tests for tensile strength have been made.

Malleability: Malleability is the property which enables a metal to be permanently deformed by compression, usually by rolling or hammering. Most ductile metals are malleable. However, there are some exceptions, such as lead. Lead lacks sufficient tensional strength to be stretched very far; therefore, it is not ductile.

Toughness: Toughness is the property which enables a metal to withstand sudden shock or impact forces without fracture. A metal ranking high in toughness generally is difficult to break. It is said to rank high in impact resistance or impact toughness. Impact tests measure the energy required to fracture a standard-size test specimen with one sharp blow. The testing devices used generally utilize a falling weight or a swinging pendulum. Two common devices utilizing a swinging pendulum are the Charpy and the Izod tester. The energy required to fracture the test specimen is expressed in foot-pounds and is a measure of impact toughness. (Impact toughness and impact testing equipment are explained in greater detail in Unit 154.)

Machinability: Machinability is a relative term which indicates the ease with which metals may be machined. Many factors are considered in arriving at machinability ratings. Some of the most important ones are rate of metal removal, quality of the finished surface, and tool life. Machinability ratings are expressed as a percentage, in comparison with AISI B1112 steel, which is rated at 100 percent. For a more detailed explanation of machinability, see Unit 139. For machinability ratings of various metals, see Table 30, appendix.

Strength: Strength of a metal is its resistance to deformation. There are several common types: *tensile* strength, *compressive* strength, *shear* strength, and *torsion* or twisting strength. Metals may be deformed when loads are applied which exert tensional forces, compression forces, forces producing a shearing action, and torsional forces producing a twisting action. See Fig. 16-5.

Tensile Strength: Tensile strength is that property of a material which resists tensional forces applied to pull the material apart. On a test specimen, tensile strength is the maximum load force per unit of original cross-sectional area before fracture of the specimen. Tensile strength of metals usu-

531

ally is expressed in terms of thousands of pounds per square inch (psi). The tensile strength of steel generally is related to its hardness. As the hardness is increased, the tensile strength is increased. Similarly, as the hardness is decreased, the tensile strength is decreased. The tensile strength for various metals is shown in Table 30, appendix.

Tensile strength is determined through use of tensile-testing machines. Although metal test specimens of standard cross-sectional size generally are used, it is possible to test the tensile strength of specimens of many different shapes and sizes. A standard tensile specimen 0.505″ in diameter (0.2 square inches cross-sectional area) commonly is used in many metallurgical and research laboratories.

An example will illustrate how the tensile strength for a test specimen is calculated. If a maximum load force of 20,000 psi is required before rupture of a steel specimen 0.505″ in diameter, what is the tensile strength of the steel?

Formula. The tensile strength is equal to the maximum load before rupture, divided by the original cross-sectional area of the specimen.

$$\text{Tensile strength} = \frac{\text{Load in pounds}}{\text{Area in sq. inches}}$$
$$\text{Tensile strength} = \frac{20,000}{0.2}$$
$$\text{Tensile strength} = 100,000 \text{ psi}$$

It is evident that the tensile-testing machine used in this example must be able to withstand a tensile load of 20,000 psi. If a tensile-testing machine of less capacity were used, the cross-sectional area of the test specimen necessarily would be smaller. It would have to be within the capacity of the machine.

The general procedure involved in making a tensile strength test on steel is illustrated in Fig. 16-6. The original length of the test specimen is noted, and the specimen is inserted into both jaws of the tensile-testing machine. A steadily increasing load then is applied. When the *yield point* is reached, the specimen exhibits a rather sharp increase in length and a decrease in diameter, as shown in Fig. 16-6C. Under a continued increase in load, when the tensile strength is exceeded, the specimen is fractured, as shown in Fig. 16-6D.

Yield Point: The yield point is determined in the process of making a tensile strength test on certain ductile metals, such as low-carbon steel. It usually is expressed in terms of thousands of pounds per square inch (psi). When a typical steel specimen is tested for tensile strength, the tensional forces are steadily increased. When the *yield point* is reached, the specimen will continue to elongate or stretch a certain amount without a further increase of the tensional load, as shown in Fig. 16-6C. The tensional load is increased steadily until failure occurs.

Some ductile and brittle metals do not behave in this manner under tensile tests. Ductile metals such as copper and aluminum deform steadily with increased tension until they fail. The *yield strength* for these metals is the

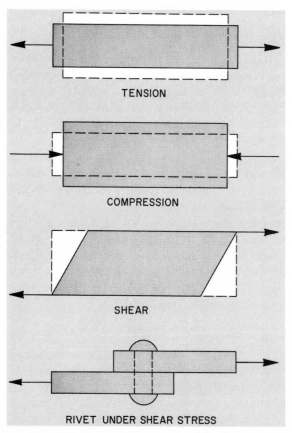

TENSION

COMPRESSION

SHEAR

RIVET UNDER SHEAR STRESS

Fig. 16-5. Types of Stress or Load Application

stress at which the test specimen exhibits a specified amount of permanent elongation or distortion. Some brittle metals, such as cast iron, also behave in a similar manner in tensile tests, except that they exhibit much less elongation before failure. The yield point for various metals is shown in Table 30, appendix.

Elongation: Elongation is the amount of permanent extension in length, in the vicinity of the fracture, on a tensile strength specimen, as shown in Fig. 16-6. It is expressed as a percentage of the original gage length of the specimen. The original gage length is usually two inches. Elongation also is a measure of ductility. The greater the per-

centage of elongation, the greater the ductility of the metal. The elongation for various metals is shown in Table 30, appendix.

Stress: Stress in a material or structural member is its internal resistance to an external force or load. Actually it is equal to the load or force applied, but it is specified in terms of force per unit of cross-sectional area.

The difference between load and load per unit of cross-sectional area can be understood more clearly with an example. A common-size, standard steel specimen for a tensile strength

A

C

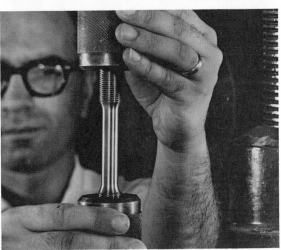

B

D

Fig. 16-6. Making a Tensile Strength Test on a Steel Specimen (U.S. Steel)
(A) Inserting specimen in lower jaw of testing ma-

chine; **(B)** Inserting specimen in upper jaw; **(C)** Effect on specimen when yield point is reached; **(D)** Specimen fractured when ultimate tensile strength is exceeded.

test has a diameter of 0.505″ (cross-sectional area 0.2 square inches). When a tensional load of 1000 pounds is applied, the specimen will be under a stress of 5000 psi (pounds per square inch). The stress is equal to the load force divided by the cross-sectional area, or in this case, 1000 divided by 0.2″.

There are three general types of stress — tension, compression, and shear. See Fig. 16-5. In *tension* stress, the forces tend to pull the material apart. In *compression* stress, the forces tend to squeeze or shorten the material under stress. In *shear* stress, there is a tendency to cause one part of the material to slide by the other part. When bending loads are applied, a combination of tension stress and compression stress is involved; see Fig. 16-7. When torsional loads are applied, all three types of stress are involved to some degree. A torsional load is shown in Fig. 16-8.

Reduction of Area: Reduction of area is the difference between the original cross-sectional area of a tensile strength test specimen and the final cross-sectional area at the point of rupture. During a tensile strength test on ductile metals, at stresses greater than the yield point, the test specimen becomes deformed. The deformation is in the form of elongation and reduced cross-sectional area, as shown in Fig. 16-6.

The reduction of area usually is expressed as the percentage of the original area. There is a much greater percentage reduction of area for ductile metals than for brittle metals. The reduction of area also is a measure of the amount of ductility. The reduction of area for various metals is shown in Table 30, appendix.

Strain: Strain is the deformation resulting from an external force applied to a material or structural member. The structural member in Fig. 16-9A is said to be under strain, since it is deformed from an external load. In this case, the deformation is in the form of a bend. When the member returns to its original form with the removal of the load, it is no longer under a strain.

The types of deformation which take place when materials are under strain include elongation, compression, shear, torsion, and bending. The type of deformation depends on how the load is applied. Methods of applying loads and the direction in which the forces are exerted are shown in Figs. 16-5, 16-8, and 16-9.

Elasticity: Elasticity is the property which enables a material to return to its original size and shape after an external, distortional force has been removed. Rubber is elastic because it returns to its original shape after deformation, not because it stretches. In this sense, steel is more elastic than rubber. When a steel beam returns to its original form after removal of the load, as in Fig. 16-9B, it exhibits elasticity.

Elastic Limit: Elastic limit is the maximum load, per unit of area, which may be applied to a material without permanent deformation. The elastic limit occurs at a stress just short of that which causes permanent deformation. When the load force on a structural member exceeds the elastic limit,

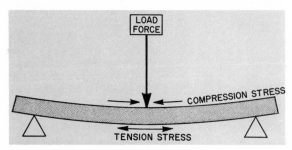

Fig. 16-7. Combination of Forces Acting on a Structural Member

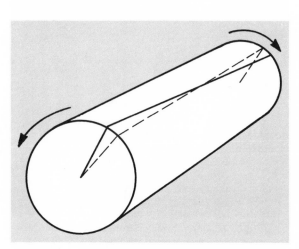

Fig. 16-8. Torsional Load

the member will be deformed permanently. The steel beam in Fig. 16-9C is an example of permanent deformation caused by a load which was greater than the elastic limit.

Plasticity: Plasticity is the property in a material which permits permanent deformation to occur without rupture. It is the opposite of elasticity. Modeling clay has excellent plasticity. Many metals exhibit plasticity when stressed beyond their elastic limits. Ductile metals generally rank high in plasticity, while brittle metals rank low. When ductile metals are machined, continuous-type chips are formed due to plasticity. See Fig. 15-4.

Fatigue: Fatigue is the property which causes a metal to fracture under a repeated or pulsating load which is considerably below the tensile strength of the material. By repeated bending, a piece of metal may be broken due to fatigue. Springs, propeller shafts, gear teeth, and other parts of machines subjected to repeated vibration sometimes fail due to fatigue. Fractures due to fatigue often occur as a result of tool marks or sharp arrises on shafts or other machine parts. Elimination of machine marks and provision for a fillet radius at intersecting surfaces will aid in preventing *fatigue failures.*

Testing machines have been devised to exert various types of cyclic stresses on different types of metal parts, as well as on standard test specimens of various metals and alloys. On the basis of the standard tests, various metals are assigned fatigue strength ratings, usually referred to as *endurance limit ratings.* This rating is defined as the greatest stress which will not produce fatigue failure in a specified number of cycles. A typical endurance limit for one type of steel is approximately 40,000 psi for 10 million cycles. Similar tests usually will reveal a lower load rating for an increased number of cycles, such as the load for 100 million cycles.

Fusibility: Fusibility is that quality which enables a metal to join readily with another metal when heated to a liquid state. Fusibility is important in welding. Metals which rank high in fusibility generally can be

Table 20
Properties of Principal Metals

Metal	Chemical Symbol	Specific Gravity	Weight per Cubic Inch, Pounds	Weight per Cubic Foot, Pounds	Average Melting Point, Deg. F.
Aluminum	Al	2.70	0.0975	168.5	1220
Antimony	Sb	6.618	0.2390	413.0	1167
Bismuth	Bi	9.781	0.3532	610.3	520
Boron	B	2.535	0.0916	158.2	4172
*Brass	—	8.60	0.3105	536.6	1560-1900
*Bronze	—	8.78	0.3171	547.9	1300-1880
Cadmium	Cd	8.648	0.3123	539.6	610
Chromium	Cr	6.93	0.2502	432.4	2939
Cobalt	Co	8.71	0.3145	543.5	2696
Copper	Cu	8.89	0.3210	554.7	1981
Gold	Au	19.3	0.6969	1204.3	1945
Iron	Fe	7.86	0.285	491.0	2802
*Iron, Cast	—	7.03-7.73	0.254-0.279	438.7-482.4	1990-2300
*Iron, Wrought	—	7.80-7.90	0.282-0.285	486.7-493.0	2750
Lead	Pb	11.342	0.4096	707.7	621
Magnesium	Mg	1.741	0.0628	108.6	1204
Manganese	Mn	7.3	0.2636	455.5	2300
Molybdenum	Mo	10.2	0.3683	636.5	4748
Nickel	Ni	8.8	0.3178	549.1	2651
Platinum	Pt	21.37	0.7717	1333.5	3224
Silver	Ag	10.42-10.53	0.376-0.380	650.2-657.1	1761
*Steel, Carbon	—	—	0.283-0.284	489.0-490.8	2500
Tantalum	Ta	16.6	0.5998	1035.8	5162
Tellurium	Te	6.25	0.2257	390.0	846
Tin	Sn	7.29	0.2633	454.9	449
Titanium	Ti	4.5	0.1621	280.1	3272
Tungsten	W	18.6-19.1	0.672-0.690	1161-1192	6098
Uranium	U	18.7	0.6753	1166.9	3362
Vanadium	V	5.6	0.2022	394.4	3110
Zinc	Zn	7.04-7.16	0.254-0.259	439.3-446.8	788

*Properties may vary according to kind and amount of alloying elements or impurities.

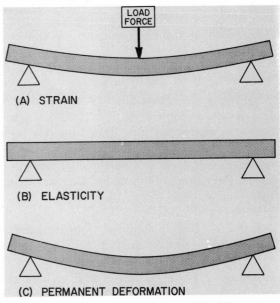

Fig. 16-9. Effects of Load Force on Steel Beam

535

welded with ease. *Weldability* is the specific term which indicates the relative ease with which metal may be welded by practical means.

Chemical Properties

The chemical properties of metals are concerned largely with chemical composition, melting temperatures, and corrosion resistance. A detailed discussion of the chemical properties of metals is not within the scope of this book. This type of information can be found in sources such as the following: standard handbooks for machinists, chemistry handbooks, manufacturer's catalogs, and the ASME handbook, *Metals Properties**. The corrosion resistance of a metal is that property which enables it to resist corrosion from weather or from chemicals.

In studying the properties of various metals, it is often necessary to know their chemical symbols, their relative density, and their melting temperatures. This information concerning some of the principal metals is listed in Table 20.

*American Society of Mechanical Engineers, *Metals Properties,* a handbook edited by Samuel L. Hoyt. New York: McGraw-Hill Book Company Inc., 1954.

The Production of Iron and Its Use

The most important ingredient in steel is iron. Many of the commonly used steels have approximately 98% iron content. The remaining content includes carbon, phosphorous, sulfur, silicon, and manganese. Other elements are added in special steels to produce properties such as hardness, toughness, and corrosion resistance.

Acquiring Raw Materials

To make steel, iron must be acquired first. Iron is not available in its pure state in quantities for commercial use. Pure iron has been found as relatively small fragments, usually as particles of meteorites which fell from outer space. Pure iron is too soft for practical structural applications.

Iron Ore: Iron is acquired from iron ore, a mineral which varies in form from a compact solid mass to powder. It varies in color from various shades of red, yellow, and purple, to black. The ore is taken from both open-pit mines and shaft mines.

There are several different types of iron ore, ranging from very low to very high iron content. The ores mined in this country vary from about 30% to 65% iron content. A large percentage of the ores used in this country are *iron oxides*, rust-like chemical combinations with up to 50% iron content. The remaining content is considered largely as impurities; these are composed of minerals which include oxygen, phosphorous, silicon, sulfur, manganese, small amounts of certain other elements, and clay. An average of about 1¾ tons of iron ore is required to make one ton of iron.

In order to conserve some of the high-grade iron ore in this country, *taconite*, a lower grade ore of about 30% iron, is gaining wider use. It is mined in rock form, ground finely, processed, and blended with higher grade ores when smelted in a blast furnace. There is sufficient taconite in the Lake Superior region to last the nation for hundreds of years.

The largest proportion of the ore mined in this country comes from the Lake Superior region of Minnesota, Wisconsin, and Michigan.

In the past, the Mesabi Range in Minnesota supplied about 80% of the iron ore used in the United States. Most of this was high-grade ore which averaged approximately 50% iron content. With a decrease in the supply of high-grade ore in the Lake Superior region, important iron ore sources have been developed in other states.

There is also an increasing amount of ore being imported from other countries. Large deposits of iron ore have been located and are being developed at high cost in Canada and Venezuela, Brazil, Peru, and other South American countries.

Other Raw Materials: Certain raw materials are required for making iron from iron ore. These include iron ore, coke, limestone, and air. Iron is made in a blast furnace, Fig. 16-10.

Additional raw materials are required to make steel. These include iron from the blast furnace, scrap iron, and other alloying elements necessary to make alloy steels.

An alloy steel is composed of one or more metallic elements in combination with iron. Though many different metallic elements may be included in special steels, the principal alloying elements include nickel, chromium, and manganese. From 80% to 90% of all steels made in the United States are plain carbon steels. The remaining steels include many varieties of alloy steels.

Furnaces

Large furnaces of several types are used with the various processes required in making iron and steel. The furnaces are lined with heat-resistant brick so that they will withstand temperatures higher than the molten metal, often above 3000°F. The furnaces commonly used to make iron and steel include the following:

1. Blast furnace, used to make iron, Fig. 16-10.
2. Open-hearth furnace, Fig. 16-10.
3. Basic oxygen furnace, Fig. 16-10.
4. Electric furnace, Fig. 16-10.
5. Bessemer converter, Fig. 16-11 (page 541).

Making Pig Iron

The first step in the steelmaking process is the making of pig iron from iron ore, as shown in Fig. 16-10. There are several methods which can be used to extract or refine metals from their ores. One of these methods is *smelting*. Pig iron is extracted from its ore by smelting in a blast furnace.

Smelting involves the chemical process called *reduction*. With this process, metallic oxide ore is heated in the presence of a reducing agent and a flux. (A *reducing agent* is a material which will combine with the unwanted elements in the ore more easily than with the metal being extracted.) The reducing agent combines with the oxygen in the metallic oxide ore, thus releasing the metal. The *flux* absorbs or combines with the impurities which remain and separates them from the metal being extracted. When iron oxide ore is smelted in a blast furnace, carbon monoxide acts as the principal reducing agent. Limestone is used as a flux.

The blast furnace is a large, cylindrical structure, approximately 100 feet tall, about 30 feet in diameter at the base, and tapered toward the top. It is lined with heat-resistant brick. Three or four large cylindrical stoves are located near the furnace for heating the air which is blown into the furnace. The air is heated to about 1200° F. and is forced into the furnace under pressure.

The blast furnace is charged by being filled with carefully controlled layers of coke, limestone, and iron ore. Thus, the coke is burned in the presence of iron ore and limestone. The strong blast of hot air, previously heated by the stoves, supports combustion and raises the temperature at the bottom of the furnace to about 3000°F. The iron melts in the range between 2200° to 2500°F., usually at about 2300°F. The temperature gradually decreases to about 400°F. near the top of the furnace.

With the intense heat developed near the bottom of the blast furnace, combustion gases are formed rapidly, and chemical reactions take place. The carbon in the coke and the oxygen in the air combine to form carbon monoxide gas, a reducing agent, and heat is

HOW STEEL IS MADE

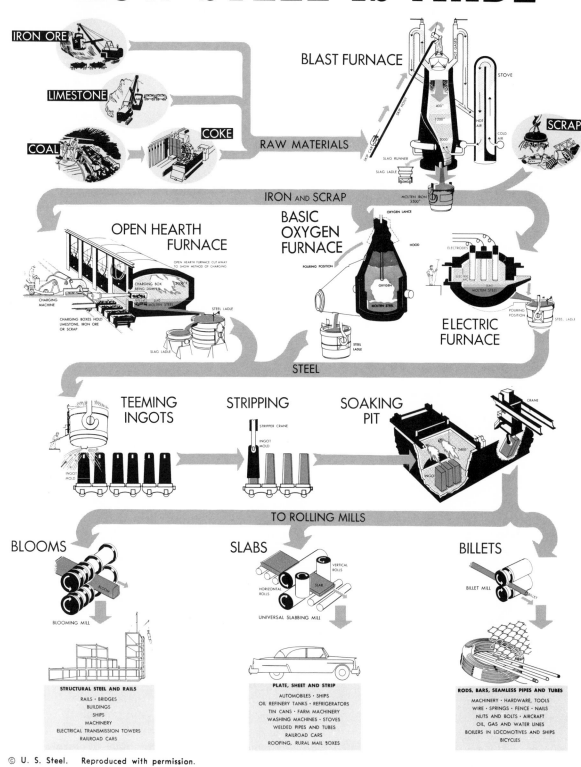

Fig. 16-10. How Steel Is Made (U.S. Steel)

released. As the gas flows up through the ore, another reaction takes place. The carbon monoxide combines with the oxygen in the ore to form carbon dioxide, thus freeing the iron. On some modern furnaces, the blast of air is enriched with oxygen, to speed up the process.

The iron which has been reduced from the ore forms droplets which fall to the bottom of the furnace. The limestone acts as a flux. It reacts with the earthy impurities in the ore, and with the coke, and forms a slag which also flows toward the bottom. Since the slag is lighter than the iron, it floats on top of the iron.

Every 4 to 6 hours, the iron is tapped through a hole at the bottom of the furnace. The amounts drawn off vary from 100 to 300 tons. The slag is drawn off more often, through a hole located above the level of the molten iron. The furnace is operated continuously until it is in need of repair or until the supply of iron exceeds the demand.

When the iron is drawn off, it generally is used to make either steel or *pig iron*. Only 7% to 8% of the iron made in the blast furnace is poured into forms to make chunks of iron called pig iron. The pig iron is sold to foundries to make various kinds of *cast iron* castings.

The iron which is drawn off from the blast furnace to make steel is poured into a special railroad-type, cauldron car. It is kept hot and is hauled (in a molten state) to the steel department, where it is poured into a steel-making furnace.

The following raw materials generally are required to make one ton of pig iron in the blast furnace: 1¾ tons of iron ore, ¾ ton of coke, ⅓ ton of limestone, and 4 tons of air. Millions of gallons of water are required daily to keep parts of the furnace cool.

The blast furnace has limited refining capabilities. During the process of smelting pig iron, the iron picks up from 3% to 4½% carbon from the coke. All of the phosphorous which was originally in the ore still remains in the iron. Also, much of the sulfur, manganese, and silicon which was originally in the ore remains in the iron. Most of these impurities, averaging a total of approximately 3%, must be removed in making steel. This is why other types of furnaces and other processes must be used to make steel.

How Steel Is Made

The properties of steel are very different from those of pig iron, which is iron drawn from a blast furnace. Pig iron is very brittle and must be cast into shape. If it were rolled, it would crush and fall apart. In contrast, steel is ductile, malleable, and tough. Steel is rolled into bars, strips, and sheets without breaking or cracking. It also can be drawn out into wire.

In its simplest terms, steelmaking is a process of removing most of the impurities from molten pig iron which comes from the blast furnace. Actually, the process also removes impurities in lesser quantities from the scrap and other materials used in making steel. The impurities are removed in steelmaking furnaces at high temperatures through *burning* or *oxidation*.

Steelmaking is a carefully-controlled process. Each type of steel must have specified amounts of elements other than iron. These elements are controlled through measurement and testing. The raw materials are tested before they are placed in the steelmaking furnace. The molten steel in the furnace also is sampled and analyzed frequently to determine the amount of both the impurities and the necessary ingredients. When the impurities have been burned out as required, other necessary elements also may have been burned out. The required elements then are added in controlled amounts to produce the particular type of steel specified.

The various types of steel are made by specific processes, each of which requires a particular type of steelmaking furnace. The following processes for making steel are illustrated in Fig. 16-10 and will be explained:

1. Open-hearth process.
2. Bessemer process.
3. Basic oxygen process.
4. Electric furnace process.

Open-Hearth Process

From 80% to 90% of all steel produced in the United States is produced by the open-hearth process. Steel made by this process is called open-hearth steel. The open-hearth furnace is so named because the molten metal lies on the open hearth (floor) of the furnace and is heated by flames which sweep across the hearth. See Fig. 16-10.

The furnaces are rectangular in shape and vary in size and capacity. Although the average open-hearth furnace has a capacity of 125 tons of steel, the range in capacity may vary from 50 to 550 tons.

In this process, the raw materials are loaded into the furnace through the side doors with charging machines. The first materials so charged are limestone and steel scrap. Sometimes iron ore also is included as an oxidizing agent. Gas, oil, or coal may be used as a fuel. A mixture of hot air and fuel is ignited, and the flame is directed over the materials in the open hearth, thus bringing them to melting temperature. The temperature in the furnace is approximately 3000°F.

With the open-hearth process, it is possible to make steel from iron ore only, or from iron ore, scrap, and molten pig iron combined.

However, the more common practice today is to make it largely from scrap and molten pig iron (which was smelted in a blast furnace). The scrap content may vary from 30% to 50% and the molten pig iron from 50% to 70%. A typical proportion is 48% scrap and 52% pig iron. Limestone always is included.

When the initial charge of scrap and limestone is nearly molten, the molten pig iron from the blast furnace is poured into the open-hearth furnace with a large ladle. With continued heat from the burning fuel and air mixture, the complete charge becomes a bubbling bath. Some modern furnaces are equipped with an oxygen lance which provides a stream of oxygen over the molten bath to speed up the process.

The purifying process then takes place. The impurities are removed largely by *oxidation*. Such impurities as carbon, manganese, and silicon in the molten pig iron unite readily with oxygen in the air, or with pure oxygen, at high temperatures to form oxides. These oxides may be gases or solids. The gases escape with the exhaust. The solids float on top of the molten steel and are absorbed in the slag.

The limestone, which melts and floats on top of the molten bath, reacts chemically to remove some of the impurities in the form of gases. It also absorbs some of the impurities, including some of the sulfur.

Thus, through a combination of the chemical action of the limestone, slag formation, and oxidation at high temperatures, the impurities gradually are removed from the hot molten metal. The impurities removed include carbon, silicon, manganese, phosphorous and sulfur.

Test samples are taken from the furnace and analyzed. When the impurities are burned out, and when necessary elements are added to bring the steel up to required specifications, the steel is ready for removal from the furnace. The furnace is tapped, and the molten steel is drawn off into large ladles. It is then *teemed* (poured into molds), where it cools enough to form solid ingots. The molds are stripped from the ingots while still hot. The ingots are then placed in *soaking* pits, where they are held at high temperature until ready for rolling in the rolling mill. See Fig. 16-10.

Bessemer Process

The Bessemer converter is used to produce steel by the Bessemer process, Fig. 16-11. In this process, cold air is blown through molten pig iron. The molten iron is at a temperature of approximately 2300°F. At this temperature, the impurities, such as carbon, silicon, and manganese, combine readily with oxygen and burn out. Thus, the impurities are used as the necessary fuel. As the impurities burn out by oxidation, the temperature of the molten metal rises.

The Bessemer converter is a large, pear-shaped container with an open mouth at the top for charging and discharging iron and steel. It is lined with fire-resistant brick and has a double bottom which forms a *wind box*. The top of the wind box, which serves as the bottom of the converter, has many holes for the air to pass through. Bessemer converters vary in size and have a capacity ranging from 5 to 25 tons of molten iron. The average capacity is about 15 tons.

The converter is tilted on an angle and is loaded from the top with molten iron from the blast furnace. As the converter is tilted upright, air is blown through the bottom at pressures which keep the molten iron from draining into the wind box. The pressures are usually 20 to 30 pounds per square inch. The air flows up through the molten iron, combining with the impurities and burning them out. Sparks appear first, followed by flames. The flames change in color and length, thereby indicating which impurities are burned out first. After about 20 minutes, the flames stop, thus indicating that the impurities are largely burned out. The process is complete, except for adding the correct amount of carbon and other elements required for meeting the specifications of the particular steel.

The steel is poured from the mouth of the converter. As the converter is tilted, the air is shut off gradually. The slag, floating on top, is separated and caught in a ladle while the steel is poured into another larger ladle. The steel is poured into large molds to form ingots which later are rolled into bars and other useful shapes.

The Bessemer process was developed for commercial purposes during the 1850's. It was the first steelmaking process which made steel available in thousands of tons rather than by the pound.

The use of the Bessemer process has declined in the United States. The heat is more difficult to control with this process than with the open-hearth process. The amount of alloying elements also is more difficult to control. The process is used for making only about 3% of the steel produced in the United States today.

Basic Oxygen Process

The basic oxygen process (BOP) for making steel is somewhat similar to the Bessemer process, and at a number of plants, it is replacing the Bessemer process.

Several different oxygen processes have been developed for making steel. Some still are being used experimentally. One of the most well known is the BOP. This newer process involves the use of the *basic oxygen furnace*, which resembles a Bessemer converter. Compare Figs. 16-10 and 16-11. However, the furnace is much larger and the process is somewhat different.

With the Bessemer process, air is blown up through the molten metal. With the BOP, oxygen is blown down on the molten metal, through a lance which enters from the top of the furnace. Nitrogen, which makes metal brit-

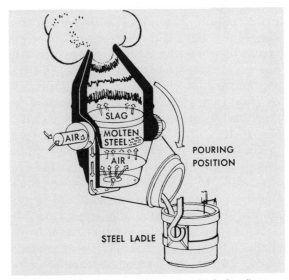

Fig. 16-11. Bessemer Converter (U.S. Steel)

541

tle, does not enter in significant amounts with the new process as it does in the Bessemer process. Also, the new process is much faster than the Bessemer process. The furnace has a capacity of about 80 tons and will produce one heat every 40 to 60 minutes.

The basic oxygen furnace in Fig. 16-10 is charged by tilting it on its side. Molten iron is charged through the mouth; sometimes scrap steel also is included. It is then turned upright, and oxygen is blown in through the lance. Burned lime, converted from limestone, is added at the same time. When the steel is purified, the necessary elements are added to meet the specifications for the type of steel required. It is then poured into a large ladle by tilting the furnace on its side.

It had been known for many years that oxygen could be used to improve steelmaking, but pure oxygen was too expensive for this purpose. Since 1950, methods have been developed for producing oxygen in large quantities, at low cost. It is estimated that during the 1970's approximately 20% of the steel produced in the United States will be produced by the basic oxygen process.

Electric Furnace Process

The electric furnace process is used primarily for making high-grade steels, such as alloy steels, stainless steels, tool and die steels, and heat-resisting steels. It is used for making steels which require control of both the furnace atmosphere and the proportion of alloying elements. Because the electric process uses no fuel which keeps building up sulfur, it is the only process by which all of the sulfur can be removed from steel. An electric furnace of the type used in modern steelmaking is shown in Fig. 16-10.

The electric furnace is a huge container, with a steel shell resembling the shape of a tea kettle. It is lined with refractory brick. Openings for charging the furnace are located on the sides or on the top (which may be swung to the side). The molten metal is discharged through a spout as the furnace is tilted. Three large carbon or graphite electrodes, 10″ to 24″ in diameter, enter through the top of the furnace. The electrodes supply the current which produces the electric arc and the intense heat necessary for melting the charge.

Although the first electric furnace developed in the United States in 1906 was very small, the furnaces used today are much larger. They vary in capacity from 5 tons to 200 tons of molten steel. A large electric furnace can produce 500 tons of steel in 24 hours.

The electric furnace provides several advantages not attainable with other steelmaking processes. The electricity does not produce any special reaction other than to produce a very high heat rapidly. Furnace temperatures of 3500°F. are obtained readily. The atmosphere inside the furnace can be controlled because air is not used for combustion. However, pure oxygen sometimes is used in controlled amounts for initial oxidation of excess carbon or other elements. The heat inside the furnace also is regulated easily. Alloying elements may be carefully controlled, due to minimum loss by oxidation.

Steel from the open-hearth furnace or the Bessemer converter sometimes is further refined in the electric furnace. However, scrap materials of known content most generally are used. The type of scrap used depends on the type of steel to be produced.

After the furnace is charged, the current is turned on. An electric arc appears at the ends of the electrodes, and flames are produced. As the scrap melts down, a puddle of metal develops. The electrodes then are adjusted for the correct distance from the molten metal. When the charge is molten and at the correct temperature, oxygen is introduced to burn out any excess impurities. With the impurities removed, and the correct temperature attained, the necessary alloys are added in controlled amounts. When test specimens reveal the right chemical analysis, the steel is poured out through the spout and into a large ladle. The molten steel is poured into molds to form ingots which are rolled into bars or other shapes.

Ingots To Finished Steel

The freshly-made steel in a large ladle is carried to a row of ingot molds, as in Fig. 16-10. The steel is *teemed* or poured into the molds. As the liquid steel cools, it solidifies to form an *ingot*, which is the first solid form of steel. Ingots may weigh as much as 15 tons.

After the ingots are cooled sufficiently to solidify, the molds are *stripped* off by an overhead stripper crane, as in Fig. 16-10. The ingots are actually large steel castings. They are poured and formed in the same manner, whether they come from the open-hearth furnace, Bessemer converter, oxygen furnace, or electric furnace. The ingot molds are tapered from one end to the other so they may be pulled off more easily. Steel produced for rolling or forging is cast in ingot molds before it is reduced to other shapes.

Soaking Pit: Before steel ingots can be rolled down to finished steel, they must be *soaked* — i.e., heated evenly to a uniform temperature of about 2200°F. This is done by placing them (while still at a high red heat) in a *soaking pit*, a large furnace usually below the level of the floor. The cover is removed to lower the ingots into the furnace. Since the ingots are still at a high heat, they can be *soaked* in a short period of time, usually from 30 minutes to 1½ hours. The soaking period for cold ingots is much longer.

Rolling the Steel: The hot steel ingots are taken from the soaking pits and are rolled into various shapes in the rolling mills. The steel passes through two or more large rollers a number of times. Each time the ingot is rolled, it is reduced in cross-sectional area and increased in length. An ingot 19″ by 23″ in cross section can be rolled down to a cross-sectional size 6″ square, in 16 passes requiring 5 minutes or less. Besides shaping the steel, rolling also improves its physical and mechanical properties. It breaks down the grain size, making the grain finer, and it improves the toughness of the steel.

The ingot is rolled on all four sides to form *blooms, billets,* or *slabs*. These are semifinished products which are further reduced in cross-sectional area in *finish rolling mills*. While still hot, they generally are sheared off in shorter lengths, before being sent to the finish rolling mill. They usually must be reheated before finish rolling.

Blooms generally are square or rectangular and are larger than 36 square inches in cross-sectional area. They are used to make rails and structural steel for purposes such as those illustrated in Fig. 16-10.

Billets may be square or rectangular, but they generally are less than 36 square inches in cross-sectional area. They are used to make rods, bars, seamless pipes, and tubes. These products are used for purposes as illustrated in Fig. 16-10.

Slabs generally are wider and flatter than billets. They are used to make plate, sheet, and strip steel. These are all flat rolled products of different widths and thicknesses. It is difficult to define the point at which one product stops and the other begins.

Forms of Steel: In conventional terms, a steel *plate* is a flat product ¼″ or more in thickness and 8″ or more in width, or 0.180″ or more in thickness when the width is more than 48″. According to the *Manufacturer's Standard Gage for Steel Sheets*, steel *sheet* is considered to be a flat product rolled to thicknesses less than ¼″, and usually 0.239″ or less. Sheet steel cut to widths of 12″ or less is called *strip*. Steel plate, sheet, and strip products are used for purposes such as those indicated in Fig. 16-10.

Confusion in the purchase of flat steel products may be avoided by indicating the decimal equivalent thickness of the material. The *Manufacturer's Standard Gage for Steel Sheets* is included in machine shop handbooks. While this is the gage now used by most manufacturers in designating the thickness of steel sheets, exceptions may be encountered.

Bars are made from billets and are available in many shapes and sizes. Typical shapes include square, round, flat, hexagonal, octagonal, oval, and diamond. Bars are used for forgings, cold-formed parts, bolts, nuts, concrete reinforcement, parts of machines, and for machined parts. The machinist is concerned largely with bar products used for machining applications.

Hot-rolled steel is steel which is rolled to finished size while hot. It is identified by the

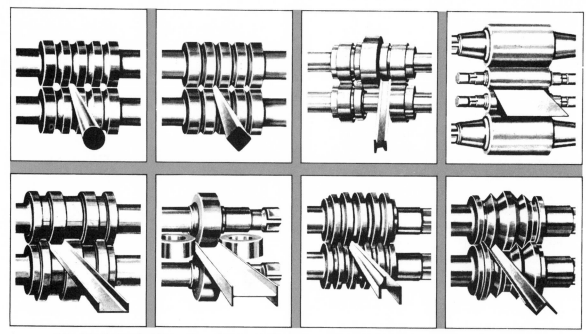

Fig. 16-12. **Steel of Many Cross-Sectional Shapes Is Produced by Rolling** (Amer. Iron and Steel)

black iron oxide scale on the surface. The scale is formed by oxidation, caused by exposure to oxygen in the air while rolling. Many steel products are available in hot-rolled form, including structural steel, bars, sheets, plates, and strip. All of these products can be produced by rolling as illustrated in Fig. 16-12.

Cold-drawn steel is steel which is drawn through dies to a finished size. It is identified by a smooth, bright surface. It is also produced to relatively accurate tolerances. Steel which is to be cold-drawn is hot-rolled slightly oversize. It is then pickled in a dilute sulfuric acid solution to remove the iron oxide scale. After pickling, it is drawn through dies. Round bars are drawn through round holes in very hard steel dies, square bars through square holes, etc. The cold-drawing process generally improves the machinability of the steel.

Cold-rolled steel is steel which has been rolled to finished size while cold. The process is similar to the cold-drawing process, except that the steel is rolled to final size instead of being drawn to size. The steel is hot-rolled slightly oversize, pickled, and then rolled cold between huge, smooth rolls under great pressure. Cold-rolled steels are produced to close

tolerances and have bright, smooth surfaces. The cold-rolling process commonly is used for sheet steel and plate requiring a clean, bright surface. It also is used for producing cold-rolled bars of various shapes.

Cast steel is steel which is poured into sand molds to form intricate shapes called castings. Steel castings are used for machine parts requiring extreme strength and shock resistance. They are used for products such as heavy mining equipment, railroad equipment, large gears, valve bodies, and parts for other heavy machinery.

Steel castings generally rank lower in machinability than the commonly-used types of cast iron and malleable iron castings. However, they rank higher in tensile strength. The tensile strength may vary from 60,000 psi to 100,000 psi for castings made of low-carbon steel and medium-carbon steel. Castings made of low-alloy steel may possess tensile strength in the range from 70,000 to 200,000 psi, depending on the type of heat treatment used. Gray iron castings range from 20,000 to 65,000 psi in tensile strength, depending on the type of cast iron and the heat treatment used on the castings.

Plain Carbon Steels

Steel is essentially an alloy of iron and carbon. Of course, very small quantities of other elements also are present, usually in the form of impurities. The properties of steel may be changed significantly through the addition of carbon or other elements. Consequently, there are hundreds of different grades of steel used in industry. Each grade has a slightly different quantity of alloying elements.

Steels may be classified in two basic groups — plain carbon steels and alloy steels. Those steels which are composed basically of iron and carbon are classified as *plain carbon steels*. Steels which have other elements intentionally added for the purpose of changing their properties usually are classified as *alloy steels*. Alloy steels usually contain one or more metallic alloying elements in addition to the iron content. Generally, they are named after the specific alloying element. Examples of alloy steels include nickel steel, nickel-chromium steel, and molybdenum steel.

In studying the various types of steel, one should first understand the properties of *commercially pure iron*. It then is easier to understand the effects of alloying elements in producing the varieties of steel developed from this base metal.

Commercially Pure Iron

Commercially pure iron is iron which is made as nearly pure as practical applications in industry demand. Usually it does not contain more than two-hundredths of one percent (0.02%) of its weight in impurities. The carbon content generally does not exceed 0.03%. Commercially pure iron may be made in either the open-hearth furnace or the Bessemer converter. This type of iron actually represents a very small percentage of ferrous metal production.

The tensile strength of commercially pure iron averages about 40,000 psi. It is very ductile, possessing an elongation rating of about 40%. It does not harden significantly through heat treatment, but it does harden a small amount through hammering, rolling, or other forms of cold-working. It can be welded or forged readily.

Commercially pure iron becomes highly magnetized when subjected to a magnetic field. Similarly, it loses its magnetism readily. Hence, it frequently is used as a magnetic material. Magnetic chucks on machine tools often are made of this type of iron.

The mechanical properties of commercially pure iron may be changed readily by the addition of small amounts of alloying elements. These may be either metallic or nonmetallic elements.

Wrought Iron: Wrought iron is a mechanical mixture of commercially pure iron and slag. Its internal structure is characterized by thread-like fibers formed by the mixture. The fibers run in the direction in which the iron was rolled. Wrought iron is an example of how alloying substances influence the properties of iron.

Wrought iron is probably the first form in which iron was used by man. It is so named because of its distinguishing properties. It is malleable, ductile, tough, fatigue-resistant, and corrosive-resistant. It has good weldability, but it ranks relatively low in machinability. It can be bent, twisted, and hammered into various shapes while hot or cold. The following are average properties of wrought iron in common use today: tensile strength, 50,000 psi; yield point, 30,000 psi; elongation, 25%; and reduction in area, 40%.

Until the development of the Bessemer and open-hearth furnaces during the 19th century, wrought iron was the most widely used ferrous metal product. Although it has been replaced largely by low-carbon steel, wrought iron still is used for a number of products. Frequently it is used in the production of water pipe, gas pipe, and pipe joints. It also is used with a galvanized coating for culverts, metal roofing, fencing, and similar items which require corrosion resistance.

Before the development of modern steel-making methods, wrought iron was made in a coal-fired *puddling furnace*. Pig iron was charged into the furnace and heated to a molten state. The furnace was lined with iron oxide. As the iron became molten, the iron oxide lining provided the necessary oxygen for burning out the excess carbon. The other impurities, including sulfur, phosphorus, manganese, and silicon, formed a molten slag which floated on top of the iron.

As the molten iron became purified, it began to solidify because of the limited temperature of the furnace. As it continued to solidify, the molten slag was manually puddled (mixed) with the molten iron, thus forming a thick plastic mass. The mass formed a mixture of relatively pure iron and slag. The iron was then hammered into billets or bars which were forged, shaped, or welded into useful objects by blacksmiths or ironworkers.

A modern method for making wrought iron produces a material similar to the earlier puddled wrought iron. However, it is more uniform in quality and can be produced economically in larger quantities. The impurities are oxidized out of pig iron as nearly as practicable. This is done by making commercially-pure iron in either an open-hearth furnace or a Bessemer converter. While still in a molten state, the iron is poured into a ladle with separately prepared molten slag from an open-hearth furnace. The slag is kept well below the temperature of the molten metal. The iron forms globules coated with slag. This material quickly solidifies and forms a paste-like mass. The mass, which weighs several tons, is squeezed in a large press. The squeezing removes excess slag and welds the material into a solid bloom or billet. The hot mass is then rolled into finished wrought iron products of various shapes.

Carbon Content of Steel

As previously mentioned, steel is essentially an alloy of iron and carbon. However, minute quantities of impurities also may exist in steel. Carbon is the most important element which is alloyed with iron to form steel. It is largely through control of the form and amount of the carbon content that the properties of various steels may be controlled.

The amount of carbon combined to form steel is rated as a percentage of the total weight. Except for very-high-carbon tool steels, the carbon content of steel is usually less than *one* percent. A typical low-carbon steel has 0.18% (eighteen-hundredths of one percent) carbon. The carbon content of steel usually is expressed in terms of *points*. Thus, steel with 0.18% carbon has 18-point carbon content.

Tensile Strength of Soft Steel: The approximate tensile strength of annealed (unhardened) steel, with carbon content up to 0.80%, can be calculated. It should be remembered that commercially pure iron has a tensile strength of approximately 40,000 psi. For each point (0.01%) of carbon content combined with iron, the tensile strength increases approximately 1000 psi. Thus, the following formula may be used to calculate the approximate tensile strength of annealed carbon steel with up to 0.80% (80-point) carbon content:

Approximate tensile strength = 40,000 + (1000 × points of carbon)

Example: Determine the approximate tensile strength (TS) of steel with 45-point carbon content.
TS = 40,000 + (1000 × 45)
TS = 40,000 + 45,000
TS = 85,000 psi

Tensile Strength of Hardened Steel: The tensile strength of steel can be increased further through heat-treatment processes. The amount of carbon largely determines the degree to which steel may be hardened by heat treatment. The tensile strength increases in proportion to the amount of increased hardness. However, as the hardness and tensile strength of steel increase, the ductility of the steel generally decreases.

The approximate tensile strength of steel may be calculated easily if its Brinell hardness is known. For an explanation of Brinell hardness, see Unit 158. The approximate tensile strength in pounds per square inch is equal to the Brinell hardness divided by two, and the quotient multiplied by 1000.

Example: Determine the approximate tensile strength (TS) of steel which has a Brinell hardness of 170.

$$TS = (\text{Brinell hardness} \div 2) \times 1000$$
$$TS = \frac{170}{2} \times 1000$$
$$TS = 85,000 \text{ psi}$$

Plain Carbon Steels

Plain carbon steel is essentially an alloy of iron and carbon. In addition, it includes small amounts of silicon, sulfur, phosphorous, and manganese, usually in the form of impurities. It does not include other metallic alloying elements intentionally added. Although all steels contain some carbon, steels which do not include other metallic alloying elements are classified as plain *carbon steels*.

The carbon content in plain carbon steels may range from 0.05% to 1.7%. However, it seldom exceeds 1.5%. The following represents a typical analysis of the range of elements in plain carbon steels:

Carbon........... 0.05 to 1.5%
Manganese....... 0.25 to 1.65%
Phosphorus....... 0.040% maximum
Sulfur........... 0.050% maximum
Iron............. 97% (The remainder, usually more)

The carbon content in the plain carbon steels is the most important factor in determining its properties. With significant increases in the carbon content, the following properties are influenced:

1. Tensile strength is increased.
2. Hardness is increased.
3. Response to various heat-treatment processes is increased. Greater hardness may be obtained.
4. Ductility decreases.

5. Malleability decreases.
6. Weldability decreases.

The plain carbon steels may be classified as low-, medium-, or high-carbon steel, according to the relative amount of carbon content.

Low-Carbon Steel: Low-carbon steel, sometimes called machinery steel or mild steel, has a range of carbon content from 0.05% to 0.30%. The low-carbon steels with less than 0.15% carbon sometimes are classified further as the *very-low-carbon* steels.

The properties of the low-carbon steels include good ductility, malleability, weldability, and good cold- and hot-working characteristics. The very-low-carbon steels rate lower in machinability than those with carbon content above 0.15%. The tensile strength for the low-carbon steels, in the as-rolled condition, varies from 45,000 to 75,000 psi, depending on the carbon content.

Direct hardening by heat treatment depends largely on the carbon content. Therefore, low-carbon steels may be hardened only a very slight amount by direct hardening. However, for special applications requiring a hard, wear-resistant surface and soft but tough inner core, the low-carbon steels may be *casehardened*. This is a special heat-treatment process by which the outer surface, or skin layer, may be carburized and hardened. Hence, these steels are also called carburizing grades.

The low-carbon steels have many uses. They are used for nails, screws, bolts, nuts, washers, wire fence, structural parts for machinery, and for forged parts. They also are used for many pressed or deep-drawn sheet metal parts, such as automobile fenders, bodies, and oil pans.

The low-carbon steels are available in the form of bars, strips, sheets, plate, shapes of various types, and wire. These steels are available in either the hot-rolled, cold-rolled, or cold-drawn condition.

Medium-Carbon Steel: Medium-carbon steels range in carbon content from 0.30% to 0.60%. These steels have less ductility than the low-carbon steels, but they are harder and possess greater tensile strength. The tensile strength in the as-rolled condition ranges from 70,000 to 100,000 psi, depending on the carbon content.

The strength of the medium-carbon steels also may be increased significantly by heat treatment. The tensile strength of steel with 0.45% carbon can be increased to 150,000 psi with proper heat treatment. The medium-carbon steels may be hardened directly in water or brine, at appropriate temperatures. The maximum degree of hardness obtainable will vary with the carbon content. In comparison with high-carbon steels, it can be stated that a moderate degree of hardness may be obtained with the medium-carbon steels.

A typical medium-carbon steel with 0.45% carbon is SAE 1045 steel. A maximum hardness value of about Rockwell C-59 can be obtained by hardening this steel with a water quench at a temperature of 1500°F. Of course, the hardness is reduced when the steel is tempered. The effect of various tempering temperatures on the hardness of SAE 1045 steel is shown in Fig. 17-29. Rockwell hardness values are shown in Table 34 in the appendix.

Medium-carbon steels are used for many parts on various types of machinery. Their use frequently involves heat treatment to control such properties as tensile strength, hardness, wear resistance, and toughness. They are used for parts which require medium strength or wear-resistant surfaces. The parts may be forgings, structural elements, or machined parts. Although they do not weld easily by the oxy-acetylene process, they may be brazed or electric welded. They are used for gears, truck axles, steering arms, crankshafts, connecting rods, shift levers, and similar items. They also are used for stampings which are not heat-treated.

The medium-carbon steels are available in rods, bars, strips, and forging stock. They may be hot-rolled, cold-rolled, cold-drawn, or annealed.

High-Carbon Steel: High-carbon steels may range in carbon content from 0.60% to 1.70%. However, the maximum carbon content seldom exceeds 1.50%. Most high-carbon steels have less than 1.30% carbon.

The plain high-carbon steels may be divided into two basic groups for ease in understanding their properties and uses. The two groups include the standard *high-carbon constructional steels* and the *plain carbon tool steels*. The high-carbon constructional steels have carbon content ranging from 0.60% to 0.95%. The plain carbon tool steels have carbon content which usually ranges from 0.60% to 1.40%.

The high-carbon steels are harder and possess greater tensile strength than the carbon steels with lower carbon content. They generally are used for products which require heat treatment. The heat treatment improves both the hardness and the tensile strength. In the as-rolled condition, the tensile strength may range up to 140,000 psi or higher. With heat treatment, this strength may be increased beyond 200,000 psi.

Maximum hardness values of about Rockwell C-66 may be obtained with the high-carbon steels. However, these values usually are decreased several points by tempering to increase toughness. The effects of various tempering temperatures on the hardness of high-carbon steel, such as SAE 1095 steel, are shown in Fig. 17-29.

A Rockwell hardness of C-60 or higher is generally required for metal cutting tools such as drills, reamers, taps, dies, and similar tools. Rockwell hardness values are shown in Table 34, appendix.

The maximum hardness obtainable by heat treatment in plain carbon steels increases with increased carbon content up to about 0.80%. Thereafter, additional carbon content does not increase the hardness significantly. However, a further increase in carbon content does increase wear resistance appreciably.

The maximum hardness obtainable increases rapidly with increased carbon content up through 0.45%. Thereafter, the increase in hardness tapers off gradually to a maximum hardness obtained with 0.70% to 0.80% carbon. The plain high-carbon steels usually are quenched in water or brine for maximum hardness.

Constructional Grades: The constructional grades of high-carbon steel are used where carbon steels with improved strength and wear-resistant characteristics are required. These applications include parts used in the construction of automobiles, farm machinery, railroad equipment, and mining equipment. They also are used widely for many types of springs, including coil springs and flat springs. Practically all of these products are heat-treated. The following are products made from the constructional grades of high-carbon steel: plow beams, plow shares, cultivator shovels, rake teeth, scraper blades, disks, hammers, cutlery, chisels, gouges, strongest steel wire, axes, saws, wear plates on machines, and many other machinery parts.

Plain Carbon Tool Steel: This is one of several widely-used types of tool steel. Actually, any steel which is used to make metal-cutting tools may be called a tool steel. However, as the term is commonly used in the tool and die making phase of industry, plain carbon tool steels are one group of tool and die steels in common use. The other types, although they may have high carbon content, are alloyed with other metals. Hence, they are *alloy tool steels.* The carbon tool steels usually are hardened in water and, therefore, may be called water-hardening tool steels. The alloy tool steels usually are oil-hardened or air-hardened.

Tool and die steels, including both the plain carbon tool steels and alloy tool steels, are classified by a special AISI classification system, which differs from that used for the standard constructional steels. According to the AISI classification system for tool and die steels, the plain carbon tool steels are designated W-1. Plain carbon steels within the W-1 group are available with various amounts of carbon content, ranging from 0.60% to 1.40%. Special data concerning tool and die steels, including properties, composition, and heat treatment, are included in standard handbooks for machinists.

There are several grades of plain carbon tool steel, based on both carbon content and quality. The grades include *special, extra, standard,* and *commercial.* The special and extra grades are the highest quality. These grades are used for tools and dies requiring higher quality material. The standard and commercial grades are produced according to less-rigid production controls, and they are used for general-purpose tools or other products which require the properties of high-carbon tool steel.

Carbon tool steels are used for the following products: punches, dies, taps, threading dies, forming dies, drills, reamers, cold chisels, razors, files, and many other special cutting tools for cutting metals or other tough materials.

The high-carbon steels are available in the hot-rolled condition, in the form of bars, plates, or other special forms specified by the purchaser. Some bars or plates are available with machined or ground surfaces. Drill rod is an example of this material with a ground surface. It is available in various diameters.

The cost of the plain carbon tool steels varies with the grade or quality. The cost per pound may vary from four to eight times the cost of cold-drawn low-carbon steel.

Resulfurized Carbon Steel

In carefully controlled amounts, sulfur improves the machinability of steel. Normally, the sulfur in carbon steels is held to a maximum of 0.05%. See Table 31, appendix. However, sulfur in amounts from approximately 0.08% to 0.33% sometimes is added to certain grades of carbon steel to improve machinability (Table 31, appendix). These grades of steel are designated *resulfurized carbon steels*, and are of two types — *Bessemer resulfurized carbon steels* and *open-hearth resulfurized carbon steels.* As can be seen, they are named according to the steelmaking process used in producing them. Both types commonly are referred to as *screw steels* or *free-machining steels.* They are used widely in making cylindrical and threaded parts in turret lathes, hand screw machines, automatic screw machines, and engine lathes.

The machinability of the resulfurized carbon steels is superior to that of the plain carbon steels. This can be understood best by comparing their approximate machinability ratings. The resulfurized steel designated AISI B1112 is given arbitrarily a machinability rating of 100%. Other steels and many other metals are given approximate machinability ratings in comparison with AISI B1112 steel; see Table 30 appendix. The corresponding plain carbon steel, AISI C1012, has a machinability rating of approximately 53%. The resulfurized carbon steel designated AISI B1113 has a machinability rating of approximately 130% to 140%. The tensile strength and the hardness of the resulfurized steels are somewhat higher than the corresponding plain carbon steels. See Table 30, appendix.

Lead sometimes is added to the resulfurized carbon steels to further improve their machinability. The lead usually is included in amounts from 0.15% to 0.35%. Generally, this is less than one third of a pound per one hundred pounds of steel. The lead is evenly distributed in the steel in extremely fine particles. It does not affect the mechanical properties of the steel, but it does improve the machinability. Modern resulfurized and leaded steels are available with machinability ratings as high as 300% or higher. Hence, these steels can be machined many times more easily and efficiently than the plain carbon steels. Since the number system used to identify some of the leaded grades of steel is not completely standardized, the properties of these steels may be secured in steel manufacturer's catalogs.

The resulfurized steels do have some shortcomings, which must be considered in the selection of the type of steel for a specific use.

The sulfur, when included greatly in excess of that used in the plain carbon steels, affects the hot-working properties of the steel. It produces an effect called *red shortness*. The steel becomes brittle and unworkable at high temperatures. Also, the grades with high amounts of sulfur do not have good forging or welding properties. Hence, they should not be selected where these hot-working operations are involved. The resulfurized steels, however, may be heat-treated.

The resulfurized carbon steels are used widely where high machinability is important. Cutting speeds may be increased from two to four times those used with the plain carbon steels. Of course, the proper cutting tool and cutting fluids must be used at these high speeds. The following are suggested cutting speeds for turning operations of average severity, using cutting tools of high-speed steel, on steels of various machinability ratings:

Machinability Rating	Cutting Speed (sfpm)
50	80
75	120
100	160
150	240
200	320

The resulfurized steels, including the leaded grades, are excellent for many projects which are turned on a school lathe. Their machining characteristics include general ease of machining, good chip formation, increased tool life, improved finish, increased cutting speeds, and increased rate of metal removal.

UNIT 146

Steel Classification and Identification

SAE and AISI Classification Code

There are hundreds of standard grades of steel available, each designated by a code number. These numbers are used on drawings, blueprints, and specification sheets to indicate the type of steel which should be used.

Two main code-number systems were developed to classify the standard constructional grades of steel, including both carbon steels and alloy steels. These systems classify types of steel according to their basic chemical composition. One classification system is the SAE code sponsored by the *Society of Automobile Engineers*. The second system is the AISI code sponsored by the *American Iron and Steel Institute*. The numbers used in both systems are now essentially the same. However, the AISI code uses a letter before the number to indicate the method used in the manufacture of the steel.

The SAE and AISI code-number systems usually have a four-numeral or four-digit series of numbers. Occasionally a five-digit series is used for certain alloy steels. The code number indicates the approximate chemical composition of the steel.

First Digit: In the SAE and AISI code classification systems, the first number frequently, but not always, indicates the basic type of steel as follows:
1 — Carbon
2 — Nickel
3 — Nickel-chrome
4 — Molybdenum
5 — Chromium
6 — Chromium-vanadium
7 — Tungsten
8 — Nickel-chromium-molybdenum
9 — Silicomanganese

All Digits: The first two digits together indicate the *series* within the basic alloy group. There may be several series within a basic alloy group, depending on the amount of principal alloying elements. Hence, the second digit very often, but not always, indicates the approximate percentage of the principal alloying element. The third, fourth, and fifth digits are intended to indicate the approximate middle of the carbon range. The carbon content is indicated in points—1-point carbon is 0.01%, 45-point carbon is 0.45%, and 100-point carbon is 1.0%.

Prefix: As previously mentioned, the AISI code system uses a letter before the number, to show the process used in making the steel. The following letters are used:

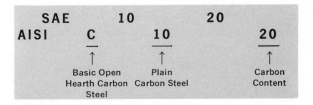

Fig. 16-13. SAE and AISI Steel Code Numbers
The example designates basic open-hearth, plain carbon steel with a range of 0.18% to 0.23% carbon content.

B — Acid Bessemer carbon steel
C — Basic open-hearth or basic electric furnace carbon steel
E — Electric furnace alloy steel

Examples: An example of the SAE and AISI code classification system used to classify a commonly used plain carbon steel is shown in Fig. 16-13.

The series designations and the types of steel which they designate are summarized in Table 21.

The standard and tentative-standard constructional steels are listed according to their SAE — AISI code numbers in Table 31, appendix. The table shows those grades of steel which were standard in 1960. Since tungsten steels generally are considered special steels, they are not listed in the above table.

Many alloy steels of constructional grade are produced to meet certain hardenability standards. The letter *H* is used after the SAE or AISI number to designate this type of steel. An example is 1340 H steel. Additional information concerning the H-steels is available in standard handbooks for machinists.

Color Code for Steel

A color code often is used by steel producers to identify various types of steel. The ends of steel bars frequently are painted at the steel mill for identification purposes. However, not all steel producers use the same color-code system. The color code used generally is listed in each steel producer's catalog. Therefore, two factors must be known in order to identify steel bars by color code — the name of the steel producer and the color code used by him.

The stock always should be removed from the unpainted end, so that the painted end remains, and the type of steel always can be identified for future use.

Spark Test

The identity of unknown types of steel often can be determined by a *spark test*. When steel is ground on a grinding wheel, sparks are produced. Different types of sparks are produced by different types of steel. Therefore, an unknown type of steel may be identified when its spark is the same as that produced by a known type of steel.

Some practice usually is required in the identification of steel or other metals by spark testing. The pressure applied to the piece against the grinding wheel should be about the same for all specimens. The types of sparks produced by each type of steel or other metal should be studied carefully. Table 22 may be used as an aid in the general identification of unknown types of steel.

The volume of sparks produced with carbon steel is quite large. The quantity of *spurts* or *spark-explosions*, however, depends on the carbon content. Thus, wrought iron, which has very low carbon content, has very few spurts. High-carbon tool steel has many spurts. Careful study of figures 1 through 3 in Table 22 will aid in determining whether a carbon steel is of the low-, medium-, or high-carbon type.

Table 21
Series Designations in SAE-AISI Steel Code

Series	Types		
10xx	Nonsulphurized carbon steels		
11xx	Resulphurized carbon steels (free machining)		
12xx	Rephosphorized and resulphurized carbon steels (free machining)		
13xx	Mn 1.75%		
*23xx	Ni 3.50%		
*25xx	Ni 5.00%		
31xx	Ni 1.25%	Cr 0.65%	
33xx	Ni 3.50%	Cr 1.55%	
40xx	Mo 0.20 or 0.25%		
41xx	Cr 0.50 or 0.95%	Mo 0.12 or 0.20%	
43xx	Ni 1.80%	Cr 0.50 or 0.80%	Mo 0.25%
44xx	Mo 0.40%		
45xx	Mo 0.52%		
46xx	Ni 1.80%	Mo 0.25%	
47xx	Ni 1.05%	Cr 0.45%	Mo 0.20 or 0.35%
48xx	Ni 3.50%	Mo 0.25%	
50xx	Cr 0.25, 0.40 or 0.50%		
50xxx	C 1.00%	Cr 0.50%	
51xx	Cr 0.80, 0.90, 0.95, or 1.00%		
51xxx	C 1.00%	Cr 1.05%	
52xxx	Cr 1.00%	Cr 1.45%	
61xx	Cr 0.60, 0.80 or 0.95%		
	V 0.12%, 0.10% min., or 0.15% min.		
81xx	Ni 0.30%	Cr 0.40%	Mo 0.12%
86xx	Ni 0.55%	Cr 0.50%	Mo 0.20%
87xx	Ni 0.55%	Cr 0.05%	Mo 0.25%
88xx	Ni 0.55%	Cr 0.50%	Mo 0.35%
92xx	Mn 0.85%	Si 2.00%	Cr 0 or 0.35%
93xx	Ni 3.25%	Cr 1.20%	Mo 0.12%
94xx	Ni 0.45%	Cr 0.40%	Mo 0.12%
98xx	Ni 1.00%	Cr 0.80%	Mo 0.25%

* Not included in the current list of standard steels.

Abbreviations:
C   Carbon   Mo Molybdenum
Cr Chromium   Ni Nickel
Mn Mangenese   Si Silicon
                    V   Vanadium

Alloy Steels

Alloy steels include steels such as manganese steels, nickel steels, nickel-chromium steels, and molybdenum steels. Steels which are classified as alloy steels have one or more alloying elements, other than iron and carbon. These elements are intentionally added, and, usually, one or more of the alloying elements is a metallic element.

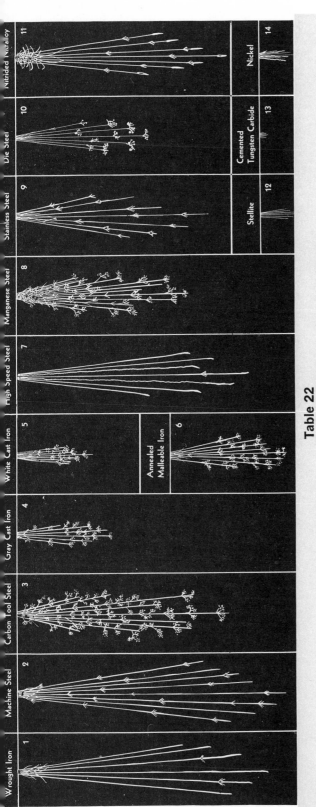

Wrought Iron 1 · Machine Steel 2 · Carbon Tool Steel 3 · Gray Cast Iron 4 · White Cast Iron 5 · Annealed Malleable Iron 6 · High Speed Steel 7 · Manganese Steel 8 · Stainless Steel 9 · Die Steel 10 · Nitrided Nitralloy 11 · Stellite 12 · Cemented Tungsten Carbide 13 · Nickel 14

Table 22
Characteristics of Sparks Generated by the Grinding of Metals

Metal	Volume of Stream	Relative Length of Stream, Inches†	Color of Stream Close to Wheel	Color of Streaks Near End of Stream	Quantity of Spurts	Nature of Spurts
1. Wrought iron	Large	65	Straw	White	Very few	Forked
2. Machine steel (AISI 1020)	Large	70	White	White	Few	Forked
3. Carbon tool steel	Moderately large	55	White	White	Very many	Fine, repeating
4. Gray cast iron	Small	25	Red	Straw	Many	Fine, repeating
5. White cast iron	Very small	20	Red	Straw	Few	Fine, repeating
6. Annealed mall. iron	Moderate	30	Red	Straw	Many	Fine, repeating
7. High speed steel (18-4-1)	Small	60	Red	Straw	Extremely few	Forked
8. Austenitic manganese steel	Moderately large	45	White	White	Many	Fine, repeating
9. Stainless steel (Type 410)	Moderate	50	Straw	White	Moderate	Forked
10. Tungsten-chromium die steel	Small	35	Red	Straw*	Many	Fine, repeating*
11. Nitrided Nitralloy	Large (curved)	55	White	White	Moderate	Forked
12. Stellite	Very small	10	Orange	Orange	None	
13. Cemented tungsten carbide	Extremely small	2	Light Orange	Light Orange	None	
14. Nickel	Very small**	10	Orange	Orange	None	
15. Copper, brass, aluminum	None				None	

†Figures obtained with 12" wheel on bench stand and are relative only. Actual length in each instance will vary with grinding wheel, pressure, etc. *Blue-white spurts. **Some wavy streaks.

(Norton)

Of course, like the plain carbon steels, alloy steels contain small amounts of impurities. These include silicon, sulfur, phosphorous, and manganese. The alloy steels are classified according to the predominating alloying element (or elements). An example of an alloy with three principal alloying elements is nickel-chromium-molybdenum steel.

Properties from Alloying Elements

Characteristics or properties not obtainable in the plain carbon steels are produced in steel through the use of alloying elements. For many applications, alloy steels are selected because of their special properties, often made possible through heat treatment. The principal properties which may be developed through the addition of alloying elements in steel include the following:

1. Increased hardenability.
2. Decrease in rate of cooling during the hardening operation, thus reducing distortion and the development of cracks.
3. Resistance to becoming soft when being tempered.
4. Retention of hardness and strength at higher temperatures without softening.
5. Increased strength through heat treatment.
6. Increased wear or abrasion resistance at both normal and increased temperatures.
7. Increased toughness.
8. Increased strength as manufactured.
9. Increased corrosion resistance at both normal and high temperatures.
10. Increased machinability.

Of the above properties, the most important are: increased hardenability, retention of basic properties at higher temperatures, and resistance to corrosion. The alloy steels are selected for applications which require properties not obtainable with the plain carbon steels. In most applications, the alloy steels must be heat-treated in order to develop their best potential properties.

The cost of alloy steel generally averages about three times that of the equivalent types of plain carbon steel. Hence, it would be uneconomical to select alloy steels for applications where plain carbon steels would be adequate.

Not all properties acquired through the addition of alloying elements are desirable. Sometimes it is necessary to accept some undesirable properties in order to obtain certain desirable characteristics. For instance, in selecting an alloy tool steel which ranks high in abrasion resistance, it may be necessary to accept a material more brittle than desired.

Classification of Alloy Steels

Alloy steels can be classified in the following three categories: 1. constructional alloy steels, 2. alloy tool steels, and 3. special alloy steels.

Constructional Alloy Steels: Constructional alloy steels include various types of steel used in the construction of many kinds of parts for machines. These include items such as gears, levers, shafts, bolts, springs, pistons, and connecting rods. This group of alloys also includes steels used for large structural members for bridges, buildings, railroads, automobile frames, and ships. The constructional alloy steels usually contain relatively low alloy content, as compared with that of alloy tool steels. The total alloy content of the constructional steels generally ranges from 0.25% to 6%.

The principal grades of constructional alloy steel are given in Table 31, appendix. They are listed by their SAE and AISI number designations, together with their chemical composition. The machinability ratings of some of these steels are listed in Table 30, appendix. Heat-treatment data are listed in Tables 32 and 33, appendix.

Alloy Tool Steels: The alloy tool steels are used in making cutting and forming tools. They are used to produce items such as drills, reamers, milling cutters, punches, dies, and wear plates. Although several types of alloy tool steel may be hardened in water, most must be hardened in oil or in air. For this reason, they often are called *oil-hardening* or *air-hardening* tool steels. Generally they rank higher in hardenability than the plain carbon tool steels; *i.e.*, they harden more deeply.

The alloy tool steels generally include higher alloy content than the constructional grades. The total alloy content usually ranges from 0.25% to more than 38%. One type of high-speed steel has a combination of alloying elements totaling 38%.

There are hundreds of different alloy tool steels. These generally are classified in several categories according to their basic properties. Each category then contains numerous grades.

A special numbering system approved by the AISI is used widely to designate each of the principal grades and types. By this system, each grade and type must meet certain minimum property specifications. There are many different manufacturers of these high-grade tool steels. Therefore, there may be variations in the quality and properties of certain grades which are sometimes considered to be equivalent.

Tool and die steels, including both the plain carbon tool steels and the alloy tool steels, are classified in the following six categories:

1. Water-hardening tool steels.
2. Shock-resisting tool steels.
3. Cold-work tool steels.
4. Hot-work tool steels.
5. High-speed tool steels.
6. Special-purpose tool steels.

A list of the basic types of tool and die steels, including both the carbon and alloy types, usually is listed according to the AISI numbering system in handbooks for machinists. Such lists include data concerning the basic properties and heat treatment of the various steels. This information also frequently is available in tool steel manufacturer's catalogs.

Special Alloy Steels: As the name implies, the special alloy steels are designed for special purposes. Included in this group are steels such as those which require very high heat resistance, or corrosion resistance. The group also may include steels which become tougher and harder with service. Steels possessing the latter characteristic often are used in making teeth on power shovels, lugs on crawler-type tractors, and jaws of rock crushers.

Effect of Alloying Elements

About twenty-six elements are used, either singly or in combination with other elements, in the production of alloy steels. It is not within the scope of this book to discuss all of these elements. However, the most important ones and their influence on the properties of alloy steels are included.

Carbon: Carbon is one of the most important elements in steel. When carbon is added in amounts up to about 0.80%, the steel becomes harder, increases in tensile strength, and increases in response to heat treatment. Carbon content in greater amounts does not cause the steel to harden significantly more, but it does increase wear resistance.

Manganese: Manganese is next in importance to carbon. Normally it is present in amounts from 0.30% to 1.50% in the constructional grades of steel. It acts as a deoxidizer and increases responsiveness to heat treatment. It increases hardenability, strength, toughness, and shock resistance.

Constructional grades of *manganese steel* usually have from 0.90% to 1.50% manganese. These steels are used for machine parts which must withstand severe duty.

Steel with 1.5% to 5% manganese is so brittle that it is useless, but with a further increase in manganese, its strength improves. Special manganese steels have from 10% to 14% manganese. These steels possess extreme hardness and ductility. The ductility is acquired through quenching in water at a high temperature, a procedure opposite from that used with carbon steels. These steels become *strain-hardened* by cold-working. With continued use, they become extremely hard and tough, and are used for rock-crushing, grinding, and railroad equipment.

Nickel: Nickel increases strength, toughness, wear resistance, and corrosion resistance of steels. It is not very effective in increasing hardenability. The usual alloying quantity is 3% to 3.7%.

The *nickel steels* have high impact resistance, especially at low temperatures. They are used for machine parts which are subject to repeated shock and stress. These steels also are used for structural purposes such as bridge construction, buildings, rails, armor plate, and heavy machinery.

Nickel often is alloyed with chromium to produce *nickel-chrome* steels of constructional grade. These steels are used for items such as spline shafts, crankshafts, steering knuckles, rear axles, parts of farm machinery, and parts of earth-moving equipment subject to severe work conditions.

Nickel is a principal alloying element in the nickel-chromium *stainless steels*. In these steels, nickel is alloyed in amounts up to 22%, together with chromium.

Chromium: Chromium is alloyed with steel to produce *chromium steels* and certain other alloy steels. Chromium steels also are called *chrome steels*. Chromium increases corrosion resistance, toughness, wear resistance, hardenability, and response to heat treatment. Like other steels, the tensile strength depends on the carbon content.

The chromium content in constructional grades ranges from about 0.30% to 1.60%. The carbon content usually ranges from about 0.20% to 1.30%. With proper hardening and tempering, the tensile strength of these steels may be doubled and the yield strength tripled in comparison with corresponding annealed steel. The ductility is reduced by heat treatment. Without proper heat treatment, these steels are not superior to carbon steels.

The chrome steels are used for machine parts such as ball bearings, races for bearings, coil springs, flat springs, gears, and shafts.

Chromium may be alloyed alone with steel, or it may be alloyed in combination with other elements such as nickel, vanadium, tungsten, and molybdenum. It is used in larger amounts in the stainless steels. In these, the chromium content generally ranges from 11% to 26%. Chromium is also one of the principal alloying elements in tool and die steels and high-speed steels.

Molybdenum: Molybdenum improves the heat-treatment properties of steel. It increases hardenability, and it increases resistance to softening at high temperatures. It also increases toughness and shock resistance. The *molybdenum steels* are used for machine parts such as bolts, coil springs, differential gears, leaf springs, and propeller and transmission shafts.

Molybdenum may be alloyed alone or in combination with other alloying elements in steel. It is alloyed with chromium in the *chromium-molybdenum steels*. It is alloyed with nickel and chromium in the *nickel-chromium-molybdenum steels*. It is alloyed with nickel in the *nickel-molybdenum steels*. In all of these constructional steels, molybdenum is alloyed in comparatively small amounts, from 0.15% to 0.40%. On the other hand, it is alloyed in tool and die steels in amounts up to 9%.

Vanadium: Vanadium promotes the development of fine grain structure in steels. In the construction grades, it is alloyed in small amounts, usually from 0.03% to 0.20%. Vanadium in amounts less than 0.20% increases tensile strength, yield strength, wear resistance, and impact toughness. These properties are increased without a corresponding loss of ductility. In amounts greater than 0.20%, vanadium generally reduces strength of steel.

In steels of constructional grade, vanadium usually is alloyed in combination with chromium. These grades, therefore, are called *chromium-vanadium* steels. They are used for items such as heat-treated and forged parts, flat springs, coil springs, valve springs, piston rods, and spline shafts.

Vanadium is included in amounts up to 5% in high-speed steels, to impart stability at high temperatures. With stability, steels tend to maintain their properties without change. The vanadium retards tempering or softening of high-speed steel cutting tools at high working temperatures. The high-speed steels are used widely for cutting tools such as drills, reamers, milling cutters, and lathe tool bits. In alloy tool steels, vanadium usually is alloyed in combination with other elements such as chromium, tungsten, molybdenum, and cobalt.

Tungsten: Tungsten is one of the principal elements in many alloy tool steels. It is alloyed in these steels in amounts from 2% to 20%. It produces a fine, dense grain structure, and it improves the heat-treatment qualities in the steel. The steels with high tungsten content possess high wear resistance. Keen cutting edges can be produced on these steels, and they retain their hardness at high temperatures after being hardened.

Tungsten is a principal ingredient in cemented-carbide cutting tools. In these tools, grains of tungsten carbide are cemented together with cobalt. The carbide grains are very hard and wear-resistant. In some grades of cemented carbide, tungsten is alloyed with certain other elements. Tungsten carbide is discussed in greater detail in Unit 140.

Cobalt: Cobalt is an important alloying element used in cutting tool materials. These materials include high-speed steels, cast alloys, and cemented carbides. The outstanding characteristic of cobalt is its ability to improve the *hot-hardness* or *red-hardness* of cutting tool materials. With high cobalt content, these materials retain their hardness at the lower red-heat temperatures. The cobalt also improves the wear resistance of these materials.

The cobalt content in high-speed steels varies from 5% to 12%. In the cast alloys, it is used in amounts from 35% to 55%. In both materials, it frequently is alloyed in combination with chromium, vanadium, and tungsten.

Cobalt also is used as an alloying element in making metal used for permanent magnets. *Alnico*, a nonferrous alloy of aluminum, nickel, and cobalt, often is used for high-quality permanent magnets.

The properties of cobalt are discussed further in Unit 140.

Other Elements: *Copper* in small amounts sometimes is alloyed with steel to improve corrosion resistance. It also tends to improve tensile and yield strengths of steel.

Lead is alloyed with steel to improve machinability. When finely divided and evenly distributed, it has no effect on the strength properties. It generally is used in amounts from 0.10% to 0.35%.

Sulfur is alloyed with steel in amounts from 0.05% to 0.33% to improve machinability. However, in larger amounts, sulfur is detrimental to the hot-working properties of steel, and thus it is detrimental for welding and forging purposes.

Silicon is used as a deoxidizer in steel production. It exists in many steels in small amounts, ranging from 0.10% to 0.40%. When the silicon is held within specified limits from 0.60% to 2.20%, the steel is considered an alloy steel and is called *silicon steel*.

Silicon may be alloyed alone or in combination with manganese or chromium in steel. In alloying amounts, silicon improves tensile strength, hardenability, elastic limit, and the electrical properties of steel. It also improves resiliency. The silicon steels often are used for cores in electrical machinery and for various types of springs.

Forms of Alloy Steel

Constructional Grades: Alloy steels of constructional grade generally are available from steel suppliers in the following standard bar shapes: squares, rounds, flats, hexagons, and octagons. Some grades are available in the form of structural members such as angles and channels. Certain grades also are available in the form of sheets, strip, and plate.

Alloy steels of constructional grade are used widely in producing forged machine parts of many kinds. Steels for forging purposes are available in the form of bars, billets, or in special forms. These steels are forged into machine parts such as: gear blanks, connecting rods, camshafts, crankshafts, piston pins, chisels, hammers, axes, wrenches, universal joints, and aircraft landing gears. The majority of these forgings must be machined and heat-treated after forging.

Tool Steels: Alloy tool steels are available in the form of standard bar shapes, including squares, rounds, octagons, hexagons, and flats. They also are available in special shapes for machining or forging applications.

The alloy tool steels generally are available with the following types of finish: hot-rolled, cold-drawn, rough-machined, ground, and ground and polished. They may be ordered in the as-rolled condition or in the annealed condition. Some suppliers will furnish these steels with heat treatment as ordered.

UNIT 148

Nonferrous Alloys

The Nature of Alloys

For commercial classification purposes, an alloy has been defined previously as a metallic substance composed of two or more metallic elements, one of which must be intentionally added. Alloys also may have nonmetallic substances included in their composition. Alloys generally are formed as either heterogeneous or homogeneous mixtures. They are composed largely of a base metal to which smaller amounts of one or more alloying elements have been added.

Alloys are manufactured to possess properties which otherwise are unobtainable in the pure base metal. Pure metals often are too soft, rust too easily, or lack other desirable properties. In contrast, alloys generally are harder, less ductile, and melt more easily than the pure base metal.

Alloys are usually produced by heating the base metal and the alloying elements to a molten state. Then they are mixed and allowed to cool to a solid. The speed of cooling affects the grain size in the alloy; the grain size, in turn, affects the properties of the alloy. Therefore, the speed of cooling sometimes is carefully controlled.

The grain size also is affected by heat-treatment processes, cold-rolling processes, hammering, and other cold-working processes. Hence, these processes also are used to control the properties of alloys.

An endless number of alloys is possible. When an alloying element is mixed in different proportions with a given base metal, different alloys result. Each alloy possesses properties somewhat different from other alloys. Two, three, four, or more alloying elements may be mixed with the base metal to produce a large number of alloys of one base metal. This is how the many copper alloys, aluminum alloys, and alloys of other types of metal were developed.

Alloys have a wide range of melting temperatures. Some melt at temperatures below that for boiling water (212° F.), while others melt at temperatures above 2750° F. When bismuth is alloyed with elements such as tin, lead, and cadmium, alloys are developed with a temperature range from about 117° to 440° F. Some types of stainless steel melt above 2800° F. The melting points of various metals and alloys are shown in Table 48, appendix.

Common Nonferrous Alloys

The general characteristics and some of the uses of several of the most important groups of nonferrous alloys are included in this unit. The most important groups of alloys are identified by the following headings, which indicate the base metal: copper, aluminum, zinc, magnesium, nickel, lead, tin, and special alloys.

A detailed explanation of specific properties of each alloy within each group is not within the scope of this book. Detailed information concerning the chemical composition, physical properties, and mechanical properties of these alloys is readily available in sources such as handbooks for machinists and handbooks of metals properties. Several sources of this type are listed in the bibliography located at the front of the book.

Copper-Base Alloys: Bronze is composed largely of copper and tin. Brass is composed basically of copper and zinc. Both of these alloys also may include a number of other alloying elements. Both bronze and brass commonly are referred to as copper alloys.

Bronze was one of the first alloys produced by man. It was used during the Bronze Age, about 3500 to 5000 years ago, to make hammers, hatchets, saws, chisels, files, and arrowheads. Tools such as these have been found and are on exhibit in museums. Some of the early copper alloys were alloyed with zinc, lead, and tin. The bronze thus formed was harder than any of the metals from which it was made.

Today there are more than 60 standard copper-base alloys, including both wrought and cast alloys. The principal alloying elements in these alloys are tin, zinc, and lead. However, small amounts of the following alloying elements also frequently are included: iron, phosphorous, antimony, aluminum, manganese, and nickel. Silver is alloyed with copper in several special copper alloys. The melting temperatures for various copper alloys may range from about 1300° to 1900° F., depending on the kind and amount of alloying elements.

Aluminum-Base Alloys: There are more than 60 common types of wrought- and cast-aluminum alloys used today. Within each of these types, there also may be several grades with different properties, depending on the kind of heat treatment employed. The tensile strength of aluminum, like that of most metals, is increased through the use of alloying elements and heat treatment. This property varies from about 13,000 pounds per square inch (psi) for soft, pure aluminum, to about 81,000 psi for special hardened alloys. The tensile strength for a number of common metals is shown in Table 30, appendix.

The characteristics of the specific aluminum alloys vary considerably. Each alloy is developed to possess special properties such as hardness, ductility, machinability, corrosion resistance, and weldability. The hardest aluminum alloys generally cannot be bent cold without breaking. However, the harder grades generally machine better. Some of the wrought-aluminum alloys have greater tensile strength than low-carbon steel, and they can be machined about three to four times faster.

The following elements are used as alloying elements in various aluminum alloys: copper, manganese, silicon, magnesium, zinc, iron, chromium, nickel, lead, bismuth, and titanium.

The melting temperatures for most aluminum alloys range from about 900° to 1215° F.

Zinc-Base Alloys: The zinc-base alloys are used widely in making die castings for items such as: engine blocks for small gas engines, housings for small engines, carburetors, automobile door handles, parts for typewriters, and many parts for electrical appliances. Zinc alloys also are available in the form of rolled products such as sheets. This material is used for items such as nameplates, weatherstrip, and photoengravings.

There are more than ten standard zinc-base alloys in common use. The following elements may be alloyed with zinc in producing these alloys: aluminum, and very small amounts of copper, magnesium, iron, lead, cadmium, and tin. The tensile strength for zinc alloys varies from about 25,000 to 47,000 psi, depending on the type of alloy. The melting temperatures of most zinc alloys range from about 727° to 787° F.

Magnesium-Base Alloys: Magnesium is noted particularly for its light weight. It is about two-thirds the weight of aluminum. Magnesium-base alloys are available in the form of sheets, wire, extruded bars, and ingots for casting.

The tensile strength of magnesium alloys may range from 12,000 psi for pure magnesium sand castings, to 50,000 psi for certain alloys which are used in extruded bars. Magnesium alloys often are used for making die castings. The tensile strength of common magnesium die-casting alloys ranges from about 30,000 to 37,000 psi.

The following elements are alloyed with magnesium in various magnesium alloys: aluminum, zinc, silicon, copper, nickel, manganese, tin, and iron. The melting temperatures for magnesium-base alloys range from about 860° to 1250° F.

Nickel-Base Alloys: There are about twenty or more nickel-base alloys. The nickel content in these may range from about 62% to 99%, depending on the particular alloy.

Nickel is a silver-colored metal, which is hard and tough. Its outstanding characteristic is its resistance to corrosion by weather, sea water, many chemicals, and a number of acids. (The five-cent coin which is called a *nickel* is a copper-base alloy composed of about three parts copper and one part nickel.)

Pure nickel is used for plating other metals. Alloys high in nickel content are used for chemical-handling equipment, and for other items which must resist the corrosive action of chemicals. *Monel* is a common nickel alloy composed of about 65% nickel and 30% copper. The remaining 5% includes small quantities of several other elements. Monel is used for items such as nonmagnetic parts of aircraft, valve stems, pump rods, and valves and pipes used in corrosive and chemical environments.

The alloying elements used in the nickel-base alloys include the following: copper, aluminum, iron, silicon, manganese, titanium, chromium, and tungsten. The melting temperatures of most nickel-base alloys range from 2350° to 2600° F.

Lead-Base Alloys: Pure lead is a very soft, heavy metal which has a low melting point of 621° F. It is so soft that it can be scratched with the fingernail. It resists corrosion by water, weather, and many chemicals. Lead may be alloyed with the following elements to improve its properties: tin, antimony, zinc, bismuth, silver, nickel arsenic, manganese, copper, and iron.

Lead and lead-base alloys are used to make several grades of soft solder, sheets and pipe to resist chemicals, storage batteries, covering for underground electrical wires, babbit for bearings, and similar uses. Soft solders often are made with 50% to 80% lead (depending on the grade), and the balance is largely tin. The solder may include very small amounts of other alloying elements, usually not exceeding more than about 1%.

Babbit is a lead-base alloy used for bearings. Several grades are available. A typical type of babbit has 15% antimony and 10% tin, with the remainder being largely lead. Small amounts of other elements may be included.

Tin-Base Alloys: Pure tin is a silvery-white metal which is relatively soft. It melts at about 449° F. It resists corrosion from weather and many foodstuffs. Tin frequently is used as a coating on steel in the production of tin-plate.

Tin may be alloyed with the following elements to acquire special properties: antimony, lead, zinc, silver, copper bismuth, and iron. Some of the principal tin-base alloys include tin solders, soft solders, tin-silver solders, and tin babbit.

A typical grade of tin solder has about 5% antimony, with the remainder being tin. Tin solders are used widely for containers which are in contact with foodstuffs. Solders with lead content usually are objectionable for this purpose. Tin foil is about 92% tin and 8% zinc. A typical type of tin-silver solder is about 95% tin and 5% silver. Several grades of tin babbit are available for use in making bearings. Tin babbit usually has from 80% to 90% tin, while the remaining content is largely lead and copper. Pewter is a tin-base alloy composed of about 92% tin and 8% antimony and copper. Pewter is used for ornamental objects.

Special Alloys: A number of alloys have been developed for special purposes. These special alloys sometimes are called *super alloys*, because of the special properties which they possess. Their properties usually are concerned with wear resistance and with maintaining strength at high temperatures. The special alloys are used for purposes such as the following: blades for gas turbines, ratchet components, conveyor mechanisms in large heat treating furnaces, wear plates on machines, and cutting tools used in the machining of metals.

The special alloys include two major classifications — the *wrought* alloys and the *cast* alloys. The special wrought alloys generally are not as hard as the cast alloys. The cast alloys are so hard that they usually are not machinable except by grinding. However, the special wrought alloys generally are very tough and difficult to machine with standard cutting tools. Hence they also are machined most frequently by grinding.

The special alloys generally are considered to be nonferrous alloys because they contain very little iron. Although some wrought alloys may include up to about 35% iron, the cast alloys usually contain much less. The cast alloys which are used for cutting tools contain no iron except that which exists in the raw materials used in their manufacture, usually less than 1%.

The principal alloying elements used to produce the various special alloys include the following: nickel, cobalt, molybdenum, tungsten, chromium, and iron. Small amounts of the following elements also may be included in the special alloys: carbon, manganese, silicon, titanium, columbium, aluminum, and tantalum.

For the machinist, a general understanding of the special cast alloys which are used for cutting tools is important. Some of the common trade names of cast alloy cutting tools include *Stellite*, *Rexalloy*, *Armaloy*, and *Tantung*. These materials are explained in greater detail in Unit 140.

Types of Cast Iron and Its Use

Cast iron gets its name from its principal use. Molten cast iron is poured into molds to form castings which are made into machinery parts. There are several basic types of cast iron, including gray cast iron, malleable cast iron, white cast iron, and ductile cast iron. Other special classes, which are subdivisions of the basic types, include alloy cast iron, chilled cast iron, and ferritic malleable and pearlitic malleable cast iron.

Cast iron is one of the most important products of the foundry industry. It is used to make many types of castings which range in weight from a few ounces to many tons. More than 15 million tons of cast iron castings are produced in the United States each year. The major output of many production machine shops is the machining of cast iron castings.

All types of cast iron are basically alloys of iron and carbon. Any iron-carbon alloy containing more than 1.7% carbon is cast iron. The carbon may range from 1.7% to 4.5%, but the more common range is from 2% to 4%, averaging 3.25%. Other elements totaling 2% to 5%, in varying amounts, include silicon, manganese, phosphorous, and sulfur. Minute quantities of other elements may exist in the form of impurities. Additional metallic elements sometimes are added to make an alloy which has special properties. The iron content of various types of cast iron may range from 91% to 97%.

Alloying Elements

The most important alloying elements in cast iron are carbon and silicon. Through their control, the properties of cast iron are largely determined.

Carbon: All types of cast iron contain more than 1.7% carbon, an amount in excess of that which will combine with iron to form steel. The carbon appears in cast iron in two forms. The *first* is free carbon, in the form of *graphite*. Graphite occurs in gray cast iron, malleable cast iron, and ductile cast iron. Examples of flakes or aggregates of graphite as they appear in three types of cast iron when viewed through a metallurgical microscope which magnifies 100 times are shown in Fig. 16-14.

The *second* form in which carbon appears in cast iron is as a chemically-combined carbon. In this form, the carbon combines chemically with iron to form *cementite*. Another name for cementite is iron carbide (Fe_3C). Cementite is a very hard substance, and, in large amounts, it makes ferrous metals hard to machine. Cementite exists in steel as well as cast iron.

Carbon exists in white cast iron in the combined form, as cementite. A photomicrograph of white cast iron, under very high magnification in Fig. 16-15, shows the light regions as *cementite* and the darker regions as *pearlite*. The pearlite is a form of steel which is made up of alternating layers of cementite and *ferrite*. The ferrite is nearly pure iron.

Since white cast iron has an extremely large proportion of cementite, it is virtually nonmachinable. It can be machined only by grinding. Consequently, control of the *form* of carbon in cast iron is important in controlling the properties of cast iron.

Silicon: A second alloying element which is important in controlling the properties of cast iron is silicon. It acts as a *graphitizer* in the production of cast iron. As such, silicon causes carbon to separate from iron

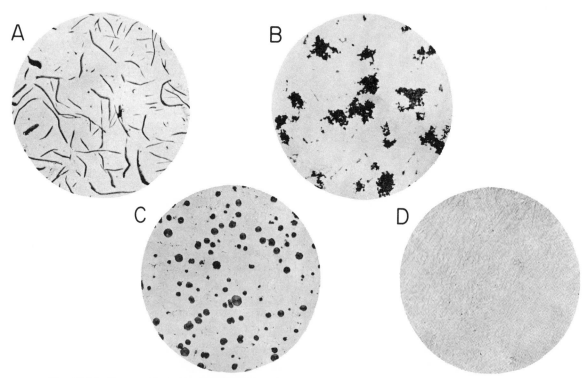

Fig. 16-14. Types of Cast Iron as Distinguished by Graphite Structure (100×) (Precision Scientific)
(A) Flake graphite in gray cast iron; **(B)** Temper carbon aggregates in malleable cast iron; **(C)** Speroidal graphite in ductile cast iron; **(D)** No free graphite in white cast iron.

more readily at elevated temperatures, thus forming flakes or globules of free graphite. This reduces the proportion of cementite formed, which, in turn, improves the machinability of the cast iron.

The opposite reaction takes place when silicon content in cast iron is reduced. A reduced amount of silicon, coupled with a reduced amount of carbon, causes an increased percentage of combined carbon or cementite. Advantage of this relationship is applied in the production of white cast iron. Most white cast iron is produced as a first step in the process of making malleable iron castings.

The properties and uses of various types of cast iron, therefore, depend largely on the form and relative amount of carbon content. The properties also may be modified by the addition of other alloying elements, by variations in casting procedures, and by heat-treatment processes.

The various types of cast iron generally are classified by their mechanical properties rather than their chemical compositions. This system is used because castings of varying chemical composition may be produced with similar mechanical properties (made possible by varying the casting procedures used). Also, castings of the same chemical composition may vary in mechanical properties because of the variation in casting, cooling, and heat-treatment procedures used. Hence, foundries can produce castings with specified properties by modification of either the *chemical composition* or the *casting and heat-treatment* procedures used.

Production of Cast Iron

Cast iron generally is produced in a *cupola* furnace. This type furnace resembles a blast furnace, but it is much smaller. Pig iron is charged into the furnace with coke, scrap cast iron, and limestone. Scrap steel also may be used in certain types of cast iron. An unheated air blast is used to support combustion of the coke. Although some refining may take place, the primary purpose of the furnace is to melt the pig iron and scrap material. The molten metal flows to the bottom of the furnace. When sufficient iron is melted, the furnace is tapped, and the molten iron is drawn

off in a ladle. It is then poured into sand molds to form castings.

The furnace may be operated continuously by recharging the materials as the iron is melted and drawn off. Scrap steel sometimes is used as an aid in controlling the carbon content of the iron. The molten metal tends to pick up additional carbon from the coke which is used as fuel.

Gray Cast Iron

Gray cast iron is so named because of the characteristic gray color at its fracture. This color appears because of the excess carbon content which is in the form of flakes. Gray cast iron contains from 1.7% to 4.5% carbon, usually averaging about 3.25%. The silicon content may vary from 1% to 3%. Other elements, totaling from 1% to 2%, include manganese, sulfur, and phosphorous.

Gray iron contains excess carbon in the form of graphite flakes, as in Fig. 16-14A. The graphite is supported in a matrix or envelope of iron or steel. Low-strength gray iron usually has a matrix composed largely of ferrite, which is nearly pure iron. High-strength gray iron usually has a matrix composed largely of pearlite, which is a form of steel.

Properties and Uses: As it is cast, gray iron is relatively brittle. When fractured, cracks generally follow along the line of the graphite flakes. The flakes form sharp cavities which enable the cast iron to

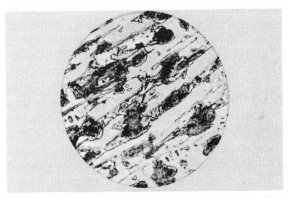

Fig. 16-15. Fine Pearlite (Dark Area) and Iron Carbide Known as Cementite (Light Area) in White Cast iron (500×) (Precision Scientific)

563

fracture easily. From a strength standpoint, the free graphite flakes contribute nothing, except to reduce strength. Gray cast iron also lacks ductility and malleability. However, these properties may be improved by various methods of heat treatment.

Gray iron must be cast or machined to shape. It has good machinability, due to the flakes of free graphite. The graphite acts as a lubricant for cutting tools, and it enables the machined chips to fracture and escape easily from the edge of cutting tools. Gray iron is a relatively inexpensive metal which is cast easily into many intricate shapes without the problems which arise in making steel castings.

There are many uses for gray cast iron. It is used chiefly for parts which do not require toughness or extremely high tensile strength, such as foundation bases for machinery, pistons, engine blocks, various structural parts on farm machinery, and similar machinery parts.

Grades: Gray iron is available in seven standard grades established by American Society for Testing Materials (ASTM). The grades are identified by numbers which represent the tensile strength, such as No. 20 for 20,000 psi, and No. 25 for 25,000 psi. The tensile strength for the seven grades range from 20,000 psi to 65,000 psi. Seven standard grades for automotive gray iron castings also have been established. Specifications for the various grades of gray iron are included in standard handbooks for machinists. In the selection of gray iron for castings, it should be remembered that with the higher hardness and tensile strengths, brittleness is increased and machinability generally is decreased.

Alloy Cast Iron

The mechanical properties of cast iron may be modified by the addition of small amounts of certain alloying elements, such as: nickel, silicon, chromium, vanadium, molybdenum, and copper. Alloyed castings are used widely in the automobile industry. Toughness, strength, and hardness are increased by the addition of the proper alloying elements.

Alloy castings have been developed which have tensile strengths up to 100,000 psi. Some of their uses include brake drums, plow shares, forging dies, piston rings, and similar items requiring high strength.

White Cast Iron

White cast iron is so named because of the silvery-white appearance of its surface where fractured. It has practically no free carbon. Rather the carbon is in the form of cementite, as in Figs. 16-14D and 16-15. Since cementite is an extremely hard substance, white cast iron is very hard and virtually nonmachinable, except by grinding.

Types and Uses: The direct use of white cast iron is limited to castings requiring hard wear surfaces, such as rolls used in rolling steel. The major use of white cast iron applies to *malleable iron* castings; the first step in their production is the production of white cast iron castings.

White cast iron may be produced accidentally when gray iron castings are cooled too rapidly. When this occurs, the casting may harden in spots, to a surface depth only, or throughout, depending on the rate of cooling. Hard spots of white cast iron so formed in gray iron castings are difficult to machine and can cause damage to cutting tools. Through careful annealing or other forms of heat treatment, the castings may be machined readily.

Chilled Cast Iron: Chilled cast iron is a term used for gray iron castings which have a very hard, wear-resistant surface layer of white cast iron. It is produced by rapid cooling of the outer surface of gray iron as it is poured into molds. The molds may be metal, or they may be equipped with metal chill plates. Such rapid cooling causes cementite to form, thus producing the hard, white cast iron surface.

Malleable Cast Iron

White cast iron can be converted to malleable cast iron by a heat-treatment process called *malleablizing*. The process involves *graphitization*, the reduction of carbon from its combined form as cementite (Figs. 16-14D and 16-15) to free carbon in the form of aggregates which are called *temper carbon* (Fig. 16-14B).

At high temperatures, the carbon combined to form cementite in white cast iron breaks down to form iron and free carbon. The carbon becomes rounded aggregates, while the soft iron forms a matrix around these aggregates. This new material is malleable iron, with properties very different from white cast iron or gray iron.

Malleablization: White cast-iron castings are malleablized by first placing them in a heat-resistant cast-iron container. The container then is placed in a furnace and gradually is heated to about 1650° F., for a period of about 50 hours. The temperature then is reduced, slowly cooling the castings during a period of about 60 hours. This completes the process. The castings are removed from the container, malleablized and annealed. They are relatively soft.

Malleable castings have many of the tough characteristics of steel. They possess good ductility, strength, and machinability. There are several standard types of malleable cast iron, and each type has several standard grades. The properties vary according to the type and grade. When greater ductility and malleability are desired, softer grades are selected. However, these grades have lower tensile strength. The various grades of malleable cast iron may be classified according to two major types — *ferritic* and *pearlitic*.

Ferritic Type: The physical grain structure of ferritic or standard malleable cast iron is largely ferrite surrounding the temper carbon. Ferrite is nearly pure iron. Hence, ferritic iron ranks high in ductility, impact resistance, and malleability. The following is the average range of properties for ferritic or standard grades of malleable cast iron: tensile strength, 50,000 to 55,000 psi; minimum yield point, 32,000 to 35,000 psi; and elongation, 10% to 18% in 2″.

Pearlitic Type: The malleablization method used in the production of pearlitic malleable cast iron is modified somewhat from that used for ferritic malleable iron. The graphitization process is stopped before all of the carbon has broken down into free temper-carbon aggregates. As a result, some cementite remains to form a mechanical mixture with the ferrite. The mixture thus formed is pearlite, which surrounds the aggregates of temper carbon. With an increased proportion of pearlite, the cast iron becomes harder. It also increases in tensile strength and becomes more difficult to machine.

Pearlitic malleable cast iron is harder, less ductile, and has higher tensile strength than the ferritic type. The following are the average ranges for the properties of the several grades of pearlitic malleable cast iron: tensile strength 65,000 to 100,000 psi, and elongation 2% to 10% in 2″.

Uses: Malleable cast iron usually is limited to castings of small cross section. This is due to the need for rapid cooling of the initial white iron castings in the first step of making the malleable cast iron. Its properties enable it to be used for purposes which otherwise would require steel. It is useful for auto parts such as gear housings, camshafts, differential housings, and brake pedals. It also is useful for many types of machinery parts.

Ductile Cast Iron

Ductile cast iron also is known as *nodular* cast iron or *spheroidal graphite* iron. Its distinguishing feature is that it contains free carbon in ball-like form as shown in Fig. 16-14C. Each nodule of graphite is surrounded by a matrix of ferrite, or ferrite and pearlite, depending on the grade.

Ductile iron is produced by adding magnesium alloys, and sometimes certain other elements, to a ladle of molten gray iron before it is poured into molds. The additional elements, together with special processing, causes the carbon to form as nodular graphite during the solidification and cooling process.

Grades and Uses: There are several grades of ductile cast iron. This type of cast iron may be heat-treated for further modification of its properties. Hence, there is a wide range of variation in its properties and uses.

The properties of ductile cast iron lie in a range between gray cast iron and steel. Basically, ductile cast iron is tough, shock-resistant, high in tensile strength, and easily machined.

The basic properties for several standard grades of ductile cast iron have a broad range. The tensile strength varies from 60,000 to 80,000 psi. The elongation varies from 3% to 10% in 2″. The tensile strength also can be increased to 100,000 psi by heat treatment. Hence, properties similar to pearlitic malleable cast iron can be obtained.

Various forms of heat treatment may be applied to ductile iron, including annealing, hardening, induction hardening, and flame hardening. Of course, as the hardness and tensile strength are increased, there is a corresponding decrease in ductility and impact or shock resistance.

Ductile cast iron has many uses in modern industry. It is used in the automobile industry for cylinder heads, crankshafts, camshafts, pistons, and similar parts. It is also used for control levers on heavy machinery, clamps, wrenches, lathe chuck bodies, and for numerous parts on farm machinery.

Semisteel

Semisteel is a term which has been used for cast iron which includes a high percentage of scrap steel. The use of this term should be discouraged. Cast iron with a high percentage of scrap steel has properties closely related to the properties of steel castings.

Test Your Knowledge of Section 16

Unit 141: Classification of Metals
1. Why were alloy metals developed?
2. Why is it important to understand how alloys form?
3. Why are metals heat-treated?
4. How can one distinguish between metallic and nonmetallic materials?
5. Explain the difference between ferrous and nonferrous metals.
6. Explain the meaning of an alloy, as the term is used in the commercial classification of metals. List several examples of alloy metals.
7. Explain the meaning of ferrous alloys. List several examples.
8. Explain the meaning of nonferrous alloys. List several examples.
9. Explain the difference between atoms and molecules.
10. Define a mixture, and list the forms in which it can exist.
11. Define a solution, and list the forms in which it can exist.
12. Explain how an alloy can form as a solid solution.
13. Explain the difference between a solid solution and a mechanical mixture.
14. Name an alloy which is formed as a combination of three forms of matter.

Unit 142: The Properties of Metals
1. Why have so many different metals been developed?
2. List several properties which are considered in the selection of a metal for a particular use.
3. List several occupations in which a knowledge of the properties of metals would be valuable.
4. Explain the meaning of chemical properties as applied to metals.
5. Explain the meaning of physical properties as applied to metals.
6. Explain the meaning of mechanical properties as applied to metals.
7. Explain the difference between hardness and hardenability of metals.
8. What is meant by ductility of metals?
9. Define malleability as applied to metals.
10. Define toughness as applied to metals.
11. What is meant by the machinability of metals?
12. List four types of strength possessed by metals.
13. What is the difference between the yield strength and the tensile strength of a metal?
14. Explain the meaning of elongation as applied to tensile strength tests.

15. Explain the meaning of reduction in area, as applied to tensile strength tests.
16. Explain the meaning of stress, as a property of metals.
17. Explain the meaning of strain, as a property of metals.
18. List three general types of stress which may be applied to a structural member.
19. Explain the meaning of elastic limit, as applied to a structural member.
20. Explain the meaning of fatigue, as applied to a structural part on a machine.
21. List the chemical symbols for the following metallic elements: aluminum, chromium, iron, manganese, molybdenum, nickel, tungsten, and vanadium.
22. List the melting points for the following metals: wrought iron, carbon steel, cast iron, bronze, aluminum, lead, and tin.

Unit 143: The Production of Iron and Its Use
1. What are the basic ingredients in steel?
2. From what source is iron acquired for making steel?
3. What are the ingredients in iron ore?
4. Approximately how much iron ore is required to make a ton of iron?
5. Where are some of the most important iron ore mines located?
6. What raw materials are required to make iron in a blast furnace?
7. List five types of furnaces used in making iron or steel.
8. Describe the general shape of a blast furnace.
9. Explain how iron is made in a blast furnace.
10. What is done with the iron which is drawn from a blast furnace?
11. What raw materials are required to make one ton of iron in a blast furnace?
12. What ingredients, other than iron, exist in the iron which is drawn from a blast furnace?

Unit 144: How Steel Is Made
1. How do the properties of steel differ from the properties of pig iron?
2. Explain the process of steelmaking in its simplest terms.

3. By what basic process are the impurities removed from iron in a steelmaking furnace?
4. How are the ingredients controlled in the process of making steel?
5. List four types of furnaces which are used in making steel.
6. Describe an open-hearth furnace, including shape, size, and its significance.
7. What raw materials are used in an open-hearth furnace?
8. What purpose is served when a stream of oxygen blows over the molten steel in an open-hearth furnace?
9. By what basic process are the impurities removed from the molten metal in an open-hearth furnace?
10. What purpose does the limestone serve in an open-hearth furnace?
11. What impurities are removed from the molten metal in an open-hearth furnace?
12. Why are test samples of the molten steel made before pouring the steel from the furnace?
13. Explain how oxidation takes place in removing impurities from molten metal in a bessemer converter.
14. Describe the general shape and construction of a bessemer converter.
15. What steelmaking process gradually is replacing the bessemer process?
16. List several ways in which the basic oxygen process (BOP) differs from the bessemer process.
17. List several types of steel which are made in an electric furnace.
18. Describe the basic structure of an electric furnace.
19. List several advantages of the electric furnace process for making steel.
20. What materials are generally charged into an electric furnace to make steel?
21. Describe a steel ingot.
22. What is the purpose of a soaking pit in steelmaking?
23. Describe how steel is rolled into various shapes.
24. What steel products are produced from blooms?

25. What steel products are produced from billets?
26. What steel products are produced from slabs?
27. Explain the basic difference between hot-rolled steel and cold-rolled steel.
28. List several uses for steel castings.
29. Why are steel castings sometimes used in place of cast iron castings?

Unit 145: Plain Carbon Steels

1. What are the basic ingredients in plain carbon steels?
2. What steels are classified as alloy steels?
3. Describe commercially pure iron.
4. What are the properties of commercially pure iron?
5. What materials are used to make wrought iron?
6. What are the properties of wrought iron?
7. What material has largely replaced wrought iron?
8. List several uses for wrought iron.
9. Describe a modern method for making wrought iron.
10. Why is carbon one of the most important elements alloyed with iron to form steel?
11. How is the amount of carbon content in steel expressed?
12. What is the tensile strength of commercially pure iron?
13. What relationship exists between the carbon content and the tensile strength of steel in the unhardened condition?
14. Calculate the tensile strength of unhardened carbon steel with 70-point carbon content.
15. What element in steel largely determines the hardness which can be obtained through heat treatment?
16. What properties are changed in steel when it is hardened by heat treatment?
17. Determine the approximate tensile strength of steel which has a Brinell hardness of 240.
18. What steels are classified as plain carbon steels?
19. What is the range of carbon content for plain carbon steels?

20. What properties are influenced in steel when the carbon content is significantly larger?
21. List the three basic groups of carbon steel, and indicate the range of carbon content for each group.
22. List several uses for low-carbon steels.
23. List the properties of medium-carbon steels.
24. List several uses for medium-carbon steels.
25. What hardness is obtainable when SAE 1045 steel, a medium-carbon steel, is hardened by quenching in water?
26. What is the range of carbon content for high-carbon steels of constructional grade?
27. What is the range of carbon content for high-carbon tool steels?
28. What hardness values are obtainable when high-carbon steels are hardened?
29. What hardness value generally is required for metal-cutting tools?
30. What purpose is served in increasing the carbon content beyond 0.80% in carbon steel?
31. What quenching mediums generally are used to harden carbon steels?
32. List several uses for constructional grades of high-carbon steel.
33. List several uses for high-carbon tool steel.
34. What source may be used to find additional information concerning tool and die steels?
35. List several grades of carbon tool steel.
36. In what forms or shapes is high-carbon tool steel available?
37. How does the cost of high-carbon tool steel compare with that of cold-drawn low-carbon steel?
38. How does the addition of sulfur affect the machinability of steel?
39. For what purposes are resulfurized screw steels widely used?
40. Explain how lead is used to improve the machinability of steel.
41. List several shortcomings or disadvantages of resulfurized steels.
42. What are the machining characteristics of resulfurized and leaded steels?

Unit 146: Steel Classification and Identification

1. List several instances where SAE or AISI code numbers are used to classify types of steel.
2. Explain the SAE and AISI code number systems used to classify the standard constructional grades of steel.
3. In what way is the AISI code number system different than the SAE system?
4. List the basic types of steel which usually are represented by the first digit of the SAE number code for steel.
5. Explain how the carbon content for steel is designated in the SAE and AISI steel code.
6. Explain the chemical content and method of manufacture of AISI C1020 steel.
7. What determines the difference between two different *series* of steel within a basic type of alloy steels?
8. What does the letter *H* designate when used with the SAE or AISI steel code number?
9. What two factors must be known when identifying steel by color code?
10. Why should stock be cut from the unpainted end of a steel bar?
11. Explain how steel can be identified by a spark test.
12. How does the amount of carbon in steel affect the type of spark produced in a spark test?

Unit 147: Alloy Steels

1. List several types of alloy steels.
2. What types of steel are classified as alloy steel?
3. Describe three of the most important properties which are developed through the addition of alloying elements in steel.
4. Why are alloy steels often selected in preference to carbon steels for certain applications?
5. How does the cost of alloy steel compare with the cost of plain carbon steel?
6. List three basic categories of alloy steel.
7. What are some uses of alloy steel of constructional grade?
8. What is the range of alloy content in alloy steels of constructional grade?
9. List several uses for alloy tool steels.

10. What is the range of alloy content in alloy tool steels?
11. List six classifications for tool and die steels.
12. In what source can you find information concerning tool and die steels?
13. Give an example of the use of a special alloy steel.
14. About how many different alloying elements are used in various alloy steels?
15. How does carbon content affect the properties of steel?
16. How does nickel content affect steel?
17. List several uses for nickel steels.
18. List several uses for nickel-chrome steels.
19. How does chromium content affect steel?
20. How does molybdenum content affect steel?
21. List several alloying elements which may be alloyed with molybdenum in steel.
22. How does vanadium content affect steel?
23. List several uses for chromium-vanadium steels.
24. List several uses for high-speed steels.
25. How does tungsten content affect steel?
26. Why are carbide cutting tools called cemented carbide?
27. What is the outstanding characteristic of cobalt?
28. List three types of cutting-tool material in which cobalt is used.
29. How does lead content affect steel?
30. How does sulfur content affect steel?
31. In what forms or shapes are alloy steels of constructional grade available?
32. In what forms or shapes are alloy tool steels available?

Unit 148: Nonferrous Alloys

1. Explain the meaning of *alloy* as used in classifying metals commercially.
2. Why were alloy metals produced?
3. Explain how alloys are produced.
4. What properties are generally improved when a base metal is alloyed with other alloying elements?
5. List several factors which affect the grain size in alloy metals.
6. About how many different alloys are possible with a given base metal? Why?

7. List one alloy with a very low melting point and one with a high melting point.
8. List several suggested sources from which one can acquire detailed information about specific alloys within any alloy group.
9. When were the copper-base alloys first used?
10. What are the principal alloying elements which are alloyed with copper to form copper-base alloys?
11. What is the approximate range of melting temperatures for copper-base alloys?
12. Approximately how many common types of aluminum alloys are available?
13. Define the meaning of tensile strength as applied to metals.
14. What is the range of tensile strength for various aluminum alloys?
15. How does the tensile strength of the strongest aluminum alloys compare with that of low-carbon steel?
16. List several elements which are alloyed with aluminum in producing aluminum alloys.
17. List several uses for zinc-base alloys.
18. What is the range of tensile strength for zinc-base alloys?
19. What is the principal property of magnesium?
20. List the tensile strength range and the melting temperature range for magnesium alloys.
21. What are the principal characteristics of nickel-base alloys?

Unit 149: Types of Cast Iron and Its Use
1. List four basic types of cast iron.
2. Approximately how many tons of cast iron castings are produced in the United States each year?
3. What is the approximate range of carbon content which may exist in cast iron?
4. What elements, other than carbon, exist in cast iron?
5. What two alloying elements are most important in controlling the properties of cast iron?

6. In what types of cast iron does free carbon exist?
7. What is cementite?
8. How does cementite affect the machinability of ferrous metals?
9. How is white cast iron machined?
10. Explain how increased silicon content helps in controlling the properties of cast iron.
11. What use is made of most white cast iron?
12. List several additional ways in which the properties of cast iron may be modified or changed.
13. Why is cast iron generally classified according to its mechanical properties rather than by chemical properties?
14. Explain the type of furnace and the process which generally is used to produce iron for castings.
15. Explain the characteristics and properties of gray cast iron.
16. How does the graphite in gray iron affect its machinability?
17. List several uses for gray cast iron.
18. Explain the code-number system used to identify the standard grades of gray cast iron.
19. Why are alloying elements sometimes included in cast iron?
20. What are the properties and uses of white cast iron?
21. Explain how white cast iron may be produced accidentally in the casting process.
22. Describe chilled cast iron and explain several of its uses.
23. Explain how malleable cast iron is produced.
24. What are the characteristics and properties of malleable cast iron?
25. Explain the characteristics and properties of ferritic malleable cast iron.
26. Explain the characteristics and properties of pearlitic malleable cast iron.
27. List some typical applications of malleable cast iron.
28. Describe the most distinguishing characteristic of ductile cast iron.
29. Explain the properties of ductile cast iron.
30. List several uses for ductile cast iron.
31. Explain the meaning of semisteel castings.

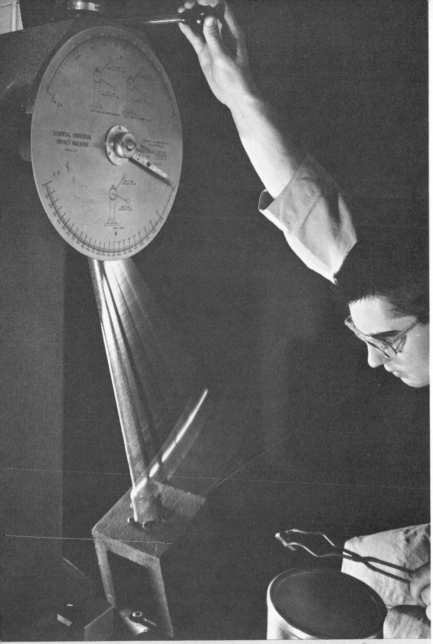

Impact Testing — Destruction with a Purpose
(U. S. Steel)

Basic Metallurgy and Heat Treatment of Steel

This section includes nine units concerning introductory metallurgy and heat-treatment processes commonly used in industry. A knowledge of Units 150, 155, and the first part of Unit 156 will enable the beginning student to harden, temper, and caseharden steel satisfactorily. With this limited study, however, the average student will not understand the metallurgical theory underlying these heat-treatment processes. For the more advanced student who wishes to understand the metallurgical theory involved in heat-treatment processes, the units in this section should be studied in the order in which they are presented.

Introduction to Heat Treatment

Heat-treatment processes involve heating and cooling of metals, in their solid state, for the purpose of changing their mechanical properties. Depending on the heat-treatment procedure used, steel may be made hard and wear-resistant, or it may be made soft, so that it can be machined easily.

Heat Treatment and Metallurgy

The theory underlying heat treatment of metals is actually one phase of the study of metallurgy. With such a basic knowledge, one can better understand the internal changes which take place in metals during heat-treatment operations. The science of *metallurgy* is a broad field. It includes the study of how metals are extracted from ores, how metals are refined, and how they are processed for various applications.

In the study of heat treatment, we are most concerned with the branch of metallurgy called *physical metallurgy* — i.e., the physical and mechanical properties of metals, which are affected by composition, mechanical working, and heat treatment. It includes study of both the internal grain structure of metals and the properties which are affected by changes in the grain structure. Heat-treatment processes affect the grain structure and the mechanical properties of metals. Metals may be made harder, stronger, tougher, or even softer through various heat-treatment processes.

Tools such as drills, milling cutters, punches, and dies possess properties which enable them to cut other metals. The materials used to produce cutting tools and other machined parts are selected because of the properties which they possess or because of the properties which they are *capable* of possessing after heat treatment. The type of steel and its chemical analysis must be known before it is heat-treated. Small amounts of certain elements, particularly the carbon content, greatly affect the properties after heat treatment.

Occupations in Heat Treatment: In modern production machine shops, heat-treating operations generally are performed by workers called *heat-treaters*. However, machinists and toolmakers frequently must perform these operations on tools, dies, and special parts which they make. Often maintenance machinists also are called upon to perform heat-treatment operations on parts which they make or repair. Consequently, the machinist should have an understanding of heat-treatment processes and procedures.

Workers in other occupational groups who frequently must possess a knowledge of heat-treatment processes include the following: tool designers, tool engineers, mechanical engineers, metallurgists, metal technicians, welders, and heat-treaters.

Heat-Treatment Processes

Although the properties of nonferrous metals may be changed by heat-treatment processes, the content in this section of the book is limited to the heat treatment of ferrous metals. The common processes used with steel and cast iron are included, the most common being hardening, tempering, and annealing.

Hardening and Tempering: The hardness of certain types of steel may be increased greatly by the heat-treatment process called *hardening*. For example, before they can be used, the cold chisel, punch, file, and milling cutter must be hardened after being machined. However, after hardening, these tools are too brittle for immediate use. They must be further heat-treated by a process called *tempering* (or drawing) to relieve internal stresses produced in the steel during the hardening process. Tempering also increases toughness. Thus, a chisel which has been hardened and tempered withstands heavy blows when used to cut other metals. Hardening and tempering will be explained in greater detail later in this section.

Annealing: Hardened steel may be softened by a heat-treatment process called *annealing*. Before high-carbon tool steel may be machined efficiently, it usually must be annealed. Annealing, therefore, is the opposite of hardening. This process also will be discussed in greater detail later.

Understanding the Processes: Hardening, tempering, and annealing include only three heat-treatment processes; numerous others often are used on steel and cast iron products. All heat-treatment processes consist of heating metal according to a *time-temperature cycle* which includes the following three steps:

1. Heating the metal to a certain temperature.
2. Holding the metal at an elevated temperature (soaking) for a certain period of time.
3. Cooling the metal at a certain rate.

During the above three steps, the properties of iron or steel may be altered in various ways,

depending on its chemical content. These operations generally alter the internal structure of the iron or steel in some way.

It is possible for the average metalworker to obtain satisfactory results in heat-treating steel, even though he does not understand the *metallurgical* theory related to heat treatment. However, it is necessary to follow the correct procedures. By following the procedures outlined in Unit 155, one may harden and temper steel with satisfactory results. The procedure there explains how to select the hardening temperature, how long to soak the steel at the hardening temperature, how to select the quenching media, and how to quench the steel for hardening.

Skilled workers engaged in the designing, machining, and heat-treating of metal products, however, often are required to possess an understanding of the basic metallurgical theory related to heat treatment. Knowledge of the following factors is essential for understanding the metallurgical theory related to heat treatment: grain structures of steel, effect of temperature changes on grain structures, effect of carbon content on obtainable hardness, effect of temperature changes on the form of carbon in steel, effect of the severity of the quench on grain structure and hardness, and effect of tempering on the toughness of steel. The metallurgical theory underlying these factors is included in the next four units of this section.

In addition to the processes and procedures which are included in succeeding units, the equipment used in the operations and the methods for determining the hardness of metals also are included in the various units of this section.

Furnaces and Temperature Control

Metal parts are heated in special furnaces during heat-treatment processes. The furnaces may be heated with gas, oil, or electricity. Modern heat-treatment furnaces usually are equipped with indicating and control devices which maintain temperature within a few degrees of that selected. The control device turns the fuel or current on and off intermittently, as necessary to maintain a constant temperature at a predetermined setting.

Temperature-indicating and control devices usually consist of an indicating pyrometer and certain accessory switches, valves, or solenoids. The pyrometer actuates the accessory parts as necessary to control the fuel or current which heats the furnace. The type of temperature device shown in Fig. 17-1 often is used to control temperatures in gas heat-treatment furnaces (Fig. 17-2).

Indicating Pyrometer: A pyrometer, as shown in Fig. 17-3, indicates the temperature inside a furnace or a molten liquid bath. It consists of a temperature indicator and a thermocouple which are connected together. When the temperature indicator is located some distance from the furnace, lead wires are used to connect the indicator with the thermocouple, as shown in Fig. 17-4. An indicating pyrometer indicates temperatures only, since it is not designed to actuate the accessory switches or valves required to control temperatures.

Thermocouple: A thermocouple is the heat-sensing device which forms part of a pyrometer. It is made up of two wires which are dissimilar metals. These are welded together at one end to form a *hot junction*. The opposite ends are connected to the indicator. Some installations require lead wires as shown in Fig. 17-4.

When the hot junction of the thermocouple is heated, a very small amount of electrical energy is developed. The voltage developed is very low and is measured in millivolts; it increases in proportion with the increase in temperature. Hence, a pyrometer is actually a millivolt meter. However, since the purpose is to measure temperatures, the graduations on the pyrometer are marked as equivalent temperatures at the hot junction of the thermocouple.

A thermocouple generally is inserted in a protective tube to prevent oxidation or damage. The tube is made of a refractory material

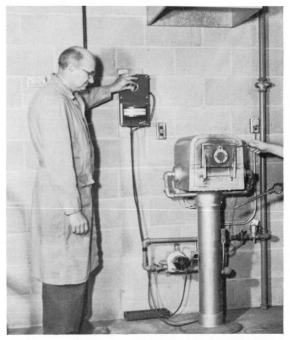

Fig. 17-2. Gas-Fired Heat-Treatment Furnace Equipped with Indicating Temperature Controls
(Johnson Gas Appliance)

Fig. 17-1. Temperature-Indicating and Control Equipment for Gas Heat-Treatment Furnace
(Johnson Gas Appliance)

Fig. 17-3. Pyrometer (Johnson Gas Appliance)

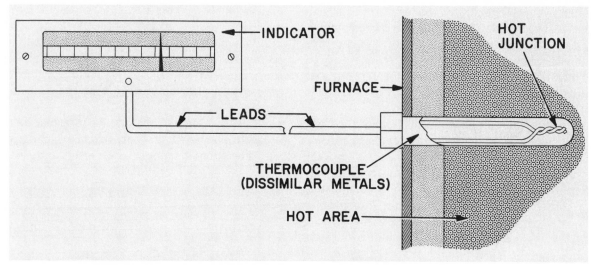

Fig. 17-4. Pyrometer Indicates Temperature Inside Furnace

Fig. 17-5. Electric Heat-Treatment Furnace with
Temperature-Indicating Control Unit (Thermolyne)

which will withstand high temperatures. Since the tube is quite brittle, it should not be bumped when placing parts in the furnace.

Types of Furnaces: The electrical furnace in Fig. 17-5 may be used for hardening, tempering, and other heat-treatment operations. It is equipped with temperature-indicating and control equipment which automatically regulates temperatures selected in the range from 300° to 2300° F.

The hardening furnace at the left in Fig. 17-6 is equipped with an air blower which supports combustion. The furnace is used for hardening carbon and high-speed steels in the

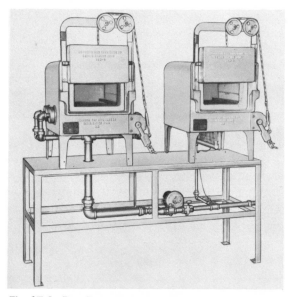

Fig. 17-6. Duo Furnace Unit (Johnson Gas Appliance)
(Left) Hardening Furnace; (Right) Drawing or
Tempering Furnace

temperature range from 1300° to 2350° F. The drawing furnace on the right is equipped with atmospheric burner tips under the hearth plate. This furnace may be used for all tempering operations from about 400° to 1150° F. Furnaces such as these usually are equipped with temperature-control units which are mounted on a wall or in a convenient location near the furnace.

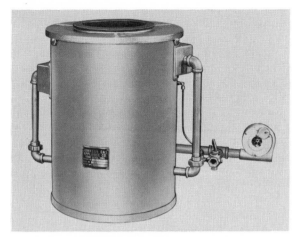

Fig. 17-7. Pot-Type Liquid Hardening Furnace
(Johnson Gas Appliance)

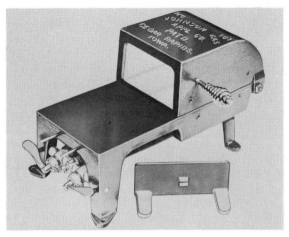

Fig. 17-8. Bench Gas Furnace (Johnson Gas Appliance)

Metals may be heated for certain hardening operations in hot, liquid baths. Parts heated in this manner are not in contact with air at elevated temperatures. Thus oxidation or scaling is reduced or prevented. Commonly used liquid baths include molten salts of various types and molten lead.

Parts which are casehardened by a process called *cyaniding* are heated in a bath of molten cyanide-carbonate-chloride salts. The parts then are quenched in water, brine, or mineral oil. A pot-type liquid hardening furnace which may be used for salt, lead, and cyanide baths is shown in Fig. 17-7. A unit which controls the temperature of the liquid bath usually is located conveniently near the furnace.

A small bench-type gas furnace, as shown in Fig. 17-8, may be used for hardening and tempering small tools or parts. A bunsen burner also is useful for tempering very small tools or parts. However, since there is usually no means for controlling temperatures with a bench furnace or bunsen burner, the temperature of the tool or part must be estimated according to its color.

Temperature Colors

When clean, bright steel is heated to about 380° F., its color starts to change. First, a very pale yellow appears. With further increases in temperature, other colors emerge. The approximate colors of steel at various temperatures

Fig. 17-9. Temperature-Indicating Products:
Pellets, Crayons, and Liquid (Tempil°)

are shown in Figs. 17-26 and 17-29, and in Table 23.

Old-time blacksmiths and heat-treaters often determined the temperature of steel by its color. However, this is not a very accurate method, even for skilled heat-treaters. For example, estimates within the tempering range from 375° to 600° may easily be off 20° to 30°. Steel appears dull red at about 1000° F. At higher red-heat temperatures, estimates based on color may be in error as much as several hundred degrees.

An inexpensive method for estimating temperatures of metals is through the use of temperature-indicating pellets, crayons, or paints, as shown in Fig. 17-9. These materials are designed to melt at various temperatures, as specified, within the range from about 100° to 2500° F. One simply selects the crayon or other material for the temperature desired and marks the workpiece; the material melts when the specified temperature is reached.

Table 23
Temperatures, Steel Colors and Related Processes

Colors	Fahrenheit	Centigrade	Processes
White	2500°	1371°	Welding
	2400°	1315°	High Speed Steel Hardening (2150-2450 F)
Yellow White	2300°	1259°	
	2200°	1204°	
	2100°	1149°	
Yellow	2000°	1093°	
	1900°	1036°	
Orange Red	1800°	981°	Alloy Tool Steel Hardening (1500-1950 F)
	1700°	926°	
	1600°	871°	
Light Cherry Red	1500°	815°	Carbon Tool Steel Hardening (1350-1550 F)
Cherry Red	1400°	760°	
	1300°	704°	
Dark Red	1200°	648°	
	1100°	593°	High Speed Steel Tempering (1000-1100 F)
Very Dark Red	1000°	538°	
	900°	482°	
Black Red in dull light or darkness	800°	426°	Carbon Tool Steel Tempering (300-1050 F)
	700°	371°	
Pale Blue (590 F)	600°	315°	
Violet (545 F) Purple (525 F)	500°	260°	
Yellowish Brown (490 F) Dark Straw (465 F)	400°	204°	
Light Straw (425 F)	300°	149°	
	200°	93°	
	100°	38°	
	0°	18°	

Heat Colors — White through Black Red in dull light or darkness

Temper Colors — Pale Blue (590 F), Violet (545 F), Purple (525 F), Yellowish Brown (490 F), Dark Straw (465 F), Light Straw (425 F)

Steel loses its magnetism when heated above temperatures indicated by line A_2 in Fig. 17-24. Hence, a magnet may be used for estimating temperatures required for hardening or annealing medium- or high-carbon steels.

Hardness Designations

In most heat-treatment operations, the hardness of the metal must meet the specifications designated. The hardness of steel and other metals may be indicated by hardness numbers according to several different hardness number systems. The most commonly used systems include: Rockwell C scale, Rockwell B scale, Brinell hardness numbers, and Shore Scleroscope hardness numbers. When the hardness is designated according to one of these number systems, it may be converted to an approximate reading in any of the other equivalent hardness number values by reading horizontally across Table 34, appendix. The method for determining the hardness of metals is included in Unit 158.

Grain Structure of Steel

Metals in the solid state have an internal crystalline structure. The *crystals* in commercial metals are called *grains*. They are formed as the metal cools and changes from a liquid to a solid state. This change in state is called *freezing*. Thus, metals freeze at high temperatures to form a solid, just as water freezes at a lower temperature to form a solid.

The rolled or cast surface of metal does not indicate its internal grain structure. However, when the metal is fractured, the surface shows a crystalline or granular structure. The grains in various metals may vary considerably in size. In some metals, the grains may be seen with the unaided eye. In other metals, they cannot be seen without magnification.

Using a Metallurgical Microscope

The grain structure of metals may be observed through a high-powered metallurgical microscope. Common types can magnify from 100 to 500 diameters the microstructure of the surface of a highly-polished metal specimen. This magnification is designated as $100\times$ to $500\times$. Some metallurgical microscopes magnify up to $2500\times$. With an electron microscope, magnification of $250,000\times$ is possible. For the study of most metals, however, the magnification of $100\times$ to $500\times$ is satisfactory.

Some metallurgical microscopes are equipped with devices for photographing the microstructure of metallic materials. A modern instrument called a *metallograph*, which is basically a metallurgical microscope equipped with a camera, is shown in Fig. 17-10. It is used for investigating and photographing the microstructure of metals. Photomicrographs of several microstructures which are common in steel are shown in Figs. 17-19 and 17-20. The study of microscopic structures of metals is called *metallography*.

A metal specimen must be specially-prepared for examination with a metallurgical microscope, since light from a source on the microscope must be reflected from the surface of the specimen. The specimen is prepared by grinding a flat surface first. The surface then is polished with finer and finer abrasives until a mirror finish is produced. As a result of the polishing procedure, a fine film of impurities is

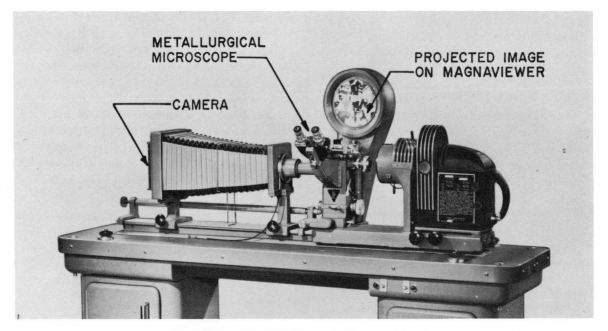

Fig. 17-10. Balphot Metallograph (Bausch & Lomb)

Fig. 17-11. Using Hot-Stage Microscope to Study and Record Photographically Transformations Occurring in Steel at Elevated Temperatures (Research and Technology Div. — U.S. Steel)

of these factors influence the properties of steel or cast iron. Also, all of these factors may be altered by the temperature changes which take place in certain heat-treatment processes.

Through the use of a hot-stage microscope, metallurgists can study the transformations which occur in steel or other metals at elevated temperatures. With this type of instrument, the changes also can be recorded photographically. Such an instrument is shown in Fig. 17-11.

It is not necessary to observe the grain structure of metal through a microscope in order to obtain good results with most heat-treatment operations. However, detailed study of this type enables one to understand heat-treatment processes more clearly. The grain structure of metals is affected by elevated temperatures and by the rate of cooling. It is largely because of these effects that the properties of steel and cast iron may be changed by heat-treatment processes.

Space Lattices

The crystalline grains in metals are composed of atoms arranged in orderly geometric patterns in three dimensions. See Fig. 17-12. The graphic representation of this systematic

produced on the surface and between the grains. This film usually is dissolved by an etching solution so that the grain boundaries may be observed. *Nital,* a solution of 5% nitric acid and alcohol, often is used as an etching solution for carbon-steel specimens.

After etching has been completed, the grain size, grain boundaries, and the form and distribution of the carbon can be investigated. All arrangement of atoms is called a *space lattice*. One common space lattice is the cubic type as shown in Fig. 17-12. The atoms in a space lattice are represented by dots or spheres. The lines actually do not exist, but they are shown graphically to help visualize the arrangement of the atoms.

The individual atoms in a metallic grain are so small that they cannot be observed directly by the most powerful microscope. Through the use of X-ray studies, however, scientists have determined that the atoms in metals and other crystalline materials have definite space lattice arrangements. Each type of metal has its own characteristic arrangement of atoms in its space lattice.

The smallest repetitive group of atoms which makes up a space lattice system is called a *unit* or *cell*. The type of unit varies with the kind of metal. The space lattice units of most common metals are of the following four types of systems:

1. Body-centered cubic unit
2. Face-centered cubic unit
3. Body-centered tetragonal unit
4. Hexagonal close-packed unit

Body-Centered Cubic Unit: The body-centered cubic unit, as illustrated in Fig. 17-13A, has nine atoms, one at each of the eight corners of the cubic arrangement and one at the center of the cube. With this arrangement, each atom has eight other atoms in its *field of influence*; this means that each atom is held in its relative position by forces acting upon it by eight other atoms.

The body-centered cubic arrangement is not as closely packed as the other unit arrangements which will be discussed. The atoms do not touch one another. In fact, in comparison with their actual size, they are spaced at great distances apart. However, in order to visualize them more easily, we can assume that they are touching one another in the form of spheres, as shown in Fig. 17-13.

If it were possible to magnify the finely-polished surface of a single metallic grain about 35 million times, the body-centered cubic lattice arrangement would appear as in the third magnification of Fig. 17-12. Repetitious body-centered cubic units unite and grow in three

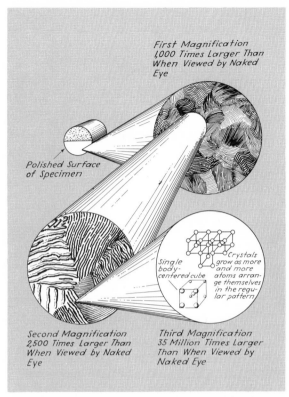

Fig. 17-12. Schematic Magnification of Steel Containing Approximately 0.83% Carbon
(Linde Div. — Union Carbide)
The magnification gives an idea of the manner in which the constituents arrange themselves. The third magnification is incomplete, but it shows how iron atoms arrange themselves as a crystal is formed. The lines joining the atoms are merely to help in visualizing the arrangement. The first and second magnifications show pearlite below 1333°F. composed of ferrite (pure iron) and cementite (iron carbide). The ferrite is the white area, and the cementite is dark.

directions, thus forming the space lattice arrangement of a single metallic grain of metal. The grains form when molten metal cools from a liquid to a solid.

Several metals which have the body-centered cubic arrangement include tungsten, molybdenum, vanadium, and columbium. Ferrite, which also is called *alpha iron*, has this arrangement at temperatures below the hardening temperature range. (The *hardening temperature* is the temperature at which steel is quenched in the hardening process.) At the hardening temperature, the lattice arrange-

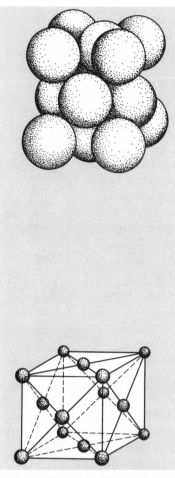

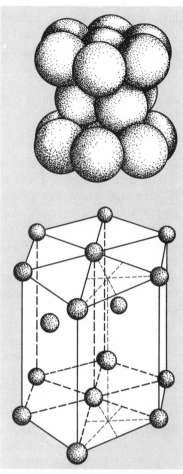

Fig. 17-13A. Body-Centered Cubic Unit Arrangement of Atoms

Fig. 17-13B. Face-Centered Cubic Unit Arrangement of Atoms

Fig. 17-13C. Hexagonal Close-Packed Unit Arrangement

ment transforms to another form — the face-centered cubic form. Metals with the body-centered cubic arrangement generally rank higher in strength and lower in cold-working characteristics than those with the face-centered cubic arrangement.

Face-Centered Cubic Unit: The face-centered cubic unit, as illustrated in Fig. 17-13B, has 14 atoms — one at each of the eight corners of the cubic unit and one at the center of the six faces of the cube. Hence, the atoms in this arrangement are more dense (closely packed) than in the body-centered arrangement. Metals which have a face-centered cubic lattice structure include nickel, aluminum, copper, lead, gold, and silver.

When steel is heated to the hardening temperature, the space lattice units in the grain structure transform from the body-centered cubic form to the face-centered cubic form. In this form, it is called *austenite* or *gamma iron*, as shown in Fig. 17-25. At the elevated temperature at which austenite forms, the carbon in the steel decomposes from its combined state as cementite (iron carbide), to free carbon. The free carbon then dissolves into the solid hot iron to form a solid solution of uniformly dispersed carbon in iron. This form of iron will dissolve up to a maximum of about 2.00% carbon. In contrast, the body-centered (alpha) form of iron (ferrite) will dissolve a maximum of about 0.05% carbon.

Hexagonal Close-Packed Unit: The hexagonal close-packed unit, as illustrated in Fig. 17-13C, has a total of 17 atoms — one at each of the six corners of the two end faces, one at the center of each end face, and three equally spaced between the two end faces. Some metals which have this type of space lattice arrangement include zinc, cadmium, cobalt, magnesium, and titanium. Metals with this type of lattice arrangement generally lack plasticity. Hence, they usually cannot be cold worked.

Body-Centered Tetragonal Unit: This type of space lattice unit is shown in Fig. 17-14. It has nine atoms arranged in a manner similar to the body-centered cubic unit in Fig. 17-13A, except that the unit is not square, but is oblong. It is essentially a body-centered cubic system with one axis elongated.

When steel is heated to the hardening temperature, the grain structure transforms to *austenite*, as shown in Fig. 17-25. Austenite has the face-centered cubic lattice arrangement shown in Fig. 17-13B. Then when the steel is quenched at the hardening temperature and cooled rapidly to a temperature below 400° F., it transforms to another form of grain structure called *martensite*, as shown in Fig. 17-27. The space lattice arrangement of martensite is made up of body-centered tetragonal units. Martensite is a supersaturated solid solution of carbon in iron. Martensite is the hardest and most brittle form of steel. The formation of martensite and other transformations which take place in the grain structure of steel during heat treatment processes are discussed further in Unit 152.

Of the four common forms of atomic space lattice arrangements, the cubic forms are the most important. Knowledge of these will aid in understanding heat-treatment processes used with steel and cast iron. Heat treatment of steel is possible largely because of the form and amount of carbon content. In turn, the form and distribution of the carbon content is dependent upon the change which takes place in the lattice structure at the hardening temperature.

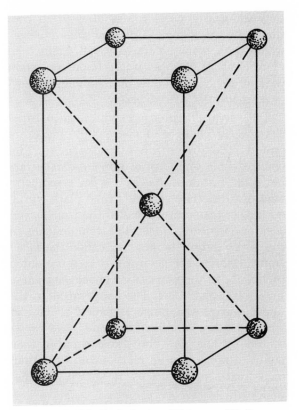

Fig. 17-14. Body-Centered Tetragonal Unit Arrangement of Atoms

Allotropy: Some metals may exist in more than one space lattice form. Iron, as previously indicated, may exist with either the *body-centered* or with the *face-centered* cubic structure, depending on its temperature. These forms are called *allotropic forms*. When the lattice structure changes from one form to another, it is called an *allotropic change*.

Pure iron, at room temperature, has the body-centered cubic lattice form and is called *alpha* iron. Upon heating above 1670° F., it changes to the face-centered cubic form, called *gamma* iron. Upon further heating to about 2550° F., it again changes to a body-centered cubic form called *delta* iron. The delta form of iron is very similar to the alpha form. Upon still further heating about 2800° F., the iron becomes liquid. In the liquid state the atoms lose any specific lattice arrangement, and thus gain fluidity. Iron has a stable cubic lattice arrangement in each of the above forms, within a specific temperature range.

583

When nearly pure iron is allowed to cool slowly from a molten state, the same changes which took place on heating will again take place, but in reverse order. However, upon cooling, the changes take place at slightly lower temperatures in each case.

The temperatures at which allotropic changes, or changes in phase, take place are called *transformation temperatures*. The changes from one form of iron to another are not often instantaneous at a specific temperature. Rather, they generally take place within a range of temperatures called the *transformation temperature range*. The temperature at the lower end of the range is called the *lower transformation temperature*. It is represented by line A_1 on the iron-carbon phase diagram in Figs. 17-23 and 17-24. The temperature at the upper end of the range is called the *upper transformation temperature*, and it is represented by line A_3. The transformation temperature range and its relationship to various heat-treatment processes is shown in Figs. 17-24 and 17-26.

When iron or steel is heated, the change from one cubic lattice form to another takes place more rapidly at the upper transformation temperature. Since the change in form involves the rearrangement of atoms throughout, considerable time is necessary for the change, even at the proper temperatures. Therefore, when heating for heat-treatment purposes, steel generally should be allowed to *soak* at the proper temperature for a period of time. The minimum soaking period should be about one hour for each inch of metal thickness. This will provide adequate time for complete transformation. For thicknesses of ¼″ or less, the change takes place almost instantaneously. For metal thickness between ¼″ and 1″, the soaking period may range from several minutes to one hour, depending on the thickness.

It was stated previously that heat-treatment operations generally have a time-temperature cycle which involves three factors: heating metal to a given temperature, holding (soaking) it at the prescribed temperature for a given period of time, and cooling it at a given rate. The second factor, *the soaking period*, provides time for the internal structural changes to take place as described above.

When steel is heated to the proper hardening temperature, the atomic lattice arrangement is transformed from the body-centered cubic type to the face-centered cubic type. Also, at the proper temperature for hardening, the grain structure will be very fine. A fine grain structure usually is required for the best combination of hardness and toughness. The grain structure increases in coarseness at temperatures significantly below or above the proper hardening temperature (which is about 50° to 100° F. above the upper transformation temperature, as shown in Fig. 17-24). The relative coarseness of the grain at this temperature is shown to the left in Fig. 17-26.

Grain Formation: The crystals or grains in metal form as the metal cools from a liquid to a solid state. The individual grains start to form in the coolest areas, usually along the edges of the molten metal. With a very slight drop in temperature, grains start to form throughout the metal in many locations. With more rapid cooling, the grains form rapidly, and the metal freezes (solidifies) quickly.

Crystallization starts with the formation of individual space lattice units in various locations throughout the molten metal. The individual units are called *seed* crystals or *unit cells*. The seed crystals grow through the addition of other lattice units which become attached and extend in three directions from the individual seed crystals. With a very slight drop in temperature, new seed crystals develop throughout the body of metal. The crystals grow by extending in three directions until their growth is obstructed by adjacent grains. In this manner, the enlarged crystals develop irregular grain boundaries as crystallization of the metal becomes complete.

The initial grain size is largely dependent upon the rate of cooling from a liquid to a solid state. When the metal cools slowly, the grains are fewer in number, but larger in size. When the metal cools more rapidly, there is less time for grain growth, and grain size is smaller. The properties of various metals often vary with the grain size. When molten steel is allowed to

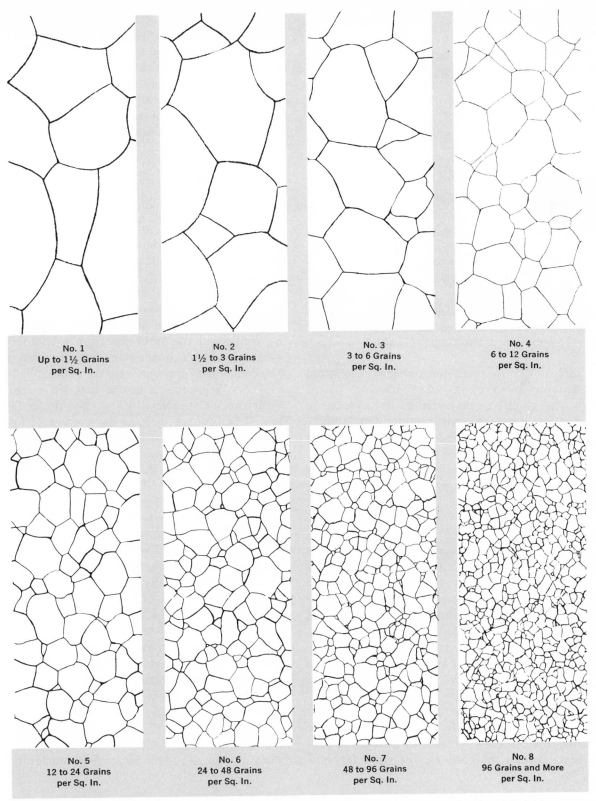

| No. 1
Up to 1½ Grains
per Sq. In. | No. 2
1½ to 3 Grains
per Sq. In. | No. 3
3 to 6 Grains
per Sq. In. | No. 4
6 to 12 Grains
per Sq. In. |
| No. 5
12 to 24 Grains
per Sq. In. | No. 6
24 to 48 Grains
per Sq. In. | No. 7
48 to 96 Grains
per Sq. In. | No. 8
96 Grains and More
per Sq. In. |

Fig. 17-15. ASTM Grain-Size Chart, Untwinned Grains (100×) (Amer. Society for Testing Materials)
The average grain size of steel after standard heat-treatment processes is measured at
100 magnifications by comparison with this chart.

Fig. 17-16. Ferrous Grain-Size Chart Mounted on Magnaviewer of Metallograph (Bausch & Lomb)

cool slowly to room temperature, the grain structure generally is quite coarse.

The grain size may change from coarse to fine, or vice versa, with certain temperature changes. The variation in grain size for carbon steel upon being heated to increasing temperatures is shown to the left in Fig. 17-26. Because of the change in grain size at different temperatures, the temperature of metals must be carefully controlled in heat-treatment operations.

At the proper temperature for hardening steel, the grain structure is very fine. If steel at this temperature is cooled rapidly by quenching in water or oil, the fine grain structure will be trapped throughout, and the steel will be hardened. Thus the third important factor involved in the time-temperature cycle, *the rate of cooling*, is applied for the purpose of controlling grain size and condition.

Grain Size: The average grain size in steel generally is determined after steel has been heat-treated by a standard process. Several methods can be used for esti-

mating the average grain size. One common method involves the use of a *grain-size comparator*. This may be in the form of a simple chart (as shown in Fig. 17-15) or in the form of printed, transparent, plastic sheets — one sheet for each grain-size range.

Grain sizes are designated by a standard number system. The most common range from 1 through 8. In estimating grain size, the grain is projected on the magnaviewer or screen of a metallurgical microscope at a magnification 100 times the actual size. See Fig. 17-16. The magnified grain is then compared with the grain sizes on the comparator chart. The comparator specimens on the chart must be at the same magnification as the grain being viewed on the microscope screen, usually $100\times$. The estimated average grain size corresponds with the nearest equivalent comparator grain size. Grain size also may be determined by comparing the grain size from a photomicrograph which is at the same magnification as the comparison specimens on the chart.

A No. 1 grain size means that the microstructure, as viewed at $100\times$, has up to $1\frac{1}{2}$ grains per square inch, or an average of one grain per square inch. The No. 2 size has from $1\frac{1}{2}$ to 3 grains per square inch. Similarly, the No. 8 size has more than 96 grains per square inch, as shown in Fig. 17-15. Steels with grain sizes ranging from 1 to 5 generally are considered coarse-grain steels; those ranging from 5 to 8 generally are considered fine-grain steels. For the best combination of hardness and toughness in hardened tool steel, a very fine grain structure usually is desirable.

The general range of grain sizes which may exist in a given type of steel, under various conditions, depends largely on the chemical constituents used in its manufacture. Therefore, some steels may be classified in a general way as coarse-grained steels, while others are fine-grained steels. However, actual grain size for a given kind of steel may vary with the temperature, with heat treatment, with hot working such as forging, and with cold working such as rolling, twisting, or machining.

How Carbon Content Affects Hardening

We have seen that steel may be hardened by the heat-treatment process called *hardening*, involving the following three steps: 1. Heat the steel to the proper temperature for hardening. 2. Hold the steel at the hardening temperature for a period of time. This step is called *soaking*. 3. Cool the steel at the proper rate by quenching in either water, oil, or air, depending upon the type of steel.

The factors involved in determining the hardening temperature, the soaking period, and selection of the quenching medium will be discussed shortly. First, however, it is important to understand how the amount and the form of carbon in steel affect its hardness. The form of the carbon and the grain structure of the steel change during each of the above three steps involved in hardening steel.

Amount of Carbon

The maximum degree of hardness obtainable in steel by direct hardening is determined largely by the amount of carbon content. Pure iron is relatively soft and cannot be hardened directly by heat treatment. Low-carbon steels can be hardened only very slightly. Medium-carbon steels may be hardened considerably by direct hardening, but generally they cannot be hardened sufficiently to cut other metals. High-carbon steels and tool steels may be hardened sufficiently to cut many other metals.

The maximum obtainable hardness in most alloy steels also is determined largely by the amount of carbon content. The use of certain alloying elements in steel, however, does improve hardenability. Hardenability, it will be recalled, refers to the depth of hardness.

The carbon steels generally are considered to be shallow-hardening steels. The depth of high hardness for carbon tool steels varies from about $\frac{4}{32}$" to $\frac{10}{32}$", depending on the hardenability rating of the particular tool steel, as indicated in Fig. 17-18. Certain alloy

tool steels, on the other hand, can be highly hardened to depths of several inches. Some alloying elements also enable alloy steels to retain their hardness at elevated temperatures where carbon steel would become softened. Whether steel is carbon steel or alloy steel, generally it cannot be hardened significantly if the carbon content is not sufficiently high.

Form of Carbon

In addition to the amount of carbon in steel, the form of carbon is important in hardening and in other common heat-treatment processes. At temperatures below approximately 1330° F., the carbon in unhardened steel is combined chemically with iron, thus forming cementite. The chemical term for cementite is iron carbide (Fe_3C). In unhardened steel, the cementite normally exists as a mechanical mixture with ferrite (nearly pure iron); this mixture is called pearlite. The pearlite, it will be recalled, is composed of tiny platelike layers of ferrite and cementite in specific proportions, Fig. 17-19. Under special heat-treatment conditions (which will be discussed later), the cementite may exist in the form of *spheroidite*, instead of pearlite, as shown in Fig. 17-20.

Solid cementite is very hard and virtually nonmachinable, except by grinding. However, when cementite is mixed with the soft ferrite, as in pearlite or spheroidite, it can be machined readily. Steel usually must have more than 0.03% (three-point) carbon before pearlite will form. Carbon in lesser amounts is dissolved in iron, thus forming the solid solution called ferrite, which is nearly pure iron, as shown in Fig. 16-4.

As the carbon content in unhardened steel is increased, up to about 0.80% to 0.85%, the proportionate amount of the grain structure which is pearlite also increases. *And* as the proportion of pearlite increases, the strength of the unhardened steel is increased. When

Hardenability Rating	P	F	Temperature	P (Depth of Case)	F (Fracture Rating of Case)
SHALLOW			1450 F	4/32″ or less	9
	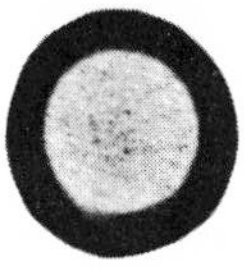	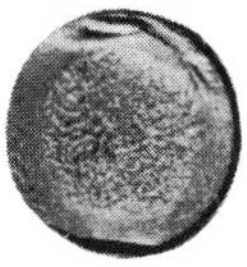	1550 F	4/32″ or less	8
MEDIUM SHALLOW		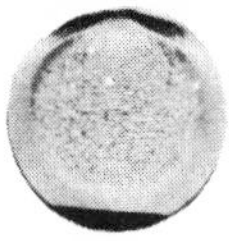	1450 F	4/32″	9
		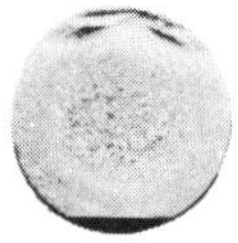	1550 F	5/32″-6/32″	8
MEDIUM DEEP	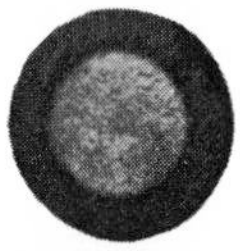	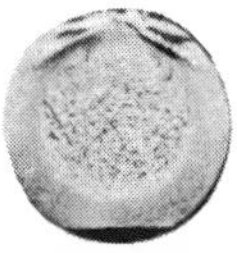	1450 F	5/32″	9
		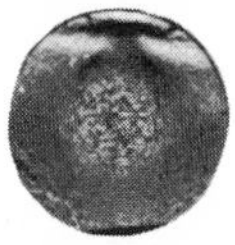	1550 F	7/32″-9/32″	8
DEEP	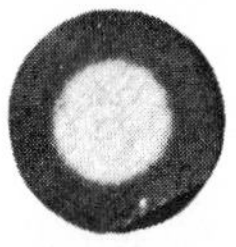	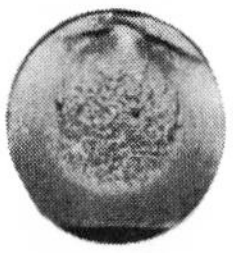	1450 F	6/32″ or over	9
			1550 F	10/32″ or over	8

Fig. 17-18. Penetration-Fracture Classifications of Carbon Tool Steels.
(©Allegheny Ludlum Steel Corp., reprinted by permission).

Figures above are based on test pieces ¾″ round (3″ long), hardening time 45 minutes in electric muffle, quenched in water at 70°F. Unless otherwise specified, **shallow** hardening is applied on rounds up to 1″ or equal, **medium shallow** on pieces from 1″ to 3″, **medium deep** on pieces 3″ to 4″, and **deep** on pieces over 4″ round or equal.

hardened by heat treatment, steel which has a high percentage of pearlite will harden to a higher hardness value than steel with a lesser proportion of pearlite.

Steel with 0.80% to 0.85% carbon is called *eutectoid* steel. In the unhardened condition, it has a grain structure which is all pearlite, as shown in Fig. 17-19. Steel with less than 0.80% to 0.85% carbon is called *hypo*eutectoid steel; in the unhardened condition, this steel has a grain structure composed of a mixture of pearlite grains and ferrite grains, as shown in Fig. 17-21. Steel with more than 0.80% to 0.85% carbon is called *hyper*eutectoid steel. In the unhardened condition, this steel has a grain structure composed of all pearlite grains and excess cementite; the latter is located in the grain boundaries, between the pearlite grains, as shown in Fig. 17-22. Since hypereutectoid steels have excess iron carbide existing in their grain boundaries, they are harder and more wear-resistant and rank lower in machinability than the hypoeutectoid steels.

Perhaps a good way to remember the difference between the two classifications of steel is to remember that *hyper*, which has five letters, represents the steel with the higher carbon content. *Hypo*, with only four letters, represents steels with the lower carbon content. *Hyper* is a prefix meaning "above" or "excessive" — much like *super*. *Hypo* has an opposite meaning of "under" or "down" — much

like *sub*. See the designations at the bottom of Fig. 17-23.

Iron-Carbon Phase Diagram

The relationship between the amount of carbon and the grain structure in steel can be understood more clearly by studying the *iron-*

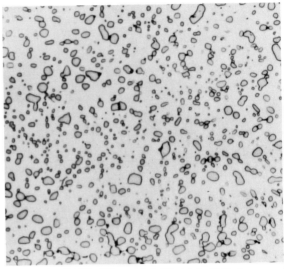

Fig. 17-20. Microscopic Structure Called Spheroidite (1000×) (U.S. Steel)

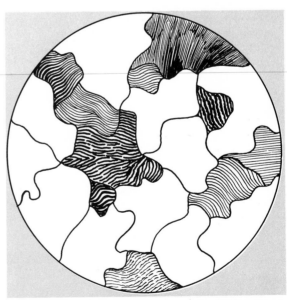

Fig. 17-21. Sketch of a Photomicrograph of Unhardened Low-Carbon Steel (Linde Div. — Union Carbide) **White area represents grains of ferrite; the shaded grains are pearlite.**

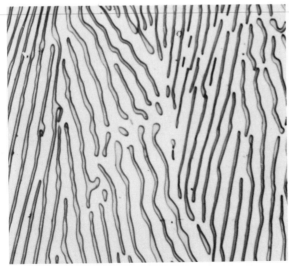

Fig. 17-19. Microscopic Structure Called Pearlite (2500×) (U.S. Steel)

**Fig. 17-22. Sketch of a Photomicrograph of
Unhardened Steel Containing About 1.1% Carbon**
(Linde Div. — Union Carbide)
**Grains of pearlite are surrounded by cementite grain
boundaries, shown as white lines.**

carbon phase diagram in Fig. 17-23. This particular diagram is only a portion of one which lists all ferrous metals, including cast iron. However, the partial diagram is sufficient for the scope of this book.

When steel is heated to certain temperatures, the form and the distribution of the carbon changes. At the same time, the grain structure also undergoes certain transformations, called *phase changes*. The iron-carbon phase diagram shows the temperatures at which these various changes occur.

It will be noted in the diagram that eutectoid steel, which is all pearlite at temperatures below 1330° F., is represented by the dotted line extending downward from the letter *S*. The line A_1, designated *PSK*, represents the *lower transformation* temperature or *lower critical* temperature of 1330° F. The line A_3, designated *GOSK*, represents the *upper transformation* temperature or *upper critical* temperature. The upper transformation temperature varies with the carbon content in the steel; it is lowered as carbon content increases toward 0.80% to 0.85%. The temperature

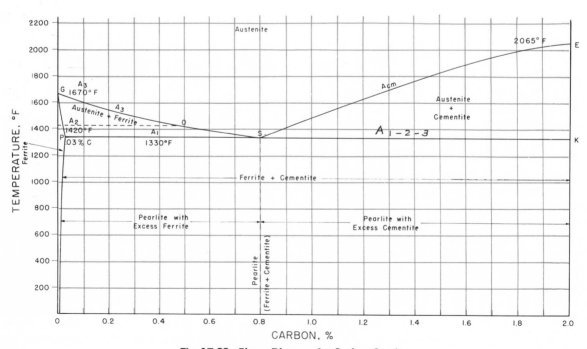

Fig. 17-23. Phase Diagram for Carbon Steels

range between lines A_1 and A_3 is called the *transformation temperature range*. It is so named because of the structural change which takes place in steel within this range. Also, it is called the *critical temperature range*.

The dotted line, designated A_2, indicates the *magnetic point*, approximately 1420° F. Above this temperature, steel is no longer magnetic. The magnetic point also continues along line *OSK*. The hardening temperature of medium- and high-carbon steel, therefore, may be estimated with a magnet if more accurate equipment is not available. Note that for hypereutectoid steels, line *SK* represents lines A_1, A_2, and A_3. The hardening temperatures of various steels are shown in Table 32, appendix. High-carbon steels usually are quenched at temperatures from 50° to 100° F. above the magnetic point, as in Fig. 17-24.

At temperatures below line A_1, the iron in steel has the body-centered cubic lattice structure called alpha iron. Upon heating steel to temperatures above line A_1, the grain structure begins to transform to the face-centered cubic lattice structure called gamma iron. This form of iron also is called *austenite*, Fig. 17-25. Transformation to austenite continues as the temperature of the steel is increased from line A_1 to line A_3. At line A_3, transformation to austenite is complete.

Austenite is a solid solution of carbon in face-centered cubic iron. When steel transforms to austenite, the carbon which was in a combined state as cementite breaks down into pure carbon and iron. The carbon then is absorbed in the iron in the form of a solid solution. In this form, the carbon is distributed uniformly, just as sugar is when dissolved in water. This condition usually is necessary for obtaining maximum hardness by quenching.

When steel is heated to the proper temperature for hardening, the internal structure not only should be transformed to austenite, but it also must possess a fine grain structure. In stress-relieved steel, the grain size is usually coarse at temperatures below line A_1. As the temperature is increased toward line A_3, the grain structure becomes finer. The finest grain structure exists at A_3, as shown at the left in Fig. 17-26. When the temperature of the austenite is increased above line A_3, the grain

size again starts to increase gradually. At temperatures more than 100° F. above line A_3, the grain size becomes quite coarse.

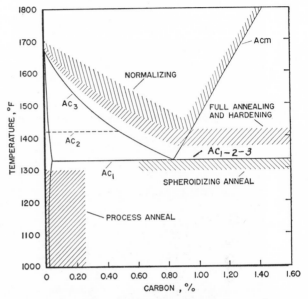

Fig. 17-24. Recommended Temperature Ranges for Heat-Treating Plain Carbon Steels*

*Thomas G. Digges, Samuel J. Rosenberg, and Glenn W. Geil, **Heat Treatment and Properties of Iron and Steel,** National Bureau of Standards Monograph 88. Washington, D.C.: U.S. Government Printing Office, 1966.

Fig. 17-25. Microscopic Structure Called Austenite (500×) (U.S. Steel)

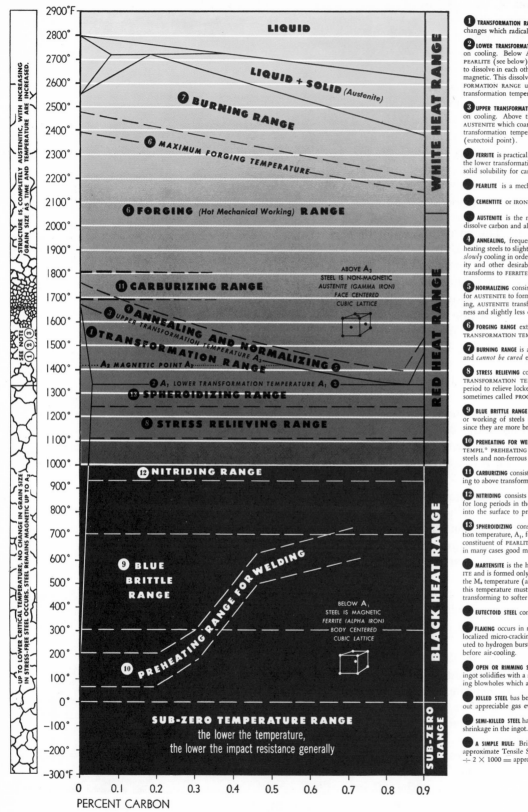

① TRANSFORMATION RANGE. In this range steels undergo internal changes which radically affect the properties of the material.

② LOWER TRANSFORMATION TEMPERATURE (A₁). Termed Ac₁ on heating on cooling. Below Ac₁ structure ordinarily consists of FERRIT PEARLITE (see below). On heating through Ac₁ these constituents to dissolve in each other to form AUSTENITE (see below) which magnetic. This dissolving action continues on heating through the FORMATION RANGE until the solid solution is complete at the transformation temperature.

③ UPPER TRANSFORMATION TEMPERATURE (A₃). Termed Ac₃ on heatir on cooling. Above this temperature the structure consists who AUSTENITE which coarsens with increasing time and temperature. transformation temperature is lowered as carbon increases to (eutectoid point).

● **FERRITE** is practically pure iron (in plain carbon steels) existing the lower transformation temperature. It is magnetic and has very solid solubility for carbon.

● **PEARLITE** is a mechanical mixture of FERRITE and CEMENTITE

● **CEMENTITE** or IRON CARBIDE is a compound of iron and carbon,

● **AUSTENITE** is the non-magnetic form of iron and has the po dissolve carbon and alloying elements.

④ ANNEALING, frequently referred to as FULL ANNEALING, cons heating steels to slightly above Ac₃, holding for AUSTENITE to form *slowly* cooling in order to produce small grain size, softness, good ity and other desirable properties. On cooling slowly the AUST transforms to FERRITE and PEARLITE.

⑤ NORMALIZING consists of heating steels to slightly above Ac₃, h for AUSTENITE to form, then followed by cooling (in still air). O ing, AUSTENITE transforms giving somewhat higher strength and ness and slightly less ductility than in annealing.

⑥ FORGING RANGE extends to several hundred degrees above the TRANSFORMATION TEMPERATURE.

⑦ BURNING RANGE is above the FORGING RANGE. Burned steel is and *cannot be cured* except by remelting.

⑧ STRESS RELIEVING consists of heating to a point below the TRANSFORMATION TEMPERATURE, A₁, holding for a sufficiently period to relieve locked-up stresses, then slowly cooling. This pr sometimes called PROCESS ANNEALING.

⑨ BLUE BRITTLE RANGE occurs approximately from 300° to 700°F. P or working of steels should not be done between these temper since they are more brittle in this range than above or below it.

⑩ PREHEATING FOR WELDING is carried out to prevent crack formatio TEMPIL° PREHEATING CHART for recommended temperature for v steels and non-ferrous metals.

⑪ CARBURIZING consists of dissolving carbon into surface of steel by ing to above transformation range in presence of carburizing comp

⑫ NITRIDING consists of heating certain *special steels* to about 1 for long periods in the presence of ammonia gas. Nitrogen is abs into the surface to produce extremely hard "skins".

⑬ SPHEROIDIZING consists of heating to just below the lower trans tion temperature, A₁, for a sufficient length of time to put the CEME constituent of PEARLITE into globular form. This produces softne in many cases good machinability.

● **MARTENSITE** is the hardest of the transformation products of AU ITE and is formed only on cooling below a certain temperature kno the M₅ temperature (about 400° to 600°F for carbon steels). Cool this temperature must be sufficiently rapid to prevent AUSTENITE transforming to softer constituents at higher temperatures.

● **EUTECTOID STEEL** contains approximately 0.85% carbon.

● **FLAKING** occurs in many alloy steels and is a defect characteri localized micro-cracking and "flake-like" fracturing. It is usually uted to hydrogen bursts. Cure consists of cycle cooling to at least before air-cooling.

● **OPEN OR RIMMING STEEL** has not been completely deoxidized as ingot solidifies with a sound surface ("rim") and a core portion c ing blowholes which are welded in subsequent hot rolling.

● **KILLED STEEL** has been deoxidized at least sufficiently to solidify out appreciable gas evolution.

● **SEMI-KILLED STEEL** has been partially deoxidized to reduce solidifi shrinkage in the ingot.

● **A SIMPLE RULE:** Brinell Hardness divided by two, times 1000, approximate Tensile Strength in pounds per square inch. (200 ÷ 2 × 1000 = approx. 100,000 Tensile Strength, p.s.i.)

Fig. 17-26. Basic Guide to Ferrous Metallurgy (Tempil°)

Hardening Temperature

The temperature at which steel usually is quenched for hardening is called the *hardening temperature*. The recommended hardening temperature is usually 50° to 100° F. above the upper critical temperature, as shown in Fig. 17-24. Generally, the grain size is not the finest obtainable when quenched from 50° to 100° F. above A_3. However, at these hardening temperatures, the grain size and structure usually give the most desirable combination of hardness and toughness. The finest obtainable grain structure is not always the most desirable.

The hardening temperature varies for different steels, depending on the carbon content. It also varies according to special alloying elements which are included in alloy steels.

For hypereutectoid steels, the recommended hardening temperature usually is in the range from 1375° to 1450° F., as shown in Fig. 17-24. For hypoeutectoid steels, the hardening temperature generally is higher, as shown in Fig. 17-24. It is advisable to follow the steel manufacturer's recommendations concerning hardening temperatures and temperatures for other heat-treating operations on specific types of steel. If these are unavailable, the hardening temperatures recommended for the various steels represented in Fig. 17-24, or in Table 32, appendix, may be used. The hardening temperatures for various steels also are listed in handbooks for machinists and in handbooks concerned with the properties of metals. A suggested list of handbooks is included in the bibliography.

Martensite Formation: When high-carbon steel is quenched at the critical temperature, and cooled rapidly to a temperature below about 400° F., the austenite transforms to a structure called *martensite*, as shown by the photomicrograph in Fig. 17-27. Martensite is the hardest and most brittle form of steel. It is a super-saturated solid solution of carbon in iron which has a body-centered tetragonal lattice arrangement (Fig. 17-14). Under magnification, this type of grain structure has an extremely fine, needlelike or acicular appearance. Pure martensite does not contain carbon in the form of cementite. For maximum hardness after quenching, the grain structure of steel usually must be completely martensitic.

Carbon steel must be cooled rapidly from the hardening temperature for complete transformation from austenite to martensite — in fact, usually from the hardening temperature to below 200° F. during a period of several seconds. With slower cooling, some pearlite will form and will be mixed in with the martensite. When this happens, the steel will not be hardened completely.

When steels are cooled from the hardening temperature, austenite begins to transform to pearlite at temperatures below 1330° F. The rate of this transformation depends on the temperature. In carbon steels, austenite decomposes rapidly to pearlite after one second in the temperature range from 1000° to 1100° F. After three seconds in this temperature range, transformation to pearlite is nearly complete. Consequently, when carbon steels are quenched at the hardening temperature, they must be cooled below the 1000° F. temperature range during a period of one second or less. So long as cooling through this range takes place in less than one second, several additional seconds may be allowed to cool the

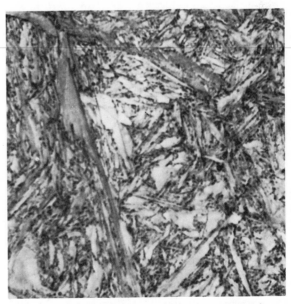

Fig. 17-27. Microscopic Structure Called Martensite (2500×) (U.S. Steel)

steel below 250° F. Therefore, it is evident that the hardening process is essentially the *avoidance of pearlite grain formation* in steel while it is being quenched.

Depth of Hardness: The depth to which steels may be uniformly hardened depends largely on the speed of cooling and the thickness of the metal. Carbon steels less than $\frac{1}{4}$" in thickness will transform from austenite to martensite almost immediately when quenched. The result is complete and uniform hardening. Carbon steels with a larger cross-sectional area, such as 1" thickness, do not transform to martensite uniformly from the surface to the center. When the transformation is incomplete, a softer structure will exist as a mixture with the martensite, toward the center of the material.

An example will illustrate the lack of uniform hardness in larger cross sections of carbon steel. When 1" diameter carbon steel, with 0.95% carbon content, is quenched in water at 1450° F., hardness indicated by the following Rockwell C numbers may result: surface hardness 63, hardness at one-half radius 47, hardness at center 43. These hardness numbers are more meaningful if it is understood that a metal-cutting tool, such as a tap or drill, generally should have a minimum hardness of

Rockwell C-60. A Rockwell C hardness value of 63 to 66 would be more desirable.

The depth of hardness for carbon tool steels with various hardenability ratings is shown in Fig. 17-18. These steels (compared to alloy tool steels) harden to relatively shallow depths.

Alloying Affects Depth: When certain alloying elements are included in steel, the rate at which austenite transforms to martensite during quenching is slowed down considerably. Consequently, steels with the proper alloying elements may be cooled more slowly from the hardening temperature. The slower cooling without pearlite formation permits more uniform hardening to greater depths, and the result is more uniform and complete transformation from austenite to martensite when the metal is quenched for hardening.

It is apparent from our discussion up to this point that rapid cooling is important for depth of hardness when quenching carbon steels. However, when the rate of cooling is too fast during quenching, warpage occurs, internal stresses develop, and cracks often appear. Of course, when the quenched part cracks, it is ruined. For these reasons, certain precautions are necessary in quenching both high-carbon steels and alloy steels for hardening. The proper quenching media and appropriate quenching procedures should be used.

Quenching Media and Their Applications

Selection of the quenching medium and use of proper quenching procedures are important factors in hardening steel. Various quenching media absorb and remove heat from steel at different rates. Cooling too rapidly often produces internal stresses which may cause cracks, particularly in high-carbon steels. Cooling too slowly may result in incomplete hardening.

Common Quenching Media

The common quenching media (or solutions) include water, brine, and oil. Air, either still or compressed, also is used to quench special types of tool and die steel. Some quenching solutions produce a more severe quench than others. (*Quenching severity* refers to the rate at which heat is removed from the article being quenched.) The severity of the quenching operation depends on the thickness of the metal, the kind of quenching medium, the temperature of the quenching solution, and the degree of agitation of the metal in this solution.

Severity of Quenching Media

Each basic quenching medium cools with a different degree of severity. The rate of cooling is most severe with brine, less rapid with water, slow with oil, and slowest in air. The rate of cooling for each quenching solution can be increased considerably by agitation of the article in the solution or by circulation of the solution. In some instances, the solution is flooded over the steel under pressure, thus producing a more severe quench than with normal agitation.

The relative severity of the common quenching solutions, in comparison with the rate of cooling by water, may be designated by numbers. For this purpose, water is assigned a rating of No. 1 when no agitation or circulation occurs. In comparison, under the same conditions, air is 0.02; oil 0.30; and brine 2.0. With good circulation or agitation, the above severity ratings may be increased by approximately 50%. With strong circulation or agitation, they may be increased by 100% or more.

The temperature of the quenching solution also affects the severity of the quench. Water or brine should be maintained at a temperature of about 60° F. Because of its increased viscosity, oil, unlike water, cools best when it is maintained at temperatures from about 100° to 140° F.

Various quenching oils are available. Some cool more slowly than others. Vegetable oils, animal oils, mineral oils, and various combinations of these have been used as quenching media. Straight mineral oil with a Saybolt viscosity rating of about 100 at 100° F. frequent-

ly is used. When metals are quenched at the lower temperatures, such as 300° to 500° F., oil will cool at only about 10% the rate of water.

Brine is a solution of 5% to 10% salt (sodium chloride) and water. Rock salt usually is used. Brine cools about twice as rapidly as water. It also has the ability to help *throw* the scale away from steel during quenching, thus enabling the steel to cool more uniformly.

Selecting Proper Quenching Medium

The proper quenching solution should be determined for each type of steel. Steel manufacturers' recommendations should be followed in selecting the quenching medium, particularly when quenching tool and die steels. If these are unavailable, the recommended solutions for various steels listed in Table 32, appendix, may be used.

The carbon steels, which are relatively shallow-hardening steels, generally require severe quenching solutions such as water or brine. Very thin sections of high-carbon steel often can be hardened satisfactorily by agitating them in oil. This procedure also is recommended in cases where the severity of water quenching causes cracks in materials of irregular cross-sectional thickness.

While some alloy steels are designed for water quenching, the majority are designed for oil quenching. Where an oil quench is recommended, it should be used, because there is less distortion and less danger of cracking. However, when an oil quench is used for water-hardening steel greater than ¼" thickness, maximum obtainable hardness generally cannot be obtained.

Agitation: Proper quenching usually involves moderate agitation of the work in the quenching bath. When steel is quenched, the liquid in contact with the hot surface vaporizes and reduces the rate of cooling. Thus, the piece should be agitated to remove the vapor film. An *up-and-down* movement or a *figure-eight* movement often is used. Where a spray quench is used, agitation is provided. Since increased agitation increases the severity of the quench, care must be taken not to agitate the work too vigorously, particularly in water or brine. The increased severity of the quench may cause cracks; this is especially true when parts with thin or irregular cross-sectional areas are quenched in water or brine.

Special Solutions: Special solutions are used in quenching special steels or steels for special purposes. Examples of special solutions include hot oil, molten salt baths, and molten lead. High-speed steels often are hardened at temperatures of 2100° to 2450° F.; they usually are quenched in molten lead or salt baths which are held at temperatures ranging from 800° to 1200° F. High-speed steels are relatively expensive, and their properties sometimes vary with different manufacturers. Consequently, it is advisable to follow the manufacturer's recommendations in heat-treating these steels.

A special molten salt solution is used for austempering in the temperature range from about 400° to 800° F. (Austempering is explained in Unit 157.) The salt melts at about 280° F. and may be used at working temperatures in the range from about 325° to 1000° F.

Several kinds or combinations of salt are available commercially for use as quenching media or as heating media for heat-treating operations. These salts are available with working temperatures ranging from about 325° to 2400° F. By comparison, lead has a total working temperature range from about 650° to 1700° F. The salts are water-soluble, thus permitting quenched parts to be cleaned easily in hot water after quenching. The salt is very corrosive when left on steel parts.

Development of Stress

When steel is hardened by quenching, internal stresses are developed. The amount of stress often is related to the severity of the quenching solution. The stresses, therefore, usually are greater when water or brine solutions are used. They occur because martensite forms near the surface first, then toward the center. The temperature difference between the center and the surface of the steel also causes uneven rates of expansion and contraction. Both factors cause internal stress.

Because of the internal stresses in hardened high-carbon steel, the material usually is so hard and brittle that it is of little practical use until it has been tempered. A piece of high-carbon steel which has been water-quenched often will fracture when struck lightly with a hammer. Hence, in most applications, before hardened steel may be used, the internal stress must be removed by a heat-treatment process called tempering. The hardened steel should be tempered as soon after hardening as possible, preferably before the piece has cooled to room temperature. When completely hardened steel gets cold, the internal stresses are further increased. If left in this condition, the steel sometimes will crack by itself.

Tempering is discussed in Unit 154. The procedures for hardening and tempering of steel are outlined in Unit 155.

Tempering, Annealing, and Normalizing

The Tempering Process

Tempering is a heating and cooling process which relieves some of the brittleness and internal stress developed in steel during the hardening operation. This process causes some loss of hardness and tensile strength, but it increases toughness. Tempering also is called drawing. To *draw* hardened steel means to *temper* it.

The tempering process follows hardening. It involves heating hardened steel to a temperature somewhere below the lower critical temperature; this is below the temperature at which steel begins to harden when quenched. The heated part then is allowed to cool in air, or it may be quenched. The rate of cooling is of little significance. However, cooling in still air often is preferred when the nature of the workpiece will permit this procedure.

The primary purposes of tempering are to relieve internal stresses and to increase toughness in hardened steel, not to reduce hardness and strength. If it were possible to increase toughness without reducing hardness and tensile strength, the ideal combination of properties would be attained. As the hardness of hardened steel is decreased by tempering, the tensile strength also is decreased, but toughness is increased.

When high-carbon steel is fully hardened, its grain structure is fully martensitic. Pure martensite is a supersaturated solution of carbon in ferrite (nearly pure iron). This is an abnormal arrangement for carbon and iron at low temperatures. Martensite is extremely hard and brittle, and it also is under great internal stress and strain. When parts in this condition are used, there is danger of fracturing. Hence, the parts must be tempered to increase toughness before use.

Tempering Temperatures

When hardened steel is tempered, the grain structure is called *tempered martensite*. There are varying degrees of tempered martensite, depending on the tempering temperature. Tempering permits the carbon (which is in solution in martensite) to be released in the form of tiny particles of cementite. At the lower tempering temperatures, some of the carbon and iron in martensite start to combine, thus forming tiny particles of cementite. This is a more normal atomic arrangement for carbon in steel at lower temperatures. Consequently, some internal stress and strain is relieved, and the steel becomes tougher. At the same time, there is some loss of hardness. With an increase in the tempering temperature, the cementite particles increase in number and size. This causes a further increase in toughness and a further loss of hardness.

Steel which has toughness also has some degree of plasticity. This means that it will deform to some extent before fracturing. The amount of plasticity depends on the degree of toughness. In turn, as previously explained, the toughness obtained in tempering varies with the tempering temperature.

The temperature to which steel is heated for tempering depends on the following factors:

1. The type of steel (carbon steel or special alloy steel).
2. The carbon content.
3. The hardness required.
4. The toughness required.

The effect of various tempering temperatures on the hardness of plain carbon steels with 0.457% and 0.95% carbon content is shown in Fig. 17-29. The hardness values indicate the surface hardness only, since carbon steels are relatively shallow-hardening. The major factors affecting maximum obtainable hardness include carbon content, hardening temperature, quenching medium, and cross-

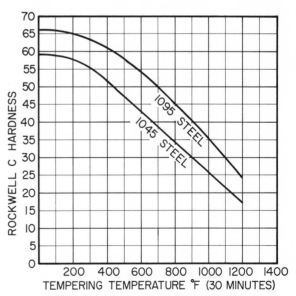

Fig. 17-29. Effect of Various Tempering Temperatures on the Hardness of Carbon Steel

Surface hardness of Carbon steel bars, SAE 1045 steel ¾" square, and SAE 1095 steel ½" diameter, after tempering at various temperatures. Both steels were hardened in a water quench, the 1045 steel at 1500°F. and the 1095 steel at 1450°F.

sectional size. The data concerning these factors are indicated below the figure just described.

It will be noted in Fig. 17-29 that there is little loss of hardness at temperatures below 250° F. At higher temperatures, the rate at which hardness decreases is more rapid. Suggested tempering temperatures for various tools are shown in Table 24.

Temperatures in the range from about 300° to 1100° F. are used for various tempering applications with carbon steels (Table 23). Temperatures as low as 300° F. are used in tempering items which require a combination of very

Fig. 17-30. Notched-Bar Specimens for Impact-Toughness Tests (U.S. Steel)

Table 24
Typical Tempering Temperatures for Various Tools

Degrees Fahrenheit	Temper Color	Tools
380	Very light yellow	Tools which require maximum hardness: lathe centers and cutting tools for lathes and shapers
425	Light straw	Milling cutters, drills, and reamers
465	Dark straw	Taps, threading dies, punches, dies, and hacksaw blades
490	Yellowish brown	Hammer faces, shear blades, rivet sets, and wood chisels
525	Purple	Center punches and scratch awls
545	Violet	Cold chisels, knives, and axes
590	Pale blue	Screwdrivers, wrenches, and hammers

high hardness and some toughness, such as ball bearings and roller bearings. Lathe centers require very high hardness and may be tempered at temperatures as low as 380° F. Temperatures within the range from about 380° to 600° F. are used for tempering many cutting tools. Articles which require very high toughness, such as steering knuckles for automobiles, are tempered in the range above 800° F., usually from 800° to 1100° F.

High-speed tool steels generally are tempered at temperatures much higher than those used for carbon steels. Usually they are tempered in the range from 1000° to 1100° F. It always is advisable to follow the manufacturer's recommendations in selecting temperatures for hardening and tempering high-speed steels and special tool and die steels.

Determining Toughness

The toughness of tempered steel often is interpreted or estimated in terms of hardness. Hardness and toughness vary indirectly with each other. As the hardness is reduced by higher tempering temperatures, toughness is increased. The hardness may be measured with hardness-testing instruments as outlined in Unit 158.

A tool such as a cold chisel may be tempered at the suggested temperature indicated in Table 24. For high-carbon tool steel, this temperature should result in a combination of hardness and toughness required to produce satisfactory results for average applications. If

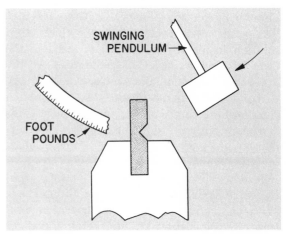

Fig. 17-31. Specimen Mounted for Izod Impact-Toughness Test

the chisel is too hard, the cutting edge may crack or chip when used. If it is too soft, the edge will dull rapidly. Cold chisels, depending on their particular applications, generally are hardened to values ranging from Rockwell C-45 to C-57. The tempering temperatures may be increased or decreased to produce the combination of hardness and toughness desired.

A tool such as a cold chisel or center punch should have a hard cutting edge and a soft head. The cutting end should be hardened and tempered for proper hardness and toughness. The head should be softer and tougher to withstand hammer blows. When only a portion of a workpiece is heat-treated, the procedure is called *selective* heat treatment. It is possible to apply any of the common heat-treatment processes to only a portion of a tool or part.

Notched-Bar Toughness: The toughness of notched-bar test specimens, of the type shown in Fig. 17-30, is determined by laboratory testing equipment. The most commonly used standard-size specimen is 10 millimeters (0.3937") square, the type shown to the left in Fig. 17-30. A pendulum is allowed to swing against the specimen, as shown in Figs. 17-31, 17-32, and 17-33. The difference in the height of the pendulum at the beginning and at the end of the swing is registered on a gage which indicates the energy absorbed in fracturing the specimen. The toughness of notched-bar specimens is indicated in *foot-pounds* of energy required to fracture the notched specimen.

Two standard tests, the Charpy and the Izod tests, utilize test specimens of the same size. A V-type notch is standard for the Izod test specimen. Although other notch designs often are used for the Charpy test, the V-type may be used for the Charpy specimen also.

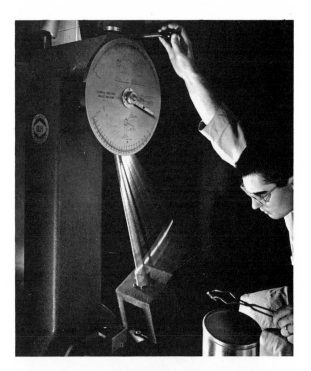

Fig. 17-33. Pendulum Impact Testing Machine
(U.S. Steel)
(A) Making Charpy test; (B) How Charpy test specimen is mounted for test.

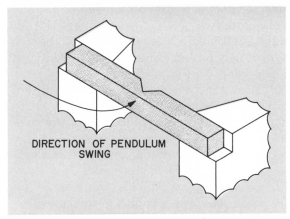

DIRECTION OF PENDULUM SWING

Fig. 17-32. Specimen Mounted for Charpy Impact-Toughness Test

It then is called the *Charpy V-notch* specimen. The V-type notched-bar specimen is shown in Fig. 17-30.

For the Izod test, the specimen is mounted in the machine by clamping it at one end, as shown in Fig. 17-31. For the Charpy test, the specimen is mounted as shown in Fig. 17-32; a knife-shaped edge on the pendulum strikes the specimen on the side opposite from the notch. The pendulum impact-testing machine in Fig. 17-33 is equipped for the Charpy impact test. Certain machines of this type also may be equipped with Izod test fixtures for use in making Izod tests.

Brittle Temperature Range: The temperature range between 400° and 700° F. often is called the *brittle temperature* range. It is so named because notched-bar specimens tempered in this range actually exhibit less toughness than those which are tempered at temperatures below or above this range. However, these toughness ratings sometimes are misleading; they usually do not apply to the toughness of specimens of similar cross-sectional size which do not possess sharp notches or fillets. This factor is not clearly understood by some heat-treaters. Consequently, the *brittle tempering* range from 400° to 700° F. too often is avoided in tempering applications.

Notched-bar tests of tempered specimens do illustrate clearly, however, that the presence of sharp notches, corners, or fillets affects the toughness of hardened and tempered parts. Therefore, parts which possess these features generally should not be tempered within the brittle temperature range, if greater toughness is required. Rather, they should be tempered at temperatures either below or above this range.

Tempering should follow immediately after hardening, particularly with high-carbon steels. After quenching, hardened steel should be allowed to cool only to the highest temperatures at which it may be handled safely with bare hands. If tempering is delayed until the part becomes cold, internal stresses increase, and there is greater possibility of cracking.

Time at Temperature: The time at which a part is held (soaked) at the tempering temperature is important. The soaking period permits time for atomic rearrangement and for relief of internal stresses. The article to be tempered should be heated uniformly to the desired temperature. It should then be soaked for a period of about one hour for each inch of thickness. Thus a part which is 3″ thick should be soaked at the tempering temperature for a minimum of three hours. Items ¼″ or less in thickness need not be soaked beyond the period necessary for bringing them up to the uniform required temperature.

Annealing

Annealing is a process which involves heating and cooling of steel to produce softening and to improve machinability. Annealing also relieves internal stress and strain caused by previous heat treatment, by machining, or by other cold-working operations.

The temperature to which steel is heated for annealing operations depends on the type of steel and the purpose for which the annealing is being done. Three types of annealing are in common industrial use. Each type is utilized to produce a somewhat different change in the metal. The common types include full annealing, process annealing, and spheroidizing.

Full Annealing: Full annealing is a process utilized primarily to produce maximum softness in steel. It also improves machinability and relieves internal stress. It may be used to soften hard steel or to soften work-hardened steel for remachining. If a file is fully annealed, a hole may be drilled through it, or it may be remachined for some other use.

Procedure for Full Annealing:

1. Heat the part uniformly to the full annealing temperature. This is about 50° F. above the upper critical temperature (represented by line A_3 in Figs. 17-23 and 17-24). The annealing temperature also is shown in Table 32, appendix.

2. Soak the part at this temperature for about one hour per inch of thickness.

3. Allow the part to cool slowly. It may be removed from the furnace and packed in

lime or ashes for slow cooling. *Or the furnace may be shut off and the part permitted to cool slowly in the furnace.*

Process Annealing: Process annealing, often termed stress-relief annealing, is utilized primarily for relieving internal stresses due to machining or other cold-working processes. Most frequently it is applied to low-carbon steels.

Procedure for Process Annealing:
1. Heat uniformly to about 30° F. below the lower critical temperature. The lower critical temperature is represented by line A_1 in Fig. 17-24. Temperatures as low as 1000° F. may be used if no further machining is involved.
2. Allow the part to soak at the desired annealing temperature for a period of about one hour per inch of thickness.
3. Remove the part from the furnace and allow it to cool in air.

Spheroidizing: Spheroidizing is a process which involves heating and cooling of steel to produce a special kind of grain structure that is relatively soft and machinable. This special microstructure has cementite in rounded globules called *spheroids*, as shown in Fig. 17-20. The spheroids are surrounded by ferrite (nearly pure iron). A microstructure of this type generally is tougher and more ductile than pearlite, which is produced by full annealing. Pearlite is shown in Fig. 17-19.

Spheroidizing generally is applied to high-carbon steels to improve machinability. It also is used to prepare high-carbon steel for cold-drawing into wire.

Procedure for Spheroidizing. The procedure for this process varies considerably with different types of steel. It also varies with the different conditions of heat treatment existing in steel parts. The following is one of several procedures which may be utilized with plain high-carbon steel which is in a fully-hardened (martinsitic) condition:

1. Heat the part uniformly to a temperature just below the lower critical temperature (represented by line A_1 in Fig. 17-24).
2. Allow the part to soak for several hours.
3. Allow the part to cool slowly in the furnace, about 50° to 100° F. per hour, to a temperature below 1000° F.
4. Remove the part from the furnace, and allow it to cool in air.

Normalizing

Normalizing is a process which involves heating steel to slightly above the hardening temperature, soaking it at this temperature, and cooling to room temperature in air. Normalizing relieves internal stresses due to machining, forging, and cold working. It removes all previous effects due to heat treatment. Normalizing also softens hardened steel and improves its machinability. However, it does not result in the uniformity and degree of softness which is produced by full annealing.

Parts of irregular cross section may lack uniformity of hardness and ductility after normalizing, particularly where thin sections are involved. The grain structure of normalized steel is generally somewhat harder, less ductile, and has a finer pearlitic grain structure than fully-annealed steel.

Procedure for Normalizing Steel:
1. Heat the part uniformly to the normalizing temperature indicated in Fig. 17-24, or in Table 32, appendix.
2. Soak the part at this temperature for about one hour per inch of diameter.
3. Remove the part from the furnace, and allow it to cool to room temperature in air. *Note:* High-carbon steel ⅛″ or less in thickness may cool rapidly enough in circulating cool air to become partially hardened. The rate of cooling may be slowed, and normalizing improved, by packing the part in lime or ashes.

How To Harden and Temper Steel

The metallurgical theory and the principles involved in hardening and tempering were discussed in the four preceding units. The more advanced student, or the student seeking a clear understanding of these two processes, should study these preceding units first. However, by carefully following the procedure outlined in this unit, steel tools or parts can be hardened and tempered with good results.

The Processes

Let us briefly review the nature of hardening and tempering so as to summarize the previous four units.

Hardening is a process which makes high-carbon steels and tool steels extremely hard and brittle — too much so for practical use. In this condition, they will fracture easily. In fact, the internal stresses developed in hardening are so great that cracks may occur in the part if it is allowed to become cold after the quenching process. Therefore, hardened parts should be tempered as soon as the part has cooled sufficiently to be handled safely in the bare hands.

Tempering is a process which relieves the internal stresses which develop in steel while it is hardened by quenching. Tempering increases the toughness of hardened parts. It also causes them to become more plastic or ductile in nature. Of course, as with most heat-treatment processes, a gain in one property often causes a loss in another. Tempering causes some loss of hardness in hardened steel. The ideal heat treatment, therefore, is a combination of maximum hardness associated with adequate toughness.

Briefly, the general procedure for hardening is:

1. Heat the work uniformly to the hardening temperature.
2. Soak the part at this temperature for the appropriate period of time.

3. Cool the part by quenching in the proper quenching medium, such as water, brine, oil, or air.

Briefly, the general procedure for tempering is:

1. Heat the part uniformly to the proper tempering temperature.
2. Allow the part to *soak* at the tempering temperature for the proper period of time.
3. Allow the part to cool in air or by quenching. Cooling in still air usually is recommended when the nature of the work permits this method. When selective areas of a part are tempered, they usually must be cooled by quenching.

Preliminary Planning

Before attempting to harden and temper steel tools or parts, you should know the type of steel you are working with. This information usually is included on the drawing or blueprint for the part, or it may be identified by your instructor. An approximate method which may be used for determining an unknown type of steel is spark testing, Unit 146.

When you have identified the kind of steel, you can determine the following information required for proper hardening and tempering of the part: the hardening temperature, the quenching medium, the combination of hardness and toughness desired, and the tempering temperature.

Hardening Temperature: The hardening temperature usually is from 50° to 100° F. above the upper critical temperature (represented as line A_3 in Fig. 17-24). Thus, the hardening temperatures for various plain carbon steels can be interpreted from Fig. 17-24. The hardening temperatures for various heat-treating grades of steel also are shown in Table 32, appendix. For high-speed steels and tool steels, the manufacturer's recommendations should be followed.

Quenching Medium: The proper quenching medium for various heat-treating grades of steels is listed in Table 32, appendix. Plain carbon steels generally are quenched in water or brine. Some alloy steels may be quenched in water, but most must be quenched in oil. High-speed steels and tool steels should be quenched as recommended by the manufacturer. Water should be at a temperature of about 60° F. Oil, as recommended in Unit 153, cools best when held at a temperature from 100° to 140° F. The average brine solution has about 8% salt, by weight.

Hardness and Toughness Desired: The combination of hardness and toughness desired will depend upon the application or desired use of the heat-treated part. Generally, maximum hardness associated with adequate toughness is most desirable. By studying Table 24 on page 598, and Fig. 17-29, you can determine the desirable degree of hardness and toughness. The hardness of metals can be determined by methods outlined in Unit 158.

Tempering Temperature: After determining the degree of hardness and toughness, the tempering temperature also may be determined from Table 24 and Fig. 17-29.

Soaking Period: When steel is heated to either the hardening or the tempering temperature, it should be allowed to soak at this temperature long enough for required internal changes to occur in the grain structure. Parts with a thickness of ¼″ or less do not require a soaking period. Parts of greater thickness usually should soak for about one hour per inch of thickness. For parts from ¼″ to 1″ in thickness, the period should be from 3 minutes to one hour, depending upon the thickness.

Heating Precautions

The following precautions should be taken when heating steel to the hardening temperature:

1. Heat parts slowly and uniformly to avoid excessive internal stresses and distortion.

The rate of heating is most rapid in a molten bath (such as a salt or lead bath), less rapid in a gas furnace, and least rapid in an electric furnace.

2. When two furnaces are available, preheat large parts in one furnace to about 1000° F. Then transfer the parts to the second furnace which is at the proper hardening temperature. More uniform heating and less distortion will result.

3. Support long parts on fire bricks or other suitable refractory material to prevent sagging or bending.

4. Avoid excessively long soaking periods. They cause decarburization (loss of carbon) of the surface, scaling, and coarseness of grain structure.

5. Adjust the fuel and air mixture so that the furnace atmosphere is neutral to slightly oxidizing, rather than carburizing. An oxidizing flame has a slight excess of air.

6. Avoid or reduce surface oxidation (scaling) and decarburization by providing a protective atmosphere in the furnace. Several methods are used for this in large industrial heat-treatment furnaces. Oxidation and decarburization also may be reduced by heating in a molten salt or lead bath. Molten baths are described in Unit 153. The rate of heating is much more rapid in molten baths than in furnaces. Certain alloy steels will crack when placed directly into molten baths at hardening temperatures.

7. Reduce surface oxidation and decarburization by *pack heating*. With this method, steel parts first are placed in a container. They then are packed with cast iron chips and are heated to the hardening temperature. After the proper soaking period, they are removed from the container for quenching.

8. If steel inadvertently is heated significantly above the proper hardening temperature, allow the part to cool in air to below 1000° F. Then reheat it to the proper hardening temperature. Otherwise the grain will become too coarse for the

best combination of hardness and toughness.

9. Quench parts immediately upon removal from the furnace or heat bath. A significant delay will permit a drop in temperature and increase the coarseness in the grain structure.

10. In general, heat alloy steels to the hardening temperature more slowly than plain carbon steels. Also, for the best surface appearance, heat them in a controlled atmosphere, either in a furnace or by the pack method.

Procedure for Hardening Steel

1. Determine the hardening temperature, and light the furnace as directed by your instructor. Allow the furnace to reach the hardening temperature. If the furnace is equipped with a temperature-control device, it should be set at this temperature.

2. With a pair of tongs, place the part in the furnace, and allow it to heat uniformly to the hardening temperature. If the furnace is equipped with a temperature control, the procedure is simple and the temperature will not be exceeded. Without temperature controls, however, care must be taken not to overheat the part. The temperature can be estimated through the use of the temperature color chart in Table 23 and Fig. 17-26. A magnet also should be used to check the temperature of the part. The hardening temperature for medium- and low-carbon steels is from 50° to 100° F. above the magnetic point — the temperature at which steel is no longer magnetic. The magnetic point is represented by line A_2 in Fig. 17-24.

3. Allow the part to soak at the hardening temperature for the proper period of time.

4. Select the proper quenching medium, and quench the part. Agitate the part in the solution, using and *up-and-down* movement. If the part is thin and flat, use a cutting motion, as with a knife, to prevent warping due to uneven cooling.

5. Determine whether the part is properly hardened. This can be done by testing with the *corner* of a file — not the flat face, since hardened steel will dull the teeth and ruin the file. If the part is properly hardened, the file either will not cut the metal or will cut with great difficulty. A properly-hardened piece is very hard and brittle, and it is under great internal stress. It should be tempered as soon as possible to prevent cracking.

Procedure for Tempering

With Temperature Controls: To temper the whole part in a furnace equipped with temperature-indicating controls:

1. Light the tempering furnace as directed by your instructor, and allow it to heat to the tempering temperature.

2. Place the part in the furnace, using a pair of tongs. Allow time for the work to heat uniformly to the tempering temperature. Then soak the work at the temperature for the desired period of time.

3. Remove the part from the furnace with tongs, and allow it to cool in still air or by quenching, as desired. Cooling in air usually is recommended.

4. Determine the hardness as outlined in Unit 158.

Without Temperature Controls: To temper the whole part in a furnace or over an open flame without the use of temperature controls:

1. Using a piece of abrasive cloth, remove the scale from the part until it is clean and bright, so that temper colors can be seen.

2. Light the furnace or flame, as directed by your instructor. A low flame is best for tempering.

3. Using a pair of tongs, hold the work over the flame, and heat slowly. Rotate the piece so that it will heat uniformly to the proper tempering temperature. The temperature is identified by the temper color, as in Table 24.

4. Remove the part from the furnace or flame, and allow it to cool as desired, either in still air, or by quenching.

5. Determine the hardness as outlined in Unit 158.

Small Cutting Tools: To temper small cutting tools, such as a small center punch or cold chisel:

1. Harden the whole tool as outlined above.

2. Using a piece of abrasive cloth, remove the scale until the tool is clean and bright.

3. Heat a scrap piece of steel red-hot.

4. Lay the tool on the hot piece of steel, being careful to extend the cutting end beyond the end of the block. Thus the opposite end will heat first.

5. Watch the temper colors. When the desired color reaches the cutting end, quench the tool in water. This will prevent the cutting end from being overheated due to the excess heat in the opposite end of the tool.

This procedure also may be used for tempering small tools over a small flame (such as that produced by a Bunsen burner), instead of a scrap steel block. Care must be taken to heat only the area or end opposite from the cutting end. As the tool is heated, the heat gradually will conduct toward the cutting end of the tool until the proper temper color appears for quenching.

Casehardening Processes

Casehardening is a process which produces a hardened layer on the surface of ferrous alloys, as shown in Fig. 17-34. The inner core below the hardened surface remains relatively soft. The steels most frequently used for casehardening include plain low-carbon steels and certain low-carbon, low-alloy steels. The low-alloy steels usually are alloyed with nickel, chromium, and molybdenum. The casehardened surface provides a combination of increased wear resistance and increased strength over a softer and tougher inner core.

Many tools and parts require only *casehardening*, rather than *through hardening*. Consequently, such items may be made from the less-expensive casehardening grades of steel. Items which frequently are casehardened include small hand tools, large wrenches, toolholders for machine tools, bolts, setscrews, pins, bearing surfaces, gears, pinions, splines, and shafts.

A casehardened surface may vary in depth from several thousandths of an inch to one-eighth inch. The depth depends upon the casehardening process and procedures used. The surface hardness is usually in the range from Rockwell C-60 to C-66. The core hardness depends largely on the carbon content of the steel. It usually is from C-20 to C-30 for steels with low-carbon content.

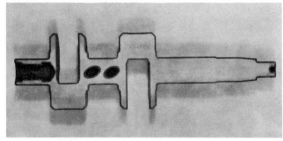

Fig. 17-34. Cross Section of Casehardened, Carburized, Outboard Motor Crankshaft (AJAX Electric)

Effects of Casehardening

Casehardening alters the chemical content and the grain structure of the surface layer of ferrous metals. Steels with low-carbon content cannot be hardened significantly by heating and quenching. Therefore, substances must be added to the surface layer to cause it to harden when properly heated and quenched. These substances include carbon, nitrogen, or various combinations of carbon and nitrogen. They can be introduced into the surface of a ferrous alloy by various casehardening processes.

When carbon is introduced in the surface layer of low-carbon steel, by a process called *carburizing*, the surface layer then becomes high-carbon steel. When heated to the proper hardening temperature and quenched, this layer will become hardened.

When nitrogen is absorbed in the surface of steel, nitrides form; these are very hard and aid in producing a hardened surface. Both nitrogen and carbon are absorbed in the surface of ferrous alloys in certain casehardening processes, which will be discussed shortly.

General Procedures

Casehardening processes, like other heat-treatment processes, include several basic procedures according to a time-and-temperature cycle. There may be variations for specific casehardening processes, depending on the materials and equipment used. However, the following basic procedures usually are involved in most casehardening processes:

1. The parts are heated to the proper case-hardening temperature.
2. The parts are soaked at this temperature while in contact with the casehardening substance being absorbed into the surface.
3. The parts are quenched, at the proper hardening temperature, in water, brine, oil, or air. Plain carbon steels generally are quenched in brine or water. Certain alloys are quenched in oil. Cooling in air sometimes is utilized for nitriding special steels.
4. When parts are to be tempered, this is done soon after hardening.

Although many casehardened parts are used without being tempered, the majority are tempered before use. Tempering is performed at low temperatures, usually in the range from 250° to 400° F. At these temperatures, there is little loss of hardness, and internal stress is adequately relieved. Deeply hardened surfaces sometimes are tempered at higher temperatures to avoid surface cracking or chipping.

The Casehardening Processes

The following casehardening processes commonly are used in industrial applications:
A. Carburizing processes
  1. Pack carburizing
  2. Gas carburizing
  3. Liquid carburizing
B. Carbonitriding processes
  1. Cyaniding (liquid carbonitriding)
  2. Carbonitriding (gas atmosphere used)
C. Nitriding processes
  1. Gas nitriding
  2. Liquid nitriding

The principal difference between carburizing, carbonitriding, and nitriding is in the materials introduced into the surfaces. In carburizing processes, the materials introduced include only carbon. In nitriding, only nitrogen is introduced. In carbonitriding, both carbon and nitrogen are introduced.

Carburizing Processes

It was previously stated that in order to caseharden ferrous alloys of low-carbon content, it is necessary first to introduce carbon, nitrogen, or a combination of these elements into the surface. *Carburizing* is a process which introduces *carbon* into the surface of solid ferrous alloys. It involves heating the steel while in contact with a carbonaceous substance. Carburizing temperatures are above the upper critical temperature of the steel, usually from 1650° to 1700° F.

In carburizing operations, the steel must be soaked at the carburizing temperature long enough to permit the carbon to penetrate to proper depth for casehardening. This depth may vary from several thousandths to one-eighth inch, depending on requirements. The time required for penetration varies with the carburizing temperatures, the carburizing substance used, and the depth of penetration desired.

The carbonaceous substances used for introducing carbon into steel include solid materials, liquids, and gases. Three common carburizing processes, therefore, often are designated according to the kind of carburizing material used. These processes include *pack*, *gas*, and *liquid* carburizing. Solid carburizing materials are used for pack carburizing.

Pack Carburizing: The pack carburizing process perhaps can be understood best when the equipment, materials, and procedures involved are explained. The parts to be carburized first are placed in a steel box. A carbonaceous substance then is packed around them. There usually is about ½″ to 1″ of material between the parts. The box generally is made of sheet or plate steel.

Several kinds of carbonaceous substances in the form of grains or fine pellets are available for pack carburizing. These materials are mixtures usually composed of various proportions of the following materials: carbonates, coke, hardwood charcoal, and binders. The binders may consist of materials such as oil, tar, or molasses. Mixtures of charred leather, bones, and charcoal sometimes are used. Carburizing materials may be reused a number of times. However, since the materials decompose with repeated use, fresh materials should be added to the used materials as necessary.

Carburizing materials of the type listed above are inflammable. Therefore, the box in which they are packed must be covered and sealed tightly enough to prevent air from entering and burning the material. However, the cover also must provide a means for exhausting gas pressure which may develop within the box. The cover may be sealed with fire clay or other suitable refractory cement.

The packed box of parts then is placed in a furnace where it is heated to the carburizing temperature. The box is allowed to soak at this temperature until the parts are carburized to the required depth. Carburizing temperatures in the range from 1500° to 1800° F. may be used. However, temperatures from 1650° to 1700° F. are used most often. At the higher

temperatures, carbon penetrates the surface more rapidly. In fact, at 1700° F., the rate of carburization is about double that at 1500° F. At 1700° F., the approximate time required to carburize to various depths is as follows: 4 hours for depths from .0.030″ to 0.045″, 8 hours for ⅟₁₆″ depth, and 24 to 30 hours for a depth of ⅛″. At the carburizing temperature, carbon monoxide is released from the carburizing compound. Carbon from the carbon monoxide is absorbed by the surface of the steel parts.

When the parts are carburized to the desired depth, the box is removed from the furnace and allowed to cool. The parts then are removed from the box and cleaned. They may be cleaned by several methods, including sandblasting, tumbling with abrasive materials in tumbling machines, or hand cleaning with a scraper and wire brush.

After Carburizing: Several different heat-treatment procedures may follow carburizing. However, each procedure involves quenching the carburized part to harden the surface. The simplest procedure is to quench the part directly from the carburizing temperature, usually from about 1650° to 1700° F. This hardens both the surface and the core, so far as the core is capable of being hardened.

Another simple treatment is used widely. The parts are allowed to cool slowly from the carburizing temperature. They then are reheated to the hardening temperature of the high-carbon steel case, about 1430° F., and quenched. This procedure hardens the surface, but not the low-carbon steel core. The hardening temperature for the core usually is from 1650° to 1700° F.

A third procedure is to *double quench*. The part is first heated to the hardening temperature of the low-carbon steel core, about 1650° F., and quenched. This hardens both the surface and the core, but the surface grain structure is relatively coarse. Hence, the part is then reheated to the hardening temperature of the surface, about 1430° F., and quenched. This refines the grain structure of the core, and it hardens the surface at a temperature which will produce a more desirable combination of hardness and toughness. The case-hardened parts may be tempered, if desired.

How to Carburize: For the school shop, one of the safest and most common methods of casehardening involves pack carburizing with a commercial material such as Kasenit, a nonpoisonous, noninflammable, carbonaceous substance. Pack carburizing with a material of this type is done in an open or well-vented container. The container may be made of sheet or plate steel construction. The following procedure generally is used.

Pack Method: (For case depths up to 0.015")

1. Place the part in an open, shallow container, and cover it with Kasenit or other equivalent carburizing compound. A well-vented cover may be placed on the container if desired.
2. Place the part in a furnace, heat to 1650° F., and soak at this temperature for 15 to 60 minutes, depending on the depth of case desired. A case depth from about 0.005" to 0.020" can be obtained in this manner.
3. Use dry tongs to remove the part from the molten compound, and quench in clean cool water.
4. The part may be tempered if desired. A tempering temperature of 300° F. is satisfactory for many applications.

Dip Method: (For a shallow case, several thousandths of an inch in depth)

1. Heat the part uniformly to about 1650° F. At this temperature, the steel will have a bright red color.
2. Dip or roll the part in Kasenit, or in an equivalent casehardening compound, until a crust is fused to the surface.
3. Reheat to about 1650° F., and quench immediately in clean cool water.
4. To increase the depth of the case, repeat steps 2 and 3 before quenching.
5. Temper if desired. Tempering very often is omitted when parts are casehardened to very shallow depths.

Gas Carburizing: In gas carburizing, parts are heated to the carburizing temperature in gas atmosphere. Common

Fig. 17-35. Gas-Carburized Roller Races Ready to be Discharged from Carburizing Furnace
(Amer. Gas Furnace)

Fig. 17-36. Rotary Gas-Carburizing Furnace Being Discharged into Quenching Tank (Amer. Gas Furnace)

fuel gases (such as natural gas, commercial gas, or propane gas) are used. The gas provides the source of carbon which is absorbed into the surface at the carburizing temperature.

Special furnaces are required for gas carburizing. The parts are placed in a sealed gas container which serves as the carburizing chamber. An inlet for circulating gas and an outlet for exhaust gases are provided for the chamber. The gas chamber is heated from an external source, usually by fuel gas or oil. Industrial-type gas-carburizing furnaces are shown in Figs. 17-35 and 17-36.

The parts are soaked in the carburizing chamber at the carburizing temperature for a period of time which depends upon the depth of case desired. With a carburizing temperature of about 1700° F., case depths of 0.020″ to 0.030″ are obtained during a period of four hours. Greater case depths are obtained with longer carburizing periods.

The parts may be quenched directly from the carburizing temperature when the design of the furnace permits this arrangement, as in Fig. 17-36. Or, the parts may be allowed to cool first. They then are reheated to the hardening temperature and quenched. Quenching directly from the carburizing chambers is preferred, as it prevents buildup of oxidation or scale on the surface. Thus, the need for surface-cleaning operations is eliminated.

Liquid Carburizing: Liquid carburizing is a process of casehardening steel parts by carburizing them in molten salt baths. These baths are mixtures composed largely of cyanides, chlorides, and carbonates. Such salts introduce both carbon and nitrogen into the surface. The proportion of either the carbon or nitrogen absorbed can be regulated by the composition of the salt bath. In liquid carburizing, the substance absorbed into the case is largely carbon. The parts shown in Fig. 17-37 are being liquid carburized in salt-bath furnaces.

Liquid carburizing temperatures usually range from about 1550° to 1700° F. A case depth of about 0.020″ can be obtained at a carburizing temperature of 1650° F. during a period of 2 hours. Case depths of $1/16$″ require more than 24 hours.

When the parts have been carburized to the desired depth, they may be quenched directly from the molten salt bath. Liquid-carburized parts generally are quenched in water or brine, although those steels requiring it may be quenched in oil. Since the molten salts are water-soluble, a water quench aids in cleaning the parts. The parts may be tempered as desired. Low tempering temperatures generally are used.

Safety Precautions

CAUTION: *Since certain solutions are potential hazards, the following safety precautions in the use of carburizing, cyaniding, and nitriding salt baths are extremely important:*

1. Cyanides are fatally poisonous if taken internally. Cyanides are included in some proportion in salt baths used for carburizing, cyaniding, and nitriding.
2. Cyanides are violently poisonous when brought into contact with open wounds or scratches.
3. Fatally poisonous fumes are developed when cyanide is brought into contact with acids.
4. The precautions exercised in handling carburizing salts containing cyanides are the same as those for handling cyaniding and nitriding salts.

Fig. 17-37. Gears Being Liquid Carburized in a Salt Bath (AJAX Electric)

5. Violent explosions or splattering will result when water or moisture comes in contact with a container of molten cyanide.

6. Workpieces must be clean and dry before being placed in contact with cyanides.

7. Slight amounts of moisture, even from the atmosphere, will cause spatter in molten cyanides. Moisture on workpieces or tongs can cause violent spatter.

8. The salt bath and rinse tanks must be carefully vented to the outdoors to remove fumes.

9. Workers and others in the area where cyanides are used should wear asbestos gloves, asbestos aprons, and safety glasses or shields.

10. If nitrate-nitrite salts come in contact with molten nitriding salts, a violent explosion will result.

11. The remelting of a frozen cyanide salt bath can be very dangerous because of the expansion of gases when the salt is reheated. This problem does not arise in furnaces equipped with immersed electrodes because the salts melt from the top down. However, when molten cyanide is allowed to freeze in other types of furnaces, a steel or cast iron wedge should be

Fig. 17-38. Parts Being Lowered into Salt-Bath Furnace for Cyanide Hardening (AJAX Electric)

placed in the center of the pot, with the tapered end down and touching the bottom. The top of the wedge should extend about 5″ above the level of the salt. Before the salt is reheated, the wedge should be removed. The wedge may be loosened by tapping it on alternate sides with a hammer. As the frozen cyanide is reheated, the gases can escape through the cavity provided. *Never* should the wedge be removed before the salt is completely frozen; molten salt may be blown out from the bottom, through the wedge opening.

Carbonitriding Processes

The two principal casehardening processes which introduce both carbon and nitrogen into the surface of the steel are *cyaniding* (liquid carbonitriding) and *carbonitriding* (gas cyaniding).

Cyaniding: Cyaniding is a liquid carbonitriding process. The parts are cyanided to the proper case depth in a molten, cyaniding salt bath and quenched. This produces a hardened case to depths which seldom exceed 0.020″. The case depth depends upon the cyaniding temperature and the composition of the salt bath. The parts shown in Fig. 17-38 are being lowered into a cyanide-salt-bath furnace for cyaniding.

The salt bath usually is composed of cyanide-carbonate-chloride salts. The proportion of cyanide salts may vary from about 30% to 97%. An increase in cyanide concentration increases the proportion of carbon in the surface case.

The cyaniding temperature is above the lower critical temperature of the steel, usually in the range from 1400° to 1600° F. For greater surface depths, the range from 1550° to 1600° F. is used most frequently.

Cyaniding generally produces a surface case which is relatively shallow in comparison with carburizing processes. It is most efficient for short immersion periods, usually from 30 to 60 minutes. At a cyaniding temperature of 1550° F., the following approximate case depths can be obtained: 0.003″ to 0.005″ in 30 minutes, 0.005″ to 0.010″ in 1 hour, and about 0.015″ in 2 hours.

Cyanided parts may be quenched directly from the salt bath, into water, brine, or mineral oil, depending on the type of steel. Although most of the salt will be removed during the quench, the parts should be thoroughly rinsed or washed off with hot water or steam after quenching. The parts may be tempered if desired, usually at temperatures from 250° to 300° F.

CAUTION: *Again, cyanide salts are highly poisonous. They are fatal if taken internally, if exposed to scratches or open wounds, or if fumes are inhaled. The safety precautions outlined on page 609 should be strictly followed when cyaniding or working with salt baths containing cyanides.*

Carbonitriding: *Carbonitriding* frequently is termed *dry cyaniding* or *gas cyaniding*. It is a process which affects steel in a manner similar to cyaniding (liquid carbonitriding) by similarly introducing carbon and nitrogen into the surface of steel parts to form a hard, wear-resistant surface.

The process involves soaking steel parts at an elevated temperature in a gaseous atmosphere. The surface of the parts absorbs both carbon and nitrogen, simultaneously, from the gas atmosphere (composed of a mixture of carburizing gas and ammonia). The ammonia supplies the nitrogen.

A special furnace, somewhat similar to a gas carburizing furnace, is used for carbonitriding. The parts do not come in contact with air, thus preventing oxidation or the buildup of scale on the parts.

The depth of the surface case depends upon the temperature and time. Temperatures ranging from about 1350° to 1650° F. may be used. The case depth generally is shallower than with gas carburizing. Case depths up to about 0.030″ can be produced during a period of 4 or 5 hours at 1600° F. However, lower temperatures often are used in order to introduce a larger proportion of nitrogen into the surface. A large percentage of carbonitrided parts is produced with case depths from 0.005″ to 0.010″ during a period of 1½ hours, at a temperature of about 1450° F.

Carbonitrided surfaces possess greater hardenability than carburized surfaces. Generally they are quenched to maximum hardness in oil. The oil quench results in less distortion of the parts.

Nitriding Processes

Nitriding is a casehardening process used to produce an exceptionally hard surface on certain alloy steel parts which have been previously machined and heat-treated. The process adds nitrogen to the surface of special alloy steels which are alloyed with nitride-forming elements. Because nitrides are exceptionally hard, they produce a harder surface than the previously heat-treated surface.

The alloy steels which are nitrided include various proportions of the following kinds of nitride-forming elements: aluminum, chromium, vanadium, and molybdenum. Nickel also is frequently alloyed with these steels to produce toughness.

Parts are nitrided by heating them at temperatures below the lower critical temperature, in a nitrogeneous atmosphere — either gas or a salt bath.

Gas Nitriding: For *gas nitriding*, ammonia gas is used most frequently. A protected atmosphere furnace is used. The nitriding temperature range usually is from 900° to 1050° F. Consequently, steels which are nitrided must have a tempering temperature which is at least 50° above the nitriding temperature.

The nitriding process is slow in comparison with other casehardening processes. The time required may take from 1 to 3 days, or longer, depending upon the case depth desired. Three days usually are required to produce a nitrided case about 0.015″ deep. Shorter periods are utilized for shallower case depths. Nitrided surfaces from 0.001″ to 0.003″ commonly are used on many high-speed steel cutting tools. No quenching is required. The low operating temperatures produce very little distortion.

Nitriding produces a harder surface than any other form of heat treatment. The surface hardness may range from Rockwell C-70 to C-75. The process does not affect the core properties of the steel.

Salt Bath: Nitriding also can be performed in a molten *salt bath*. The nitriding salt introduces nitrogen only into the surface of the steel. Several kinds of salt mixtures, which include cyanide salts, are available for this purpose. The working temperatures used are about the same as those used for gas nitriding. Nitriding salts, like carburizing salts and cyaniding salts, are highly poisonous. They are dangerous if not handled properly and safely. The safety precautions which should be followed when using nitriding salts are listed on page 609.

Nitriding improves surface hardness, wear resistance, resistance to galling, and fatigue resistance. It also improves corrosive resistance, except on stainless steels. Items made from high-speed steel, tool and die steel, and stainless steel often are nitrided. Common items include taps, dies, reamers, milling cutters and other cutting tools. The tool life of cutting tools often is doubled or tripled by nitriding.

157 Special Hardening Processes

This unit explains three heat treating processes used in special situations. *Flame hardening* and *induction hardening* require no furnace and the two are similar except for their source of heat. *Austempering* is a furnace-hardening process using a special quench to produce a grain structure (bainite) which is especially tough.

Flame Hardening

Flame hardening is a process used to harden selected surface areas of ferrous metals to depths from about $\frac{1}{32}''$ to $\frac{1}{4}''$, as desired. The selected area is heated rapidly to above the upper critical temperature with a concentrated flame. Quenching follows immediately. The part is spray-quenched with water from water jets located conveniently near the flame burners. Air-hardened steels usually are quenched with compressed air or circulating air. A cross-sectional view of a gear tooth which has been flame-hardened is shown in Fig. 17-41.

The flame is produced by mixtures of fuel gas and air or by an oxyacetylene flame. Burners or torches of special design are used to concentrate the flame in the area where hardening is desired. Small parts often are located in a stationary position under the flame. With very large parts, the flame may be guided steadily over the area to be hardened. In other setups, the part may be guided or revolved over the flame. A setup used to flame-harden the ways on a lathe bed is shown in Fig. 17-42. In this case, the flame is guided automatically

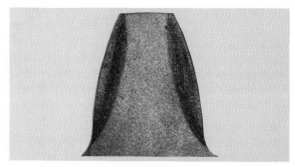

Fig. 17-41. Photograph of Etched Section of a Flame-Hardened Gear Tooth
(Linde Div. — Union Carbide)

along the lathe bed. The surface is heated and quenched in a single pass.

Flame-hardened parts generally should be tempered immediately following hardening. Usually they are tempered in the same manner in which furnace-hardened parts are tempered. Very large parts may be tempered by the *flame method*. This involves the use of a special low-temperature flame head designed to follow immediately behind the quench, thus heating the surface to the desired tempering temperature. On some very large parts, there is considerable residual heat below the hardened surfaces after quenching. This heat often is sufficient to temper the hardened surface.

Flame hardening may be applied to ferrous metals, including steels and certain kinds of cast iron, which are capable of being hardened. Thus, the metal must possess sufficient carbon content to be hardenable. Steel generally should have carbon content of 0.30% or more for flame hardening. Large cast-iron castings are very often flame-hardened, as in Fig. 17-41. Certain oil-hardening steels will crack when quenched in water. However, some of these steels may be quenched adequately with compressed air.

Flame hardening also may be used to through-harden steel up to about 3″ in diameter, depending on the hardenability of the steel. The design of the burner head, the method of work or flame movement, and the heating time may be varied as required for particular hardening applications.

Applications: Flame hardening has definite advantages for the following applications:

1. It permits making parts with the less-costly medium-carbon steels, rather than the more costly high-carbon steels.
2. It may be used where only selected areas should be hardened for the purpose of increasing hardness or wear resistance.
3. It may be used for applications where through-hardening would cause excess distortion.
4. It may be used for very large objects which cannot be furnace-hardened efficiently.
5. The following items often are flame-hardened: ways and flat bearing surfaces of machine tools; gear teeth, bearing surfaces on shafts, splines on shafts, ends of push rods, cams, large rolls, forming dies, crankshafts, and camshafts.

Induction Hardening

Induction hardening, like flame hardening, is a process used to harden selected areas of ferrous metals to depths ranging up to $\frac{1}{4}$″. The heat for induction hardening is generated electromagnetically by a high-frequency induction coil. Parts which are cylindrical in shape are heated by inserting them through an induction coil as shown in Fig. 17-43. The selected surface to be hardened is heated dur-

Fig. 17-42. Flame Hardening the Ways on a Lathe Bed
(Clausing Div. — Atlas Press)

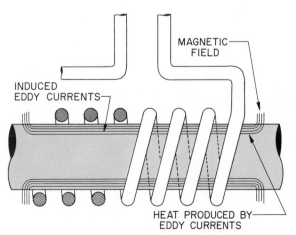

Fig. 17-43. Heating Surface of Steel Shaft with High-Frequency Induction Coil

613

ing several seconds to above the upper critical temperature. Hardening by quenching follows immediately. Water-hardening steels are quenched with a spray of water from a water jacket located conveniently near the coil. The part shown in Figs. 17-44 and 17-45 were heated and quenched in this manner. The hardened parts should be tempered as soon as possible after hardening.

The principles involved in induction heating can be understood quite readily by studying Fig. 17-43. The figure shows an induction coil of the type commonly used to harden parts which are cylindrical in shape. When high-frequency alternating current passes through the coil, a magnetic field is established around the coil and through the core. In this case, the core is the workpiece to be hardened. The magnetic field causes eddy currents to be developed in the surface of the workpiece. These generate the heat required for hardening the surface layer of the workpiece.

Frequencies ranging from 1 kc (1000 cycles) to 2 mc (2,000,000 cycles) per second may be used. The lower frequencies are used for heating to the deeper hardening depths, which may range from $\frac{1}{16}''$ to $\frac{1}{4}''$. The higher frequencies

generally are used for heating to shallow hardening depths, ranging from 0.010″ to $\frac{1}{16}''$. The very high frequencies tend to heat only a skin layer on the surface.

Induction coils of special design, and in various arrangements, are used to heat parts with different shapes. The pattern of the heated area is determined by the shape and design of the coil, the operating frequency, and the input current. Induction heating equipment is available for either manual or automatic operation. With the latter, the complete heating, quenching, and tempering cycle may be controlled automatically.

A

B

C

Fig. 17-45. High-Frequency Induction Hardening of Four Track Rollers Simultaneously
(TOCCO Div. — Ohio Crankshaft)
(A) Assembly setup; (B) Parts being heated;
(C) Parts being water-quenched.

Fig. 17-44. Cross Section of Induction-Hardened Gear Achieved with High-Frequency Heating
(TOCCO Div. — Ohio Crankshaft)

Quenching media used for induction hardening include water, oil, or compressed air, depending on the type of metal being hardened. Either spray-quenching or bath-quenching methods may be used, according to the production procedure.

Induction-hardened parts may be tempered in a tempering furnace in the same manner in which regular quench-hardened parts are tempered. They also may be heated for tempering with an induction coil at low temperatures. This is done in a manner similar to the method employed in heating for induction hardening.

Many different steels and certain grades of cast iron may be induction-hardened. However, the steel must possess sufficient carbon to be hardenable, generally more than 0.30%. Medium-carbon steels and many alloy steels are well suited for induction hardening.

Induction heating also may be applied to through-hardening applications. Shafts or rods may be through-hardened by using continuous-line heating and quenching equipment. Selected areas such as gear teeth also may be through-hardened by using induction coils of standard design. Through heating is achieved by using lower frequencies, usually in the range from 180 to 3000 cycles per second.

Applications: Induction hardening may be used for many of the applications for which flame hardening is used. The following are typical advantages and applications of induction hardening:

1. It permits making parts with less-costly, medium-carbon steels, rather than the more-costly, high-carbon steels.
2. It may be used for selective hardening of surfaces or areas.
3. It increases hardness and wear resistance.
4. It may be used for long bars which cannot be furnace-hardened efficiently.
5. Generally, it results in less distortion, less oxidation or scaling, and less warpage than conventional quench-hardening.
6. The following items often are induction-hardened: gear teeth, splines on shafts, bearing surfaces on shafts, rolls, tubing, crankshafts, camshafts, and connecting rods.

Austempering

Austempering is a process which involves heat-treating steel in a manner which will produce a *bainite* grain structure, which is softer than martensite, but harder than pearlite. (Bainite will be explained shortly.) Austempering generally involves the following basic procedure:

1. The steel parts are heated uniformly to the hardening temperature, thus producing an austenitic grain structure.
2. The parts are quenched in a molten salt bath at a temperature which produces a bainite grain structure. The quenching temperatures for bainite, as shown in Fig. 17-48 (page 616), may range from about 400° to 900° F.; however, those from about 500° to 750° F. generally are used. The salt bath is maintained at the temperature which produces the desired kind of bainite.
3. The part is soaked in the salt bath for sufficient time to permit complete transformation from austenite to bainite.
4. The part is then removed from the salt bath, and it is rinsed in hot water or steam to remove the salt.

Bainite Formation: If steel is quenched from the critical temperature to a temperature in the range from about 400° to 900° F., and if it is soaked at this temperature long enough, the austenite will transform to a grain structure called *bainite*, as shown in Figs. 17-46 and 17-47. Bainite is a finer mixture of ferrite and cementite than is pearlite. It appears more acicular or needlelike than the pearlite grain, which has alternate layers of ferrite and cementite. Bainite is formed in the transformation temperature range below the pearlite range, but above the martensite range, as shown in Fig. 17-48. Its hardness also lies in the range between the softer pearlite and the harder martensite, as shown in Fig. 17-48.

In order for bainite to form, the austenite must be quenched and cooled rapidly to the desired austempering temperature, say 600° F., in order to avoid pearlite formation. Since pearlite begins to form at 1000° F., the steel must be cooled to a point below this temperature in less than one second. However, more time may be allowed for further cooling to the 600° F. temperature selected. The molten salt bath should be maintained at (or slightly below) the desired austempering temperature.

The time required for complete transformation to bainite depends on the kind of steel and the austempering temperature selected. For plain carbon steel, the transformation period varies from about one minute at a temperature of 800° F., four minutes at 700° F., fifteen minutes at 600° F., to one hour at 500° F.

Fig. 17-46. Microstructure Called Bainite (Partial) (2500×) (U.S. Steel)

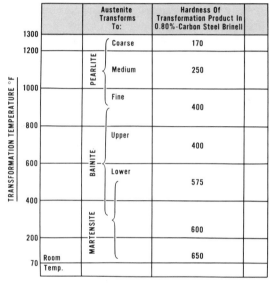

TRANSFORMATION TEMPERATURE °F		Austenite Transforms To:	Hardness Of Transformation Product In 0.80%-Carbon Steel Brinell	
1300	PEARLITE	Coarse	170	
1200		Medium	250	
1000		Fine	400	
800	BAINITE	Upper	400	
600		Lower	575	
400	MARTENSITE			
200			600	
70	Room Temp.		650	

Fig. 17-48. Transformation Products from Austenite, and Their Hardness (U.S. Steel)

Fig. 17-47. Microstructure Called Bainite (Complete) (2500×) (U.S. Steel)

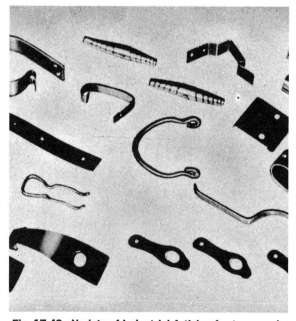

Fig. 17-49. Variety of Industrial Articles Austempered (U.S. Steel)

Applications: Austempering has several advantages over regular quench-hardening and tempering for certain applications. First, greater toughness is obtainable at equal hardness values. This is particularly true for parts which would suffer a loss of notch-toughness when tempered in the brittle temperature range. Austempered parts in the hardness range from Rockwell C-45 to C-55 generally possess much greater notch-toughness than quench-hardened and tempered parts of equal hardness.

A second major advantage of austempering is that it produces less distortion. There is also less possibility of quench cracks because of the higher quenching temperatures.

Austempering, however, has several limitations. Its use is limited to certain types of steel. Plain high-carbon steels and certain alloy steels may be austempered with good results. Plain carbon steels with less than 0.50% carbon usually cannot be austempered efficiently.

Austempering applications generally are limited to thicknesses of less than $\frac{3}{16}$" where a complete bainite structure is required. Plain carbon steels with less than 0.80% carbon generally are limited to less thickness. With modern production methods, austempering is much less expensive than the quench-harden and temper method. Typical examples of austempered parts include items such as lock washers, stamped nuts, spring nuts, spring-type toolholders, steel shanks in shoes, and many other thin steel parts which require hardness, toughness, and resilience. See Fig. 17-49.

Hardness Testing

UNIT

158

The hardness of metals or metal parts normally is designated by a hardness number. Several common hardness-number systems may be used, depending on the type of hardness-testing instrument employed. The more common systems include:

Rockwell C Scale (RC or Rc)
Rockwell B Scale (RB or Rb)
Rockwell Superficial hardness scales
Brinell hardness number (BHN)
Shore scleroscope hardness number
Knoop hardness scale
Diamond Pyramid hardness number (DPH), also known as the Vickers Scale

The hardness value for a part to be made usually is specified on the drawing or blueprint for the part. A hardness number designated according to one system, such as a Rockwell number, may be converted to an approximate equivalent hardness number of another system through the use of special tables. For example, equivalent hardness values for steel may be determined by reading horizontally across Table 34, appendix.

Hardness values for thin sheet metal, thin metal parts, tubing, or for the thin case-hardened surfaces, usually are inaccurate when determined with conventional Brinell or Rockwell testers. Instead, these products may be measured by the less-common Rockwell Superficial hardness scales, including both the Rockwell N and Rockwell T scales. The hardness of these kinds of products also may be determined more accurately with a microhardness tester, as explained later in this unit.

The general principles involved in hardness testing according to the Rockwell, Brinell, Shore scleroscope, and Knoop hardness number scales are explained in this unit. However, there are numerous variations in the mechanical design of instruments developed by various manufacturers for testing hardness according to these scales. Therefore, the specific procedures recommended by the instrument manufacturer should be reviewed and followed before using a specific hardness tester.

Estimating Hardness with a File

The approximate hardness of a piece of metal may be estimated *roughly* simply by using the corner of a sharp file and noting the ease or difficulty encountered in making the file cut. The corner of the file should be used, since the teeth on the face of the file could be ruined on very hard steel. The data in Table 25 may be used as a guide for estimating the hardness of metal parts.

Rockwell Hardness Test

The Rockwell hardness test is based on the depth of penetration made by a specific type of penetrator, into the surface of a metal specimen, while under a specific load. The hardness number is based on the difference in depth of penetration caused by a minor load and a major load on the penetrator. Deep penetration indicates a low hardness number; shallower penetration, a higher hardness number. The hardness number generally is read directly in Rockwell numbers on the dial of the tester. The Rockwell hardness test is simple to perform, requires only a few seconds, and is widely used.

Several types of hardness testers are available for measuring the hardness of metals according to standard Rockwell scales. Some are portable, while others are stationary, usually being mounted on a bench or stand, Fig. 17-52. The load on Rockwell testers generally is applied through a system involving weights, levers, screws, or a combination of these mechanisms. Some testers are hand-operated, while others are motor-driven. A hand-operated portable tester is shown in Fig. 17-53.

Testers are available for testing according to the *standard Rockwell hardness scales* only or the *Rockwell Superficial hardness scales* only. Combination models, which may be used for testing according to either scale, also are available. A motor-driven combination tester of this type is shown in Fig. 17-52.

Several different Rockwell hardness scales may be used for determining the hardness of various metals and other materials. Each scale is based on the use of a specified size and type of penetrator, which is used with a specified load. The various Rockwell hardness scales, the loads applied, and the type of penetrator employed are shown in Table 26. The most common scales used for determining the hardness of steel and other metals, however, include the Rockwell C and the Rockwell B scales. The hardness numbers for these scales are included in Table 34, appendix.

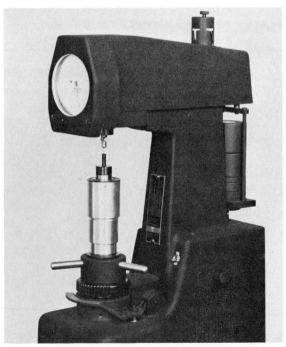

Fig. 17-52. Motorized Combination Tester for Rockwell Hardness Testing and for Rockwell Superficial Hardness Testing (Wilson Mech. Instr. Div. — Amer. Chain & Cable)

Table 25
Estimating Hardness with a File

Rockwell C Hardness No.	Action of File on Steel
20	File removes metal easily with slight pressure
30	File starts to resist cutting metal
40	File cuts metal with difficulty
50	File barely cuts metal with great difficulty
57	File glides over metal without cutting

Standard Rockwell Hardness Scales: The Rockwell C scale is used to determine the hardness of hardened steel and other metals which are harder than RB 100. In testing hardness according to the RC scale, a standard 120-degree, sphero-conical, diamond penetrator (called a *Brale*, Fig. 17-54) is used, with a *major load* of 150 kilograms (330.7 lbs.). A minor load of 10 kilograms (22 lbs.) is used.

The Rockwell B scale is used to determine the hardness of unhardened steel, cast iron, and nonferrous metals which have a hardness of less than RC 20. In testing hardness according to the RB scale, a $\frac{1}{16}$″ diameter hardened steel ball penetrator (Fig. 17-54) is used, with a minor load of 10 kilograms and a major load of 100 kilograms (220.5 lbs.). The RB hardness numbers are read according to the red figures on the dial.

The penetrator always should be in good condition, and the tester should be checked for accuracy before use. It is checked with test blocks which have known hardness values; these generally are supplied with the tester.

Rockwell hardness test values are more accurate when three hardness tests are made, each at a different spot on the specimen. An average of the three readings then is the correct hardness number value.

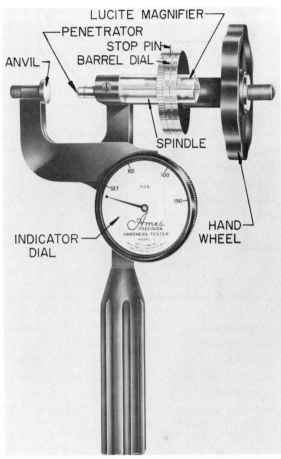

Fig. 17-53. Portable Tester for Rockwell Hardness Testing (Ames Precision Machine)

Table 26
Rockwell Hardness Scales

Scale or Prefix	Type of Penetrator	Major Loads in Kgs.	Dial Hardness Numbers
Standard Scales			
B	$\frac{1}{16}$″ Ball	100	Red
C	Diamond	150	Black
Special Scales			
A	Diamond	60	Black
D	Diamond	100	Black
E	$\frac{1}{8}$″ Ball	100	Red
F	$\frac{1}{16}$″ Ball	60	Red
G	$\frac{1}{16}$″ Ball	150	Red
H	$\frac{1}{8}$″ Ball	60	Red
K	$\frac{1}{8}$″ Ball	150	Red
Superficial Hardness Scales			
15N	Diamond	15	N (Green)
30N	Diamond	30	N (Green)
45N	Diamond	45	N (Green)
15T	$\frac{1}{16}$″ Ball	15	T (Green)
30T	$\frac{1}{16}$″ Ball	30	T (Green)
45T	$\frac{1}{16}$″ Ball	45	T (Green)

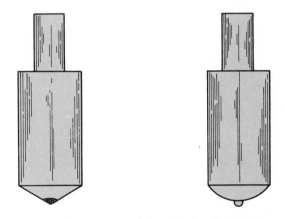

Fig. 17-54. Penetrator Points Used on Rockwell Hardness Tester (Left) 120° diamond point; (Right) 1/16″ diameter ball point.

Rockwell Superficial Hardness Scales: These hardness number scales are used to determine the hardness of materials or products which are limited to very shallow penetration or to the application of lighter loads. With a lighter load, the indentation left on the surface of the part is less severe. Thus, less damage is caused on thin tubing, thin strips, and highly-finished surfaces.

The following kinds of products often are tested according to the Rockwell Superficial hardness scales: thin strip metal, safety razor blades, cutters on electric shavers, casehardened steel parts, plug and ring gages, wire and small rounds, laminated metal.

The Rockwell Superficial hardness scales, as shown in Table 26, include both the N scales and the T scales. With these, major load weights of 15, 30, or 45 kg (kilograms) are applied with a minor load weight of 3 kg. A special N diamond (Brale) penetrator is used when measuring according to the N scales. A $\frac{1}{16}''$ diameter ball penetrator is used with the T scales. The Rockwell Superficial hardness numbers for the N scales are shown in Table 34, appendix.

Procedure: Become familiar with the particular Rockwell hardness tester available. Read and follow any special recommendations made by the manufacturer of the tester. The mechanical design of testers may vary with different manufacturers, but the general principles involved in making a test are similar.

The specimen or part to be tested should be free from rust, scale, or deep scratches. Hardened steel should be tested with a diamond penetrator. Soft steel, cast iron, and nonferrous metals generally should be tested with a $\frac{1}{16}''$ diameter hardened steel ball penetrator.

The following are the general steps of procedure to be followed in Rockwell hardness testing:

1. Select the proper type of penetrator. For the RC scale, a diamond penetrator is used. For the RB scale, a $\frac{1}{16}''$ diameter steel ball is used. See Table 26 for other Rockwell scales.

2. Check that the indicator hand is in the proper position for starting a test. On an instrument of the type shown in Fig. 17-53, the indicator hand must be over the *dot*. The *dial* may be turned to align the hand over the dot.

3. Place the specimen to be tested on the anvil of the tester. Then bring the penetrator into contact with the specimen. This is done by raising the anvil or lowering the penetrator, depending upon the design of the tester. On the tester in Fig. 17-53, the penetrator is brought into contact with the specimen by turning the handwheel.

4. Apply a minor load of 10 kg, as indicated by the appropriate mark on the tester dial. (On the tester in Fig. 17-53, the minor load is applied when the indicator hand is over the *set* mark.) Then set the hardness reading dial to zero. (On the tester in Fig. 17-53, this is done by turning the *barrel dial* on the spindle until the stop pin touches the lucite magnifier.)

5. Apply the major load. For the RC scale, a major load of 150 kg is applied. For the RB scale, 100 kg is applied. The major load for other Rockwell scales is shown in Table 26.

6. Reduce the major load to the minor load setting; then read the hardness directly, according to the Rockwell hardness number scale being used. Generally, the RC numbers are black, while the RB numbers are red. On the tester in Fig. 17-53, the hardness number is on the barrel dial and is read through the lucite magnifier.

7. Release the minor load, and remove the specimen from the tester. Several tests should be made; the correct hardness number is an average of these. The accuracy of the tester should be checked periodically by making tests on the test blocks provided with the tester.

Brinell Hardness Test

The Brinell hardness of metal is determined with a testing machine which forces a hardened ball into the smooth surface of a metal specimen or part, as in Fig. 17-55. The hardened ball is a specified size, and it is forced into the surface under a special load for a definite period of time. The ball is 10 millimeters in diameter and may be a hardened steel ball, a hultgren ball, or a carbide ball.

For the standard Brinell hardness test on steel, the load is 3000 kilograms (6600 lbs.). The load must be applied steadily, for a period of at least 15 seconds for iron or steel and at least 30 seconds for nonferrous metals.

A standard load of 500 kg (1100 lbs.) generally is applied for nonferrous metals in the hardness range from 26-100 BHN. A load of 1500 kg sometimes is used for testing nonferrous metals in the range from 80 to 300 BHN. Other loads are used for special applications. In this unit, we are concerned primarily with the standard Brinell hardness for steel.

The Brinell hardness number is determined by measuring the width of the dent produced in the surface of the metal specimen. Generally, this is done through the use of a microscope (similar to the one shown in Fig. 17-56), which has a calibrated lens for measuring the width of the dent. A comparison chart, supplied with the tester, is used to determine the hardness for dents of various widths. Wide dents are produced in soft metals, which have a low hardness number. The dents in harder metals have less width, thus resulting in a higher hardness number. The Brinell hardness numbers for steel are shown in Table 34, appendix.

On a Brinell hardness tester, the load generally is applied through a system of weights, levers, and screws. Brinell hardness testers are available in hand-operated models (Fig. 17-55) or in motorized models. With the latter, the load may be applied more rapidly, thus reducing the time required for each test.

A Brinell hardness tester generally works best on metals which do not rank exceedingly high in hardness. This includes nonferrous metals, soft steels, and medium hardened steels. It is not recommended for testing materials harder than BHN 630. On highly hardened steels, the dent is so small that its size is difficult to measure accurately. The Brinell hardness of steel may range from 150 for low-carbon annealed steel to 739 for hardened high-carbon tool steel.

A carbide ball may be used for testing the hardness of hardened steel and other materials with hardness up to BHN 630; a hultgren ball, for materials with hardness up to BHN 500; and a steel ball, up to BHN 450.

The Shore Scleroscope Test

Metal specimens are tested according to the Shore scleroscope system with a scleroscope

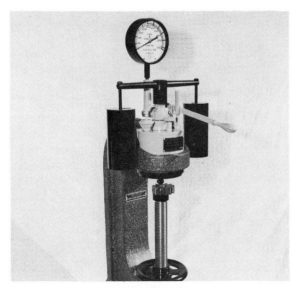

Fig. 17-55. Brinell Hardness Tester
(Pittsburgh Instr. & Machine)

Fig. 17-56. Brinell Microscope for Measuring Diameter of Impression Made by Brinell Hardness Tester
(Bausch & Lomb)

hardness tester, as shown in Figs. 17-57 and 17-58. The tester measures the height to which a diamond-tipped hammer rebounds after being dropped on the surface of a specimen being tested. The rebounding is caused by elasticity. Thus, the scleroscope actually measures elasticity, but, since elasticity is closely associated with hardness, the hardness is measured indirectly. Harder metals cause the hammer to rebound to greater heights, thus resulting in higher hardness numbers. See Table 34, appendix.

The scleroscope hardness test is essentially a nonmarring test, particularly on the harder metals. A minute dent may result on softer metals. For accurate readings, the scleroscope should be held in a vertical position.

Scleroscope hardness testers are available in several models. The hardness numbers may be located on the vertical barrel column, as shown in Fig. 17-57. On another model, the hardness numbers are located on a dial which also shows equivalent Rockwell C numbers and Brinnel hardness numbers, Fig. 17-58.

The scleroscope shown in Fig. 17-57 may be removed from the stand for portable use on large workpieces. However, care must be taken to hold the instrument steadily, firmly against the test specimen, and in a vertical position.

The scleroscope shown in Fig. 17-58 is mounted in a clamping stand which should be placed on a sturdy bench to minimize vibration. The instrument is equipped with an adjustment screw and a spirit level for use in leveling the stand. Small parts of many sizes and shapes may be held firmly in the clamping stand for testing; small round parts are placed on a vee block. The scleroscope tester shown in Fig. 17-57 also may be equipped with a clamping stand.

Steel of the following minimum thicknesses may be tested with a scleroscope tester: hardened steel, 0.005″; cold, rolled, unannealed brass and steel, about 0.010″; and annealed sheets, about 0.015″.

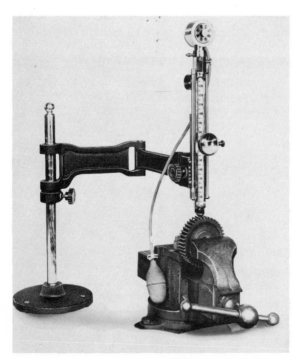

Fig. 17-57. Shore Scleroscope Hardness Tester Mounted on Swinging Arm and Post (Shore Instr. and Manufacturing)

Fig. 17-58. Dial-Recording Shore Scleroscope Hardness Tester (Shore Instr. and Manufacturing)

Procedure: The test specimen should be clean, smooth, and free from dust or scale. The tester should be placed on a sturdy bench or stand to eliminate vibration.

1. Mount the tester on the swing arm and post (Fig. 17-57) or on the clamping stand (Fig. 17-58), depending on the shape and size of the specimen to be tested. Small parts up to 3″ in height may be held in the clamping stand. Adjust the leveling screws and a spirit level so that the barrel is as nearly vertical as possible.

2. Mount the specimen in the clamping stand (Fig. 17-58) or in a vise (Fig. 17-57), depending on the nature of the test specimen. With the use of the hand knob, lower the vertical barrel, holding the barrel cap firmly in contact with the test specimen until the test is complete.

3. Draw the hammer to the *up* position by rapidly squeezing the rubber bulb, Fig. 17-57. While holding the barrel firmly against the specimen, again squeeze and release the rubber bulb; at the same time, observe the extreme height to which the hammer rebounds on the first bounce. Immediately again squeeze the rubber bulb to raise the hammer to the up position, preparatory for the next test. This will prevent the hammer from rebounding a second time. The height of the first rebound indicates the hardness number. Record the hardness reading. On the tester shown in Fig. 17-58, the hammer is released with a controller knob instead of a rubber bulb.

4. Repeat step 3 until at least three tests have been made. Each test should be made at a different spot, since the surface is partially work hardened by the impact of the hammer. Thus additional tests on the same spot will read high. The average hardness is the average of several tests made on the test specimen. The accuracy of the tester should be checked periodically by testing the hardness of the *reference* test bar supplied with the tester. The hardness is indicated on the reference test bar.

Microhardness Tester

A microhardness tester is used to determine the microhardness of metals and other hard materials according to the Knoop hardness scale. Some microhardness testers also may be used to determine hardness according to the Diamond Pyramid hardness number (Vickers Scale), provided that a 136-degree Diamond Pyramid indenter (Vickers Type) is used. With the use of the Knoop diamond and the Diamond Pyramid indenter, a microhardness tester of the type shown in Fig. 17-59 may be used to determine hardness on both hardness scales. Microhardness testers are used widely to determine the hardness of individual grains or constituents in the microstructure of metals and other materials.

In a microhardness test, a diamond penetrator is pressed into the surface of the specimen being tested. The surface should be very smooth and free from nicks, scale, or other surface irregularities. A given force is applied to the penetrator for a given period of time. The depth of penetration will depend upon the

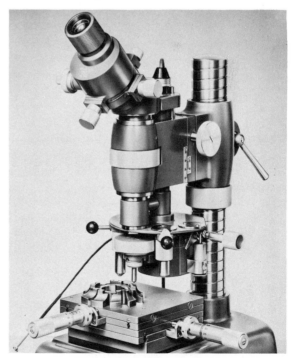

Fig. 17-59. Microhardness Tester (Scientific Instr. Div. — E. Leitz)

623

amount of load and the hardness of the test specimen. Since the pressure applied is low, in the range from 25 to 3600 grams (about 8 lbs. max.), the impression in the surface is minute. It is so small that its size must be determined with the microscope provided on the tester. The hardness is established by the size of the dent in the surface.

Several advantages accrue through the use of the microhardness tester. The dent produced is so small that it does not damage the surface significantly. The use of the microhardness tester is by no means limited to the testing of microstructures. It may be used to determine the hardness of very small or thin parts, such as parts for watches and precision instruments and thinly hardened surfaces, thin tubing, thin sheet metals, or thin parts like razor blades.

The microhardness tester may be used with the Knoop diamond penetrator to determine the hardness of minerals and other materials which are too hard to test by other methods. The Knoop hardness scale, as used to determine the hardness of abrasives under a 100-gram load, is explained in Unit 110. The Knoop hardness number is based on a relationship between the load and the long dimension of the indentation in the surface. A conversion chart which includes these factors usually is supplied with the tester.

Test Your Knowledge of Section 17

Unit 150: Introduction to Heat Treatment
1. Why are metals heat-treated?
2. What major divisions of content are included in the study of metallurgy?
3. What major factors in the study of physical metallurgy are related to the study of heat-treatment processes?
4. List several properties of metals which can be changed by heat treatment.
5. On what basis are metals selected for the manufacture of cutting tools?
6. Why should a machinist or tool and die maker possess an understanding of heat-treatment processes?

7. List several occupational groups, other than machinists, who frequently should possess an understanding of heat-treatment operations.
8. Give several examples of tools which must be hardened and tempered.
9. Why must a hardened tool be tempered before use?
10. List the three steps involved in the time-temperature cycle of all heat-treatment operations.
11. For what purposes are indicating pyrometers used?
12. Explain how a pyrometer operates to indicate temperatures.
13. What are the principal parts of a temperature-indicating control, and how does it control temperatures?
14. List several types of furnaces which may be used for hardening.
15. List several types of furnaces or heating devices which may be used for tempering.
16. List several kinds of molten baths which are used in pot-type furnaces for heat-treatment operations.
17. List the principal advantage of heating parts in a liquid bath, rather than in an air atmosphere.
18. Explain how temperature colors aid in determining temperatures for heat-treating operations.
19. List three different methods by which temperatures of steel can be determined for heat-treatment purposes.
20. List four common hardness number systems used to designate the hardness of steel.

Unit 151: Grain Structure of Steel
1. Explain the nature of the internal structure of metals.
2. For what purpose is a metallurgical microscope used?
3. What is a metallograph, and for what purposes is it used?
4. Define metallography.
5. Describe, briefly, how a metal specimen is prepared for investigation with a metallurgical microscope.
6. What principal parts of an etched metal specimen are investigated with a microscope?

7. How is the study of the grain structure of metals related to the study of heat treatment?
8. What is meant by a space lattice?
9. List four common types of space lattice units or cells.
10. Describe a body-centered cubic space lattice unit.
11. Describe a face-centered cubic space lattice unit.
12. What is meant by an allotropic change in grain structure?
13. Describe an allotropic change which takes place when steel is heated to the hardening temperature.
14. How does the form and arrangement of carbon change in steel at the hardening temperature?
15. Explain the meaning of transformation temperature.
16. What is meant by a transformation temperature range?
17. Why should heated metals be allowed to soak at certain temperatures during heat-treatment operations?
18. Describe the nature of the grain structure of steel at the hardening temperature.
19. Explain how the crystalline grains form in metals.
20. How does the speed of cooling generally affect grain fineness?
21. Describe one method used to determine the grain size of metals.

Unit 152: How Carbon Content Affects Hardening
1. List the basic steps involved in hardening steel.
2. Explain the relationship between the amount of carbon content in steel and the degree of hardness obtainable by heat treatment.
3. What largely determines the degree of hardness obtainable in alloy steels through heat treatment?
4. What is the basic difference in the meaning of the terms hardness and hardenability?
5. In comparison with alloy steels, how do carbon steels generally rank in hardenability?

6. Describe pearlite and the form in which carbon exists in it.
7. Explain the difference between hypoeutectoid and hypereutectoid steel.
8. How does an increase in pearlite content affect the strength of unhardened steel?
9. Explain the meaning of the transformation temperature range on the iron-carbon phase diagram for steel.
10. Explain the change which takes place in the lattice structure of steel when it is heated to the hardening temperature.
11. Describe the form of carbon in austenite.
12. Describe the hardening temperature of steel in relation to the upper critical temperature on the iron-carbon phase diagram.
13. Describe the grain structure which exists at the hardening temperature of steel.
14. Explain how a magnet may be used as an aid in determining the hardening temperature of steel.
15. Describe how martensite is formed.
16. Describe the properties of martensite.
17. Explain why austenite must be cooled so rapidly to form martensite.
18. How do alloying elements in steel generally affect the speed of cooling required for hardening?
19. How do alloying elements in steel generally affect the depth of hardening?
20. How does excessively rapid cooling affect steel which is quenched?

Unit 153: Quenching Media and Their Applications
1. List four quenching media which are used to quench steel in heat-treatment operations.
2. Define the meaning of quenching severity.
3. What factors determine the severity of the quench for hardening?
4. Compare the rate of cooling for oil, water, air, and brine.
5. How can the rate of cooling be increased for a given quenching medium, such as oil?

6. At what temperatures should water, brine, and oil be maintained for best quenching results?

7. What may be expected if the wrong quenching medium is used to quench steel?

8. What quenching medium generally is used for most plain carbon steels?

9. What quenching medium generally is used for most alloy steels?

10. Describe two common movements used for agitating work in a quenching solution.

11. Describe the method generally used to quench high-speed steels for hardening.

12. Why should hardened steel be tempered soon after hardening?

Unit 154: Tempering, Annealing and Normalizing

1. What is the purpose of tempering?

2. What relationship exists between hardness and toughness when steel is tempered?

3. Describe, briefy, how steel is tempered.

4. Describe the grain structure and the properties of fully-hardened steel.

5. What is the form of carbon in tempered martensite?

6. What changes in properties take place in hardened steel as tempering temperatures are increased?

7. What relationship exists between plasticity and toughness of steel?

8. What factors determine the tempering temperature of steel?

9. What factors determine maximum obtainable hardness in steel when it is quenched for hardening?

10. What is the range of tempering temperatures which may be used for various tempering applications?

11. What range of tempering temperatures is used for tempering most cutting tools?

12. List a method which may be used for estimating or determining the toughness of steel.

13. What is meant by selective heat treatment?

14. Explain how notched-bar toughness is determined.

15. Explain the meaning of the brittle temperature range.

16. Why are notch-bar toughness ratings sometimes misleading?

17. What tempering temperature range should be avoided for parts designed with sharp notches, fillets, or corners?

18. How soon after hardening should tempering be done?

19. What is the purpose of annealing?

20. Explain the full annealing process.

21. Define process annealing and its purpose.

22. Define the nature and purpose of spheroidizing.

23. What is the purpose of normalizing?

24. Compare the grain structure of normalized steel with that of fully-annealed steel.

25. Explain the procedure for normalizing a steel part.

Unit 156: Casehardening Processes

1. What is casehardening?

2. What types of steel most frequently are casehardened?

3. What is the purpose of casehardening?

4. List several kinds of tools or parts which commonly are casehardened.

5. What is the range in depth for casehardened surfaces?

6. What is the range in Rockwell hardness for most casehardened surfaces?

7. Upon what does the core hardness of casehardened parts depend?

8. What substances can be added to the surface of steel to cause it to harden when quenched?

9. How does nitrogen aid in producing a surface which can become hardened?

10. Explain the basic procedures in the time-temperature cycle which are involved in most casehardening processes.

11. At what temperatures are casehardened parts usually tempered?

12. List several common casehardening processes.

13. In general terms, explain the carburizing process.

14. Upon what factors does the time required for carburizing depend?

15. What kind of carbonaceous substances are used for pack carburizing?
16. What type of box is used for pack carburizing with inflammable substances?
17. What temperatures are used most often for pack carburizing?
18. Briefly describe several different hardening procedures which may follow pack carburizing.
19. Describe the properties of a pack carburizing material such as Kasenit.
20. Briefly describe the pack method of case-hardening with Kasenit.
21. Briefly describe the dip method of case-hardening with Kasenit.
22. Briefly describe the cyaniding process.
23. How do the depths of the hardened case compare for carburized and cyanided surfaces?
24. Briefly describe the carbonitriding process.
25. Briefly describe the nitriding process.
26. How does a nitrided surface affect the life of cutting tools?

Unit 157: Special Hardening Processes

1. Describe the flame-hardening process.
2. To what depths may surfaces be hardened by flame hardening?
3. What types of fuel are used for flame hardening?
4. How may flame-hardened parts be tempered?
5. What types of ferrous metal may be flame-hardened?
6. List several advantages of flame hardening in comparison with the standard furnace heating and quenching method for hardening.
7. List several products which may be flame hardened.
8. Describe the induction-hardening process.
9. Explain how an induction coil operates to heat the surface of a part.
10. What frequency ranges are used for induction heating purposes?
11. How is the pattern of the heated area regulated with induction-heating equipment?
12. List the quenching media which may be used for induction hardening.
13. How may induction-hardened parts be tempered?

14. What types of ferrous metal may be induction-hardened?
15. List several advantages of induction hardening in comparison with the standard furnace heating and quenching method for hardening.
16. List several typical items which may be induction-hardened.
17. How is a bainite grain structure produced in steel?
18. Describe a bainite grain structure and its approximate hardness.
19. Explain the basic procedures used for austempering steel parts.
20. List several advantages of austempering in comparison with regular quench hardening and tempering.
21. List several limitations of the austempering process.
22. List several kinds of items which may be austempered.

Unit 158: Hardness Testing

1. How is the hardness of metals designated?
2. List four hardness number systems.
3. Describe how the hardness of steel may be determined with a file.
4. Explain how a Brinell hardness tester operates.
5. What types of penetrators are used on Brinell hardness testers?
6. Explain a Rockwell hardness tester.
7. What are the most commonly used Rockwell hardness scales?
8. For what range of hardness is the Rockwell C scale recommended?
9. For what range of hardness is the Rockwell B scale used?
10. Describe the type of penetrator used for the Rockwell C and B scales.
11. Explain how a scleroscope hardness tester operates.
12. On what hardness scale is a microhardness tester generally used?
13. Explain how a microhardness tester functions.
14. List several advantages of a microhardness tester in comparison with other standard hardness testers.

627

Apprenticeship — Combines Earning and Learning
(Pontiac Motor Div. — General Motors)

Employment Opportunities

Fig. 18-1. A Skilled Machinist Operating Large Vertical Boring and Turning Machine (G.A. Gray)

Nearly every product of modern industry either contains metal parts or is produced on a machine which is made of metal parts. Many of these are machined parts which are made by machining workers. A major proportion of the labor force in America is employed directly or indirectly in metalworking occupations. Of all of the occupational groups classified under metalworking, the machining occupations employ the largest number of workers. In 1965, more than one million workers were employed in machining occupations. An estimated 370,000 were employed as machinists, layout men, and instrument makers; 140,000 as tool and die makers; 40,000 as setup men and layout men; and 500,000 as machine tool operators.

Machining workers make useful metal objects or parts for machines by shaping them from metal castings, forgings, stampings, or from solid metal bars. The parts are shaped to exact size by removing excess metal with machine tools. Machining workers operate many types of machine tools such as engine lathes, shapers, planers, milling machines, drill presses, power saws, and many other specialized production machine tools, Fig. 18-1. Many machining workers, particularly the more highly skilled workers, must be able to use all of the common metalworking hand tools and measuring tools.

Skilled machining workers must be able to read blueprints and drawings and must be able to use measuring instruments skillfully. Accuracy in workmanship is a requirement, since many metal parts must be machined to tolerances of plus or minus one ten-thousandth of an inch. Some highly skilled toolmakers make special precision gage blocks and other specialized measuring tools which are accurate to plus or minus two microinches (0.000 001″ or one millionth inch).

Learning Through Apprenticeship

A common method of learning a skilled metal machining occupation is through serving an "apprenticeship" in the trade. Apprenticeship is a period of formal, on-the-job training during which the worker learns all of the aspects of his trade. The apprentice machinist learns blueprint reading, shop mathematics, and science related to his trade. He also learns other related or technical information essential for becoming an efficient worker in his trade.

Apprenticeship involves training on the job under the supervision of a skilled worker. It also includes classroom instruction in related trade information by a skilled worker or qualified instructor. One can become an all-around machinist, a tool and die maker, or prepare to become a setup man or an instrument maker by serving an apprenticeship. The typical apprenticeship period for becoming a machinist is four years (although some companies have training programs through which they qualify machinists in less than four years). It usually requires a total minimum of 8,000 hours (2,000 hours per year) of supervised training. This usually includes a specified minimum number of hours on each of the basic machine tools and also experience on several specialized machine tools. See Fig. 18-2. In addition, the apprentice usually must receive a minimum of 144 hours per year of instruction in theory related to his trade. The apprenticeship period for a tool and die maker varies from 4 to 5 years.

Apprenticeship training programs may be sponsored independently by large industrial companies. They also may be sponsored by employers in joint cooperation with local, state, and federal *joint apprenticeship committees*. The latter committees cooperate with the Federal Bureau of Apprenticeship and Training, under the Department of Labor. The Federal Bureau of Apprenticeship makes recommendations concerning the training requirements of apprentices in various occupations, including several skilled machining occupations.

Upon completion of a recognized apprenticeship, the apprentice becomes a journeyman and has met minimum qualifications for entrance into his trade. He usually receives a written document which indicates satisfactory completion of his apprenticeship, including the type of work for which he received training. This document is recognized by many employers and labor unions as satisfactory qualification for employment in the trade.

If the new journeyman in a metal machining occupation wishes to become highly skilled and wishes to advance in his work, he must continue his study of new tools, machines, methods, and procedures related to his trade.

Fig. 18-2. Apprentice Die Maker Receiving Instructions on Safe Die-Tryout Procedures (Pontiac Motor Div. — General Motors)

To qualify for an apprenticeship in a skilled metal machining occupation, one should have better than average mechanical ability. He also should have the ability to learn blueprint reading, shop mathematics, basic principles of machines, and scientific principles related to the machining of metals. Many sponsors of apprenticeship programs require that applicants be high school graduates or possess equivalent education. Graduates of a high school or vocational school, who have a good background of mathematics, science, English, drafting, and machine shop or metalworking, frequently are sought as apprentices to learn the machinist or tool and die making trades.

The apprentice "earns while he learns" his trade. Usually he is placed on a graduated pay scale with periodic increases throughout his training period. Upon completion of his apprenticeship, he receives journeyman's pay as a skilled worker.

The Pick-Up Method of Learning

Most machine tool operators and many machinists, tool and die makers, and instrument makers have entered the machining occupations by the "pick-up" method. They acquired their skills and knowledge by working on different machine tools on several different jobs. Many of these workers also attended vocational schools and studied blueprint reading, shop mathematics, and technical theory related to their work in order to improve their qualifications. Nevertheless, it is becoming increasingly difficult to enter the skilled metal machining occupations through this method.

All-Around Machinists

The all-around machinist, also referred to as a machinist or general machinist, is a skilled worker who is able to make all types of machined metal parts with machine tools. In 1965, more than 370,000 machinists were employed in the United States.

The all-around machinist must be able to set up and operate all of the basic machine tools and many different specialized production machine tools. Usually he must be able to set up and operate any machine in the shop, Fig. 18-1. He must know how to read blueprints and how to use all of the common metalworking hand tools and precision measuring instruments, Fig. 18-3. There is much variety in his work, since he frequently is called upon to perform many different types of machining jobs on many different machines. The all-around machinist must be able to work accurately to tolerances of one ten-thousandth of an inch and, sometimes, to within several millionths of an inch.

The machinist must know of the properties and characteristics of the different metals which he machines. He must know the heat-treating properties of many metals, since these will be used in making metal parts and cutting tools which must be "heat-treated" after machining. He also must be able to compute feeds and speeds on machines.

Types of Shops: The all-around machinist may be employed in any one of three types of machine shops — a production shop, a job shop, or a maintenance shop. A *production shop* usually is a large plant or factory which makes a great number of identical machined parts. Examples of items machined in a production shop are tractor and automotive engine blocks, crankshafts, and plumbing fixtures. See Fig. 18-4.

A *job shop* usually is a smaller machine shop which makes limited numbers of machined parts for manufacturers. The job shop also may build special machines or equipment ranging from small experimental items to very large machines.

The machinist employed in a *maintenance machine shop* usually specializes as a *maintenance machinist.* He performs all types of machine work with many types of machine tools. His work involves the repair and maintenance of all types of machines, both machine tools and other manufacturing machinery. In all large factories (both metalworking and nonmetalworking), machinery must be repaired and adjusted by the maintenance machinist. He frequently must build new or specialized production machinery needed in a factory. Examples of plants or factories which employ maintenance machinists are farm machine factories, large foundries, electrical appliance factories, chemical plants, paper mills, textile plants, and large food making and packaging plants.

The employment outlook is good for machinists during the 1960's and 1970's. Many new jobs will be available because of industrial expansion and increased mechanization in industry. Many new machinists will be needed each year to replace those who transfer to other fields of work. In addition, about 7,000 new jobs will be available each year due to retirement and deaths alone in this relatively large occupational group.

The pay for all-around machinists compares favorably with other highly skilled factory

Fig. 18-3. The All-Around Machinist Must Be Able to Use Precision Measuring Instruments (Caterpillar) **Accurately measuring diameter of a hole.**

Fig. 18-4. Machine Operator Milling Engine Blocks in Large Production Machine Shop (Caterpillar)

workers. According to statistics compiled by the United States Department of Labor, in 1965 maintenance machinists in various manufacturing industries in 62 areas surveyed received average, straight-time, hourly earnings ranging from $2.15 in Greenville, S. C., to $3.60 in Milwaukee, Wisconsin.

Most companies employing machinists provide paid holidays, paid vacations, and other benefits such as paid life insurance, medical insurance, and retirement pensions.

Machine Tool Operators

The machine tool operator is a semi-skilled worker. In 1965 more than 500,000 machine tool operators were employed in metal machining work in the United States. The machine tool operator usually is skilled in the operation of a single machine tool, such as a drill press, engine lathe, or milling machine, Figs. 18-4 and 18-5. He often performs repetitive work, making many identical parts. Over a long period of time, he may become highly skilled on one particular machine, having performed many different operations on different jobs.

The training period for machine tool operators may vary from several days to more than

Fig. 18-5. Drill Press Operator Using Heavy-Duty, Special Radial Drilling Machine (Caterpillar)

a year. For example, it may take only a few days to learn the operation of a small drill press. On the other hand, it may take more than a year to become highly skilled on a large radial drill press or universal milling machine. There are no specific educational requirements for the machine tool operator. However, a background of study in drafting, blueprint reading, industrial arts metalwork, or vocational classes in metalwork is valuable in securing employment and advancing more rapidly. Machine tool operators frequently are paid according to their rating, which depends on training and experience. They often are rated as class A, class B, or class C, with class A being the highest rating. Class A operators average about 34 cents per hour more than class B operators. Similarly, class B operators average about 40 cents per hour more than class C operators.

According to statistics compiled by the Department of Labor, in 1965 class A machine tool operators employed in twenty-one selected areas received average straight-time, hourly earnings ranging from $2.66 in Dallas, Texas to $3.61 in St. Louis, Missouri. There will be some increase in employment of machine tool operators during the 1960's. Due to retirements and deaths alone, at least 10,000 job openings will be available each year. With continued development of automatic and more versatile machine tools, production per worker will increase. Continued development of automated machine tools also may affect the number employed. However, the machine tool operators with the previously mentioned educational qualifications can easily adjust to technical changes and secure new jobs.

Tool and Die Makers

The tool and die maker is a highly skilled worker who makes many types of cutting tools, dies, punches, and holding devices. These products are used on production machine tools and are the basis for mass production of many products, both metal and nonmetal. The tool and die maker produces dies for stamping sheet metal parts in punch presses, dies for die casting machines which make cast metal parts, and dies for use in plastic molding machines. An example of a die used for stamping automobile radiator mounting brackets from sheet metal is shown in Fig. 18-6. The die is mounted for use in the large press in Fig. 18-2. The tool and die maker makes *jigs* and *fixtures* (holding or guiding devices) for use on production machines and for certain types of rapid assembly work.

The tool and die maker operates all of the basic machine tools. He must be able to work accurately with all metalworking hand tools, and he must be able to use all of the basic measuring tools and precision measuring instruments. He must have a broad knowledge of shop mathematics, blueprint reading, machining operations, and of the various metals and their heat-treatment properties.

Approximately 140,000 tool and die makers were employed in the United States in 1965. They are employed in large industrial metalworking plants, smaller tool and die making shops, and in job machine shops. Many also are employed in industrial maintenance shops where they repair or make dies and fixtures for production machine tools and other machinery.

One of the best methods for learning to become a tool and die maker is through serving an apprenticeship. The length of the apprenticeship period varies from four to five years, depending on the company sponsoring the program and the content included. The training program is sometimes broader and requires more related theory than that required for the all-around machinist.

Frequently, machine tool operators become tool and die makers after many years of experience and study. They acquire extensive training in vocational schools, through correspondence study, and through self study. With the knowledge and ability to perform all of the machining operations necessary for tool and die making, they are employed as tool and die makers. Frequently, also, all-around machinists further extend and broaden their knowledge so that they may be employed as tool and die makers.

The tool and die maker usually receives higher pay than a machinist. In 1965 the Bureau of Labor Statistics reported the pay of tool and die makers employed in various manufacturing industries in 13 selected areas. The report indicated that these workers were paid average, straight-time hourly earnings ranging from $2.74 in Miami, Florida, to $3.98 in San Francisco-Oakland, California.

The outlook for employment in the 1960's and 1970's is excellent for tool and die makers. Because of their extensive skills and the shortage of workers in this field, there is little probability of unemployment. Tool and die makers are needed in many industries, and their experience usually enables them to transfer for employment as machinists, instrument makers, and other occupations in industry.

Instrument Makers

Instrument makers are highly skilled machine tool workers. They make precision instruments, gages, experimental equipment, non-standard instruments, and experimental models. They work very closely with scientists and engineers, translating new ideas into working models. Their work is very important because of the increasing use of instruments, gages, and special controls needed with modern production methods.

The skills and knowledge required of the instrument maker are similar to those required of the machinist and tool and die maker, except that he usually requires more experience and broader training. Generally, he must work to closer tolerances than the average machinist, Fig. 18-7. He works with many different materials and precision measuring devices which usually are not required for the ma-

Fig. 18-6. Die Used to Cam Pierce Holes in Automobile Radiator Mounting Bracket (Pontiac Motor Div. — General Motors)
Die was built by seventh-period apprentice die maker.

635

chinist or tool maker. He must be more creative, since he often works from very rough sketches rather than from finished blueprints. Usually he must perform all of the operations necessary to make the complete instrument.

Instrument workers are employed by industrial research centers, the federal government, and university scientific laboratories. They also are employed in conjunction with many other experimental and developmental laboratories.

Instrument workers learn their trade by serving a four- or five-year apprenticeship or by transfer from the machinist or tool and die making trades, after considerable experience in those trades. Some instrument workers also have learned their trade by the "pick-up" method. They acquired broad machining experience on many different machining jobs, together with extensive independent study and study in vocational schools.

According to the Bureau of Labor Statistics, in 1964 the average hourly earnings of instrument workers in a small number of selected locations ranged from $3.05 to $3.80 per hour. There is little unemployment among instrument workers, since they are also highly skilled in most phases of machinist work. If necessary, they can transfer easily to most types of work which require a skilled machinist or to some types of tool making.

Fig. 18-7. Skilled Instrument Maker Machining a Typical Job to Very Close Tolerances (Research and Tech. Div. — U.S. Steel)

Setup Men

Setup men are skilled workers employed in large production plants where they "set up" machine tools. The machines then are operated by semi-skilled machine tool operators or, in some cases, by unskilled operators. Setup men frequently specialize in setting up one type of production machine, such as a turret lathe. They may maintain and install the proper cutting tools, fixtures, and gages necessary for machining a particular part. They set the proper cutting speeds and feeds on the machine and make the first several pieces in order to check the tool settings. Then they often must instruct the machine tool operator in the proper methods of checking the parts being machined.

Some setup men are highly skilled machinists who can set up many types of production machines or any of the basic machine tools. They often must give instructions to the unskilled machine tool operator on how to operate the machine and check his work. The setup man must be able to analyze and set up machining operations in the proper sequence. When the machine needs resetting or tooling because of tool wear, the setup man makes the necessary adjustments for the less-skilled machine tool operator.

The setup man must work from blueprints and must have a broad knowledge of different metals and their machining properties. He must know cutting lubricants, coolants, and cutting speeds and feeds. To qualify for employment as a setup man, one must be an all-around machinist or a highly qualified specialist on one of the basic production-type machine tools. Jobs for setup men frequently are filled from within the shop by promotion or reassignment.

Continued growth in the use of numerically-controlled production machines may limit the number of setup men needed during the next several decades. There is little unemployment of setup men, however, since they are highly skilled and can easily transfer to other metal machining jobs.

Layout Men

The layout man makes marks on metal castings, forgings, and other metal workpieces, indicating where and how they are to be machined. After the metal workpiece has been laid out, it can be machined by unskilled or semi-skilled machine operators. The layout man must be able to read blueprints and analyze the sequence of machine operations. He must understand the operation of all the basic and many of the specialized machine tools. He must have a broad knowledge of the properties of many metals. The layout man is a specialist who is particularly skilled in using all of the various hand layout tools, measuring instruments, and gages.

In order to qualify as a layout man, one must serve an apprenticeship as a machinist or must have equivalent training. In addition, one must have considerable broad machining experience in order to understand the various possible sequences of metal machining operations.

There is little probability of unemployment for the layout man, since his skills enable him to transfer to other machining work if the demand for layout men decreases.

Inspectors

The inspector in the production machine shop checks machined parts to determine whether they meet the specifications indicated on the drawing or blueprint. He must be able to read drawings and blueprints and must be able to use many types of precision measuring tools, gages, and instruments. See Fig. 18-8. If the parts do not meet specifications, they will not fit together in the final assembly, or they will not be interchangeable with other similar parts.

The accurate work of the inspector in the machine shop is very important in mass production. When a workpiece or casting is machined on a production machine, it must be inspected carefully. If any errors are not detected, the remaining parts produced on the same machine also may be spoiled. In the case of large machined castings, the loss may amount to hundreds or thousands of dollars.

The work of the inspector may require varying degrees of skill, depending on the size, type, cost, and tolerances required on the machined workpieces. Some simple inspection jobs require little training, while others require considerable technical knowledge and skill. The inspector's pay depends largely on his training and skill. The range in pay may vary from the pay of a semi-skilled machine operator to that of a skilled machinist.

There are no specific educational requirements for becoming an inspector. The training may vary from several weeks to several years on the job, depending on the particular job requirements. However, a good knowledge of blueprint reading and basic shop mathematics, plus experience in industrial arts metalwork or vocational metalwork courses, is valuable in securing employment and seeking advancement in this field.

Related Occupations

Some knowledge and experience with the basic methods, hand tools, and machine tools used in the machining of metals is valuable in several occupations which do not directly involve the machining of metals.

One group of such occupations includes those who manage or are responsible for supervising plant production. Men such as managers, superintendents, foremen, production or quality control supervisors, estimators, salesmen, teachers, training directors, and technologists of several specialties are professionals or semi-professionals who must have extensive knowledge of machines, materials, processes, workers, and marketing.

Fig. 18-8. Inspector Using Precision Measuring Instruments to Check Accuracy of Machined Work
(Caterpillar)

637

Fig. 18-9. Engineers Constantly Explore Better Design for Products (Caterpillar)
Supervising engineer and design engineers discuss redesign of a track link for large tractors.

Another group includes the machine draftsmen, machine designers, tool designers, and mechanical engineers, who design and make drawings of machines, machine tools, and other mechanical devices to be constructed. They can understand their work and be more creative when they have a background knowledge of the basic machine operations. See Fig. 18-9.

In working in a machine shop where basic metalworking hand tools, machine tools, and precision measuring tools are used, one learns about the need for accuracy of measurement.

The student who takes a basic course in machine shop develops work habits and understanding which are valuable in many mechanical occupations involving the repair and maintenance of various types of mechanical equipment.

Examples of some workers who can profit from such knowledge and experience in basic machine shop work are auto mechanics, aircraft mechanics, diesel engine mechanics, electrical appliance repairmen, office machine repairmen, and factory maintenance repairmen.

The student who takes a basic course in machine shop work in high school or vocational school will find it very helpful in providing a background of understanding valuable for performing the work required in any of the occupations named in this chapter.

Test Your Knowledge of Section 18

Unit 159: Employment Opportunities

1. What occupational group classified under "metalworking" includes the largest number of workers?
2. What was the approximate number of workers employed in the metal machining occupations in 1965?
3. What types of work do machining workers perform?
4. Why must the more skilled machine worker know how to read blueprints or drawings?
5. Why must machining workers know how to use many types of measuring instruments and know how to measure accurately?
6. Explain what apprenticeship means.
7. What are some of the things which an apprentice machinist must learn?
8. What skilled machining occupations may one prepare for by serving an apprenticeship?
9. How long is the typical apprenticeship period for becoming a machinist?
10. What is the usual minimum number of hours of instruction per year which an apprentice receives in theory related to his trade?
11. Who sponsors or provides apprenticeship programs for training skilled metal machining workers?
12. What is the purpose of the Federal Bureau of Apprenticeship?
13. What is meant by a *journeyman* in a trade?
14. Does a new journeyman know all there is to know in his trade? Explain.
15. What qualifications must one usually have in order to be employed as an apprentice in a skilled metal machining occupation?
16. Does an apprentice receive pay while learning his trade?
17. Explain what it means to learn a trade through the "pick-up" method.
18. What types of work must the all-around machinist be able to do?
19. What types of shops employ all-around machinists?

20. Explain what a production machine shop is.
21. Explain what type of machine work is done in a job shop.
22. Explain what type of work is performed by a maintenance machinist.
23. What types of industries employ maintenance machinists?
24. How does the pay of all-around machinists compare with that of other skilled factory workers?
25. What type of work is performed by a machine tool operator?
26. What are the educational requirements for a machine tool operator?
27. How long is the training period for a machine tool operator?
28. How are machine tool operators usually classified?
29. What type of work does a tool and die maker do?
30. What uses are made of the dies made by a tool and die maker?
31. What are jigs and fixtures used for?
32. What types of skill should a tool and die maker possess?
33. What basic knowledge should a tool and die maker possess?
34. What types of establishments employ tool and die makers?
35. How can one learn the tool and die making trade?
36. How does the pay of a tool and die maker compare with that of other machining occupations?
37. What is the employment outlook for tool and die makers?

38. What type of work is performed by instrument makers?
39. What are the training requirements for becoming an instrument maker?
40. What types of establishments generally employ instrument makers?
41. What type of work is performed by a setup man?
42. What types of establishments usually employ setup men?
43. What are the educational or training requirements for becoming a setup man?
44. What types of knowledge must a setup man possess in order to perform his work well?
45. What type of work is performed by a layout man?
46. What are the educational and training requirements for becoming a layout man?
47. Name some professional occupations related to machining.
48. Why is a basic knowledge about the machining of metals valuable to the machine draftsman or machine designer?
49. How can a mechanical engineer profit from a knowledge about the machining of metals?
50. List five non-machining occupations where some knowledge of the machining of metals would be valuable for success.
51. Approximately what percentage of the workers engaged in metal machining occupations are classified as skilled workers?
52. Locate a source of recent occupational information for the machine tool area of work.

Appendix

Table 30
Machinability Ratings and Other Properties of Various Metals

SAE Number	AISI Number	Tensile Strength, psi	Yield Point, psi	Elongation in 2 in., Percent	Reduction in Area, Percent	Hardness, Brinell	Machinability Rating, Percent
Carbon Steels							
1015	C1015	65,000	40,000	32	65	137	50
1020	C1020	67,000	45,000	32	65	137	52
x1020	C1022	69,000	47,000	30	58	143	62
1025	C1025	70,000	41,000	31	58	130	58
1030	C1030	75,000	46,000	30	56	138	60
1035	C1035	88,000	55,000	30	56	175	60
1040	C1040	93,000	58,000	27	52	190	60
1045	C1045	99,000	60,000	24	47	200	55
1095	C1095	100,000	60,000	23	47	201	45
Free-Cutting Steels							
x1113	B1113	83,000	73,000	15	45	193	120-140
1112	B1112	67,000	40,000	27	47	140	100
....	C1120	69,000	36,000	32	55	117	80
Manganese Steels							
x1314	....	71,000	45,000	28	52	135	94
x1335	A1335	95,000	60,000	20	35	185	70
Nickel Steels							
2315	A2317	85,000	56,000	29	60	163	50
2330	A2330	98,000	65,000	25	50	207	45
2340	A2340	110,000	80,000	22	47	225	40
2345	A2345	108,000	75,000	23	46	235	50
Nickel-Chromium Steels							
3120	A3120	75,000	60,000	30	65	151	50
3130	A3130	100,000	72,000	24	55	212	45
3140	A3140	96,000	64,000	26	56	195	57
3150	A3150	104,000	73,000	19	51	229	50
3250	....	107,000	75,000	24	55	217	44
Molybdenum Steels							
4119	....	91,000	52,000	28	62	179	60
x4130	A4130	89,000	60,000	32	65	179	58
4140	A4140	90,000	63,000	27	58	187	56
4150	A4150	105,000	71,000	21	54	220	54
x4340	A4340	115,000	95.000	18	45	235	58
4615	A4615	82,000	55,000	30	61	167	58
4640	A4640	100,000	87,000	21	50	201	60
4815	A4815	105,000	73,000	24	58	212	55

Table 30 (continued)
Machinability Ratings and Other Properties of Various Metals

SAE Number	AISI Number	Tensile Strength, psi	Yield Point, psi	Elongation in 2 in., Percent	Reduction in Area, Percent	Hardness, Brinell	Machinability Rating, Percent
Chromium Steels							
5120	A5120	73,000	55,000	32	67	143	50
5140	A5140					174-229	60
52100	E52101	109,000	80,000	25	57	235	45
Chromium-Vanadium Steels							
6120	A6120					179-217	50
6150	A6150	103,000	70,000	27	51	217	50
Other Alloys and Metals							
Aluminum (11S)		49,000	42,000	14		95	300-2,000
Brass, Leaded		55,000	45,000	32		RF 100	150-600
Brass, Red or Yellow		25-35,000	15-30,000			40-55	200
Bronze, Lead-Bearing		22-32,000	8-20,000	3-16	5-18	30-65	200-500
Cast Iron, Hard		45,000				220-240	50
Cast Iron, Medium		40,000				193-220	65
Cast Iron, Soft		30,000				160-193	80
Cast Steel (0.35 C)		86,000	55,000	25	34	170-212	70
Copper (F.M.)		35,000	33,000	34		RF 85	65
Ingot Iron		41-45,000	18-25,000	45	70	101-131	50
Low-Alloy, High-Strength Steel		98,000	65,000	18	34	187	80
Magnesium Alloys							500-2,000
Malleable Iron							
Standard		53-60,000	35-40,000	18-25		110-145	120
Pearlitic		80,000	55,000	14		180-200	90
Pearlitic		97,000	75,000	4		227	80
Stainless Steel (12% Cr F.M.)		120,000	86,000	23	64	207	70
18-8 Stainless Steel (Type 303 F.M.)		80,000	30,000	60	75	150	45
18-8 Stainless Steel (Type 304)		80,000	40,000	65	70	150	25

1. All properties given for wrought materials in hot-rolled condition. As a general rule the machinability rating decreases considerably after hardening heat-treatment and increases slightly after cold-drawing.

2. The properties given in this table are presented as a rough guide to the machining characteristics of various common steels and alloys. They are by no means considered accurate enough for specifications.

(Courtesy Union Carbide Corp., Steelite Division)

Table 31. Composition Limits of Standard Steels

Nonresulphurized Carbon Steels[a]

Designation Number	Chemical Composition Limits, Percent				Designation Number	Chemical Composition Limits, Percent			
AISI	C	Mn	P(max)	S(max)	AISI	C	Mn	P(max)	S(max)
*C 1005	0.06 max	0.35 max	0.040	0.050	C 1042	0.40/0.47	0.60/0.90	0.040	0.050
*C 1006	.08 max	0.25/0.40	.040	.050	C 1043	.40/0.47	.70/1.00	.040	.050
C 1008	.10 max	.25/0.50	.040	.050	C 1044	.43/0.50	.30/0.60	.040	.050
C 1010	0.08/0.13	.30/0.60	.040	.050	C 1045	.43/0.50	.60/0.90	.040	.050
*C 1011	.08/0.13	.60/0.90	.040	.050	C 1046	.43/0.50	.70/1.00	.040	.050
C 1012	.10/0.15	.30/0.60	.040	.050	C 1048	.44/0.52	1.10/1.40	.040	.050
*C 1013	.11/0.16	.50/0.80	.040	.050	C 1049	.46/0.53	.60/0.90	.040	.050
C 1015	.13/0.18	.30/0.60	.040	.050	C 1050	.48/0.55	.60/0.90	.040	.050
C 1016	.13/0.18	.60/0.90	.040	.050	C 1051	.45/0.56	.85/1.15	.040	.050
C 1017	.15/0.20	.30/0.60	.040	.050	C 1052	.47/0.55	1.20/1.50	.040	.050
C 1018	.15/0.20	.60/0.90	.040	.050	C 1053	.48/0.55	.70/1.00	.040	.050
C 1019	.15/0.20	.70/1.00	.040	.050	C 1055	.50/0.60	.60/0.90	.040	.050
C 1020	.18/0.23	.30/0.60	.040	.050	*C 1059	.55/0.65	.50/0.80	.040	.050
C 1021	.18/0.23	.60/0.90	.040	.050	C 1060	.55/0.65	.60/0.90	.040	.050
C 1022	.18/0.23	.70/1.00	.040	.050	*C 1061	.55/0.65	.75/1.05	.040	.050
C 1023	.20/0.25	.30/0.60	.040	.050	*C 1064	.60/0.70	.50/0.80	.040	.050
C 1024	.19/0.25	1.35/1.65	.040	.050	*C 1065	.60/0.70	.60/0.90	.040	.050
C 1025	.22/0.28	0.30/0.60	.040	.050	*C 1066	.60/0.70	.85/1.15	.040	.050
C 1026	.22/0.28	.60/0.90	.040	.050	*C 1069	.65/0.75	.40/0.70	.040	.050
C 1027	.22/0.29	1.20/1.50	.040	.050	C 1070	.65/0.75	.60/0.90	.040	.050
C 1029	.25/0.31	0.60/0.90	.040	.050	*C 1072	.65/0.75	1.00/1.30	.040	.050
C 1030	.28/0.34	.60/0.90	.040	.050	*C 1074	.70/0.80	.50/0.80	.040	.050
*C 1034	.32/0.38	.50/0.80	.040	.050	*C 1075	.70/0.80	.40/0.70	.040	.050
C 1035	.32/0.38	.60/0.90	.040	.050	C 1078	.72/0.85	.30/0.60	.040	.050
C 1036	.30/0.37	1.20/1.50	.040	.050	C 1080	.75/0.88	.60/0.90	.040	.050
C 1037	.32/0.38	0.70/1.00	.040	.050	C 1084	.80/0.93	.60/0.90	.040	.050
C 1038	.35/0.42	.60/0.90	.040	.050	*C 1086	.80/0.93	.30/0.50	.040	.050
C 1039	.37/0.44	.70/1.00	.040	.050	C 1090	.85/0.98	.60/0.90	.040	.050
C 1040	.37/0.44	.60/0.90	.040	.050	C 1095	.90/1.03	.30/0.50	.040	.050
C 1041	.36/0.44	1.35/1.65	.040	.050					

Resulphurized Carbon Steels[b]

Designation Number	Chemical Composition Limits, Percent				Designation Number	Chemical Composition Limits, Percent			
AISI	C	Mn	P(max)	S	AISI	C	Mn	P(max)	S
C 1108	0.08/0.13	0.50/0.80	0.040	0.08/0.13	C 1137	0.32/0.39	1.35/1.65	0.040	0.08/0.13
C 1109	.08/0.13	.60/0.90	.040	.08/0.13	C 1139	.35/0.43	1.35/1.65	.040	.12/0.20
C 1110	.08/0.13	.30/0.60	.040	.08/0.13	C 1140	.37/0.44	.70/1.00	.040	.08/0.13
C 1116	.14/0.20	1.10/1.40	.040	.16/0.23	C 1141	.37/0.45	1.35/1.65	.040	.08/0.13
C 1117	.14/0.20	1.00/1.30	.040	.08/0.13	C 1144	.40/0.48	1.35/1.65	.040	.24/0.33
C 1118	.14/0.20	1.30/1.60	.040	.08/0.13	C 1145	.42/0.49	.70/1.00	.040	.04/0.07
C 1119	.14/0.20	1.00/1.30	.040	.24/0.33	C 1146	.42/0.49	.70/1.00	.040	.08/0.13
C 1132	.27/0.34	1.35/1.65	.040	.08/0.13	C 1151	.48/0.55	.70/1.00	.040	.08/0.13

Acid Bessemer Resulphurized Carbon Steels[c] / Rephosphorized and Resulphurized Carbon Steels[d]

Designation Number	Chemical Composition Limits, Percent				Designation Number	Chemical Composition Limits, Percent			
AISI	C	Mn	P	S	AISI	C	Mn	P	S
B 1111	0.13 max	0.60/0.90	0.07/0.12	0.08/0.15	C 1211	0.13 max	0.60/0.90	0.07/0.12	0.08/0.15
B 1112	.13 max	.70/1.00	.07/0.12	.16/0.23	C 1212	.13 max	.70/1.00	.07/0.12	.16/0.23
B 1113	.13 max	.70/1.00	.07/0.12	.24/0.33	C 1213	.13 max	.70/1.00	.07/0.12	.24/0.33
					C 1215	.09 max	.75/1.05	.04/0.09	.26/0.35
					‡C 12L14	.15 max	.80/1.20	.04/0.09	.25/0.35

Open Hearth and Electric Furnace Alloy Steels[e]

Designation Number	Chemical Composition Limits, Percent								
AISI	C	Mn	P(max)	S(max)	Si	Ni	Cr	Mo	V
1330	0.28/0.33	1.60/1.90	0.035	0.040	0.20/0.35				
1335	.33/0.38	1.60/1.90	.035	.040	.20/0.35				
1340	.38/0.43	1.60/1.90	.035	.040	.20/0.35				
1345	.43/0.48	1.60/1.90	.035	.040	.20/0.35				
*3140	.38/0.43	0.70/0.90	.035	.040	.20/0.35	1.10/1.40	0.55/0.75		
E 3310	.08/0.13	.45/0.60	.025	.025	.20/0.35	3.25/3.75	1.40/1.75		

abcde See notes on page xxx.
‡ Lead = 0.15/0.35 percent.

644

Open Hearth and Electric Furnace Alloy Steels[e]—(continued)

Designation Number AISI	Chemical Composition Limits, Percent								
	C	Mn	P(max)	S(max)	Si	Ni	Cr	Mo	V
4012	.09/0.14	.75/1.00	.035	.040	.20/0.35			0.15/0.25	
4023	.20/0.25	.70/0.90	.035	.040	.20/0.35			.20/0.30	
4024	.20/0.25	.70/0.90	.035	0.035/0.050	.20/0.25			.20/0.30	
4027	.25/0.30	.70/0.90	.035	.040	.20/0.35			.20/0.30	
4028	.25/0.30	.70/0.90	.035	.035/0.050	.20/0.35			.20/0.30	
4037	.35/0.40	.70/0.90	.035	.040	.20/0.35			.20/0.30	
*4042	.40/0.45	.70/0.90	.035	.040	.20/0.35			.20/0.30	
4047	.45/0.50	.70/0.90	.035	.040	.20/0.35			.20/0.30	
*4063	.60/0.67	.75/1.00	.035	.040	.20/0.35			.20/0.30	
4118	.18/0.23	.70/0.90	.035	.040	.20/0.35		0.40/0.60	.08/0.15	
4130	.28/0.33	.40/0.60	.035	.040	.20/0.35		.80/1.10	.15/0.25	
*4135	.33/0.38	.70/0.90	.035	.040	.20/0.35		.80/1.10	.15/0.25	
4137	.35/0.40	.70/0.90	.035	.040	.20/0.35		.80/1.10	.15/0.25	
4140	.38/0.43	.75/1.00	.035	.040	.20/0.35		.80/1.10	.15/0.25	
4142	.40/0.45	.75/1.00	.035	.040	.20/0.35		.80/1.10	.15/0.25	
4145	.43/0.48	.75/1.00	.035	.040	.20/0.35		.80/1.10	.15/0.25	
4147	.45/0.50	.75/1.00	.035	.040	.20/0.30		.80/1.10	.15/0.25	
4150	.48/0.53	.75/1.00	.035	.040	.20/0.35		.80/1.10	.15/0.25	
4161	.56/0.64	.75/1.00	.035	.040	.20/0.35		.70/0.90	.25/0.35	
4320	.17/0.22	.45/0.65	.035	.040	.20/0.35	1.65/2.00	.40/0.60	.20/0.30	
*4337	.35/0.40	.60/0.80	.035	.040	.20/0.35	1.65/2.00	.70/0.90	.20/0.30	
E 4337	.35/0.40	.65/0.85	.025	.025	.20/0.35	1.65/2.00	.70/0.90	.20/0.30	
4340	.38/0.43	.60/0.80	.035	.040	.20/0.25	1.65/2.00	.70/0.90	.20/0.30	
E 4340	.38/0.43	.65/0.85	.025	.025	.20/0.35	1.65/2.00	.70/0.90	.20/0.30	
4419	.18/0.23	.45/0.65	.035	.040	.20/0.35			.45/0.60	
*4422	.20/0.25	.70/0.90	.035	.040	.20/0.35			.35/0.45	
*4427	.24/0.29	.70/0.90	.035	.040	.20/0.35			.35/0.45	
4615	.13/0.18	.45/0.65	.035	.040	.20/0.35	1.65/2.00		.20/0.30	
*4617	.15/0.20	.45/0.65	.035	.040	.20/0.35	1.65/2.00		.20/0.30	
4620	.17/0.22	.45/0.65	.035	.040	.20/0.35	1.65/2.00		.20/0.30	
4621	.18/0.23	.70/0.90	.035	.040	.20/0.35	1.65/2.00		.20/0.30	
4626	.24/0.29	.45/0.65	.035	.040	.20/0.35	.70/1.00		.15/0.25	
4718	.16/0.21	.70/0.90	.035	.040	.20/0.35	.90/1.20	.35/0.55	.30/0.40	
4720	.17/0.22	.50/0.70	.035	.040	.20/0.35	.90/1.20	.35/0.55	.15/0.25	
4815	.13/0.18	.40/0.60	.035	.040	.20/0.35	3.25/3.75		.20/0.30	
4817	.15/0.20	.40/0.60	.035	.040	.20/0.35	3.25/3.75		.20/0.30	
4820	.18/0.23	.50/0.70	.035	.040	.20/0.35	3.25/2.75		.20/0.30	
5015	.12/0.17	.30/0.50	.035	.040	.20/0.35		.30/0.40		
*5046	.43/0.50	.75/1.00	.035	.040	.20/0.35		.20/0.35		
*5115	.13/0.18	.70/0.90	.035	.040	.20/0.35		.70/0.90		
5120	.17/0.22	.70/0.90	.035	.040	.20/0.35		.70/0.90		
5130	.28/0.33	.70/0.90	.035	.040	.20/0.35		.80/1.10		
5132	.30/0.35	.60/0.80	.035	.040	.20/0.35		.75/1.00		
5135	.33/0.38	.60/0.80	.035	.040	.20/0.35		.80/1.05		
5140	.38/0.43	.70/0.90	.035	.040	.20/0.35		.70/0.90		
5145	.43/0.48	.70/0.90	.035	.040	.20/0.35		.70/0.90		
5147	.45/0.52	.70/0.90	.035	.040	.20/0.35		.85/1.15		
5150	.48/0.53	.70/0.90	.035	.040	.20/0.35		.70/0.90		
5155	.50/0.60	.70/0.90	.035	.040	.20/0.35		.70/0.90		
5160	.55/0.65	.75/1.00	.035	.040	.20/0.35		.70/0.90		
*E 50100	0.95/1.10	0.25/0.45	0.025	0.040	0.20/0.35		0.40/0.60		
E 51100	.95/1.10	.25/0.45	.025	.025	.20/0.35		.90/1.15		
E 52100	.95/1.10	.25/0.45	.025	.025	.20/0.35		1.30/1.60		
6118	.16/0.21	.50/0.70	.035	.040	.20/0.35		.50/0.70		0.10/0.15
*6120	.17/0.22	.70/0.90	.035	.040	.20/0.35		.70/0.90		.10 min
6150	.48/0.53	.70/0.90	.035	.040	.20/0.35		.80/1.10		.15 min
*8115	.13/0.18	.70/0.90	.035	.040	.20/0.35	0.20/0.40	.30/0.50	0.08/0.15	
8615	.13/0.18	.70/0.90	.035	.040	.20/0.35	.40/0.70	.40/0.60	.15/0.25	
8617	.15/0.20	.70/0.90	.035	.040	.20/0.35	.40/0.70	.40/0.60	.15/0.25	
8620	.18/0.23	.70/0.90	.035	.040	.20/0.35	.40/0.70	.40/0.60	.15/0.25	
8622	.20/0.25	.70/0.90	.035	.040	.20/0.35	.40/0.70	.40/0.60	.15/0.25	
8625	.23/0.28	.70/0.90	.035	.040	.20/0.35	.40/0.70	.40/0.60	.15/0.25	
8627	.25/0.30	.70/0.90	.035	.040	.20/0.35	.40/0.70	.40/0.60	.15/0.25	
8630	.28/0.33	.70/0.90	.035	.040	.20/0.35	.40/0.70	.40/0.60	.15/0.25	
8637	.35/0.40	.75/1.00	.035	.040	.20/0.35	.40/0.70	.40/0.60	.15/0.25	
8640	.38/0.43	.75/1.00	.035	.040	.20/0.35	.40/0.70	.40/0.60	.15/0.25	
8642	.40/0.45	.75/1.00	.035	.040	.20/0.35	.40/0.70	.40/0.60	.15/0.25	
8645	.43/0.48	.75/1.00	.035	.040	.20/0.35	.40/0.70	.40/0.60	.15/0.25	
*8650	.48/0.53	.75/1.00	.035	.040	.20/0.35	.40/0.70	.40/0.60	.15/0.25	
8655	.50/0.60	.75/1.00	.035	.040	.20/0.35	.40/0.70	.40/0.60	.15/0.25	
*8660	.55/0.65	.75/1.00	.035	.040	.20/0.35	.40/0.70	.40/0.60	.15/0.25	
8720	.18/0.23	.70/0.90	.035	.040	.20/0.35	.40/0.70	.40/0.60	.20/0.30	
*8735	.33/0.38	.75/1.00	.035	.040	.20/0.35	.40/0.70	.40/0.60	.20/0.30	
8740	.38/0.43	.75/1.00	.035	.040	.20/0.35	.40/0.70	.40/0.60	.20/0.30	
*8742	.40/0.45	.75/1.00	.035	.040	.20/0.35	.40/0.70	.40/0.60	.20/0.30	
8822	.20/0.25	.75/1.00	.035	.040	.20/0.35	.40/0.70	.40/0.60	.30/0.40	
9255	.50/0.60	.70/0.95	.035	.040	1.80/2.20				
9260	.55/0.65	.70/1.00	.035	.040	1.80/2.20				
*9262	.55/0.65	.75/1.00	.035	.040	1.80/2.20		.25/0.40		
*E 9310	.08/0.13	.45/0.65	.025	.025	.20/0.35	3.00/3.50	1.00/1.40	.08/0.15	
*9840	.38/0.43	.70/0.90	.035	.040	.20/0.35	.85/1.15	.70/0.90	.20/0.30	
*9850	.48/0.53	.70/0.90	.035	.040	.20/0.35	.85/1.15	.70/0.90	.20/0.30	

Table 32. Recommended Heat Treatments for Various Grades of Steel

(No tempering treatments are given, as these temperatures depend upon the desired hardness)

AISI or SAE Number	Normalizing Temperature	Annealing Temperature	Hardening Temperature	Quenching Medium	AISI or SAE Number	Normalizing Temperature	Annealing Temperature	Hardening Temperature	Quenching Medium
	°F	°F	°F			°F	°F	°F	
1030	1,625/1,725	1,525/1,575	1,550/1,600	Water or brine.	5046	1,600/1,700	1,475/1,525	1,500/1,550	Oil.
1040	1,600/1,700	1,475/1,525	1,500/1,550	Do.	5130	1,600/1,700	1,500/1,550	1,550/1,600	Oil or water.
1050	1,550/1,650	1,450/1,500	1,475/1,525	Do.	5145	1,600/1,700	1,475/1,525	1,525/1,575	Oil.
1060	1,500/1,600	1,425/1,475	1,450/1,500	Do.	5160	1,600/1,700	1,450/1,500	1,500/1,550	Do.
1070	1,500/1,600	1,425/1,475	1,450/1,500	Do.	50100	1,600/1,700	1,400/1,450	1,450/1,500	Do.
1080	1,475/1,575	1,375/1,425	1,400/1,450	Do.	51100	1,600/1,700	1,400/1,450	1,475/1,525	Do.
1090	1,475/1,575	1,375/1,425	1,400/1,450	Do.	52100	1,600/1,700	1,400/1,450	1,500/1,550	Do.
1132	1,625/1,725	1,525/1,575	1,550/1,600	Do.	6150	1,600/1,700	1,500/1,550	1,550/1,600	Do.
1140	1,600/1,700	1,475/1,525	1,500/1,550	Do.	8630	1,600/1,700	1,500/1,550	1,525/1,575	Do.
1151	1,550/1,650	1,450/1,500	1,475/1,525	Do.	8645	1,660/1,700	1,475/1,525	1,500/1,550	Do.
1330	1,600/1,700	1,500/1,550	1,525/1,575	Oil or water.	8660	1,600/1,700	1,450/1,500	1,475/1,525	Do.
1340	1,550/1,650	1,475/1,525	1,500/1,550	Do.	8735	1,600/1,700	1,500/1,550	1,525/1,575	Do.
3140	1,550/1,650	1,475/1,525	1,475/1,525	Oil.	8742	1,600/1,700	1,500/1,550	1,525/1,575	Do.
4028	1,600/1,700	1,525/1,575	1,550/1,600	Oil or water.	9260	1,600/1,700	1,500/1,550	1,550/1,600	Do.
4042	1,550/1,650	1,475/1,525	1,500/1,550	Oil.	9840	1,600/1,700	1,475/1,525	1,500/1,550	Do.
4063	1,550/1,650	1,450/1,500	1,475/1,525	Do.	9850	1,600/1,700	1,475/1,525	1,500/1,550	Do.
4130	1,600/1,700	1,525/1,575	1,550/1,600	Oil or water.					
4140	1,600/1,700	1,500/1,550	1,525/1,575	Oil.					
4150	1,600/1,700	1,475/1,525	1,500/1,550	Do.					
4340	1,600/1,700	1,500/1,550	1,500/1,550	Do.					

Table 33. Recommendations for Carburizing Various Grades of Steel

AISI or SAE Number	Carburizing Temperature	Cooling Method	Reheat	Cooling Medium	2d Reheat	Cooling Medium	Tempering Temperature
	°F		°F		°F		°F
1008 to 1024; 1108 to 1119; 1211 to 1215	1,650/1,700	Brine or water					250/300
		Water or oil	1,400/1,450	Brine or water			
		Cool slowly	1,400/1,450	do			
		do	1,650/1,700	Water or oil	1,400/1,450	Brine or water	
3310	1,650/1,700	Oil					250/300
		do	1,375/1,425	Oil			
		Cool slowly	1,375/1,425	do			
		do	1,525/1,575	do	1,375/1,425	Oil	
4012 to 4024; 4118	1,650/1,700	Oil					250/300
		do	1,425/1,475	Oil			
		Cool slowly	1,425/1,475	do			
		do	1,600/1,650	do	1,425/1,475	Oil	
4419,4422 and 4427; 8822	1,650/1,700	Oil					250/300
		do	1,450/1,500	Oil			
		Cool slowly	1,450/1,500	do			
		do	1,625/1,675	do	1,450/1,500	Oil	
4520	1,650/1,700	Oil					250/300
		do	1,475/1,525	Oil			
		Cool slowly	1,475/1,525	do			
		do	1,650/1,700	do	1,475/1,525	Oil	
4320; 4615 to 4626; 4718 and 4720	1,650/1,700	Oil					250/300
		do	1,425/1,475	Oil			
		Cool slowly	1,375/1,425	do			
		do	1,525/1,575	do	1,375/1,425	Oil	
4815 to 4820	1,650/1,700	Oil					250/300
		do	1,350/1,400	Oil			
		Cool slowly	1,350/1,400	do			
		do	1,550/1,600	do	1,350/1,400	Oil	
5015; 5115 and 5120	1,650/1,700	Oil					250/300
		do	1,425/1,475	Oil			
		Cool slowly	1,425/1,475	do			
		do	1,600/1,650	do	1,425/1,475	Oil	
6118 and 6120	1,650/1,700	Oil					300/400
		do	1,450/1,500	Oil or water			
		Cool slowly	1,450/1,500	do			
		do	1,600/1,650	Oil	1,450/1,500	Oil or water	
8115; 8615 to 8622; 8720; 8822; 9310 and 94B17.	1,650/1,700	Oil					250/300
		do	1,450/1,500	Oil			
		Cool slowly	1,450/1,500	do			
		do	1,550/1,600	do	1,450/1,500	Oil	

Note: "Do" is the abbreviation for "ditto" — meaning the same as above.

Tables 31, 32, and 33 are from **Heat Treatment and Properties of Iron and Steel,** by Thomas G. Digges, Samuel J. Rosenberg, and Glenn W. Geil. National Bureau of Standards Monograph 88, Washington: U.S. Government Printing Office, 1966.

a Silicon: When required, the following ranges are common:
Up to C 1015 excl..0.10% max.
C 1015 to C 1025 incl..............0.10% max., 0.10/0.20%, or 0.15/0.30%
Over C 1025....................................0.10/0.20%, or 0.15/0.30%
Copper: When required, copper is specified as an added element.
Lead: When required, lead is specified as an added element.

b Silicon: When required, the following ranges are common:
Up to C 1110 incl..0.10% max.
C 1116 and over................0.10% max., 0.10/0.20%, or 0.15/0.30%
Lead: When required, lead is specified as an added element.

c Silicon: Because of the nature of the process, acid bessemer steels are not produced with specified silicon content.
Lead: When required, lead is specified as an added element.

d Silicon: Usually these steels have specified silicon limits.
Lead: When required, lead is specified as an added element.

e Grades with prefix E in Table 31 generally are made in a basic electric furnace, and all others normally by the basic open hearth process but the basic electric furnace process can be used if phosphorus and sulphur are adjusted. The phosphorus and sulphur limits for various processes are:

	P(max)	S(max)
Basic electric furnace........................	0.025%	0.025%
Basic open hearth...........................	0.035%	0.040%
Acid electric furnace........................	0.050%	0.050%
Acid open hearth............................	0.050%	0.050%

(Minimum silicon for alloy steel from last two is 0.15%)

Small quantities of certain elements which are not specified or required are present in alloy steels. These elements are incidental and may be present to the following maximums: 0.35% copper, 0.25% nickel, 0.20% chromium, and 0.06% molybdenum. Where minimum and maximum sulphur content is shown, it is indicative of resulphurized steels.

Table 34. Hardness Numbers for Steel Approximately Equivalent to Rockwell C Scale

Rockwell C-Scale Hardness No.	Diamond Pyramid Hardness No.	Brinell Hardness No. (10-mm Ball, 3000-kg load)			Rockwell Hardness No.			Rockwell Superficial Hardness No. (Superficial Brale Penetrator)			Shore Scleroscope Hardness No.	Tensile Strength (Approx.) 1000 psi
		Standard Ball	Hultgren Ball	Carbide Ball	A Scale (60-kg Brale)	B Scale (100-kg 1/16" Ball)	D Scale (100-kg Brale)	15-N Scale (15 kg)	30-N Scale (30 kg)	45-N Scale (45 kg)		
68	940	...	...	...	85.6	...	76.9	93.2	84.4	75.4	97	...
67	900	...	...	...	85.0	...	76.1	92.9	83.6	74.2	95	...
66	865	...	...	...	84.5	...	75.4	92.5	82.8	73.3	92	...
65	832	...	...	(739)	83.9	...	74.5	92.2	81.9	72.0	91	...
64	800	...	...	(722)	83.4	...	73.8	91.8	81.1	71.0	88	...
63	772	...	...	(705)	82.8	...	73.0	91.4	80.1	69.9	87	...
62	746	...	...	(688)	82.3	...	72.2	91.1	79.3	68.8	85	...
61	720	...	...	(670)	81.8	...	71.5	90.7	78.4	67.7	83	...
60	697	...	(613)	(654)	81.2	...	70.7	90.2	77.5	66.6	81	...
59	674	...	(599)	(634)	80.7	...	69.9	89.8	76.6	65.5	80	326
58	653	...	(587)	615	80.1	...	69.2	89.3	75.7	64.3	78	315
57	633	...	(575)	595	79.6	...	68.5	88.9	74.8	63.2	76	305
56	613	...	(561)	577	79.0	...	67.7	88.3	73.9	62.0	75	295
55	595	...	(546)	560	78.5	...	66.9	87.9	73.0	60.9	74	287
54	577	...	(534)	543	78.0	...	66.1	87.4	72.0	59.8	72	278
53	560	...	(519)	525	77.4	...	65.4	86.9	71.2	58.6	71	269
52	544	(500)	(508)	512	76.8	...	64.6	86.4	70.2	57.4	69	262
51	528	(487)	494	496	76.3	...	63.8	85.9	69.4	56.1	68	253
50	513	(475)	481	481	75.9	...	63.1	85.5	68.5	55.0	67	245
49	498	(464)	469	469	75.2	...	62.1	85.0	67.6	53.8	66	239
48	484	451	455	455	74.7	...	61.4	84.5	66.7	52.5	64	232
47	471	442	443	443	74.1	...	60.8	83.9	65.8	51.4	63	225
46	458	432	432	432	73.6	...	60.0	83.5	64.8	50.3	62	219
45	446	421	421	421	73.1	...	59.2	83.0	64.0	49.0	60	212
44	434	409	409	409	72.5	...	58.5	82.5	63.1	47.8	58	206
43	423	400	400	400	72.0	...	57.7	82.0	62.2	46.7	57	201
42	412	390	390	390	71.5	...	56.9	81.5	61.3	45.5	56	196
41	402	381	381	381	70.9	...	56.2	80.9	60.4	44.3	55	191
40	392	371	371	371	70.4	...	55.4	80.4	59.5	43.1	54	186
39	382	362	362	362	69.9	...	54.6	79.9	58.6	41.9	52	181
38	372	353	353	353	69.4	...	53.8	79.4	57.7	40.8	51	176
37	363	344	344	344	68.9	...	53.1	78.8	56.8	39.6	50	172
36	354	336	336	336	68.4	(190.0)	52.3	78.3	55.9	38.4	49	168
35	345	327	327	327	67.9	(108.5)	51.5	77.7	55.0	37.2	48	163
34	336	319	319	319	67.4	(108.0)	50.8	77.2	54.2	36.1	47	159
33	327	311	311	311	66.8	(107.5)	50.0	76.6	53.3	34.9	46	154
32	318	301	301	301	66.3	(107.0)	49.2	76.1	52.1	33.7	44	150
31	310	294	294	294	65.8	(106.0)	48.4	75.6	51.3	32.5	43	146
30	302	286	286	286	65.3	(105.5)	47.7	75.0	50.4	31.3	42	142
29	294	279	279	279	64.7	(104.5)	47.0	74.5	49.5	30.1	41	138
28	286	271	271	271	64.3	(104.0)	46.1	73.9	48.6	28.9	41	134
27	279	264	264	264	63.8	(103.0)	45.2	73.3	47.7	27.8	40	131
26	272	258	258	258	63.3	(102.5)	44.6	72.8	46.8	26.7	38	127
25	266	253	253	253	62.8	(101.5)	43.8	72.2	45.9	25.5	38	124
24	260	247	247	247	62.4	(101.0)	43.1	71.6	45.0	24.3	37	121
23	254	243	243	243	62.0	100.0	42.1	71.0	44.0	23.1	36	118
22	248	237	237	237	61.5	99.0	41.6	70.5	43.2	22.0	35	115
21	243	231	231	231	61.0	98.5	40.9	69.9	42.3	20.7	35	113
20	238	226	226	226	60.5	97.8	40.1	69.4	41.5	19.6	34	110
(18)	230	219	219	219	...	96.7	...	...	...	...	33	106
(16)	222	212	212	212	...	95.5	...	...	...	...	32	102
(14)	213	203	203	203	...	93.9	...	...	...	...	31	98
(12)	204	194	194	194	...	92.3	...	...	...	...	29	94
(10)	196	187	187	187	...	90.7	...	...	...	...	28	90
(8)	188	179	179	179	...	89.5	...	...	...	...	27	87
(6)	180	171	171	171	...	87.1	...	...	...	...	26	84
(4)	173	165	165	165	...	85.5	...	...	...	...	25	80
(2)	166	158	158	158	...	83.5	...	...	...	...	24	77
(0)	160	152	152	152	...	81.7	...	...	...	...	24	75

The values in boldface type correspond to the values in the joint SAE-ASM-ASTM hardness conversions as printed in ASTM E140-65, Table 2. Values in parentheses are beyond normal range and are given for information only. Data from **Metals Handbook,** 8th Edition, American Society for Metals.
(Reprinted with permission)

Table 35
Coarse Thread Dimensions — Unified and American National Course Series, UNC, NC

Size of Thread and Threads per inch	Major Diameter in Inches	Pitch Diameter in Inches	Minor Diameter of External Threads In inches*	Commercial Tap Drill for About 75% Thread	Decimal Equivalent of Tap Drill in Inches
1 x64	.0730	.0629	.0538	No. 53	.0595
2 x56	.0860	.0744	.0641	No. 50	.0700
3 x48	.0990	.0855	.0734	No. 47	.0785
4 x40	.1120	.0958	.0813	No. 43	.0890
5 x40	.1250	.1088	.0943	No. 38	.1015
6 x32	.1380	.1177	.0997	No. 36	.1065
8 x32	.1640	.1437	.1257	No. 29	.1360
10 x24	.1900	.1629	.1389	No. 25	.1495
12 x24	.2160	.1889	.1649	No. 16	.1770
¼ x20	.2500	.2175	.1887	No. 7	.2010
⁵⁄₁₆x18	.3125	.2764	.2443	F	.2570
⅜ x16	.3750	.3344	.2983	⁵⁄₁₆	.3125
⁷⁄₁₆x14	.4375	.3911	.3499	U	.3680
½ x13	.5000	.4500	.4056	²⁷⁄₆₄	.4219
⁹⁄₁₆x12	.5625	.5084	.4603	³¹⁄₆₄	.4844
⅝ x11	.6250	.5660	.5135	¹⁷⁄₃₂	.5312
¾ x10	.7500	.6850	.6273	²¹⁄₃₂	.6562
⅞ 9	.8750	.8028	.7387	⁴⁹⁄₆₄	.7656
1 x 8	1.0000	.9188	.8466	⅞	.8750
1⅛x 7	1.1250	1.0322	.9497	⁶³⁄₆₄	.9844
1¼x 7	1.2500	1.1572	1.0747	1⁷⁄₆₄	1.1094
1⅜x 6	1.3750	1.2667	1.1705	1⁷⁄₃₂	1.2187
1½x 6	1.5000	1.3917	1.2955	1²¹⁄₆₄	1.3281
1¾x 5	1.7500	1.6201	1.5046	1³⁵⁄₆₄	1.5469
2 x 4½	2.0000	1.8557	1.7274	1²⁵⁄₃₂	1.7812
2¼x 4½	2.2500	2.1057	1.9774	2¹⁄₃₂	2.0312
2½x 4	2.5000	2.3376	2.1933	2¼	2.2500
2¾x 4	2.7500	2.5876	2.4433	2½	2.5000
3 x 4	3.0000	2.8376	2.6933	2¾	2.7500
3¼x 4	3.2500	3.0876	2.9433	3	3.0000
3½x 4	3.5000	3.3376	3.1933	3¼	3.2500
3¾x 4	3.7500	3.5876	3.4433	3½	3.5000
4 x 4	4.0000	3.8376	3.6933	3¾	3.7500

Table 36
Fine Thread Dimensions — Unified and American National Fine Series, UNF, NF

Size of Thread and Threads per inch	Major Diameter in Inches	Pitch Diameter in Inches	Minor Diameter of External Threads in Inches*	Commercial Tap Drill for About 75% Thread	Decimal Equivalent of Tap Drill in Inches
0 x80	.0600	.0519	.0447	³⁄₆₄	.0469
1 x72	.0730	.0640	.0560	No. 53	.0595
2 x64	.0860	.0759	.0668	No. 50	.0700
3 x56	.0990	.0874	.0771	No. 45	.0820
4 x48	.1120	.0985	.0864	No. 42	.0935
5 x44	.1250	.1102	.0971	No. 37	.1040
6 x40	.1380	.1218	.1073	No. 33	.1130
8 x36	.1640	.1460	.1299	No. 29	.1360
10 x32	.1900	.1697	.1517	No. 21	.1590
12 x28	.2160	.1928	.1722	No. 14	.1820
¼ x28	.2500	.2268	.2062	No. 3	.2130
⁵⁄₁₆x24	.3125	.2854	.2614	I	.2720
⅜ x24	.3750	.3479	.3239	Q	.3320
⁷⁄₁₆x20	.4375	.4050	.3762	²⁵⁄₆₄	.3906
½ x20	.5000	.4675	.4387	²⁹⁄₆₄	.4531
⁹⁄₁₆x18	.5625	.5264	.4943	³³⁄₆₄	.5156
⅝ x18	.6250	.5889	.5568	³⁷⁄₆₄	.5781
¾ x16	.7500	.7094	.6733	¹¹⁄₁₆	.6875
⅞ x14	.8750	.8286	.7874	¹³⁄₁₆	.8125
1 x14	1.0000	.9536	.8978	¹⁵⁄₁₆	.9375
1⅛x12	1.1250	1.0709	1.0228	1³⁄₆₄	1.0469
1¼x12	1.2500	1.1959	1.1478	1¹¹⁄₆₄	1.1719
1⅜x12	1.3750	1.3209	1.2728	1¹⁹⁄₆₄	1.2969
1½x12	1.5000	1.4459	1.3978	1²⁷⁄₆₄	1.4219

*Design form, maximum metal condition. See Fig. 4-7A.
Based on external thread height = 0.61343 Pitch

Table 37
Standard Series of Unified Screw Threads

| Sizes | | Basic Major Diameter | Series with Graded Pitches | | | Series with Constant Pitches | | | | | | | | Sizes |
Primary	Secondary		Coarse UNC	Fine UNF	Extra Fine UNEF	4UN	6UN	8UN	12UN	16UN	20UN	28UN	32UN	
0		0.0600	..	80	..	..	..	..	..	..	..	..	..	0
	1	0.0730	64	72	..	..	..	..	..	..	..	..	..	1
2		0.0860	56	64	..	..	..	..	..	..	..	..	..	2
	3	0.0990	48	56	..	..	..	..	..	..	..	..	..	3
4		0.1120	40	48	..	..	..	..	..	..	..	..	..	4
5		0.1250	40	44	..	..	..	..	..	..	..	..	..	5
6		0.1380	32	40	..	..	..	..	..	..	..	..	UNC	6
8		0.1640	32	36	..	..	..	..	..	..	..	..	UNC	8
10		0.1900	24	32	..	..	..	..	..	..	..	..	UNF	10
	12	0.2160	24	28	32	..	..	..	..	..	..	UNF	UNEF	12
¼		0.2500	20	28	32	..	..	..	..	..	UNC	UNF	UNEF	¼
5⁄16		0.3125	18	24	32	..	..	..	..	..	20	28	UNEF	5⁄16
⅜		0.3750	16	24	32	..	..	..	..	UNC	20	28	UNEF	⅜
7⁄16		0.4375	14	20	28	..	..	..	..	16	UNF	UNEF	32	7⁄16
½		0.5000	13	20	28	..	..	..	..	16	UNF	UNEF	32	½
9⁄16		0.5625	12	18	24	..	..	..	UNC	16	20	28	32	9⁄16
⅝		0.6250	11	18	24	..	..	..	12	16	20	28	32	⅝
	11⁄16	0.6875	..	..	24	..	..	..	12	16	20	28	32	11⁄16
¾		0.7500	10	16	20	..	..	..	12	UNF	UNEF	28	32	¾
	13⁄16	0.8125	..	..	20	..	..	..	12	16	UNEF	28	32	13⁄16
⅞		0.8750	9	14	20	..	..	..	12	16	UNEF	28	32	⅞
	15⁄16	0.9375	..	..	20	..	..	..	12	16	UNEF	28	32	15⁄16
1		1.0000	8	12	20	..	..	UNC	UNF	16	UNEF	28	32	1
	1 1⁄16	1.0625	..	..	18	..	..	8	12	16	20	29	..	1 1⁄16
1⅛		1.1250	7	12	18	..	..	8	UNF	16	20	28	..	1⅛
	1 3⁄16	1.1875	..	..	18	..	..	8	12	16	20	28	..	1 3⁄16
1¼		1.2500	7	12	18	..	..	8	UNF	16	20	28	..	1¼
	1 5⁄16	1.3125	..	..	18	..	..	8	12	16	20	28	..	1 5⁄16
1⅜		1.3750	6	12	18	..	UNC	8	UNF	16	20	28	..	1⅜
	1 7⁄16	1.4375	..	..	18	..	6	8	12	16	20	28	..	1 7⁄16
1½		1.5000	6	12	18	..	UNC	8	UNF	16	20	28	..	1½
	1 9⁄16	1.5625	..	..	18	..	6	8	12	16	20	..	..	1 9⁄16
1⅝		1.6250	..	..	18	..	6	8	12	16	20	..	..	1⅝
	1 11⁄16	1.6875	..	..	18	..	6	8	12	16	20	..	..	1 11⁄16
1¾		1.7500	5	..	..	..	6	8	12	16	20	..	..	1¾
	1 13⁄16	1.8125	..	..	..	..	6	8	12	16	20	..	..	1 13⁄16
1⅞		1.8750	..	..	..	..	6	8	12	16	20	..	..	1⅞
	1 15⁄16	1.9375	..	..	..	..	6	8	12	16	20	..	..	1 15⁄16
2		2.0000	4½	..	..	..	6	8	12	16	20	..	..	2
	2⅛	2.1250	..	..	..	..	6	8	12	16	20	..	..	2⅛
2¼		2.2500	4½	..	..	..	6	8	12	16	20	..	..	2¼
	2⅜	2.3750	..	..	..	..	6	8	12	16	20	..	..	2⅜
2½		2.5000	4	..	..	UNC	6	8	12	16	20	..	..	2½
	2⅝	2.6250	..	..	..	4	6	8	12	16	20	..	..	2⅝
2¾		2.7500	4	..	..	UNC	6	8	12	16	20	..	..	2¾
	2⅞	2.8750	..	..	..	4	6	8	12	16	20	..	..	2⅞
3		3.0000	4	..	..	UNC	6	8	12	16	20	..	..	3
	3⅛	3.1250	..	..	..	4	6	8	12	16	..	..	..	3⅛
3¼		3.2500	4	..	..	UNC	6	8	12	16	..	..	..	3¼
	3⅜	3.3750	..	..	..	4	6	8	12	16	..	..	..	3⅜
3½		3.5000	4	..	..	UNC	6	8	12	16	..	..	..	3½
	3⅝	3.6250	..	..	..	4	6	8	12	16	..	..	..	3⅝
3¾		3.7500	4	..	..	UNC	6	8	12	16	..	..	..	3¾
	3⅞	3.8750	..	..	..	4	6	8	12	16	..	..	..	3⅞
4		4.0000	4	..	..	UNC	6	8	12	16	..	..	..	4
	4⅛	4.1250	..	..	..	4	6	8	12	16	..	..	..	4⅛
4¼		4.2500	..	..	..	4	6	8	12	16	..	..	..	4¼
	4⅜	4.3750	..	..	..	4	6	8	12	16	..	..	..	4⅜
4½		4.5000	..	..	..	4	6	8	12	16	..	..	..	4½
	4⅝	4.6250	..	..	..	4	6	8	12	16	..	..	..	4⅝
4¾		4.7500	..	..	..	4	6	8	12	16	..	..	..	4¾
	4⅞	4.8750	..	..	..	4	6	8	12	16	..	..	..	4⅞
5		5.0000	..	..	..	4	6	8	12	16	..	..	..	5
	5⅛	5.1250	..	..	..	4	6	8	12	16	..	..	..	5⅛
5¼		5.2500	..	..	..	4	6	8	12	16	..	..	..	5¼
	5⅜	5.3750	..	..	..	4	6	8	12	16	..	..	..	5⅜
5½		5.5000	..	..	..	4	6	8	12	16	..	..	..	5½
	5⅝	5.6250	..	..	..	4	6	8	12	16	..	..	..	5⅝
5¾		5.7500	..	..	..	4	6	8	12	16	..	..	..	5¾
	5⅞	5.8750	..	..	..	4	6	8	12	16	..	..	..	5⅞
6		6.0000	..	..	..	4	6	8	12	16	..	..	..	6

Extracted from American Standard Unified Screw Threads (ASA B1.1 — 1960) with permission of the publisher, The American Society of Mechanical Engineers, 29 West 39th Street, New York, N. Y.

Table 38. Taps for Various Classes of Unified and American Screw Threads — Numbered Sizes

No. Size	Threads Per Inch NC	Threads Per Inch NF	Recommended Tap Class 2	Recommended Tap Class 3	Recommended Tap Class †2B	Recommended Tap Class 3B	Min All Classes (Basic)	Max Class 2	Max Class 3	Max Class 2B	Max Class 3B
0	..	80	G H1	G H1	G H2	G H1	0.0519	0.0536	0.0532	0.0542	0.0536
1	64	..	G H1	G H1	G H2	G H1	0.0629	0.0648	0.0643	0.0655	0.0648
1	..	72	G H1	G H1	G H2	G H1	0.0640	0.0658	0.0653	0.0665	0.0659
2	56	..	G H1	G H1	G H2	G H1	0.0744	0.0764	0.0759	0.0772	0.0765
2	..	64	G H1	G H1	G H2	G H1	0.0759	0.0778	0.0773	0.0786	0.0779
3	48	..	G H1	G H1	G H2	G H1	0.0855	0.0877	0.0871	0.0885	0.0877
3	..	56	G H1	G H1	G H2	G H1	0.0874	0.0894	0.0889	0.0902	0.0895
4	40	..	G H2	G H1	G H2	G H2	0.0958	0.0982	0.0975	0.0991	0.0982
4	..	48	G H1	G H1	G H2	G H1	0.0985	0.1007	0.1001	0.1016	0.1008
5	40	..	G H2	G H1	G H2	G H2	0.1088	0.1112	0.1105	0.1121	0.1113
5	..	44	G H1	G H1	G H2	G H1	0.1102	0.1125	0.1118	0.1134	0.1126
6	32	..	G H2	G H1	G H3	G H2	0.1177	0.1204	0.1196	0.1214	0.1204
6	..	40	G H2	G H1	G H2	G H2	0.1218	0.1242	0.1235	0.1252	0.1243
8	32	..	G H2	G H1	G H3	G H2	0.1437	0.1464	0.1456	0.1475	0.1465
8	..	36	G H2	G H1	G H2	G H2	0.1460	0.1485	0.1478	0.1496	0.1487
10	24	..	G H3	G H1	G H3	G H3	0.1629	0.1662	0.1653	0.1672	0.1661
10	..	32	G H2	G H1	G H3	G H2	0.1697	0.1724	0.1716	0.1736	0.1726
12	24	..	G H3	G H1	G H3	G H3	0.1889	0.1922	0.1913	0.1933	0.1922
12	..	28	G H3	G H1	G H3	G H3	0.1928	0.1959	0.1950	0.1970	0.1959

Table 39. Taps for Various Classes of Unified and American Screw Threads — Fractional Sizes

Inch Size	Threads Per Inch NC and UNC	Threads Per Inch NF and UNF	Recommended Tap Class 2	Recommended Tap Class 3	Recommended Tap Class †2B	Recommended Tap Class 3B	Min All Classes (Basic)	Max Class 2	Max Class 3	Max Class 2B	Max Class 3B
¼	20	..	G H3	G H2	G H5	G H3	0.2175	0.2211	0.2201	0.2223	0.2211
¼	..	28	G H2	G H1	G H4	G H2	0.2268	0.2299	0.2299	0.2311	0.2300
5/16	18	..	G H3	G H2	G H5	G H3	0.2764	0.2805	0.2794	0.2817	0.2803
5/16	..	24	G H3	G H1	G H4	G H3	0.2854	0.2887	0.2878	0.2902	0.2890
3/8	16	..	G H3	G H2	G H5	G H3	0.3344	0.3389	0.3376	0.3401	0.3387
3/8	..	24	G H3	G H1	G H4	G H3	0.3479	0.3512	0.3503	0.3528	0.3516
7/16	14	..	G H5	G H3	G H5	G H3	0.3911	0.3960	0.3947	0.3972	0.3957
7/16	..	20	G H3	G H1	G H5	G H3	0.4050	0.4086	0.4076	0.4104	0.4091
½	13	..	G H5	G H3	G H5	G H3	0.4500	0.4552	0.4537	0.4565	0.4548
½	..	20	G H3	G H1	G H5	G H3	0.4675	0.4711	0.4701	0.4731	0.4717
9/16	12	..	G H5	G H3	G H5	G H3	0.5084	0.5140	0.5124	0.5152	0.5135
9/16	..	18	G H3	G H2	G H5	G H3	0.5264	0.5305	0.5294	0.5323	0.5308
5/8	11	..	G H5	G H3	G H5	G H3	0.5660	0.5719	0.5702	0.5732	0.5714
5/8	..	18	G H3	G H2	G H5	G H3	0.5889	0.5930	0.5919	0.5949	0.5934
¾	10	..	G H5	G H3	G H5	G H5	0.6850	0.6914	0.6895	0.6927	0.6907
¾	..	16	G H3	G H2	G H5	G H3	0.7094	0.7139	0.7126	0.7159	0.7143
7/8	9	..	G H6	G H4	G H6	G H4	0.8028	0.8098	0.8077	0.8110	0.8089
7/8	..	14	G H4	G H2	G H6	G H4	0.8286	0.8335	0.8322	0.8356	0.8339
1	8	..	G H6	G H4	G H6	G H4	0.9188	0.9264	0.9242	0.9276	0.9254
1	..	12	G H4	G H2	G H6	G H4	0.9459	0.9515	0.9499	0.9535	0.9516
1		14 NS	G H4	G H2	G H6	G H4	0.9536	0.9585	0.9572	0.9609	0.9590
1⅛	7	..	G H8	G H4	G H8	G H4	1.0322	1.0407	1.0381	1.0416	1.0393
1⅛	..	12	G H4	G H4	G H6	G H4	1.0709	1.0765	1.0749	1.0787	1.0768
1¼	7	..	G H8	G H4	G H8	G H4	1.1572	1.1657	1.1631	1.1668	1.1644
1¼	..	12	G H4	G H4	G H6	G H4	1.1959	1.2015	1.1999	1.2039	1.2019
1⅜	6	..	G H8	G H4	G H8	G H4	1.2667	1.2768	1.2738	1.2771	1.2745
1⅜	..	12	G H4	G H4	G H6	G H4	1.3209	1.3265	1.3249	1.3291	1.3270
1½	6	..	G H8	G H4	G H8	G H4	1.3917	1.4018	1.3988	1.4022	1.3996
1½	..	12	G H4	G H4	G H6	G H4	1.4459	1.4515	1.4499	1.4542	1.4522

Note: Class 1B tapped holes can be produced with CUT thread taps.

†Cut thread taps in sizes 3 — 12 NC and NF inclusive may be used under normal conditions and in average materials for producing tapped holes to this classification.

The taps recommended above normally produce the Class of Thread indicated in average materials when used with reasonable care. However, if the tap specified does not give a satisfactory gage fit in the work, a choice of some other limit tap will be necessary.

Tables 38 and 39 are extracted from **American Standard Taps — Cut and Ground Threads** (ASA B5.4 — 1959) with permission of the publisher, The American Society of Mechanical Engineers, 29 West 39th Street, New York, N. Y.

Table 40. Hole Sizes for Tapping Threads of Various Percentages

When tapping drilled holes, if the hole is the same size as the minor diameter of the tap, the thread produced will be 100% height; in holes larger than the tap minor diameter, the height of thread will be less than 100%. To vary the height of thread, the size of the drilled hole must be varied.

Thread strength tests show that for the vast majority of requirements 55% to 75% is adequate. Soft metals or small engagements require the higher percentages.

For depths more than one and one-half times tap diameter, drills giving 50% thread height may be entirely satisfactory.

Nominal Size of Thread	Theoretical Hole Size to Give Various Percentages of Thread Height							Recommended Hole Size Limits for Various Lengths of Engagement							
								⅓ diameter		⅓-⅔ diameter		⅔-1½ diameters		1½-3 diameters	
	83-⅓%	75%	70%	65%	60%	55%	50%	Min.	Max.	Min.	Max.	Min.	Max.	Min.	Max.
0-80	.0465	.0479	.0486	.0494	.0502	.0510	.0519	.0465	.0500	.0479	.0514	.0479	.0514	.0479	.0514
1-64	.0561	.0578	.0588	.0599	.0609	.0619	.0629	.0561	.0599	.0585	.0623	.0585	.0623	.0585	.0623
1-72	.0580	.0595	.0604	.0613	.0622	.0631	.0640	.0580	.0613	.0596	.0629	.0602	.0635	.0602	.0635
2-56	.0667	.0686	.0698	.0710	.0721	.0732	.0744	.0667	.0705	.0686	.0724	.0699	.0737	.0699	.0737
2-64	.0691	.0708	.0718	.0729	.0739	.0749	.0759	.0691	.0724	.0707	.0740	.0720	.0753	.0720	.0753
3-48	.0764	.0788	.0801	.0815	.0828	.0841	.0855	.0764	.0804	.0785	.0825	.0805	.0845	.0806	.0846
3-56	.0797	.0816	.0828	.0840	.0851	.0862	.0874	.0797	.0831	.0814	.0848	.0831	.0865	.0833	.0867
4-36	.0819	.0849	.0867	.0886	.0904	.0922	.0940	.0819	.0869	.0844	.0894	.0869	.0919	.0878	.0919
4-40	.0849	.0877	.0893	.0909	.0926	.0942	.0958	.0849	.0894	.0871	.0916	.0894	.0939	.0902	.0947
4-48	.0894	.0918	.0931	.0945	.0958	.0971	.0985	.0894	.0931	.0912	.0949	.0931	.0968	.0939	.0976
5-40	.0979	.1007	.1023	.1039	.1056	.1072	.1088	.0979	.1020	.1000	.1041	.1021	.1062	.1036	.1077
5-44	.1004	.1029	.1044	.1059	.1073	.1087	.1102	.1004	.1041	.1023	.1060	.1042	.1079	.1060	.1097
6-32	.1042	.1076	.1096	.1117	.1137	.1157	.1177	.1042	.1091	.1066	.1115	.1091	.1140	.1115	.1164
6-40	.1109	.1137	.1153	.1169	.1185	.1201	.1218	.1109	.1148	.1128	.1167	.1147	.1186	.1166	.1205
8-32	.1302	.1336	.1356	.1377	.1397	.1417	.1437	.1302	.1345	.1324	.1367	.1346	.1389	.1367	.1410
8-36	.1339	.1370	.1388	.1406	.1424	.1442	.1460	.1339	.1377	.1359	.1397	.1378	.1416	.1397	.1435
10-24	.1449	.1495	.1522	.1549	.1576	.1602	.1629	.1449	.1502	.1475	.1528	.1502	.1555	.1528	.1581
10-32	.1562	.1596	.1616	.1637	.1657	.1677	.1697	.1562	.1601	.1581	.1621	.1601	.1641	.1621	.1661
12-24	.1709	.1755	.1782	.1809	.1836	.1862	.1889	.1709	.1758	.1733	.1782	.1758	.1807	.1782	.1831
12-28	.1773	.1813	.1836	.1859	.1882	.1905	.1928	.1773	.1815	.1794	.1836	.1815	.1857	.1836	.1878
14-20	.1879	.1933	.1965	.1998	.2030	.2063	.2095	.1879	.1933	.1906	.1960	.1933	.1987	.1960	.2014
14-24	.1969	.2014	.2041	.2068	.2095	.2122	.2149	.1969	.2014	.1992	.2037	.2014	.2059	.2037	.2082
¼-20	.1959	.2012	.2046	.2078	.2111	.2143	.2175	.1959	.2013	.1986	.2040	.2013	.2067	.2040	.2094
¼-28	.2113	.2153	.2176	.2199	.2222	.2245	.2268	.2113	.2152	.2131	.2171	.2150	.2190	.2169	.2209
5⁄16-18	.2524	.2584	.2620	.2656	.2692	.2728	.2764	.2524	.2577	.2551	.2604	.2577	.2630	.2604	.2657
5⁄16-24	.2674	.2720	.2747	.2774	.2801	.2827	.2854	.2674	.2714	.2694	.2734	.2714	.2754	.2734	.2774
3⁄8-16	.3073	.3142	.3182	.3223	.3263	.3303	.3344	.3073	.3127	.3101	.3155	.3128	.3182	.3155	.3209
3⁄8-24	.3299	.3345	.3372	.3399	.3426	.3452	.3479	.3299	.3336	.3314	.3354	.3332	.3372	.3351	.3391
7⁄16-14	.3602	.3680	.3726	.3772	.3819	.3865	.3911	.3602	.3660	.3630	.3688	.3659	.3717	.3688	.3746
7⁄16-20	.3834	.3888	.3921	.3953	.3986	.4018	.4050	.3834	.3875	.3855	.3896	.3875	.3916	.3896	.3937
½-13	.4167	.4251	.4301	.4351	.4401	.4450	.4500	.4167	.4225	.4196	.4254	.4226	.4284	.4255	.4313
½-20	.4459	.4513	.4546	.4578	.4611	.4643	.4675	.4459	.4498	.4477	.4517	.4497	.4537	.4516	.4556
9⁄16-12	.4723	.4814	.4868	.4922	.4976	.5030	.5084	.4723	.4783	.4753	.4813	.4783	.4843	.4813	.4873
9⁄16-18	.5024	.5084	.5120	.5156	.5192	.5228	.5264	.5024	.5065	.5045	.5086	.5065	.5106	.5086	.5127
5⁄8-11	.5266	.5365	.5424	.5483	.5542	.5601	.5660	.5266	.5328	.5298	.5360	.5329	.5391	.5360	.5422
5⁄8-18	.5649	.5709	.5745	.5787	.5817	.5853	.5889	.5649	.5690	.5670	.5711	.5690	.5730	.5711	.5752
11⁄16-11	.5891	.5989	.6048	.6107	.6166	.6225	.6285	.5891	.5952	.5921	.5982	.5951	.6012	.5982	.6043
11⁄16-16	.6198	.6266	.6307	.6347	.6388	.6438	.6469	.6198	.6241	.6219	.6262	.6241	.6284	.6263	.6306
¾-10	.6417	.6526	.6591	.6656	.6721	.6785	.6850	.6417	.6481	.6449	.6513	.6481	.6545	.6513	.6577
¾-16	.6823	.6892	.6932	.6973	.7013	.7053	.7094	.6823	.6866	.6844	.6887	.6865	.6908	.6886	.6929
7⁄8-9	.7547	.7668	.7740	.7812	.7884	.7956	.8028	.7547	.7614	.7580	.7647	.7614	.7681	.7647	.7714
7⁄8-14	.7977	.8055	.8101	.8147	.8194	.8240	.8286	.7977	.8022	.8000	.8045	.8023	.8068	.8045	.8090
1 -8	.8647	.8783	.8864	.8945	.9026	.9107	.9188	.8647	.8722	.8684	.8759	.8722	.8797	.8760	.8835
1 -12	.9098	.9188	.9242	.9296	.9350	.9404	.9459	.9098	.9148	.9123	.9173	.9148	.9198	.9173	.9223
1 -14	.9227	.9304	.9350	.9397	.9443	.9490	.9536	.9227	.9271	.9249	.9293	.9271	.9315	.9293	.9337
1 ⅛-7	.9704	.9859	.9951	1.0044	1.0137	1.0229	1.0322	.9704	.9790	.9747	.9833	.9789	.9875	.9832	.9918
1 ⅛-12	1.0348	1.0439	1.0493	1.0547	1.0601	1.0655	1.0709	1.0348	1.0398	1.0373	1.0423	1.0398	1.0448	1.0423	1.0473
1 ¼-7	1.0954	1.1109	1.1201	1.1294	1.1387	1.1479	1.1572	1.0954	1.1040	1.0997	1.1083	1.1039	1.1125	1.1082	1.1168
1 ¼-12	1.1598	1.1689	1.1743	1.1797	1.1851	1.1905	1.1959	1.1598	1.1648	1.1623	1.1673	1.1648	1.1698	1.1673	1.1723
1 ⅜-6	1.1946	1.2127	1.2235	1.2343	1.2451	1.2559	1.2667	1.1946	1.2046	1.1996	1.2096	1.2046	1.2146	1.2096	1.2196
1 ⅜-12	1.2848	1.2939	1.2993	1.3047	1.3101	1.3155	1.3209	1.2848	1.2898	1.2873	1.2923	1.2898	1.2948	1.2923	1.2973
1 ½-6	1.3196	1.3377	1.3485	1.3593	1.3701	1.3809	1.3917	1.3196	1.3296	1.3246	1.3346	1.3296	1.3396	1.3346	1.3446
1 ½-12	1.4098	1.4189	1.4243	1.4297	1.4351	1.4405	1.4459	1.4098	1.4148	1.4123	1.4173	1.4148	1.4198	1.4173	1.4223

(Greenfield Tap and Die Corporation)

651

Table 41
Cutting Speeds for Various Diameters

Feet per Min. Diameter Inches	30'	40'	50'	60'	70'	80'	90'	100'	110'	120'	130'	140'	150'
						Revolutions per Minute							
1/16	1833	2445	3056	3667	4278	4889	5500	6111	6722	7334	7945	8556	9167
1/8	917	1222	1528	1833	2139	2445	2750	3056	3361	3667	3973	4278	4584
3/16	611	815	1019	1222	1426	1630	1833	2037	2241	2445	2648	2852	3056
1/4	458	611	764	917	1070	1222	1375	1528	1681	1833	1986	2139	2292
5/16	367	489	611	733	856	978	1100	1222	1345	1467	1589	1711	1833
3/8	306	407	509	611	713	815	917	1019	1120	1222	1324	1426	1528
7/16	262	349	437	524	611	698	786	873	960	1048	1135	1222	1310
1/2	229	306	382	458	535	611	688	764	840	917	993	1070	1146
5/8	183	244	306	367	428	489	550	611	672	733	794	856	917
3/4	153	203	255	306	357	407	458	509	560	611	662	713	764
7/8	131	175	218	262	306	349	393	436	480	524	568	611	655
1	115	153	191	229	267	306	344	382	420	458	497	535	573
1 1/8	102	136	170	204	238	272	306	340	373	407	441	475	509
1 1/4	92	122	153	183	214	244	275	306	336	367	397	428	458
1 3/8	83	111	139	167	194	222	250	278	306	333	361	389	417
1 1/2	76	102	127	153	178	204	229	255	280	306	331	357	382
1 5/8	70	94	117	141	165	188	212	235	259	282	306	329	353
1 3/4	65	87	109	131	153	175	196	218	240	262	284	306	327
1 7/8	61	81	102	122	143	163	183	204	224	244	265	285	306
2	57	76	95	115	134	153	172	191	210	229	248	267	287
2 1/4	51	68	85	102	119	136	153	170	187	204	221	238	255
2 1/2	46	61	76	92	107	122	137	153	168	183	199	214	229
2 3/4	42	56	69	83	97	111	125	139	153	167	181	194	208
3	38	51	64	76	89	102	115	127	140	153	166	178	191

This table can be used to determine the approximate rpm for drilling, milling, turning, and boring operations for diameters up to 3 inches. It also gives the cutting speeds produced by various rpm with the diameters given.

(Courtesy: The Cleveland Twist Drill Co.)

Table 42
Metric Units of Measure and English Equivalents

1 millimeter (mm) = ...(about 1/25") 0.03937079"
10 millimeters = 1 Centimeter (cm) = ...0.3937079"
10 centimeters = 1 Decimeter (dm) = ...3.937079"
10 decimeters = 1 Meter (m) = ...39.37079"
    or 3.2808992 feet, or 1.09361 yards
10 meters = 1 Decameter (dkm) = ...   32.808992 feet
10 decameters = 1 Hectometer (hm) = ...109.36 yards
10 Hectometers = 1 Kilometer (km) = ...0.6213824 mile
10 kilometers = 1 Myriameter (mm) = ...6.213824 miles
1 inch = ...25.4 mm or 2.54 cm
1 foot = ...304.8 mm or .3048 m
1 yard = ...91.14 cm or .9114 m
1 mile = ...1.609 km
1 square centimeter (sq cm or cm²).............155 sq. in.
1 square inch = ...6.452 sq. cm.
1 cubic inch = ...16.393 cu. cm.
1 cubic centimeter (cucm, cc, or cm³)............061 cu. in.
1 cubic decimeter = ...61.023 cu. in. or .0353 cu. ft.
1 liter (l) = ...1 cu. dm. or 61.023 cu. in.
1 cubic foot = ...28.317 l
1 gallon = ...3.785 l
1 kilogram (kg) = ...2.2046 lbs.
1 pound = ...4536 kg.

Table 42 (continued)
Fractional Inches to Millimeters

Inches	mm	Inches	mm	Inches	mm	Inches	mm
1/64 =	.397	17/64 =	6.747	33/64 =	13.097	49/64 =	19.447
1/32 =	.794	9/32 =	7.144	17/32 =	13.494	25/32 =	19.844
3/64 =	1.191	19/64 =	7.541	35/64 =	13.890	51/64 =	20.240
1/16 =	1.587	5/16 =	7.937	9/16 =	14.287	13/16 =	20.637
5/64 =	1.984	21/64 =	8.334	37/64 =	14.684	53/64 =	21.034
3/32 =	2.381	11/32 =	8.731	19/32 =	15.081	27/32 =	21.431
7/64 =	2.778	23/64 =	9.128	39/64 =	15.478	55/64 =	21.828
1/8 =	3.175	3/8 =	9.525	5/8 =	15.875	7/8 =	22.225
9/64 =	3.572	25/64 =	9.922	41/64 =	16.272	57/64 =	22.622
5/32 =	3.969	13/32 =	10.319	21/32 =	16.669	29/32 =	23.019
11/64 =	4.366	27/64 =	10.716	43/64 =	17.065	59/64 =	23.415
3/16 =	4.762	7/16 =	11.113	11/16 =	17.462	15/16 =	23.812
13/64 =	5.159	29/64 =	11.509	45/64 =	17.859	61/64 =	24.209
7/32 =	5.556	15/32 =	11.906	23/32 =	18.256	31/32 =	24.606
15/64 =	5.953	31/64 =	12.303	47/64 =	18.653	63/64 =	25.003
1/4 =	6.350	1/2 =	12.700	3/4 =	19.050	1 =	25.400

Table 42 (continued)
Millimeters to Decimal Inches

mm	Inches	mm	Inches	mm	Inches	mm	Inches
.01 =	.00039	.34 =	.01339	.67 =	.02638	1. =	.03937
.02 =	.00079	.35 =	.01378	.68 =	.02677	2. =	.07874
.03 =	.00118	.36 =	.01417	.69 =	.02717	3. =	.11811
.04 =	.00157	.37 =	.01457	.70 =	.02756	4. =	.15748
.05 =	.00197	.38 =	.01496	.71 =	.02795	5. =	.19685
.06 =	.00236	.39 =	.01535	.72 =	.02835	6. =	.23622
.07 =	.00276	.40 =	.01575	.73 =	.02874	7. =	.27559
.08 =	.00315	.41 =	.01614	.74 =	.02913	8. =	.31496
.09 =	.00354	.42 =	.01654	.75 =	.02953	9. =	.35433
.10 =	.00394	.43 =	.01693	.76 =	.02992	10. =	.39370
.11 =	.00433	.44 =	.01732	.77 =	.03032	11. =	.43307
.12 =	.00472	.45 =	.01772	.78 =	.03071	12. =	.47244
.13 =	.00512	.46 =	.01811	.79 =	.03110	13. =	.51181
.14 =	.00551	.47 =	.01850	.80 =	.03150	14. =	.55118
.15 =	.00591	.48 =	.01890	.81 =	.03189	15. =	.59055
.16 =	.00630	.49 =	.01929	.82 =	.03228	16. =	.62992
.17 =	.00669	.50 =	.01969	.83 =	.03268	17. =	.66929
.18 =	.00709	.51 =	.02008	.84 =	.03307	18. =	.70866
.19 =	.00748	.52 =	.02047	.85 =	.03346	19. =	.74803
.20 =	.00787	.53 =	.02087	.86 =	.03386	20. =	.78740
.21 =	.00827	.54 =	.02126	.87 =	.03425	21. =	.82677
.22 =	.00866	.55 =	.02165	.88 =	.03465	22. =	.86614
.23 =	.00906	.56 =	.02205	.89 =	.03504	23. =	.90551
.24 =	.00945	.57 =	.02244	.90 =	.03543	24. =	.94488
.25 =	.00984	.58 =	.02283	.91 =	.03583	25. =	.98425
.26 =	.01024	.59 =	.02323	.92 =	.03622	26. =	1.02362
.27 =	.01063	.60 =	.02362	.93 =	.03661	27. =	1.06299
.28 =	.01102	.61 =	.02402	.94 =	.03701	28. =	1.10236
.29 =	.01142	.62 =	.02441	.95 =	.03740	29. =	1.14173
.30 =	.01181	.63 =	.02480	.96 =	.03780	30. =	1.18110
.31 =	.01220	.64 =	.02520	.97 =	.03819	31. =	1.22047
.32 =	.01260	.65 =	.02559	.98 =	.03858	32. =	1.25984
.33 =	.01299	.66 =	.02598	.99 =	.03898	33. =	1.29921

Table 43
Selection Chart For Cutting Fluids

		FERROUS METALS				NON-FERROUS METALS	
	Group:	I	II	III	IV	V	VI
	Machinability:*	Above 70%	50–70%	40–50%	Below 40%	Above 100%	Below 100%
	Materials:	Low-carbon Steels High-carbon Steels Malleable Iron Cast Steel Stainless Iron	Cast Iron	Stainless Steels Ingot Iron Wrought Iron	Tool Steels High-speed Steels	Aluminum and Alloys Brasses and Bronzes Magnesium and Alloys Zinc	Copper Nickel Inconel Monel
Severity	Type of Machining Operation						
(Greatest) 1.	Broaching; internal	Em. Sul.	Sul. Em.	Sul. Em.	Sul. Em.	MO. Em.	Sul. ML.
2.	Broaching; surface	Em. Sul.	Em. Sul.	Sul. Em.	Sul. Em.	MO. Em.	Sul. ML.
2.	Threading; pipe	Sul.	Sul. ML.	Sul.	Sul.		Sul.†
3.	Tapping; plain	Sul.	Sul.	Sul.	Sul.	Em. Dry	Sul. ML.
3.	Threading; plain	Sul.	Sul.	Sul.	Sul.	Em. Sul.	Sul.†
4.	Gear shaving	Sul. L.	Sul. L.	Sul. L.	Sul. L.		
4.	Reaming; plain	ML. Sul.	ML. Sul.	ML. Sul.	ML. Sul.	ML. MO. Em.	ML. MO. Sul.
4.	Gear cutting	Sul. ML. Em.	Sul.	Sul.	Sul. ML.		Sul. ML.
5.	Drilling; deep	Em. ML.	Em. Sul.	Sul.	Sul.	MO. ML. Em.	Sul. ML.
6.	Milling; plain	Em. ML. Sul.	Em.	Em.	Sul.	Em. MO. Dry	Sul. Em.
6.	Milling; multiple cutter	ML.	Sul.	Sul.	Sul. ML.	Em. MO. Dry	Sul. Em.
7.	Boring; multiple head	Sul. Em.	Sul. HDS	Sul. HDS	Sul. Em.	K. Dry Em.	Sul. Em.
7.	Multiple-spindle automatic screw machines and turret lathes: drilling, forming, turning, reaming. cutting-off, tapping, threading	Sul. Em. ML.	Sul. Em. ML.	Sul. Em. ML. HDS	Sul. ML. Em. HDS	Em. Dry ML.	Sul.
8.	High speed, light feed automatic screw machines: drilling, forming, tapping, threading, turning, reaming, box milling, cutting off	Sul. Em. ML.	Sul. Em. ML.	Sul. Em. ML.	Sul. ML. Em.	Em. Dry ML.	Sul.
9.	Drilling	Em.	Em.	Em.	Em. Sul.	Em. Dry	Em.
9.	Planing, shaping	Em. Sul. ML.	Em. Sul. ML.	Sul. Em.	Em. Sul.	Em. Dry	Em.
9.	Turning; single point tool, form tools	Em. Sul. ML.	Em. Sul. ML.	Em. Sul. ML.	Em. Sul. ML.	Em. Dry ML.	Em. Sul.
(Least) 10.	Sawing; circular, hack	Sul. ML. Em.	Sul. Em. ML.	Sul. Em. ML.	Sul. Em. ML.	Dry MO. Em.	Sul. Em. ML.
	Grinding; 1. plain	Em.	Em.	Em.	Em.	Em.	Em.
	2. form (thread, etc.)	Sul.	Sul.	Sul.	Sul.	MO. Sul.	Sul.

Key
K.—Kerosene
L.—Lard Oil
MO.—Mineral oils
ML.—Mineral-lard oils
Sul.—Sulphurized oils, with or without chlorine
Em.—Soluble or emulsifiable oils and compounds
Dry—No cutting fluid needed
HDS—Heavy duty soluble oil

*Machinability rating based on 100% for cold drawn Bessemer screw stock (specification B 1112).

†Palm oil is frequently used to thread copper.

Compiled from Metals Handbook, Machinery's Handbook, and AISI Steel Products Manual.
Reproduced from: **Metal Machining with Cutting Fluids** by Gulf Oil Corporation.

Table 44
Decimal Equivalents of Common Fractions

Fraction	Decimal		Fraction	Decimal
1/64	.015625		33/64	.515625
1/32	.03125		17/32	.53125
3/64	.046875		35/64	.546875
1/16	.0625		9/16	.5625
5/64	.078125		37/64	.578125
3/32	.09375		19/32	.59375
7/64	.109375		39/64	.609375
1/8	.125		5/8	.625
9/64	.140625		41/64	.640625
5/32	.15625		21/32	.65625
11/64	.171875		43/64	.671875
3/16	.1875		11/16	.6875
13/64	.203125		45/64	.703125
7/32	.21875		23/32	.71875
15/64	.234375		47/64	.734375
1/4	.250		3/4	.750
17/64	.265625		49/64	.765625
9/32	.28125		25/32	.78125
19/64	.296875		51/64	.796875
5/16	.3125		13/16	.8125
21/64	.328125		53/64	.828125
11/32	.34375		27/32	.84375
23/64	.359375		55/64	.859375
3/8	.375		7/8	.875
25/64	.390625		57/64	.890625
13/32	.40625		29/32	.90625
27/64	.421875		59/64	.921875
7/16	.4375		15/16	.9375
29/64	.453125		61/64	.953125
15/32	.46875		31/32	.96875
31/64	.484375		63/64	.984375
1/2	.500		1	1.0000

Table 45. Four Place Trigonometric Functions

Angles	Sines Nat.	Sines Log.	Cosines Nat.	Cosines Log.	Tangents Nat.	Tangents Log.	Cotangents Nat.	Cotangents Log.	Angles
0° 00′	.0000	∞	1.0000	0.0000	.0000	∞	∞	∞	90° 00′
10	.0029	7.4637	1.0000	0000	.0029	7.4637	343.77	2.5363	50
20	.0058	7648	1.0000	0000	.0058	7648	171.89	2352	40
30	.0087	9408	1.0000	0000	.0087	9409	114.59	0591	30
40	.0116	8.0658	.9999	0000	.0116	8.0658	85.940	1.9342	20
50	.0145	1627	.9999	0000	.0145	1627	68.750	8373	10
1° 00′	.0175	8.2419	.9998	9.9999	.0175	8.2419	57.290	1.7581	89° 00′
10	.0204	3088	.9998	9999	.0204	3089	49.104	6911	50
20	.0233	3668	.9997	9999	.0233	3669	42.964	6331	40
30	.0262	4179	.9997	9999	.0262	4181	38.188	5819	30
40	.0291	4637	.9996	9998	.0291	4638	34.368	5362	20
50	.0320	5050	.9995	9998	.0320	5053	31.242	4947	10
2° 00′	.0349	8.5428	.9994	9.9997	.0349	8.5431	28.636	1.4569	88° 00′
10	.0378	5776	.9993	9997	.0378	5779	26.432	4221	50
20	.0407	6097	.9992	9996	.0407	6101	24.542	3899	40
30	.0436	6397	.9990	9996	.0437	6401	22.904	3599	30
40	.0465	6677	.9989	9995	.0466	6682	21.470	3318	20
50	.0494	6940	.9988	9995	.0495	6945	20.206	3055	10
3° 00′	.0523	8.7188	.9986	9.9994	.0524	8.7194	19.081	1.2806	87° 00′
10	.0552	7423	.9985	9993	.0553	7429	18.075	2571	50
20	.0581	7645	.9983	9993	.0582	7652	17.169	2348	40
30	.0610	7857	.9981	9992	.0612	7865	16.350	2135	30
40	.0640	8059	.9980	9991	.0641	8067	15.605	1933	20
50	.0669	8251	.9978	9990	.0670	8261	14.924	1739	10
4° 00′	.0698	8.8436	.9976	9.9989	.0699	8.8446	14.301	1.1554	86° 00′
10	.0727	8613	.9974	9989	.0729	8624	13.727	1376	50
20	.0756	8783	.9971	9988	.0758	8795	13.197	1205	40
30	.0785	8946	.9969	9987	.0787	8960	12.706	1040	30
40	.0814	9104	.9967	9986	.0816	9118	12.251	0882	20
50	.0843	9256	.9964	9985	.0846	9272	11.826	0728	10
5° 00′	.0872	8.9403	.9962	9.9983	.0875	8.9420	11.430	1.0580	85° 00′
10	.0901	9545	.9959	9982	.0904	9563	11.059	0437	50
20	.0929	9682	.9957	9981	.0934	9701	10.712	0299	40
30	.0958	9816	.9954	9980	.0963	9836	10.385	0164	30
40	.0987	9945	.9951	9979	.0992	9966	10.078	0034	20
50	.1016	9.0070	.9948	9977	.1022	9.0093	9.7882	0.9907	10
6° 00′	.1045	9.0192	.9945	9.9976	.1051	9.0216	9.5144	0.9784	84° 00′
10	.1074	0311	.9942	9975	.1080	0336	9.2553	9664	50
20	.1103	0426	.9939	9973	.1110	0453	9.0098	9547	40
30	.1132	0539	.9936	9972	.1139	0567	8.7769	9433	30
40	.1161	0648	.9932	9971	.1169	0678	8.5555	9322	20
50	.1190	0755	.9929	9969	.1198	0786	8.3450	9214	10
7° 00′	.1219	9.0859	.9925	9.9968	.1228	9.0891	8.1443	0.9109	83° 00′
10	.1248	0961	.9922	9966	.1257	0995	7.9530	9005	50
20	.1276	1060	.9918	9964	.1287	1096	7.7704	8904	40
30	.1305	1157	.9914	9963	.1317	1194	7.5958	8806	30
40	.1334	1252	.9911	9961	.1346	1291	7.4287	8709	20
50	.1363	1345	.9907	9959	.1376	1385	7.2687	8615	10
8° 00′	.1392	9.1436	.9903	9.9958	.1405	9.1478	7.1154	0.8522	82° 00′
10	.1421	1525	.9899	9956	.1435	1569	6.9682	8431	50
20	.1449	1612	.9894	9954	.1465	1658	6.8269	8342	40
30	.1478	1697	.9890	9952	.1495	1745	6.6912	8255	30
40	.1507	1781	.9886	9950	.1524	1831	6.5606	8169	20
50	.1536	1863	.9881	9948	.1554	1915	6.4348	8085	10
9° 00′	.1564	9.1943	.9877	9.9946	.1584	9.1997	6.3138	0.8003	81° 00′
10	.1593	2022	.9872	9944	.1614	2078	6.1970	7922	50
20	.1622	2100	.9868	9942	.1644	2158	6.0844	7842	40
30	.1650	2176	.9863	9940	.1673	2236	5.9758	7764	30
40	.1679	2251	.9858	9938	.1703	2313	5.8708	7687	20
50	.1708	2324	.9853	9936	.1733	2389	5.7694	7611	10
10° 00′	.1736	9.2397	.9848	9.9934	.1763	9.2463	5.6713	0.7537	80° 00′
10	.1765	2468	.9843	9931	.1793	2536	5.5764	7464	50
20	.1794	2538	.9838	9929	.1823	2609	5.4845	7391	40
30	.1822	2606	.9833	9927	.1853	2680	5.3955	7320	30
40	.1851	2674	.9827	9924	.1883	2750	5.3093	7250	20
50	.1880	2740	.9822	9922	.1914	2819	5.2257	7181	10
11° 00′	.1908	9.2806	.9816	9.9919	.1944	9.2887	5.1446	0.7113	79° 00′
10	.1937	2870	.9811	9917	.1974	2953	5.0658	7047	50
20	.1965	2934	.9805	9914	.2004	3020	4.9894	6980	40
30	.1994	2997	.9799	9912	.2035	3085	4.9152	6915	30
40	.2022	3058	.9793	9909	.2065	3149	4.8430	6851	20
50	.2051	3119	.9787	9907	.2095	3212	4.7729	6788	10
12° 00′	.2079	9.3179	.9781	9.9904	.2126	9.3275	4.7046	0.6725	78° 00′
10	.2108	3238	.9775	9901	.2156	3336	4.6382	6664	50
20	.2136	3296	.9769	9899	.2186	3397	4.5736	6603	40
30	.2164	3353	.9763	9896	.2217	3458	4.5107	6542	30
40	.2193	3410	.9757	9893	.2247	3517	4.4494	6483	20
50	.2221	3466	.9750	9890	.2278	3576	4.3897	6424	10
13° 00′	.2250	9.3521	.9744	9.9887	.2309	9.3634	4.3315	0.6366	77° 00′
10	.2278	3575	.9737	9884	.2339	3691	4.2747	6309	50
20	.2306	3629	.9730	9881	.2370	3748	4.2193	6252	40
30	.2334	3682	.9724	9878	.2401	3804	4.1653	6196	30
40	.2363	3734	.9717	9875	.2432	3859	4.1126	6141	20
50	.2391	3786	.9710	9872	.2462	3914	4.0611	6086	10
14° 00′	.2419	9.3837	.9703	9.9869	.2493	9.3968	4.0108	0.6032	76° 00′
10	.2447	3887	.9696	9866	.2524	4021	3.9617	5979	50
20	.2476	3937	.9689	9863	.2555	4074	3.9136	5926	40
30	.2504	3986	.9681	9859	.2586	4127	3.8667	5873	30
40	.2532	4035	.9674	9856	.2617	4178	3.8208	5822	20
50	.2560	4083	.9667	9853	.2648	4230	3.7760	5770	10
15° 00′	.2588	9.4130	.9659	9.9849	.2679	9.4281	3.7321	0.5719	75° 00′
10	.2616	4177	.9652	9846	.2711	4331	3.6891	5669	50
20	.2644	4223	.9644	9843	.2742	4381	3.6470	5619	40
30	.2672	4269	.9636	9839	.2773	4430	3.6059	5570	30
40	.2700	4314	.9628	9836	.2805	4479	3.5656	5521	20
50	.2728	4359	.9621	9832	.2836	4527	3.5261	5473	10
16° 00′	.2756	9.4403	.9613	9.9828	.2867	9.4575	3.4874	0.5425	74° 00′
10	.2784	4447	.9605	9825	.2899	4622	3.4495	5378	50
20	.2812	4491	.9596	9821	.2931	4669	3.4124	5331	40
30	.2840	4533	.9588	9817	.2962	4716	3.3759	5284	30
40	.2868	4576	.9580	9814	.2994	4762	3.3402	5238	20
50	.2896	4618	.9572	9810	.3026	4808	3.3052	5192	10
Angles	Nat. Cosines	Log. Cosines	Nat. Sines	Log. Sines	Nat. Cotangents	Log. Cotangents	Nat. Tangents	Log. Tangents	Angles

Angles	Sines Nat.	Sines Log.	Cosines Nat.	Cosines Log.	Tangents Nat.	Tangents Log.	Cotangents Nat.	Cotangents Log.	Angles
17° 00′	.2924	9.4659	.9563	9.9806	.3057	9.4853	3.2709	0.5147	73° 00′
10	.2952	4700	.9555	9802	.3089	4898	3.2371	5102	50
20	.2979	4741	.9546	9798	.3121	4943	3.2041	5057	40
30	.3007	4781	.9537	9794	.3153	4987	3.1716	5013	30
40	.3035	4821	.9528	9790	.3185	5031	3.1397	4969	20
50	.3062	4861	.9520	9786	.3217	5075	3.1084	4925	10
18° 00′	.3090	9.4900	.9511	9.9782	.3249	9.5118	3.0777	0.4882	72° 00′
10	.3118	4939	.9502	9778	.3281	5161	3.0475	4839	50
20	.3145	4977	.9492	9774	.3314	5203	3.0178	4797	40
30	.3173	5015	.9483	9770	.3346	5245	2.9887	4755	30
40	.3201	5052	.9474	9765	.3378	5287	2.9600	4713	20
50	.3228	5090	.9465	9761	.3411	5329	2.9319	4671	10
19° 00′	.3256	9.5126	.9455	9.9757	.3443	9.5370	2.9042	0.4630	71° 00′
10	.3283	5163	.9446	9752	.3476	5411	2.8770	4589	50
20	.3311	5199	.9436	9748	.3508	5451	2.8502	4549	40
30	.3338	5235	.9426	9743	.3541	5491	2.8239	4509	30
40	.3365	5270	.9417	9739	.3574	5531	2.7980	4469	20
50	.3393	5306	.9407	9734	.3607	5571	2.7725	4429	10
20° 00′	.3420	9.5341	.9397	9.9730	.3640	9.5611	2.7475	0.4389	70° 00′
10	.3448	5375	.9387	9725	.3673	5650	2.7228	4350	50
20	.3475	5409	.9377	9721	.3706	5689	2.6985	4311	40
30	.3502	5443	.9367	9716	.3739	5727	2.6746	4273	30
40	.3529	5477	.9356	9711	.3772	5766	2.6511	4234	20
50	.3557	5510	.9346	9706	.3805	5804	2.6279	4196	10
21° 00′	.3584	9.5543	.9336	9.9702	.3839	9.5842	2.6051	0.4158	69° 00′
10	.3611	5576	.9325	9697	.3872	5879	2.5826	4121	50
20	.3638	5609	.9315	9692	.3906	5917	2.5605	4083	40
30	.3665	5641	.9304	9687	.3939	5954	2.5386	4046	30
40	.3692	5673	.9293	9682	.3973	5991	2.5172	4009	20
50	.3719	5704	.9283	9677	.4006	6028	2.4960	3972	10
22° 00′	.3746	9.5736	.9272	9.9672	.4040	9.6064	2.4751	0.3936	68° 00′
10	.3773	5767	.9261	9667	.4074	6100	2.4545	3900	50
20	.3800	5798	.9250	9661	.4108	6136	2.4342	3864	40
30	.3827	5828	.9239	9656	.4142	6172	2.4142	3828	30
40	.3854	5859	.9228	9651	.4176	6208	2.3945	3792	20
50	.3881	5889	.9216	9646	.4210	6243	2.3750	3757	10
23° 00′	.3907	9.5919	.9205	9.9640	.4245	9.6279	2.3559	0.3721	67° 00′
10	3934	5948	.9194	9635	.4279	6314	2.3369	3686	50
20	3961	5978	.9182	9629	.4314	6348	2.3183	3652	40
30	.3987	6007	.9171	9624	.4348	6383	2.2998	3617	30
40	4014	6036	.9159	9618	.4383	6417	2.2817	3583	20
50	4041	6065	.9147	9613	.4417	6452	2.2637	3548	10
24° 00′	4067	9.6093	.9135	9.9607	.4452	9.6486	2.2460	0.3514	66° 00′
10	.4094	6121	.9124	9602	.4487	6520	2.2286	3480	50
20	4120	6149	.9112	9596	.4522	6553	2.2113	3447	40
30	.4147	6177	.9100	9590	.4557	6587	2.1943	3413	30
40	.4173	6205	.9088	9584	.4592	6620	2.1775	3380	20
50	.4200	6232	.9075	9579	.4628	6654	2.1609	3346	10
25° 00′	4226	9.6259	.9063	9.9573	.4663	9.6687	2.1445	0.3313	65° 00′
10	.4253	6286	.9051	9567	.4699	6720	2.1283	3280	50
20	.4279	6313	.9038	9561	.4734	6752	2.1123	3248	40
30	.4305	6340	.9026	9555	.4770	6785	2.0965	3215	30
40	.4331	6366	.9013	9549	.4806	6817	2.0809	3183	20
50	.4358	6392	.9001	9543	.4841	6850	2.0655	3150	10
26° 00′	.4384	9.6418	.8988	9.9537	.4877	9.6882	2.0503	0.3118	64° 00′
10	.4410	6444	.8975	9530	.4913	6914	2.0353	3086	50
20	.4436	6470	.8962	9524	.4950	6946	2.0204	3054	40
30	.4462	6495	.8949	9518	.4986	6977	2.0057	3023	30′
40	.4488	6521	.8936	9512	.5022	7009	1.9912	2991	20
50	.4514	6546	.8923	9505	.5059	7040	1.9768	2960	10
27° 00′	.4540	9.6570	.8910	9.9499	.5095	9.7072	1.9626	0.2928	63° 00′
10	.4566	6595	.8897	9492	.5132	7103	1.9486	2897	50
20	.4592	6620	.8884	9486	.5169	7134	1.9347	2866	40
30	.4617	6644	.8870	9479	.5206	7165	1.9210	2835	30
40	.4643	6668	.8857	9473	.5243	7196	1.9074	2804	20
50	.4669	6692	.8843	9466	.5280	7226	1.8940	2774	10
28° 00′	.4695	9.6716	.8829	9.9459	.5317	9.7257	1.8807	0.2743	62° 00′
10	.4720	6740	.8816	9453	.5354	7287	1.8676	2713	50
20	.4746	6763	.8802	9446	.5392	7317	1.8546	2683	40
30	.4772	6787	.8788	9439	.5430	7348	1.8418	2652	30
40	.4797	6810	.8774	9432	.5467	7378	1.8291	2622	20
50	.4823	6833	.8760	9425	.5505	7408	1.8165	2592	10
29° 00′	.4848	9.6856	.8746	9.9418	.5543	9.7438	1.8040	0.2562	61° 00′
10	.4874	6878	.8732	9411	.5581	7467	1.7917	2533	50
20	.4899	6901	.8718	9404	.5619	7497	1.7796	2503	40
30	.4924	6923	.8704	9397	.5658	7526	1.7675	2474	30
40	.4950	6946	.8689	9390	.5696	7556	1.7556	2444	20
50	.4975	6968	.8675	9383	.5735	7585	1.7437	2415	10
30° 00′	.5000	9.6990	.8660	9.9375	.5774	9.7614	1.7321	0.2386	60° 00′
10	.5025	7012	.8646	9368	.5812	7644	1.7205	2356	50
20	.5050	7033	.8631	9361	.5851	7673	1.7090	2327	40
30	.5075	7055	.8616	9353	.5890	7701	1.6977	2299	30
40	.5100	7076	.8601	9346	.5930	7730	1.6864	2270	20
50	.5125	7097	.8587	9338	.5969	7759	1.6753	2241	10
31° 00′	.5150	9.7118	.8572	9.9331	.6009	9.7788	1.6643	0.2212	59° 00′
10	.5175	7139	.8557	9323	.6048	7816	1.6534	2184	50
20	.5200	7160	.8542	9315	.6088	7845	1.6426	2155	40
30	.5225	7181	.8526	9308	.6128	7873	1.6319	2127	30
40	.5250	7201	.8511	9300	.6168	7902	1.6212	2098	20
50	.5275	7222	.8496	9292	.6208	7930	1.6107	2070	10
32° 00′	.5299	9.7242	.8480	9.9284	.6249	9.7958	1.6003	0.2042	58° 00′
10	.5324	7262	.8465	9276	.6289	7986	1.5900	2014	50
20	.5348	7282	.8450	9268	.6330	8014	1.5798	1986	40
30	.5373	7302	.8434	9260	.6371	8042	1.5697	1958	30
40	.5398	7322	.8418	9252	.6412	8070	1.5597	1930	20
50	.5422	7342	.8403	9244	.6453	8097	1.5497	1903	10
33° 00′	.5446	9.7361	.8387	9.9236	.6494	9.8125	1.5399	0.1875	57° 00′
10	.5471	7380	.8371	9228	.6536	8153	1.5301	1847	50
20	.5495	7400	.8355	9219	.6577	8180	1.5204	1820	40
30	.5519	7419	.8339	9211	.6619	8208	1.5108	1792	30
40	.5544	7438	.8323	9203	.6661	8235	1.5013	1765	20
50	.5568	7457	.8307	9194	.6703	8263	1.4919	1737	10
Angles	Nat. Cosines	Log. Cosines	Nat. Sines	Log. Sines	Nat. Cotangents	Log. Cotangents	Nat. Tangents	Log. Tangents	Angles

Table 45. Four Place Trigonometric Functions (continued)

Angles	Sines Nat.	Sines Log.	Cosines Nat.	Cosines Log.	Tangents Nat.	Tangents Log.	Cotangents Nat.	Cotangents Log.	Angles
34° 00′	.5592	9.7476	.8290	9.9186	.6745	9.8290	1.4826	0.1710	56° 00′
10	.5616	7494	.8274	9177	.6787	8317	1.4733	1683	50
20	.5640	7513	.8258	9169	.6830	8344	1.4641	1656	40
30	.5664	7531	.8241	9160	.6873	8371	1.4550	1629	30
40	.5688	7550	.8225	9151	.6916	8398	1.4460	1602	20
50	.5712	7568	.8208	9142	.6959	8425	1.4370	1575	10
35° 00′	.5736	9.7586	.8192	9.9134	.7002	9.8452	1.4281	0.1548	55° 00′
10	.5760	7604	.8175	9125	.7046	8479	1.4193	1521	50
20	.5783	7622	.8158	9116	.7089	8506	1.4106	1494	40
30	.5807	7640	.8141	9107	.7133	8533	1.4019	1467	30
40	.5831	7657	.8124	9098	.7177	8559	1.3934	1441	20
50	.5854	7675	.8107	9089	.7221	8586	1.3848	1414	10
36° 00′	.5878	9.7692	.8090	9.9080	.7265	9.8613	1.3764	0.1387	54° 00′
10	.5901	7710	.8073	9070	.7310	8639	1.3680	1361	50
20	.5925	7727	.8056	9061	.7355	8666	1.3597	1334	40
30	.5948	7744	.8039	9052	.7400	8692	1.3514	1308	30
40	.5972	7761	.8021	9042	.7445	8718	1.3432	1282	20
50	.5995	7778	.8004	9033	.7490	8745	1.3351	1255	10
37° 00′	.6018	9.7795	.7986	9.9023	.7536	9.8771	1.3270	0.1229	53° 00′
10	.6041	7811	.7969	9014	.7581	8797	1.3190	1203	50
20	.6065	7828	.7951	9004	.7627	8824	1.3111	1176	40
30	.6088	7844	.7934	8995	.7673	8850	1.3032	1150	30
40	.6111	7861	.7916	8985	.7720	8876	1.2954	1124	20
50	.6134	7877	.7898	8975	.7766	8902	1.2876	1098	10
38° 00′	.6157	9.7893	.7880	9.8965	.7813	9.8928	1.2799	0.1072	52° 00′
10	.6180	7910	.7862	8955	.7860	8954	1.2723	1046	50
20	.6202	7926	.7844	8945	.7907	8980	1.2647	1020	40
30	.6225	7941	.7826	8935	.7954	9006	1.2572	0994	30
40	.6248	7957	.7808	8925	.8002	9032	1.2497	0968	20
50	.6271	7973	.7790	8915	.8050	9058	1.2423	0942	10
39° 00′	.6293	9.7989	.7771	9.8905	.8098	9.9084	1.2349	0.0916	51° 00′
10	.6316	8004	.7753	8895	.8146	9110	1.2276	0890	50
20	.6338	8020	.7735	8884	.8195	9135	1.2203	0865	40
30	.6361	8035	.7716	8874	.8243	9161	1.2131	0839	30
40	.6383	8050	.7698	8864	.8292	9187	1.2059	0813	20
50	.6406	8066	.7679	8853	.8342	9212	1.1988	0788	10
	Nat.	Log.	Nat.	Log.	Nat.	Log.	Nat.	Log.	
Angles	Cosines		Sines		Cotangents		Tangents		Angles

Angles	Sines Nat.	Sines Log.	Cosines Nat.	Cosines Log.	Tangents Nat.	Tangents Log.	Cotangents Nat.	Cotangents Log.	Angles
40° 00′	.6428	9.8081	.7660	9.8843	.8391	9.9238	1.1918	0.0762	50° 00′
10	.6450	8096	.7642	8832	.8441	9264	1.1847	0736	50
20	.6472	8111	.7623	8821	.8491	9289	1.1778	0711	40
30	.6494	8125	.7604	8810	.8541	9315	1.1708	0685	30
40	.6517	8140	.7585	8800	.8591	9341	1.1640	0659	20
50	.6539	8155	.7566	8789	.8642	9366	1.1571	0634	10
41° 00′	.6561	9.8169	.7547	9.8778	.8693	9.9392	1.1504	0.0608	49° 00′
10	.6583	8184	.7528	8767	.8744	9417	1.1436	0583	50
20	.6604	8198	.7509	8756	.8796	9443	1.1369	0557	40
30	.6626	8213	.7490	8745	.8847	9468	1.1303	0532	30
40	.6648	8227	.7470	8733	.8899	9494	1.1237	0506	20
50	.6670	8241	.7451	8722	.8952	9519	1.1171	0481	10
42° 00′	.6691	9.8255	.7431	9.8711	.9004	9.9544	1.1106	0.0456	48° 00′
10	.6713	8269	.7412	8699	.9057	9570	1.1041	0430	50
20	.6734	8283	.7392	8688	.9110	9595	1.0977	0405	40
30	.6756	8297	.7373	8676	.9163	9621	1.0913	0379	30
40	.6777	8311	.7353	8665	.9217	9646	1.0850	0354	20
50	.6799	8324	.7333	8653	.9271	9671	1.0786	0329	10
43° 00′	.6820	9.8338	.7314	9.8641	.9325	9.9697	1.0724	0.0303	47° 00′
10	.6841	8351	.7294	8629	.9380	9722	1.0661	0278	50
20	.6862	8365	.7274	8618	.9435	9747	1.0599	0253	40
30	.6884	8378	.7254	8606	.9490	9772	1.0538	0228	30
40	.6905	8391	.7234	8594	.9545	9798	1.0477	0202	20
50	.6926	8405	.7214	8582	.9601	9823	1.0416	0177	10
44° 00′	.6947	9.8418	.7193	9.8569	.9657	9.9848	1.0355	0.0152	46° 00′
10	.6967	8431	.7173	8557	.9713	9874	1.0295	0126	50
20	.6988	8444	.7153	8545	.9770	9899	1.0235	0101	40
30	.7009	8457	.7133	8532	.9827	9924	1.0176	0076	30
40	.7030	8469	.7112	8520	.9884	9949	1.0117	0051	20
50	.7050	8482	.7092	8507	.9942	9975	1.0058	0025	10
45° 00′	.7071	9.8495	.7071	9.8495	1.0000	0.0000	1.0000	0.0000	45° 00′
	Nat.	Log.	Nat.	Log.	Nat.	Log.	Nat.	Log.	
Angles	Cosines		Sines		Cotangents		Tangents		Angles

Table 46
Commonly Used Measures and Formulas

Linear Measure

12 inches (in.)	equals 1 foot.............ft.
3 feet	equals 1 yard...........yd.
5½ yards	equals 1 rod.............rd.

Square Measure

144 square inches (sq. in).	equals 1 square foot......sq. ft.
9 square feet	equals 1 square yard......sq. yd.
30¼ square yards	equals 1 square rod.......sq. rd.

Cubic Measure

1728 cubic inches (cu. in.)	equals 1 cubic foot........cu. ft.
27 cubic feet	equals 1 cubic yard.......cu. yd.

Measure of Angles or Arcs

60 seconds (″)	equals 1 minute..........
60 minutes (′)	equals 1 degree.........°
90 degrees (°)	equals 1 right angle.......L
360 degrees	equals 1 circle..........cir.

Liquid Measure

4 gills (gi.)	equals 1 pint............pt.
2 pints	equals 1 quart..........qt.
4 quarts	equals 1 gallon.........gal.
31½ gallons	equalls 1 barrel.........bbl.
2 barrels	equals 1 hogshead.......hhd.

Dry Measure

2 pints (pt.)	equals 1 quart..........qt.
8 quarts	equals 1 peck...........pk.
4 pecks	equals 1 bushel.........bu.

Avoirdupois Weight

16 ounces (oz.)	equals 1 pound..........lb.
100 pounds	equals 1 hundredweight...cwt.
20 cwt. or 2000 pounds	equals 1 ton.............t

Miscellaneous Measures

12 Articles	equals 1 dozen..........doz.
12 dozen	equals 1 gross...........gross

1 pint of water equals 1.043125 pounds or approximately 1 pound.

1 cubic foot of water weighs 62.425 pounds.

Formulas:

1. The circumference of a circle is equal to π or 3.1416 times the diameter.

   cir. = 3.1416 x dia.

2. The area of a circle is equal to π times the radius squared

   $a = 3.1416 \times r^2$

3. The area of a rectangle or parallelogram is equal to length times the width.

   $a = L \times W$

4. The area of a trapezoid is equal to the sum of one half of the parallel sides times the height.

   $A = \frac{1}{2}h(a+b)$ or $A = \frac{a+b}{2}h$

5. The area of a triangle is equal to the altitude times the base divided by 2.

   $A = \frac{(ab)}{2}$ or $A = \frac{1}{2}ab$

656

Table 47
Drill Sizes — Number, Letter and Fractional
Note that letter drills are larger than number drills and they begin where number drills end.

Number and Letter Drills	Fractional Drills	Decimal Equivalents	Number and Letter Drills	Fractional Drills	Decimal Equivalents	Number and Letter Drills	Fractional Drills	Decimal Equivalents	Number and Letter Drills	Fractional Drills	Decimal Equivalents
80	...	.0135	42	...	.0935		13/64	.2031		13/32	.4062
79	...	.0145		3/32	.0937	6	...	.2040	Z	...	.4130
	1/64	.0156	41	...	.0960	5	...	.2055		27/64	.4219
78	...	.0160	40	...	.0980	4	...	.2090		7/16	.4375
77	...	.0180	39	...	.0995	3	...	.2130		29/64	.4531
76	...	.0200	38	...	.1015		7/32	.2187		15/32	.4687
75	...	.0210	37	...	.1040	2	...	.2210		31/64	.4844
74	...	.0225	36	...	.1065	1	...	.2280		1/2	.5000
73	...	.0240		7/64	.1094	A	...	.2340			
72	...	.0250	35	...	.1100		15/64	.2344		33/64	.5156
71	...	.0260	34	...	.1110	B	...	.2380		17/32	.5312
70	...	.0280	33	...	.1130	C	...	.2420		35/64	.5469
69	...	.0292	32	...	.1160	D	...	.2460		9/16	.5625
68	...	.0310	31	...	.1200	E	1/4	.2500		37/64	.5781
	1/32	.0312		1/8	.1250	F	...	.2570		19/32	.5937
67	...	.0320	30	...	.1285	G	...	.2610		39/64	.6094
66	...	.0330	29	...	.1360		17/64	.2656		5/8	.6250
65	...	.0350	28	...	.1405	H	...	.2660			
64	...	.0360		9/64	.1406	I	...	.2720		41/64	.6406
63	...	.0370	27	...	.1440	J	...	.2770		21/32	.6562
62	...	.0380	26	...	.1470	K	...	.2810		43/64	.6719
61	...	.0390	25	...	.1495		9/32	.2812		11/16	.6875
60	...	.0400	24	...	.1520	L	...	.2900		45/64	.7031
59	...	.0410	23	...	.1540	M	...	.2950		23/32	.7187
58	...	.0420		5/32	.1562		19/64	.2969		47/64	.7344
57	...	.0430	22	...	.1570	N	...	.3020		3/4	.7500
56	...	.0465	21	...	.1590		5/16	.3125			
	3/64	.0469	20	...	.1610	O	...	.3160		49/64	.7656
55	...	.0520	19	...	.1660	P	...	.3230		25/32	.7812
54	...	.0550	18	...	.1695		21/64	.3281		51/64	.7969
53	...	.0595		11/64	.1719	Q	...	.3320		13/16	.8125
	1/16	.0625	17	...	.1720	R	...	.3390		53/64	.8281
52	...	.0635	16	...	.1770		11/32	.3437		27/32	.8437
51	...	.0670	15	...	.1800	S	...	.3480		55/64	.8594
50	...	.0700	14	...	.1820	T	...	.3580		7/8	.8750
49	...	.0730	13	...	.1850		23/64	.3594			
48	...	.0760		3/16	.1875	U	...	.3680		57/64	.8906
	5/64	.0781	12	...	.1890		3/8	.3750		29/32	.9062
47	...	.0785	11	...	.1910	V	...	.3770		59/64	.9219
46	...	.0810	10	...	.1935	W	...	.3860		15/16	.9375
45	...	.0820	9	...	.1960		25/64	.3906		61/64	.9531
44	...	.0860	8	...	.1990	X	...	.3970		31/32	.9687
43	...	.0890	7	...	.2010	Y	...	.4040		63/64	.9844
										1	1.0000

Table 48. Melting Points of Metals and Alloys of Practical Importance

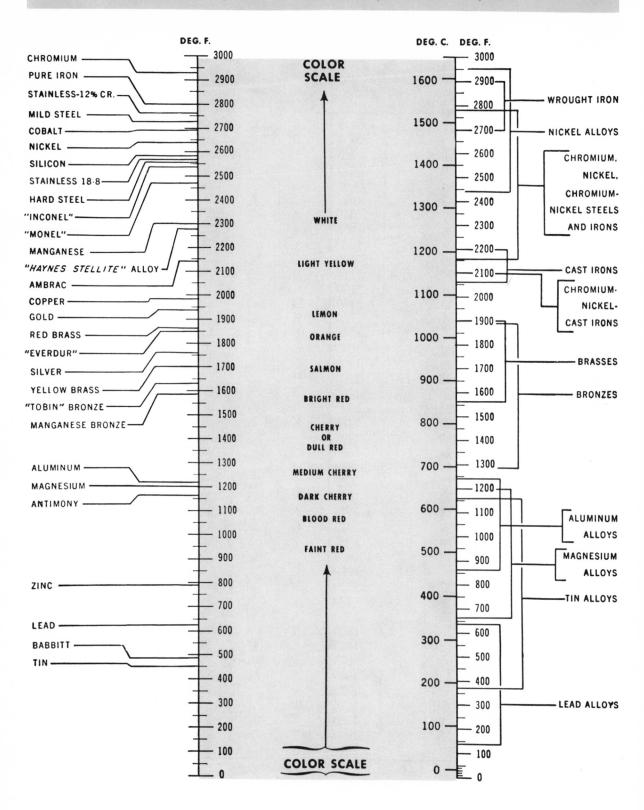

(Courtesy Linde Co., Div. of Union Carbide Corp.)

658

Index